Principles of

Heat Transfer

Principles of

Heat Transfer

FRANK KREITH

Associate Professor of
Mechanical Engineering

LEHIGH UNIVERSITY

1958 *International Textbook Company · Scranton*

Preface

This book is an amplification of lecture notes used by the author in teaching a one-semester course in heat transfer for engineering students at the senior and first-year graduate level. The material has been organized as a text, but it can also serve as a convenient reference for practicing engineers interested in fundamental techniques of analyzing heat-transfer problems. It is assumed that the reader has an elementary knowledge of thermodynamics, fluid dynamics, d-c circuit theory, calculus, and differential equations, although a certain amount of review of these topics has been included.

The purpose of the book is to present a basic introduction to the field of engineering heat transfer. The presentation endeavors to convey to the reader a physical understanding of the processes by which heat is transferred and to provide him with the tools necessary to obtain quantitative solutions to engineering problems involving one or more of the basic modes of heat flow. An effort has been made to present information from recent and authoritative sources, but the amount of empirical data included is no more than considered necessary to give the reader a sufficiently broad background to use the available literature effectively. No attempt has been made to present rigorous mathematical solutions which, although available for numerous problems, require a more advanced mathematical background than most engineering students acquire in their undergraduate curriculum.

Although the field of heat transfer is generally subdivided into conduction, radiation, and convection, in most practical situations heat is transferred by several of these modes simultaneously. The author deemed it desirable, therefore, to introduce a general method for handling heat-transfer problems in the first chapter. This method makes use of the similarity between the equations governing the flow of heat and the flow of electric current to develop an analogy between electrical and thermal systems. With the aid of this analogy, heat-transfer problems can be reduced to thermal networks which can be analyzed with simple and familiar principles of d-c circuit theory. The thermal-circuit method of analysis also makes it possible to consider realistic problems throughout the book, and the reader can thereby acquire a "feel" for the order of magnitude of thermal resistances under various conditions. This is often of help in spotting errors in the solution to a particular problem when the numerical answer seems unreasonable in the light of past experience.

Interpreting a heat-transfer problem as a thermal circuit is not difficult once one has acquired a physical understanding of the analogies involved. However, the elements of the circuit can be evaluated quantitatively only after a detailed knowledge of the basic modes of heat transfer has been acquired. To this end, each heat-flow mechanism and its analysis is considered separately in subsequent chapters.

In the chapters dealing with conduction heat transfer, numerical, graphical, and electrical-model-analogue methods of solution have been freely employed. Although numerical and graphical methods do not lend themselves to parameterizations, they yield rapid approximations to individual problems and are therefore widely used in industry. They also appeal to the students because the temperature field can be visualized.

A modified analogue-network method has been applied to the solution of radiant-heat-transfer problems. This approach circumvents the need for matrix algebra in the solution of more complex problems and integrates radiant heat transfer into the over-all scheme of analysis.

In the treatment of convection, the interrelationship between the flow of heat and the flow of the fluid has been emphasized. Prandtl's concept of the boundary layer has been presented and one problem, namely the flow over a flat plate, has been treated in detail. This problem is not only the simplest case to analyze, but is perhaps also the most important because many practical situations approximate flow over a plate, while others are described by equations which can be reduced by appropriate transformation to the flat-plate boundary-layer equations.

In as complex a field as convective heat transfer, the practicing engineer is forced to rely considerably on available experimental results. The derivation and interpretation of dimensionless parameters used to correlate empirical data can therefore not be overlooked. To acquaint the reader with the use of dimensional analysis in correlating heat-transfer data, the basic aspects of the Buckingham pi theorem have been presented in the introductory chapter on convection and several pertinent examples have been worked out. The European method of deducing similarity parameters from differential equations is illustrated in the chapter on free convection.

The evaluation of convective-heat-transfer coefficients from empirical equations is taken up in separate chapters for free convection, forced convection inside conduits, and flow over tubes and other bodies. Heat transfer of boiling and condensing fluids is treated in the chapter on heat transfer with phase change, in which melting and freezing processes are also considered. The amount of empirical data presented has been limited to configurations of widest practical interest, but the effect of variable fluid properties on heat transfer and friction coefficients has been emphasized.

In the chapter dealing with the design and thermal analysis of heat exchangers, the concept of effectiveness has been emphasized. Basic material on the mean-temperature-difference method of analysis has been included because this technique is widely used in industry.

In Professor Andersen's chapter on mass transfer, the analogy between the transfer of mass, heat, and momentum has been emphasized. The material has been organized in such a manner that it can be presented immediately after, or simultaneously with, heat transfer by convection.

The appendix contains a survey of thermal properties. The property tables are designed to supplement the discussion and to provide a handy source of data for solving the problems at the end of each chapter. Wherever answers are given, they have been obtained with the physical properties listed in the appendix.

One of the most difficult and probably the most controversial task in preparing an introductory text for a field as broad as heat transfer is the selection of the material. The author has tried to avoid overspecialization as much as possible but has illustrated the basic principles by applying them to the solution of specific problems dealing with nuclear reactors, temperature-measuring techniques, solar radiation, high-speed flow, rocket-motor cooling systems, compact heat exchangers, and many other devices of current interest. Highly specialized areas such as regenerator theories, film cooling, and heat transfer at extreme temperatures and pressures have not been treated because the author believes that these problems do not fall within the scope of an introductory text. Wherever practical, however, a sufficiently complete bibliography has been included to enable the reader to pursue his special interest more fully.

This text makes no claim to originality. The author has merely attempted to collect pertinent material and present it in a teachable form. The material itself has been selected from the literature, and wherever possible the author has given credit to the original sources. In his approach the author has been greatly influenced by the philosophy of Dean L. M. K. Boelter and his coworkers, especially the late Mr. Earl Morrin.

The author acknowledges with pleasure the help and encouragement given him by his colleagues and students. Several members of the staff of the Mechanical Engineering Department at the University of California at Berkeley, particularly Professor H. A. Johnson, Dr. R. Drake (now at Princeton University), Professor R. V. Dunkel, and Dr. R. A. Seban, have offered suggestions and contributed some of the student exercises. Professor J. T. Anderson, Michigan State University, Professor W. M. Kays, Stanford University, Professor J. F. Lee, North Carolina State College, Dr. P. J.

Schneider, University of Minnesota, and Dr. L. B. Andersen, Lehigh University, have read the manuscript in its entirety and have contributed many valuable suggestions.

Dr. O. P. Bergelin, University of Delaware, Dr. A. J. Chabai, Lehigh University, and Dr. W. M. Rohsenow, Massachusetts Institute of Technology, have given technical advice. Mr. Kun Min checked the illustrative problems and prepared some of the drawings. Miss Joyce Broadhead and Mrs. Helen Farrell typed portions of the manuscript. Particular thanks are due to Marion Kreith for helping in many tangible and many more intangible ways.

FRANK KREITH

Bethlehem, Pennsylvania
January, 1958

Contents[1]

[1] Sections marked with an * can be omitted in an undergraduate course without interrupting the continuity of the presentation.

Principles of

Heat Transfer

1 Introduction

1–1. THE RELATION OF HEAT TRANSFER TO THERMODYNAMICS

Whenever a temperature gradient exists within a system, or when two systems at different temperatures are brought into contact, energy is transferred. The process by which the energy transport takes place is known as *heat transfer*. The thing in transit, called heat, cannot be measured or observed directly, but the effects it produces are amenable to observation and measurement. The flow of heat, as the performance of work, is a process by which the internal energy of a system is changed.

The branch of science which deals with the relation between heat and other forms of energy is called *thermodynamics*. Its principles, like all laws of nature, are based on observations and have been generalized into laws which are believed to hold for all processes occurring in nature, because no exceptions have ever been detected. The first of these principles, the first law of thermodynamics, states that energy can be neither created nor destroyed but only changed from one form to another. It governs all energy transformations quantitatively but places no restrictions on the direction of the transformation. It is known, however, from experience that no process is possible whose sole result is the net transfer of heat from a region of lower temperature to a region of higher temperature. This statement of experimental truth is known as the second law of thermodynamics.

All heat-transfer processes involve the transfer and conversion of energy. They must therefore obey the first as well as the second law of thermodynamics. At a first glance one might therefore be tempted to assume that the principles of heat transfer can be derived from the basic laws of thermodynamics. This, however, would be an erroneous conclusion because classical thermodynamics is restricted primarily to the study of equilibrium states, including mechanical and chemical as well as thermal equilibriums, and is therefore, by itself, of little help in determining quantitatively the transformations which occur from a lack of equilibrium in engineering processes. Since heat flow is the result of temperature nonequilibrium, its quantitative treatment must be based on other branches of science. The same reasoning applies to other types of transport processes such as mass transfer and diffusion.

3

Limitations of classical thermodynamics. Classical thermodynamics deals with the states of systems from a macroscopic view and makes no hypotheses about the structure of matter. To perform a thermodynamic analysis it is necessary to describe the state of a system in terms of gross characteristics, such as pressure, volume, and temperature, which can be measured directly and involve no special assumptions regarding the structure of matter. These variables or thermodynamic properties are of significance for the system as a whole only when they are uniform throughout it, i.e., when the system is in equilibrium. Thus, classical thermodynamics is not concerned with the details of a process but rather with equilibrium states and the relations among them. The processes employed in a thermodynamic analysis are idealized processes, devised merely to give information concerning equilibrium states.

From a thermodynamic viewpoint, the amount of heat transferred during a process simply equals the difference between the energy change of the system and the work done. It is evident that this type of analysis considers neither the mechanism of heat flow nor the time required to transfer the heat. It simply prescribes how much heat to supply to, or reject from, a system during a process between specified end states without taking care of whether or how this could be accomplished. The reason for this lack of information obtainable from a thermodynamic analysis is the absence of time as a variable. The question of how long it would take to transfer a specified amount of heat, although it is of great practical importance, does not usually enter into the thermodynamic analysis.

Engineering heat transfer. From an engineering viewpoint, the determination of the *rate of heat transfer at a specified temperature difference* is the key problem. To estimate the cost, the feasibility, and the size of equipment necessary to transfer a specified amount of heat in a given time, a detailed heat-transfer analysis must be made. The dimensions of boilers, heaters, refrigerators, and heat exchangers depend not only on the amount of heat to be transmitted, but rather on the rate at which the heat is to be transferred under given conditions. The successful operation of equipment components such as, for example, turbine blades or the walls of combustion chambers depends on the possibility of cooling certain metal parts by removing heat continuously at a rapid rate from a surface. Also, in the design of electric machines, transformers, and bearings, a heat-transfer analysis must be made to avoid conditions which will cause overheating and damage the equipment. These varied examples show that in almost every branch of engineering, heat-transfer problems are encountered which are not capable of solution by thermodynamic reasoning alone, but require an analysis based on the science of heat transfer.

In heat transfer, as in other branches of engineering, the successful solution of a problem requires assumptions and idealizations. It is almost impossible to describe physical phenomena exactly, and in order to express a problem in the form of an equation that can be solved it is necessary to make some approximations. In electric-circuit calculations, for example, it is usually assumed that the values of the resistances, capacitances, and inductances are independent of the current flowing through them. This assumption simplifies the analysis but may in certain cases limit the accuracy of the results severely.

It is important to keep the assumptions, idealizations, and approximations made in the course of an analysis in mind when the final results are interpreted. Sometimes insufficient information on physical properties makes it necessary to use engineering approximations to solve a problem. For example, in the design of machine parts for operation at elevated temperatures it may be necessary to estimate the proportional limit or the fatigue strength of the material from low-temperature data. To assure satisfactory operation of the part, the designer should apply a factor of safety to the results he obtains from his analysis. Similar approximations are also necessary in heat-transfer problems. Physical properties, such as the thermal conductivity or the viscosity, change with temperature, but if suitable average values are selected, the calculations can be considerably simplified without introducing an appreciable error in the final result. When heat is transferred from a fluid to a wall, as for example in a boiler, a scale forms under continued operation and reduces the rate of heat flow. To assure satisfactory operation over a long period of time, a factor of safety must be applied to provide for this contingency.

When it becomes necessary to make an assumption or approximation in the solution of a problem, the engineer must rely on his ingenuity and past experience. There are no simple guides to new and unexplored problems, and an assumption valid for one problem may be misleading in another. Experience has shown, however, that the first and foremost requirement for making sound engineering assumptions or approximations is a complete and thorough physical understanding of the problem at hand. In the field of heat transfer, this requires not only a familiarity with the laws and physical mechanisms of heat flow, but also with those of fluid mechanics, physics, and mathematics.

1-2. MODES OF HEAT FLOW

Heat transfer can be defined as the transmission of energy from one region to another as a result of a temperature difference between them. Since differences in temperatures exist all over the universe, the phenomena of heat flow are as universal as those associated with gravitational attractions. Unlike gravity, however, heat flow is governed not by a unique relationship, but rather by a combination of various independent laws of physics.

The literature of heat transfer generally recognizes three distinct modes of heat transmission: *conduction, radiation,* and *convection.* Strictly speaking, only conduction and radiation should be classified as heat-transfer processes, because only these two mechanisms depend for their operation on the mere existence of a temperature difference. The last of the three, convection, does not strictly comply with the definition of heat transfer because it depends for its operation on mechanical mass transport also. But since convection also accomplishes transmission of energy from regions of higher temperature to regions of lower temperature, the term "heat transfer by convection" has become generally accepted.

Each of these modes of heat transfer will be described and analyzed separately. Yet it should be emphasized that, in most situations occurring in nature, heat flows not by one, but by several of these mechanisms acting simultaneously. It is particularly important in engineering to be aware of the confluence of the various modes of heat transfer because, in practice, when one mechanism dominates quantitatively, useful approximate solutions are obtained by neglecting all but the dominant mechanism. However, a change of external conditions will often require that one or both of the previously neglected mechanisms be taken into account.

Conduction. Conduction is a process by which heat flows from a region of higher temperature to a region of lower temperature within a medium (solid, liquid, or gaseous) or between different mediums in direct physical contact. In conduction heat flow, the energy is transmitted by direct molecular communication without appreciable displacement of the molecules. According to the kinetic theory, the temperature of an element of matter is proportional to the mean kinetic energy of its constituent molecules. The energy possessed by an element of matter by virtue of the velocity and relative position of the molecules is called *internal energy.* Thus, the more rapidly the molecules are moving, the greater will be the temperature as well as the internal energy of an element of matter. When molecules in one region acquire a mean kinetic energy greater than that of molecules in an adjacent region, as manifested by a difference in temperature, the molecules possessing the greater energy will transmit part of their energy to the molecules in the lower-temperature region. The transfer of energy could take place by elastic impact (e.g., in fluids) or by diffusion of faster-moving electrons from the higher- to the lower-temperature regions (e.g., in metals). Irrespective of the exact mechanism, which is by no means fully understood, the observable effect of heat conduction is an equalization of temperature. However, if differences in temperature are maintained by addition and removal of heat at different points, a continuous flow of heat from the hotter to the cooler region will be established.

Conduction is the only mechanism by which heat can flow in opaque solids. Conduction is also important in fluids, but in nonsolid mediums it is usually combined with convection, and in some cases with radiation also.

Radiation. Radiation is a process by which heat flows from a high-temperature body to a body at a lower temperature when the bodies are separated in space, even when a vacuum exists between them. The term "radiation" is generally applied to all kinds of electromagnetic-wave phenomena, but in heat transfer only those phenomena which are the result of temperature and can transport energy through a transparent medium or through space are of interest. The energy transmitted in this manner is termed *radiant heat*.

All bodies emit radiant heat continuously. The intensity of the emissions depends on the temperature and the nature of the surface. Radiant energy travels at the speed of light (186,000 mps) and resembles phenomenologically the radiation of light. In fact, according to the electromagnetic theory, light and thermal radiation differ only in their respective wavelengths.

Radiant heat is emitted by a body in the form of finite batches, or *quanta*, of energy. The motion of radiant heat in space is similar to the propagation of light and can be described by the wave theory. When the radiation waves encounter some other object, their energy is absorbed near its surface. Heat transfer by radiation becomes increasingly important as the temperature of an object increases. In engineering problems involving temperatures approximating those of the atmosphere, radiant heating may often be neglected.

Convection. Convection is a process of energy transport by the combined action of heat conduction, energy storage, and mixing motion. Convection is most important as the mechanism of energy transfer between a solid surface and a liquid or a gas.

The transfer of energy by convection from a surface whose temperature is above that of a surrounding fluid takes place in several steps. First, heat will flow by conduction from the surface to adjacent particles of fluid. The energy thus transferred will serve to increase the temperature and the internal energy of these fluid particles. Then the fluid particles will move to a region of lower temperature in the fluid where they will mix with, and transfer a part of their energy to, other fluid particles. The flow in this case is of fluid as well as energy. The energy is actually stored in the fluid particles and is carried as a result of their mass motion. This mechanism does not depend for its operation merely on a temperature difference and therefore does not strictly conform to the definition of heat transfer. The net effect, however, is a transport of energy, and since it occurs in the direction of a temperature gradient, is also classified as a mode of heat transfer and is referred to as *heat flow by convection*.

Convection heat transfer is classified according to the mode of motivating flow into *free convection* and *forced convection*. When the mixing motion takes place merely as a result of density differences caused by temperature gradients, we speak of *natural,* or *free,* convection. When the mixing motion is induced by some external agency, such as a pump or a blower, the process is called forced convection.

The effectiveness of heat transfer by convection depends largely upon the mixing motion of the fluid. Consequently a study of convective heat transfer is predicated on a knowledge of the characteristics of the fluid flow.

In the solution of heat-transfer problems, it is necessary not only to recognize the modes of heat transfer which play a role but also to determine whether a process is *steady* or *unsteady*. When the rate of heat flow in a system does not vary with time, i.e., when it is constant, the temperature at any point does not change and steady-state conditions prevail. Under steady-state conditions, the rate of heat influx at any point of the system must be exactly equal to the rate of heat efflux, and no change in internal energy can take place. The majority of engineering heat-transfer problems are concerned with steady-state systems. Typical examples are the flow of heat from the products of combustion to water in the tubes of a boiler, the cooling of an electric light bulb by the surrounding atmosphere, or the heat transfer from the hot to the cold fluid in a heat exchanger.

The heat flow in a system is *transient,* or unsteady, when the temperatures at various points in the system change with time. Since a change in temperature indicates a change of internal energy, we conclude that energy storage is part and parcel of unsteady heat flow. Unsteady-heat-flow problems are more complex than are those of steady state and can often be solved only by approximate methods. Unsteady-heat-flow problems are encountered during the warm-up periods of furnaces, boilers, and turbines or in the heat treatment and stress-relieving of metal castings.

A special case of unsteady heat flow occurs when a system is subjected to cyclic variations in the temperature of its environment. In such problems the temperature at a particular point in the system returns periodically to the same value; also, the rate of heat flow and the rate of energy storage undergo periodic variations. Problems of this type come under the classification of *periodic* or *quasi-steady-state heat transfer*. Typical examples are the variation of temperature of a building during any twenty-four-hour period or the heat flow through the cylinder walls of a reciprocating engine when the temperature of the gases within the cylinder changes periodically.

1–3. BASIC LAWS OF HEAT TRANSFER

Any meaningful engineering analysis demands a quantitative answer. To perform such an analysis of heat-transfer problems we must investigate the physical laws and relations which govern the various mechanisms of heat flow. In this section we shall make a preliminary survey of the basic equations governing each of the three modes of heat transfer. Later we shall show how to combine these relations when several of the heat-flow mechanisms are operating concurrently, either in series or in parallel. Our preliminary aim is to obtain a broad perspective of the field without becoming involved in the details of any particular mechanism. We shall, therefore, consider only simple cases and postpone more complex problems for later chapters.

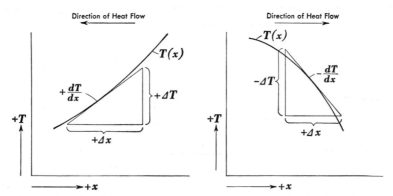

Fig. 1–1. Sketch illustrating sign convention for conduction heat flow.

Conduction. The basic relation for heat transfer by conduction was proposed by the French scientist, J. B. J. Fourier, in 1822. It states that q_k, the *rate of heat flow by conduction* in a material, is equal to the product of the following three quantities:

1. k, the thermal conductivity of the material.
2. A, the area of the section through which heat flows by conduction, to be measured perpendicularly to the direction of heat flow.
3. dT/dx, the temperature gradient at the section, i.e., the rate of change of temperature T with respect to distance in the direction of heat flow x.

To write the heat conduction equation in mathematical form, we must adopt a sign convention. We specify that the direction of increasing distance x is to be the direction of positive heat flow. Then, since according to the second law of thermodynamics heat will automatically flow from points of higher temperature to points of lower temperature, heat flow will be positive when the temperature gradient is negative (Fig. 1–1). Accordingly, the elementary equation for one-dimensional conduction in the steady state is written

$$q_k = -kA \frac{dT}{dx} \tag{1-1}$$

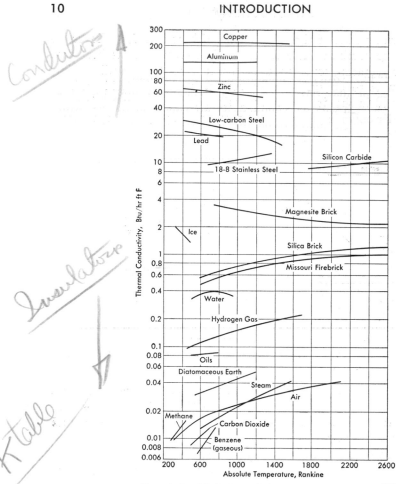

Conductors

Insulators

K table

FIG. 1–2. Variation of thermal conductivity of
solids, liquids, and gases with temperature.

For dimensional consistency of Eq. 1–1, the rate of heat flow q_k is
expressed in Btu/hr, the area A in sq ft, and the temperature gradient
dT/dx in F/ft.   The thermal conductivity k is a property of the material
and indicates the quantity of heat that will flow across a unit area if the
temperature gradient is unity.   The units for k used in this text are
British thermal units per hour per square foot per unit temperature
gradient in degrees Fahrenheit per foot, i.e.,

$$K = \frac{\text{Btu/hr sq ft}}{\text{F/ft}} \quad \text{or} \quad \frac{\text{Btu}}{\text{hr ft F}} \quad [1]$$

[1] Throughout the remainder of this book units of physical quantities will be given
in conventionally abbreviated form without expanding them.

Thermal conductivities of engineering materials at atmospheric pressure range from about 4×10^{-3} for gases through about 1×10^{-1} for liquids to 2.4×10^{2} for copper. Orders of magnitudes of the thermal conductivity of various classes of material are shown in Table 1–1 and Fig. 1–2. Materials having a high thermal conductivity are called *conductors*, while materials of low thermal conductivity are referred to as *insulators*. In general, the thermal conductivity varies with temperature, but in many engineering problems the variation is sufficiently small to be neglected.

TABLE 1–1

ORDER OF MAGNITUDE OF THERMAL CONDUCTIVITY

Material	k in Btu/hr ft F
Gases at atmospheric pressure	0.004–0.10
Insulating materials	0.02–0.12
Nonmetallic liquids	0.05–0.40
Nonmetallic solids (brick, stone, concrete)	0.02–1.5
Liquid metals	5.0–45
Alloys	8.0–70
Pure metals	30–240

For the simple case of steady-state heat flow through a plane wall, the temperature gradient and the heat flow do not vary with time and the cross-sectional area along the heat-flow path is uniform. The variables in Eq. 1–1 can be separated and the resulting equation is

$$\frac{q_k}{A} \int_0^L dx = -\int_{T_{\text{hot}}}^{T_{\text{cold}}} k \, dT$$

The limits of integration can be checked by inspection of Fig. 1–3, where the temperature at the left-hand face ($x = 0$) is uniform at T_{hot} and the temperature at the right-hand face ($x = L$) is uniform at T_{cold}.

If k is independent of T, we obtain, after integration, the following expression for the rate of heat conduction through the wall

$$q_k = \frac{Ak}{L}(T_{\text{hot}} - T_{\text{cold}}) = \frac{\Delta T}{L/Ak} \qquad (1\text{-}2)$$

In this equation ΔT, the temperature difference between the higher temperature T_{hot} and the lower temperature T_{cold}, is the driving potential which causes the flow of heat. L/Ak is equivalent to a *thermal resistance* R_k, which the wall offers to the flow of heat by conduction and we have

$$\text{Thermal Resistance} = R_k = \frac{L}{Ak} = \frac{F \cdot Hr}{BTU} \qquad (1\text{-}3)$$

The reciprocal of the thermal resistance is referred to as the *thermal conductance*

$$K_k = \frac{Ak}{L} = \frac{BTU}{HR \cdot F}$$ (1-4)

and k/L, the thermal conductance per unit area, is called the *unit thermal conductance for conduction heat flow*. The subscript k indicates that the transfer mechanism is by conduction. The thermal conductance has the units of Btu/hr F temperature difference and the thermal resistance has the units hr F/Btu. The concepts of resistance and conductance are helpful in the analysis of thermal systems where several modes of heat transfer occur simultaneously.

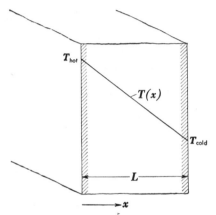

FIG. 1-3. Temperature distribution for steady-state conduction through a plane wall.

Radiation. The quantity of energy leaving a surface as radiant heat depends upon the *absolute temperature* and the nature of the surface. A perfect *radiator* or *black body*[2] emits radiant energy from its surface at a rate q_r given by

$$q_r = \sigma A_1 T_1{}^4 \qquad \text{Btu/hr} \qquad (1-5)$$

where A_1 is the surface area in sq ft, T_1 is the surfacet emperature in degrees Rankine (R), and σ is a dimensional constant with a value of 0.1714×10^{-8} Btu/hr sq ft R^4. The quantity σ is named the *Stefan-Boltzmann constant* after two Austrian scientists, J. Stefan, who in 1879 found Eq. 1-5 experimentally, and L. Boltzmann, who in 1884 derived it theoretically.

An inspection of Eq. 1-5 shows that any black-body surface above a temperature of absolute zero radiates heat at a rate proportional to the

[2] A detailed discussion of the meaning of these terms is presented in Chapter 5.

fourth power of the *absolute temperature*. While the rate of emission is independent of the conditions of the surroundings, a *net* transfer of radiant heat requires a difference in the surface temperature of any two bodies between which the exchange is taking place. If the black body radiates to an enclosure which completely surrounds it and whose surface is also *black,* i.e., absorbs all the radiant energy incident upon it, the net rate of radiant heat transfer is given by

$$q_r = \sigma A_1(T_1{}^4 - T_2{}^4) \qquad \text{(1-6)}$$

where T_2 is the surface temperature of the enclosure in degrees Fahrenheit absolute.

Real bodies do not meet the specifications of an ideal radiator but emit radiation at a lower rate than black bodies. If they emit, at a temperature equal to that of a black body, a constant fraction of black-body emission at each wavelength, they are called *gray bodies.* The net rate of heat transfer from a gray body at a temperature T_1 to a black surrounding at T_2 is

$$q_r = \sigma A_1 \epsilon_1(T_1{}^4 - T_2{}^4) \qquad \text{(1-7)}$$

where ϵ_1 is the *emissivity* of the gray surface and is equal to the ratio of emission from the gray surface to the emission from a perfect radiator at the same temperature.

If neither of two bodies is a perfect radiator and if the two bodies possess a given geometrical relationship to each other, the net heat transfer by radiation between them is given by

$$q_r = \sigma A_1 \mathfrak{F}_{1-2}(T_1{}^4 - T_2{}^4) \qquad \text{(1-8)}$$

where $\mathfrak{F}_{1-2}$ is a modulus which modifies the equation for perfect radiators to account for the emissivities and relative geometries of the actual bodies.

In many engineering problems, radiation is combined with other modes of heat transfer. The solution of such problems can often be simplified by using a thermal conductance K_r, or a thermal resistance R_r, for radiation. The definition of K_r is similar to that of K_k, the thermal conductance for conduction. If the heat transfer by radiation is written

$$q_r = K_r(T_1 - T_2') \qquad \text{(1-9)}$$

the conductance, by comparison with Eq. 1-8, is given by

$$K_r = \frac{\sigma A_1 \mathfrak{F}_{1-2}(T_1{}^4 - T_2{}^4)}{T_1 - T_2'} \qquad \text{Btu/hr F} \qquad \text{(1-10)}$$

and the unit thermal conductance for radiation $\bar{h}_r$ by

$$\bar{h}_r = \frac{K_r}{A_1} = \frac{\sigma \mathfrak{F}_{1-2}(T_1{}^4 - T_2{}^4)}{T_1 - T_2'} \qquad \text{Btu/hr sq ft F} \qquad \text{(1-11)}$$

where T_2' is any convenient reference temperature whose choice is often dictated by the convection equation, which will be discussed next. Similarly, the thermal resistance for radiation is

$$R_r = \frac{T_1 - T_2'}{\sigma A_1 \mathfrak{F}_{1-2}(T_1{}^4 - T_2{}^4)} \text{ hr sq ft F/Btu} \qquad (1\text{--}12)$$

Convection. The rate of heat transfer by convection between a surface and a fluid may be computed by the relation

$$q_c = \bar{h}_c A \Delta T \qquad (1\text{--}13)$$

where q_c = rate of heat transfer by convection, Btu/hr;
A = heat transfer area, sq ft;
ΔT = difference between the surface temperature T_s and a temperature of the fluid T_∞ at some specified location (usually far away from the surface), F;
$\bar{h}_c$ = average unit thermal convective conductance (sometimes called the film heat-transfer factor, surface coefficient of heat transfer, or convective heat transfer coefficient), Btu/hr sq ft F.

The relation expressed by Eq. 1–13 was originally proposed by the British scientist, Isaac Newton, in 1701. Engineers have used this equation for many years, even though it is a definition of $\bar{h}_c$ rather than a phenomenological law of convection. The evaluation of the convective heat-transfer coefficient is difficult because convection is a very complex phenomenon. The methods and techniques available for a quantitative evaluation of $\bar{h}_c$ will be presented in later chapters. At this point it is sufficient to note that the numerical value of $\bar{h}_c$ in a system depends on the geometry of the surface and the velocity, as well as on the physical properties of the fluid and often even on the temperature difference ΔT. In view of the fact that these quantities are not necessarily constant over a surface, the convective heat-transfer coefficient may also vary from point to point. For this reason we must distinguish between a *local* and an *average* convective heat-transfer coefficient. The local coefficient h_c is defined by

$$dq_c = h_c dA (T_s - T_\infty) \qquad (1\text{--}14)$$

while the average coefficient $\bar{h}_c$ can be defined in terms of the local value by

$$\bar{h}_c = \frac{1}{A} \int\int_A h_c dA \qquad (1\text{--}15)$$

For most engineering applications, we shall be interested in average values. For general orientation, typical values of the order of magnitude of average convective heat-transfer coefficients encountered in engineering practice are presented in Table 1–2.

TABLE 1–2

ORDER OF MAGNITUDE OF CONVECTIVE HEAT-TRANSFER COEFFICIENTS

Condition	$\hbar$ in Btu/hr sq ft F
Air, free convection	1–5
Superheated steam or air, forced convection	5–50
Oil, forced convection	10–300
Water, forced convection	50–2000
Water, boiling	500–10,000
Steam, condensing	1000–20,000

Using Eq. 1–13, we can define the thermal conductance K_c for convective heat transfer as

$$K_c = \bar{h}_c A \tag{1–16}$$

and the thermal resistance to convective heat transfer R_c, which is equal to the reciprocal of the conductance, as

$$R_c = \frac{1}{\bar{h}_c A} \tag{1–17}$$

1–4. COMBINED HEAT-TRANSFER MECHANISMS

In the preceding section the three mechanisms of heat transfer have been considered separately. In practice, however, heat is usually transferred in steps through a number of different series-connected sections, the transfer frequently occurring by two mechanisms in parallel for a given section in the system. The transfer of heat from the products of combustion in the combustion chamber of a rocket motor through a thin wall to a coolant flowing in an annulus over the outside of the wall will illustrate such a case (Fig. 1–4).

Products of combustion contain gases, such as CO, CO_2, and H_2O which emit and absorb radiation. In the first section of this system, heat is therefore transferred from the hot gas to the inner surface of the wall of the rocket motor by the mechanisms of convection and radiation acting in parallel. The total rate of heat flow q is

$$q = q_c + q_r$$
$$= \bar{h}_c A (T_g - T_{sg}) + \bar{h}_r A (T_g - T_{sg}) \tag{1–18}$$

or

$$q = (\bar{h}_c A + \bar{h}_r A)(T_g - T_{sg})$$
$$= (K_c + K_r)(T_g - T_{sg})$$
$$= \frac{T_g - T_{sg}}{R_1}$$

where T_g = temperature of hot gas;

T_{sg} = temperature at inner surface of wall;

R_1 = combined or effective thermal resistance of the first section,
$R_1 = 1/(\bar{h}_r + \bar{h}_c)A$.

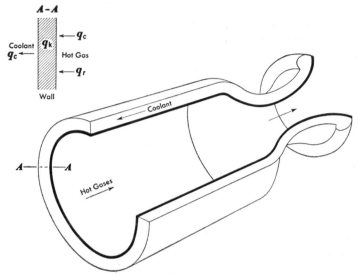

FIG. 1–4. Heat transfer in a rocket motor.

In the steady state, heat is conducted through the shell, the second section of the system, at the same rate and

$$q = q_k = \frac{kA}{L}(T_{sg} - T_{sc}) \qquad (1\text{--}19)$$

$$= K_k(T_{sg} - T_{sc})$$

$$= \frac{T_{sg} - T_{sc}}{R_2}$$

where T_{sc} = surface temperature at wall on coolant side;

R_2 = thermal resistance of second section.

After passing through the wall, the heat flows through the third section of the system by convection to the coolant. Assuming that radiant heat transfer is negligible compared to convection, the rate of heat flow in the last step is

$$q = q_c = \bar{h}_c A(T_{sc} - T_c) \qquad (1\text{--}20)$$

$$= \frac{T_{sc} - T_c}{R_3}$$

where T_c = temperature of the coolant;

R_3 = thermal resistance in the third section of the system.

It should be noted that the symbol $\bar{h}_c$ stands for the unit-surface conductance in general, but the numerical values of the conductances in the first and third sections of the system depend on many factors and will in general be different. Also the areas of the three heat-flow sections are not equal. But since the wall is very thin, the change in the heat-flow area is so small that it can be neglected in this system.

In practice, often only the temperatures of the hot gas and the coolant are known. The intermediate temperatures can be eliminated by algebraic addition of Eqs. 1–18, 1–19, and 1–20, or

$$q = \frac{T_g - T_c}{R_1 + R_2 + R_3} = \frac{\Delta T_{\text{total}}}{R_1 + R_2 + R_3} \tag{1-21}$$

where the thermal resistances of the three series-connected sections or heat-flow steps in the system are defined in Eqs. 1–18, 1–19, and 1–20.

In Eq. 1–21 the rate of heat flow is expressed only in terms of an overall temperature potential and the heat-transfer characteristics of individual sections in the heat-flow path. From these relations it is possible to evaluate quantitatively the importance of each individual thermal resistance in the path. An inspection of the order of magnitudes of the individual terms in the denominator often indicates means of simplifying a problem. When one or the other term dominates quantitatively, it is sometimes permissible to neglect the rest. As we gain facility in the techniques of determining individual thermal resistances and conductances, there will be numerous occasions where such approximations will be illustrated. There are, however, certain types of problems, notably in the design of heat exchangers, where it is convenient to simplify the writing of Eq. 1–21 by combining the individual resistances or conductances of the thermal system into one quantity, called the *over-all unit conductance, the over-all transmittance,* or the *over-all coefficient of heat transfer, U.* The use of an over-all coefficient is a convenience in notation, and it is important not to lose sight of the significance of the individual factors which determine the numerical value of U.

Writing Eq. 1–21 in terms of an over-all coefficient gives

$$q = UA\Delta T_{\text{total}} \tag{1-22}$$

where
$$UA = \frac{1}{(R_1 + R_2 + R_3)} \tag{1-23}$$

The over-all coefficient U may be based on any chosen area. To avoid misunderstandings, the area basis of an over-all coefficient should therefore always be stated.

The numerical evaluation of the various resistances or conductances of a thermal system is generally the most difficult part of any engineering heat-transfer problem. In fact, the material to which most of the following chapters is devoted deals with the determination of individual resistances and conductances from external conditions which can either be measured or specified. Once the individual resistances or conductances have been evaluated, the over-all coefficient of heat transfer can be obtained and, for steady-state conditions, the rate of heat transfer can be determined for a specified temperature difference. For heat flow along a path consisting of n thermal sections in series, the over-all conductance UA is equal to the reciprocal of the sum of the resistances of the individual sections, or

$$UA = \frac{1}{R_1 + R_2 + \cdots + R_n} \tag{1-24}$$

where each resistance is the reciprocal of the sum of the conductances for that section.

The over-all heat-transfer coefficient will be found useful primarily in problems involving thermal systems consisting of several series-connected sections. The analysis of heat flow at boundaries of complicated geometry and in unsteady-state conduction problems can be simplified by using a combined unit-thermal-surface conductance $\bar{h}$. The combined unit-thermal-surface conductance, or *unit-surface conductance* for short, combines the effects of heat flow by convection and radiation between a surface and a fluid and is defined by

$$\bar{h} = \bar{h}_c + \bar{h}_r \tag{1-25}$$

The unit-surface conductance specifies the average total rate of heat flow per unit area between a surface and a fluid per degree temperature difference. Its units are Btu/hr sq ft F.

1–5. ANALOGY BETWEEN HEAT FLOW AND ELECTRICAL FLOW

Two systems are said to be analogous when both obey similar equations and also have similar boundary conditions. This means that the equation describing the behavior of one system can be transformed into the equation for the other system by simply changing the symbols of the variables. For example, the flow of heat through a thermal resistance is analogous to the flow of direct current through an electrical resistance because both types of flow obey similar equations. If we replace, in the heat-flow equation

$$q = \frac{\Delta T}{R} \tag{1-26}$$

the symbol for the temperature potential ΔT by the symbol for the electric potential, i.e., the voltage difference, ΔE and the symbol for the thermal resistance R by the symbol for the electrical resistance R_e, we obtain the equation for i, the flow rate of electricity, i.e., the current

$$i = \frac{\Delta E}{R_e} \tag{1-27}$$

Having once established the basic analogy, we can apply certain concepts from direct-current theory to heat-transfer problems. For instance, an

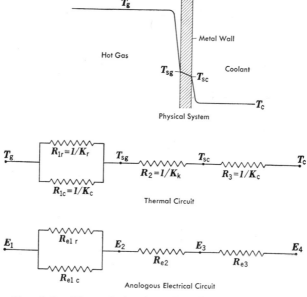

Fig. 1–5. Thermal circuit and analogous electric circuit for heat flow from a hot gas through a metal wall to a coolant.

electric circuit has a corresponding thermal circuit, and vice versa. In the problem of the preceding section, the heat flow from the hot gases to the coolant can be visualized as analogous to the flow of current in a simple direct-current circuit. In the equation for the current flow, analogous to Eq. 1–21 for the heat flow, we find that

$$i = \frac{\Delta E}{R_{e1} + R_{e2} + R_{e3}} \tag{1-28}$$

where R_{e1} is the effective resistance of two parallel resistances. One of them is analogous to the thermal resistance encountered by the convection heat flow, the other to the thermal resistance met by the heat flow from the gas to the wall by radiation. The thermal circuit and the electrical circuit for this problem are shown in Fig. 1–5.

Example 1–1. In the design of a heat exchanger for aircraft application, the maximum wall temperature is not to exceed 1000 F. For the conditions tabulated below, determine the maximum permissible thermal resistance per square foot area of the metal wall between hot gas on the one side and cold gas on the other.

Hot-gas temperature = 1900 F
Unit-surface conductance on hot side $\bar{h}_1$ = 40 Btu/hr sq ft F
Unit-surface conductance on cold side $\bar{h}_3$ = 50 Btu/hr sq ft F
Cold-gas temperature = 100 F

Solution: In the steady state we can write q/A from gas to hot side of wall = q/A from hot side of wall through wall to cold gas

or
$$\frac{T_g - T_{sg}}{R_1} = \frac{T_{sg} - T_c}{R_2 + R_3}$$

Substituting numerical values for the thermal resistances and temperatures yields

$$\frac{1900 - 1000}{1/40} = \frac{1000 - 100}{R_2 + 1/50}$$

Solving for R_2 gives

$$R_2 = 0.005 \text{ hr sq ft F/Btu} \qquad\qquad Ans.$$

A thermal resistance per unit area larger than 0.005 hr sq ft F/Btu would raise the inner wall above 1000 F.

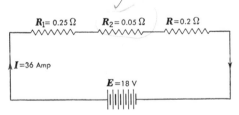

Fig. 1–6. Electric circuit analogous to the thermal circuit for Example 1–2.

Example 1–2. Draw the analogous electrical circuit for the preceding problem and determine the values of the electrical resistances in ohms if an 18-volt (v) d-c battery is used to provide the electrical potential, and a heat-flow rate of 1000 Btu/hr sq ft corresponds to 1 ampere (amp) of current.

Solution: We first determine the heat-flow rate per unit area in the thermal system

$$\frac{q}{A} = h_1(T_g - T_{sg}) = (40)(900) = 36,000 \text{ Btu/hr sq ft}$$

The current in the electric circuit is therefore 36 amp and the total electrical resistance of the three elements in series is $18/36 = 0.5$ ohms.

For the two circuits to be analogous, the ratio of each electrical resistance to the over-all resistance must be equal to the corresponding ratio in the thermal circuit. The values of the respective electrical resistances are indicated on the circuit diagram (Fig. 1–6) and should be checked by the reader. A tabulation of quantities analogous in both systems is given below:

Quantity	Thermal System	Electrical System
Potential.........	1 F	0.01 v
Flow............	1 Btu/hr sq ft	0.001 amp
Resistance.......	1 hr F/Btu	10.0 ohm

The analogy between the flow of heat and the flow of electricity may be used as an aid in visualizing relations in a thermal system by relating them to a more familiar electrical system. The analogy is also an aid in the quantitative analysis of a thermal circuit because methods and techniques familiar from d-c-circuit theory can be applied. There are numerous instances where solutions to heat-transfer problems are available in terms of an analogous system.

The analogy between electrical and thermal systems illustrated in this section is by no means complete. Other useful analogies will be considered in later chapters in connection with problems in two-dimensional heat conduction and in transient thermal systems.

PROBLEMS

1–1. Heat is transferred through a plane wall from the inside of a room at 70 F to the outside air at 30 F. The unit-surface conductances at the inside and outside surfaces are 2 and 3 Btu/hr sq ft F, respectively. The thermal resistance of the wall per unit area is 3 hr sq ft F/Btu. Determine the temperature at the outer surface of the wall and the rate of heat flow through the wall per unit area.

1–2. Draw the thermal circuit for heat transfer from the sun through a window to the air in a room. Identify each circuit element.

1–3. Steam is condensing inside a pipe at 134 psia. The unit-surface conductance on the steam side is 1000 Btu/hr sq ft F. The thermal resistance of the pipe per unit area is 0.001 hr sq ft F/Btu and the unit-surface conductance at the outside of the pipe is 5 Btu/hr sq ft F. (a) Estimate the per cent of the over-all thermal resistance offered by (1) the steam, (2) the pipe, and (3) the steam and the pipe. (b) Determine the temperature at the outer surface of the pipe if the pipe is suspended in a room at 70 F. The values of the unit conductances and the resistance are based on the outside area of the pipe.

1–4. Using Table 1–2 as a guide, prepare a similar table showing the order of magnitudes of the thermal resistances per unit area for convection between a surface and various fluids.

1–5. Draw the thermal circuit, determine the rate of heat flow per unit area from a furnace wall, and estimate the exterior surface temperature under the following conditions:

1. Convective heat-transfer coefficient at the interior surface is 10 Btu/hr sq ft F.
2. Rate of heat flow by radiation from hot gases and particles (3500 F) to interior wall surface is 20,000 Btu/hr sq ft.

3. Unit thermal conductance of wall (interior surface temperature about 1500 F) is 40 Btu/hr sq ft F.

4. Free convection from outer surface.

1–6. A thermocouple ($\frac{1}{32}$-in.-OD wire) is used to measure the temperature of quiescent gas in a furnace. The thermocouple reading is 300 F. It is known, however, that the rate of radiant heat flow per inch length from hotter furnace walls to the thermocouple wire is 0.1 Btu/hr and the unit conductance between the wire and the gas is 1.2 Btu/hr sq ft F. With this information, *estimate* the true gas temperature. State your assumptions and indicate the equations used.

1–7. The thermal conductivity of cork at 86 F is given in Table A-2 of Appendix III in Btu/hr ft F. What is its value in watts per square centimeter per degree centigrade per centimeter (w/cm C)?   *Ans.* 4.32 $\times$ 10^{-4}

1–8. Determine the rate of radiant heat emission in Btu per hr per sq ft from a black body at (a) 300 F; (b) 3000 F; (c) 3000 R; (d) 10,000 R.

          Ans. (a) 5.8 $\times$ 10^2; (b) 2.46 $\times$ 10^5; (c) 1.39 $\times$ 10^5; (d) 1.7 $\times$ 10^7

1–9. A flat plate placed in the sunlight receives 200 Btu/hr sq ft of radiant heat from the sun and the atmosphere. If the air temperature is 80 F and the unit-surface conductance between the plate and the air is 2 Btu/hr sq ft F, determine the plate temperature. Neglect heat losses from the bottom of the plate.

1–10. How much Fiberglas insulation (k = 0.02 Btu/hr ft F) is needed to enable a guarantee that the outside temperature of a kitchen oven will not exceed 120 F? The maximum oven temperature to be maintained by the conventional type of thermostatic control is 550 F, the kitchen temperature may vary from 60 F to 90 F and the average heat-transfer coefficient between the oven surface and the kitchen is 2 Btu/hr sq ft F.

1–11. A hot acid storage tank wall is to be constructed with $\frac{1}{8}$-in.-thick lead (k = 20 Btu/hr ft F) lining, an insulating layer of brick (k = 0.5 Btu/hr ft F), and $\frac{1}{4}$-in.-thick steel (k = 26 Btu/hr ft F) outer case. With the inside surface of the lead at 190 F and the room at 80 F, the temperature of the outside surface of the steel case is to be no higher than 140 F, selected as the maximum to prevent burns to workmen. Determine the necessary thickness of insulating brick to permit an inside lead surface temperature of 280 F.

2 Steady One-Dimensional Heat Conduction

2-1. WALLS OF SIMPLE GEOMETRICAL CONFIGURATION

In this section we shall consider steady-state heat conduction through simple systems in which the temperature and the heat flow are functions of a single coordinate.

Plane wall. The simplest case of one-dimensional heat flow, namely heat conduction through a plane wall, was treated in Sec. 1–3. We found that, for uniform temperatures over the hot and the cold surfaces, the rate of heat flow by conduction through a homogeneous material is given by

$$q_k = \frac{Ak}{L} (T_{\text{hot}} - T_{\text{cold}}) = \frac{\Delta T}{R_k} = K_k \Delta T \qquad [\,1\text{-}2\,]$$

Example 2–1. The interior surfaces of the walls in a large building are to be maintained at 70 F while the outer surface temperature is -10 F. The walls are 10 in. thick and constructed from a brick material having a thermal conductivity of 0.4 Btu/hr ft F. Calculate the heat loss for each square foot of wall surface per hour.

Solution: If we neglect the effect of the corners where the walls meet and the effect of mortared brick joints, Eq. 1–2 applies. Substituting the thermal conductivity and the pertinent dimensions in their proper units (e.g., $L = \frac{10}{12}$ ft) we obtain

$$\frac{q}{A} = \frac{(0.4)[70 - (-10)]}{10/12} = 38.4 \text{ Btu/hr sq ft}$$

Thus, 38.4 Btu will be lost from the building per hour through each square foot of wall-surface area. *Ans.*

Effect of nonuniform thermal conductivity. It has already been mentioned that the thermal conductivity varies with temperature. The variation of thermal conductivity with temperature may be neglected if the temperature range under consideration is not large or if the temperature dependence of the conductivity is not too severe. On the other hand, if the temperature difference in a system causes substantial variations in the thermal conductivity, the temperature dependence must be taken into account.

For numerous materials, especially within a limited temperature range,

23

the variation of the thermal conductivity with the temperature can be represented by the linear function.

$$k(T) = k_0(1 + \beta_k T) \tag{2-1}$$

where k_0 is the thermal conductivity at $T = 0$ and β_k is a constant called the *temperature coefficient of thermal conductivity*. When the variation of thermal conductivity is available in the form of a curve showing how k varies with T, the temperature coefficient can be obtained approximately by drawing a straight line between the temperatures of interest and measuring its slope. Then k_0 is a hypothetical value of the thermal conductivity equal to the ordinate intercept at zero temperature. It is determined graphically by continuing the straight line representing the

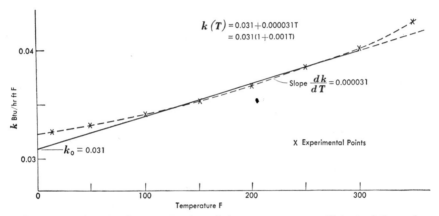

FIG. 2-1. Graphical determination of the temperature coefficient of thermal conductivity.

actual thermal conductivity over a limited temperature range through the axis of conductivity at zero temperature (Fig. 2-1).

With a linear approximation to the temperature variation of the thermal conductivity, the rate of heat flow by conduction through a plane wall is, from Eq. 1-2,

$$\frac{q_k}{A} \int_0^L dx = -\int_{T_{\text{hot}}}^{T_{\text{cold}}} k_0(1 + \beta_k T) dT \tag{2-2}$$

Integration of Eq. 2-2 gives

$$q_k = \frac{k_0 A}{L} \left[T_{\text{hot}} - T_{\text{cold}} + \frac{\beta_k}{2} (T_{\text{hot}}^2 - T_{\text{cold}}^2) \right] \tag{2-3}$$

which can be written more conveniently as

$$q_k = \frac{A(T_{\text{hot}} - T_{\text{cold}})}{L} k_0 \left(1 + \beta_k \frac{T_{\text{hot}} + T_{\text{cold}}}{2} \right) = \frac{\Delta T}{L/Ak_m} \quad (2\text{-}4)$$

where $k_m = k_0 [1 + \beta_k (T_{\text{hot}} + T_{\text{cold}})/2]$ represents a mean value of the thermal conductivity. For a linear variation of k with T, the thermal conductivity in Eq. 1-2 should therefore be evaluated at the arithmetic mean temperature $(T_{\text{hot}} + T_{\text{cold}})/2$.

Example 2-2. The conductivity of an 85 per cent magnesia insulating material is shown as a function of temperature in Fig. 2-1. (a) Determine β_k and k_0 for a linear approximation between 100 and 300 F. (b) Estimate the rate of heat flow per unit area between these temperatures for a slab of 3-in. thickness.

Solution: (a) By means of the graphical method illustrated in Fig. 2-1, the slope of the straight line connecting the thermal-conductivity curve between 100 and 300 F is found to be +0.000031. The ordinate intercept at 0 degrees (deg) is 0.031. Thus we have

$$k(T) = 0.031 \ (1 + 0.001 \ T) \qquad \text{for } 100 \text{ F} < T < 300 \text{ F}$$

The mean temperature is 200 F and the mean value of the thermal conductivity is

$$k_m = 0.031 \ (1 + 0.001 \times 200) = 0.0372 \text{ Btu/hr ft F} \qquad Ans.$$

b) The rate of heat flow per unit area is, from Eq. 2-4,

$$\frac{q_k}{A} = \frac{\Delta T}{L/k_m} = \frac{200}{(3/12)/(0.0372)} = 2.15 \text{ Btu/hr sq ft} \qquad Ans.$$

Hollow cylinders. Radial heat flow by conduction through a hollow circular cylinder is another one-dimensional conduction problem of considerable practical importance. Typical examples are conduction through pipes and through pipe insulation.

If the cylinder is homogeneous and sufficiently long that end effects may be neglected and the inner surface temperature is constant at T_i while the outer surface temperature is maintained uniformly at T_o, the rate of heat conduction is, from Eq. 1-1,

$$q_k = - kA \frac{dT}{dr}$$

where dT/dr = temperature gradient in the radial direction.

For the hollow cylinder (Fig. 2-2), the area is a function of the radius and

$$A = 2\pi r l$$

where r is the radius and l the length of the cylinder. The rate of heat flow by conduction can thus be expressed as

$$q_k = -k 2\pi r l \frac{dT}{dr} \tag{2-5}$$

Separating the variables and integrating between T_o at r_o and T_i at r_i yields

$$T_i - T_o = \frac{q_k}{k 2\pi l} \ln \frac{r_o}{r_i} \tag{2-6}$$

Solving Eq. 2–6 for q_k yields

$$q_k = \frac{T_i - T_o}{\dfrac{\ln (r_o/r_i)}{2\pi k l}} \tag{2-7}$$

the equation for calculating the rate of heat conduction through a hollow circular cylinder such as a pipe. An inspection of Eq. 2–7 shows that the

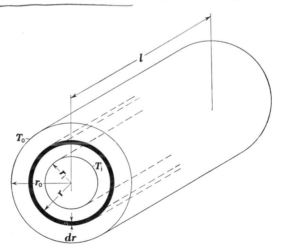

Fig. 2–2.   Sketch illustrating nomenclature for conduction through a hollow cylinder.

rate of radial heat flow varies directly with the cylinder length l, the thermal conductivity k, the temperature difference between the inner and outer surfaces $T_i - T_o$, and inversely as the *natural logarithm*[1] of the ratio of the outside and inside radii r_o/r_i or the corresponding diameter ratio D_o/D_i. By analogy to the case of a plane wall and Ohm's law, the thermal resistance of the hollow cylinder is

[1] The natural logarithm of a number, ln, is 2.3026 times the logarithm to base 10.

$$R_k = \frac{\ln (r_o/r_i)}{2\pi k l} \tag{2-8}$$

The temperature distribution in the curved wall is obtained by integrating Eq. 2–5 from the inner radius r_i and the corresponding temperature T_i to an arbitrary radius r and the corresponding temperature T, or

$$\int_{r_i}^{r} \frac{q_k}{k(2\pi l)} \frac{dr}{r} = -\int_{T_i}^{T(r)} dT$$

which gives

$$T(r) = T_i - \frac{T_i - T_o}{\ln (r_o/r_i)} \ln \frac{r}{r_i}$$

Thus the temperature in a hollow circular cylinder is a logarithmic function of the radius r (Fig. 2–3), while for a plane wall the temperature distribution is linear.

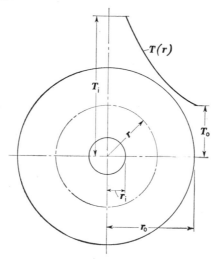

Fig. 2–3. Temperature distribution in a hollow cylinder.

For some applications it is helpful to have the equation for heat conduction through a curved wall in the same form as Eq. 1–2 for a plane wall. To obtain this form of equation we equate the right-hand sides of Eqs. 2–7 and 1–2, using, however, $L = (r_o - r_i)$, the thickness through which heat is conducted, and $A = \bar{A}$ in Eq. 1–2. This yields

$$\frac{k\bar{A}\Delta T}{r_o - r_i} = \frac{2\pi k l \Delta T}{\ln (r_o/r_i)}$$

from which $\bar{A}$ is

$$\bar{A} = \frac{2\pi(r_o - r_i)l}{\ln(r_o/r_i)}$$

Noting that $2\pi r_o l = A_o$, the area of the outside surface, and that $r_o/r_i = A_o/A_i$, we can express $\bar{A}$ as

$$\bar{A} = \frac{A_o - A_i}{\ln(A_o/A_i)} \tag{2-9}$$

The area $\bar{A}$ defined by Eq. 2–9 is called the *logarithmic mean area*. The rate of heat conduction through a hollow circular cylinder can then be expressed as

$$q_k = \frac{T_o - T_i}{(r_o - r_i)/k\bar{A}} \tag{2-10}$$

The rate of heat flow q_k will be in Btu/hr if $T_o - T_i$ is in F, $r_o - r_i$ is in ft, k is in Btu/hr ft F, and $\bar{A}$ is in sq ft.

For values of $A_o/A_i < 2$ (i.e., $r_o/r_i < 2$) the arithmetic mean area $(A_o + A_i)/2$ is within 4 per cent of the logarithmic mean area and may be used with satisfactory accuracy. For thicker walls this approximation is generally not acceptable.

Example 2–3. Calculate the heat loss from 10 ft of 3-in. nominal-diameter pipe covered with $1\frac{1}{2}$ in. of an insulating material having a thermal conductivity of 0.040 Btu/hr ft F. Assume that the inner and outer surface temperatures of the insulation are 400 and 80 F, respectively.

Solution: The outside diameter of a nominal 3-in. pipe is 3.50 in. This is also the inside diameter of the insulation. The outside diameter of the insulation is 6.50 in. The logarithmic mean area is

$$\bar{A} = \frac{A_o - A_i}{\ln(A_o/A_i)} = \frac{10\pi(6.50 - 3.50)/12}{\ln(6.50/3.50)}$$

$$= \frac{7.85}{0.62} = 12.70 \text{ sq ft}$$

Since $r_o/r_i < 2$, the arithmetic mean area would be an acceptable approximation and

$$\frac{A_o + A_i}{2} = \frac{1}{2}\frac{6.50 + 3.50}{12} = 13.10 \text{ sq ft}$$

Applying Eq. 2–10, the rate of heat loss is

$$q_k = \frac{400 - 80}{(3/12)/(0.04)(12.7)} = 650 \text{ Btu/hr} \qquad Ans.$$

Radial heat conduction through a hollow cylinder made of a material whose thermal conductivity varies linearly with temperature can be handled in a manner analogous to that used for the plane wall.   Substituting Eq. 2–1 into Eq. 2–5, separating the variables, and integrating yields

$$q_k = \frac{T_i - T_o}{(r_o - r_i)/k_m \bar{A}} \tag{2-11}$$

where $k_m = k_0 [1 + \beta_k (T_i + T_o)/2]$, the thermal conductivity at the arithmetic mean of the temperatures at the inner and outer surfaces.

Equations 2–7 and 2–10 apply only to radial heat flow at right angles to the cylinder axis.   If the length of the cylinder is short in comparison with its diameter, end effects become important because the direction of heat flow near the ends is no longer perpendicular to the axis.   Such cases come under the classification of two-dimensional heat flow.

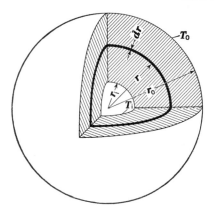

Fig. 2–4.   Sketch illustrating no-menclature for conduction through spherical shell.

Spherical and parallelepiped shells.   A sphere has the largest volume per outside surface area of any geometrical configuration.   For this reason a hollow sphere is sometimes used in the chemical industry for low-temperature work, when heat losses are to be kept at a minimum.   Conduction through a spherical shell is also a one-dimensional steady-state problem if the interior and exterior surface temperatures are uniform and constant. The rate of heat conduction for this case (Fig. 2–4) is

$$q_k = \frac{4\pi\, r_i\, r_o\, k(T_o - T_i)}{r_o - r_i} = k\sqrt{A_o A_i}\, \frac{T_o - T_i}{r_o - r_i} \tag{2-12}$$

if the material is homogeneous.   If the thermal conductivity is a linear function of temperature, then it should be calculated at the arithmetic mean value between the inner and outer surface temperatures.

Equation 2–12 can also be used as an approximation for parallelepiped shells which have a small inner cavity surrounded by a thick wall. An example of such a system would be a small furnace surrounded by a large thickness of insulating material. For this type of geometry the heat flow, especially in the corners, is not perpendicular to the bounding surfaces, and hence cannot strictly be considered one-dimensional. However, when the cavity is roughly cubic and the surrounding walls are thick ($A_o/A_i > 2$), the rate of heat flow can be estimated according to Schumann (1) by multiplying the geometric mean area in Eq. 2–12, $\sqrt{A_o A_i}$, by the semi-empirical correction factor 0.725. More accurate correction factors have been determined by Langmuir et al. (2) and are summarized in Ref. 3.

Example 2–4. The working chamber of an electrically heated laboratory furnace is 6 by 8 by 12 in. and the walls, 6 in. thick on all sides, are made of a refractory brick ($k = 0.2$ Btu/hr ft F). If the temperature at the interior surface is to be maintained at 2000 F while the outside surface temperature is 300 F, estimate the power consumption in kilowatts (kw).

Solution: Under steady-state conditions the power consumption will equal the heat loss. The inner surface area A_i is

$$A_i = 2\,\frac{(6 \times 8) + (6 \times 12) + (8 \times 12)}{144} = 3 \text{ sq ft}$$

The outer surface area A_o is

$$A_o = 2\,\frac{(18 \times 20) + (18 \times 24) + (20 \times 24)}{144} = 17.7 \text{ sq ft}$$

Since $A_o/A_i > 2$, we can use Eq. 2–12 with the empirical correction factor 0.725, and the heat loss is

$$q_k = (0.2)(0.725)\sqrt{3 \times 17.7}\left(\frac{1700}{6/12}\right) = 7500 \text{ Btu/hr}$$

Since 1 Btu/hr = 2.93×10^{-4} kw, the power consumption is about 2.56 kw.   *Ans.*

2–2. COMPOSITE STRUCTURES

The general method for analyzing problems of steady-state heat flow through composite structures has been presented in Sec. 1–4. In this section we shall consider some examples of composite structures in which the heat flow is one-dimensional, or at least approximately so. In order to make the treatment applicable to practical cases where the surface temperatures are generally not known, heat flow through thermal resistances at the boundaries will be included in the treatment. We shall assume that the system is exposed to a high-temperature medium, i.e., a *heat source*, of known and constant temperature on one side and to a low-temperature medium, i.e., a *heat sink*, of known and constant temperature on the other

side.   The surface conductances between the medium and the surface will
be taken as constant over a given surface.

Composite walls.   A composite wall, typical of the type used in a large
furnace, is shown in Fig. 2–5.   The inner layer, which is exposed to the
high-temperature gases, is made of firebrick.   The intermediate layer
consists of an insulating brick and is followed by an outer layer of ordinary
red brick.   The temperature of the hot gases is T_i and the unit-surface
conductance over the interior surface is $\bar{h}_i$.   The atmosphere surrounding
the furnace is at a temperature T_o and the unit-surface conductance over
the exterior surface is $\bar{h}_o$.   Under these conditions there will be a continuous heat flow from the hot gases through the wall to the surroundings.

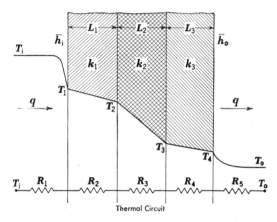

Fig. 2–5.   Temperature distribution and thermal circuit for heat flow through a series composite plane wall.

Since the heat flow through a given area A is the same for any section,
we obtain

$$q = h_i A (T_i - T_1) = \frac{k_1 A}{L_1} (T_1 - T_2)$$

$$= \frac{k_2 A}{L_2} (T_2 - T_3) = \frac{k_3 A}{L_3} (T_3 - T_4) = \bar{h}_o A (T_4 - T_o) \quad \textbf{(2–13)}$$

The symbols in Eq. 2–13 can be identified by inspection of Fig. 2–5.
Equation 2–13 can be written in terms of the thermal resistances of the
various sections as

$$q = \frac{T_i - T_1}{R_1} = \frac{T_1 - T_2}{R_2} = \frac{T_2 - T_3}{R_3} = \frac{T_3 - T_4}{R_4} = \frac{T_4 - T_o}{R_5} \quad \textbf{(2–14)}$$

where the resistances may be determined from Eqs. 1–3 and 1–13 or by

$R_i = $ Thermal Resistance

comparison of corresponding terms in Eqs. 2–13 and 2–14. Solving for the various temperature differences in Eq. 2–14 we obtain

$$
\begin{aligned}
T_i - T_1 &= qR_1 \\
T_1 - T_2 &= qR_2 \\
T_2 - T_3 &= qR_3 \\
T_3 - T_4 &= qR_4 \\
T_4 - T_o &= qR_5
\end{aligned}
\tag{2-15}
$$

Adding the left- and right-hand sides of these equations yields

$$
T_i - T_o = q(R_1 + R_2 + R_3 + R_4 + R_5)
\tag{2-16}
$$

or

$$
q = \frac{T_i - T_o}{\sum\limits_{n=1}^{n=5} R_n}
\tag{2-17}
$$

The result expressed by Eq. 2–17, namely that the heat flow through the five sections in series is equal to the over-all temperature potential divided by the sum of the thermal resistances in the path of the heat flow, can also be obtained from the thermal circuit shown in Fig. 2–5. Using the analogy between the flow of heat and the flow of electric current, Eq. 2–17 can be written directly.

Example 2–5. A furnace wall consists of two layers, 9 in. of firebrick ($k = 0.8$ Btu/hr ft F) and 5 in. of insulating brick ($k = 0.1$ Btu/hr ft F). The temperature inside the furnace is 3000 F and the unit-surface conductance at the inside wall is 12 Btu/hr sq ft F. The temperature of the surrounding atmosphere is 80 F and the unit-surface conductance at the outer wall is 2 Btu/hr sq ft F. Neglecting the thermal resistance of the mortar joints, estimate (a) the rate of heat loss per square foot of wall and the temperatures at the (b) inner surface and (c) outer surface.

Solution: (a) The rate of heat flow is obtained from Eq. 2–17 as

$$
\frac{q}{A} = \frac{3000 - 80}{\frac{1}{12} + \frac{9}{12}/0.8 + \frac{5}{12}/0.1 + \frac{1}{2}} = \frac{2920}{0.083 + 0.94 + 4.17 + 0.50}
$$

$$
= \frac{2920}{5.69} = 513 \text{ Btu/hr sq ft} \qquad\qquad Ans.
$$

It is of interest to note that the insulating brick, while representing only about one-third of the wall thickness, accounts for three-quarters of the total thermal resistance.

Applying Eq. 2–14, the temperature drop between the furnace gases and the interior surface is $T_i - T_1 = q\,R_1 = (5.13)(0.083) = 43$ F

This relatively small temperature difference is in accordance with previous considerations indicating that the thermal resistance of the first section in the circuit is negligible. Thus, heat can flow without a large potential and the temperature at the interior wall is nearly equal to that of the gases, that is, $T_i = T_1 - 43 \text{ F} = 3000 - 43 = 2957$ F   *Ans.*

b) The temperature of the outer surface, obtained in a like manner, is 336 F.   *Ans.*

In numerous practical applications, combinations of series- and parallel-connected heat-flow paths are encountered. An example of such a case is illustrated by the composite wall shown in Fig. 2–6. An approximate solution can be obtained by assuming that the heat flow is essentially one-dimensional. The composite wall can then be divided into three sections. The thermal resistance of each section can be determined with the aid of the thermal circuit shown in Fig. 2–6. The intermediate layer consists

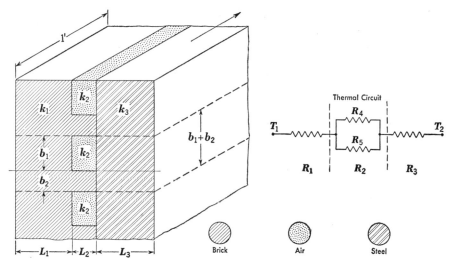

FIG. 2–6. Thermal circuit for a parallel-series composite wall. ($L_1 = 1$ in.; $L_2 = \frac{1}{32}$ in.; $L_3 = \frac{1}{4}$ in.; for Example 2–6.)

of two separate thermal paths in parallel and its thermal conductance is the sum of the individual conductances. For a wall section of height $b_1 + b_2$ (Fig. 2–6) the conductance is

$$K_2 = \frac{k_2 b_1}{L_2} + \frac{k_1 b_2}{L_2}$$

per unit length of wall. Using Eq. 1–24, the over-all unit transmittance U from surface to surface is

$$U = \frac{1}{R_1 + R_2 + R_3} = \frac{1}{\dfrac{L_1}{k_1} + \dfrac{b_1 + b_2}{(k_1 b_2/L_1) + (k_2 b_1/L_2)} + \dfrac{L_3}{k_3}}$$

Example 2–6. A layer of 2-in.-thick firebrick ($k_b = 1.0$ Btu/hr ft F) is placed between two $\frac{1}{4}$-in.-thick steel plates ($k_s = 30$ Btu/hr ft F). The faces of the brick adjacent to the plates are rough, having solid-to-solid contact only over 30 per cent of the total area, with the average height of the asperities being $\frac{1}{32}$ in. If the outer steel-plate surface temperatures are 200 and 800 F respectively, specify the rate of heat flow per unit area.

Solution: The real system is first idealized by assuming that the asperities of the surface are distributed, as shown in Fig. 2–6. We note that the composite wall is symmetrical with respect to the center plane and therefore only consider one-half of the system. The over-all heat-transfer coefficient for the composite wall is then

$$U = \frac{1/2}{R_1 + \dfrac{R_4 R_5}{R_4 + R_5} + R_3}$$

from an inspection of the thermal circuit.

The thermal resistance of the steel plate R_3 is, on the basis of a unit area, equal to

$$R_3 = \frac{L_3}{k_s} = \frac{1/4}{(12)(30)} = 0.694 \times 10^{-3} \text{ hr sq ft F/Btu}$$

The thermal resistance of the brick asperities R_4 is, on the basis of a unit area, equal to

$$R_4 = \frac{L_2}{0.3 k_b} = \frac{1/32}{(12)(0.3)(1.0)} = 8.7 \times 10^{-3} \text{ hr sq ft F/Btu}$$

Since the air is trapped in very small compartments, the effects of convection are small and it will be assumed that heat flows through the air by conduction. At a temperature of 280 F, the conductivity of air k_a is 0.02 Btu/hr ft F. Then R_5, the thermal resistance of the air trapped between the asperities, is, on the basis of unit area, equal to

$$R_5 = \frac{L_2}{0.7 k_a} = \frac{1/32}{(12)(0.7)(0.02)} = 187 \times 10^{-3} \text{ hr sq ft F/Btu}$$

The factors of 0.3 and 0.7 in R_4 and R_5 respectively, represent the per cent of the total area for the two separate heat-flow paths.

The total thermal resistance for the two paths, R_4 and R_5 in parallel, is

$$R_2 = \frac{R_4 R_5}{R_4 + R_5} = \frac{(8.7)(187) \times 10^{-6}}{(8.7 + 187) \times 10^{-3}} = 8.3 \times 10^{-3} \text{ hr sq ft F/Btu}$$

The thermal resistance of *one half* of the solid brick, R_1, is

$$R_1 = \frac{1}{2} \frac{L_1}{k_b} = \frac{1}{2} \frac{2}{(12)(1.0)} = 83.5 \times 10^{-3} \text{ hr sq ft F/Btu}$$

and U, the over-all heat-transfer coefficient, is

$$U = \frac{1/2 \times 10^3}{83.5 + 8.3 + 0.69} = 5.4 \text{ Btu/hr sq ft F}$$

An inspection of the values for the various thermal resistances shows that the steel offers a negligible resistance, while the contact section, although only $\frac{1}{32}$ in. thick, contributes 10 per cent to the total resistance. From Eq. 1–21, the rate of heat flow per unit area is

$$\frac{q}{A} = U \Delta T = 5.4(800 - 200) = 3250 \text{ Btu/hr sq ft} \qquad \textit{Ans.}$$

The thermal resistance between two surfaces is called *contact resistance*. The analysis of the contact resistance in the preceding problem is only approximate because, in addition to roughness, the contact resistance depends on the contact pressure. For more information on contact resistance, see Refs. 4 and 5.

Concentric cylinders. Radial heat flow through concentric cylinders of different thermal conductivity is encountered in many industrial installations. An insulated pipe, with a hot fluid flowing inside and exposed to a colder medium on the outside, is typical of such problems (Fig. 2–7). If the pipe is relatively long, then the heat flow through the walls will be

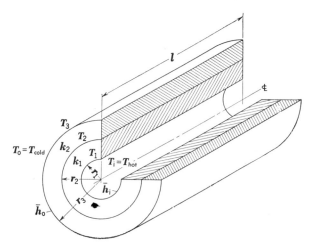

Fig. 2–7.   Sketch illustrating nomenclature of composite cylinder wall.

in a radial direction. In the steady state, the rate of heat flow through each section is the same and is represented by

$$q = 2\pi r_1 l \bar{h}_i \, (T_i - T_1) = \frac{T_{\text{hot}} - T_1}{R_1} \qquad \text{for the inner surface}$$

$$q = \frac{2\pi k_1 l}{\ln(r_2/r_1)} \, (T_1 - T_2) = \frac{T_1 - T_2}{R_2} \qquad \text{for the inner cylinder}$$

$$q = \frac{2\pi k_2 l}{\ln \, (r_1/r_2)} \, (T_2 - T_3) = \frac{T_2 - T_3}{R_3} \qquad \text{for the outer cylinder}$$

$$q = 2\pi r_3 l \bar{h}_o (T_3 - T_o) = \frac{T_3 - T_{\text{cold}}}{R_4} \qquad \text{for the outer surface}$$

In most practical applications the temperature of the fluid inside and the temperature of the medium surrounding the insulation are known or specified. The intermediate temperatures can be eliminated by addition of the temperature-difference terms and transposition. The resulting expression for the rate of heat flow through two concentric cylinders then becomes

$$q = \frac{T_i - T_o}{\dfrac{1}{2\pi r_1 l \bar{h}_i} + \dfrac{\ln(r_2/r_1)}{2\pi k_1 l} + \dfrac{\ln(r_3/r_2)}{2\pi k_2 l} + \dfrac{1}{2\pi r_3 l \bar{h}_o}} = \frac{T_{hot} - T_{cold}}{\displaystyle\sum_{n=1}^{n=4} R_n} \quad (2\text{–}18)$$

The over-all heat-transfer coefficient U for this system can be based on any area, but its numerical value will depend on the area selected. Since the outer diameter is the easiest to measure in practice, $A_o = 2\pi r_3 l$ is usually chosen as the base area and the rate of heat flow is

$$q = U A_o (T_{hot} - T_{cold})$$

Then, by comparison with Eq. 2–18, the over-all heat-transfer coefficient becomes

$$U = \frac{1}{\dfrac{r_3}{r_1 \bar{h}_i} + \dfrac{r_3 \ln(r_2/r_i)}{k_1} + \dfrac{r_3 \ln(r_3/r_2)}{k_2} + \dfrac{1}{\bar{h}_o}} \quad (2\text{–}19)$$

Example 2–7. Calculate the heat loss per linear foot from a 3-in.- steel sched. 40 pipe (3.07 in. ID, 3.500 in. OD, $k = 25$ Btu/hr ft F) covered with a $\frac{1}{2}$-in. thickness of asbestos insulation ($k = 0.11$ Btu/hr ft F). The pipe transports a fluid at 300 F with an inner unit-surface conductance of 20 Btu/hr sq ft F and is exposed to ambient air at 80 F with an average outer unit-surface conductance of 2.0 Btu/hr sq ft F.

Solution: Using Eq. 2–18, the rate of heat transfer for $l = 1$ is

$$q = \frac{T_i - T_o}{R_1 + R_2 + R_3 + R_4}$$

$$= \frac{220}{\dfrac{1}{\pi(3.07/12)20} + \dfrac{\ln(3.5/3.07)}{2\pi 25} + \dfrac{\ln(4.5/3.5)}{2\pi 0.11} + \dfrac{1}{\pi(4.5/12)2}}$$

$$= \frac{220}{0.0312 + 0.00085 + 0.363 + 0.212} = 362 \text{ Btu/hr ft} \qquad Ans.$$

It is to be noted that the thermal resistance is concentrated in the insulation and in the low surface conductance at the outer surface, while the resistance of the metal wall is negligible. If the pipe were bare, the heat loss would be 722 Btu/hr ft, or nearly twice as large as with the insulation.

Critical thickness of insulation. The addition of insulation to the outside of small pipes or wires does not always reduce the heat transfer. We have previously noted that the radial rate of heat flow through a hollow cylinder is inversely proportional to the logarithm of the outer radius and the rate of heat dissipation from the outer surface is directly proportional to this radius. Thus, for a single-wall tube of fixed inner radius r_i, an increase in outer radius r_o (e.g., the insulation thickness) increases the thermal resistance due to conduction *logarithmically* and at the same time reduces the thermal resistance at the outer surface *linearly* with r_o. Since the total thermal resistance is proportional to the sum of these two resistances, the rate of heat flow may increase as insulation is added to a bare pipe or wire. If the insulation thickness is then further increased, the heat loss gradually drops below the loss for a bare surface. This principle is widely utilized in electrical engineering where lagging is provided for current-carrying wires and cables, not to reduce the heat loss, but to increase it. It is also of importance in refrigeration, where heat flow to the cold refrigerant should be kept at a minimum. In many such installations where small-diameter pipes are used, insulation on the outside surface would increase the rate of heat flow.

The relation between heat transfer and insulation thickness can be studied quantitatively with the aid of Eq. 2–18. In many practical situations the thermal resistance is concentrated in the insulation and at the outer surface. We shall therefore simplify Eq. 2–18 by assuming that T_i is the temperature at the inner surface of the insulation. This boundary condition applies to an insulated electric wire whose outer surface temperature T_i is fixed by the current density, the wire size, and the material. Then,

$$q = \frac{2\pi kl(T_i - T_o)}{\ln(r_o/r_i) + k/\bar{h}_o r_o} \tag{2–20}$$

where r_o is the outer radius, r_i the inner radius, and k the thermal conductivity of the insulation.

For a fixed value of r_i, the rate of heat flow is a function of r_o, i.e., $q = q(r_o)$, and will be a maximum at that value of r_o for which

$$\frac{dq}{dr_o} = \frac{-2\pi kl(T_i - T_o)[1/r_o - (k/\bar{h}_o r_o^2)]}{[\ln(r_o/r_i) + k/\bar{h}_o r_o]^2} = 0 \tag{2–21}$$

From Eq. 2–21 the radius for maximum heat transfer, called the *critical radius*, is $r_{oc} = k/\bar{h}_o$.

Example 2–8. An electrical cable, $\frac{1}{2}$ in. OD, is to be insulated with rubber ($k = 0.09$ Btu/hr ft F). The cable is to be located in air ($\bar{h}_o = 1.5$ Btu/hr sq ft F) at 70 F. Investigate the effect of insulation thickness on the heat dissipation, assuming a cable surface temperature of 150 F.

Solution: Applying Eq. 2–20, the rate of heat dissipation per unit length is

$$q = \frac{2\pi(0.09)(150-70)}{\ln(r_o/\frac{1}{4}) + (0.09)(12/1.5r_o)} = \frac{45.2}{\ln 4r_o + (0.72/r_o)} \text{ Btu/hr ft}$$

if r_o is in inches.   The first term of the denominator is proportional to the thermal resistance of the insulation, the second term to the surface resistance.   In Fig. 2–8 each of these terms is plotted against the outer radius r_o.   The dotted line, representing the sum of both terms, has a minimum at $r_{oc} = 0.72$ in.   This is the critical radius at which the rate of heat dissipation reaches a maximum value of

$$q = \frac{45.2}{2.08} = 22.8 \text{ Btu/hr ft length}$$

If the wire were bare, the rate of heat dissipation would be 15.7 Btu/hr ft length, a reduction of 45 per cent.

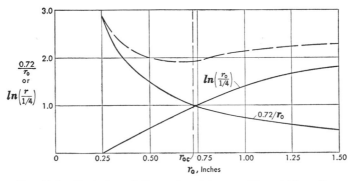

FIG. 2–8.   Variation of thermal resistance with outside radius for an insulated electric wire.

In a practical situation, the selection of the insulating thickness also requires a cost analysis, and usually a compromise between the desirability of dissipating as much heat as possible and the necessity of keeping cost down must be made.   Such a compromise might be an insulation thickness of $\frac{1}{8}$ in. ($r_o = 0.5$ in.), which requires only about 50 per cent of the material, yet dissipates heat at a rate equal to 98 per cent of the maximum rate.

For cases when r_i is larger than $k/\bar{h}_o$, addition of insulation will always reduce the rate of heat transfer, and the optimum insulation thickness must be determined by a cost analysis that takes into account the cost and depreciation of the insulation, the cost and depreciation of the equipment required to make up for the energy lost as heat, and sometimes the space occupied by the insulation.

2–3. SYSTEMS WITH HEAT SOURCES

Systems with heat sources (or sinks) are encountered in many branches of engineering.   Typical examples are electric coils, resistance heaters, nuclear reactors, and the combustion of fuel in the fuel bed of a boiler furnace.   The dissipation of heat from internal sources is also an important consideration in rating electric motors, generators, and transformers.

In this section we shall consider two simple cases: steady-state heat conduction in a flat plate and a circular cylinder with homogeneous internal heat generation.   For a treatment of more complicated problems such as systems with nonuniform heat sources, constant local heat sources, or moving heat sources, see Refs. 3 and 8.

Flat plate with uniformly distributed heat sources.   Consider a flat plate in which heat is generated uniformly.   This plate could be a heating element such as a flat bus bar in which heat is generated by passing an

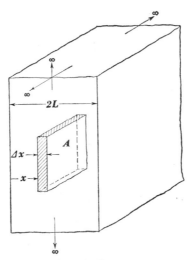

Fig. 2–9.   Sketch illustrating nomenclature for heat conduction in a plane wall with internal heat generation.

electric current through it.   If we assume that steady state exists, that the material is homogeneous, and that the plate is large enough that end effects may be neglected, an energy equation for a differential element (Fig. 2–9) can be expressed semantically as

| Heat conducted in through the left face during time $\Delta\theta$ | + | heat generated by sources in the element during time $\Delta\theta$ | = | heat conducted out through the right face during time $\Delta\theta$ |

The corresponding algebraic expression is

$$-kA \left.\frac{dT}{dx}\right|_{\text{at } x} \Delta\theta + \dot{q}(A\,\Delta x)\Delta\theta = -kA \left.\frac{dT}{dx}\right|_{\text{at } (x + \Delta x)} \Delta\theta \quad \textbf{(2–22)}$$

where $\dot{q}$ is the heat-source-strength per unit volume and unit time.

According to the mean-value theorem $f(x)$, the value of a function of x at x, is related to $f(x + \Delta x)$, the value of that same function at $(x + \Delta x)$, by

$$f(x + \Delta x) = f(x) + \frac{d}{dx} [f(x)]\Big|_{\text{at } M} \Delta x$$

where M is located somewhere between x and $(x + \Delta x)$. In particular, if we take $f(x) = [dT(x)/dx]$, the temperature gradients at x and $(x + \Delta x)$ are related by the mean-value theorem

$$\frac{dT}{dx}\Big|_{\text{at } (x + \Delta x)} = \frac{dT}{dx}\Big|_{\text{at } x} + \left[\frac{d}{dx}\left(\frac{dT}{dx}\right)\right]\Big|_{\text{at } M} \Delta x \qquad (2\text{--}23)$$

where M is located somewhere between x and $(x + \Delta x)$ as shown in Fig. 2–10. Substituting Eq. 2–23 for the temperature gradient at $(x + \Delta x)$ in Eq. 2–22 yields, after dividing each term by $\Delta \theta$,

$$-kA \frac{dT}{dx}\Big|_x + \dot{q}(A\Delta x) = -kA \frac{dT}{dx}\Big|_x - kA\left[\frac{d}{dx}\left(\frac{dT}{dx}\right)\right]_M \Delta x \qquad (2\text{--}24)$$

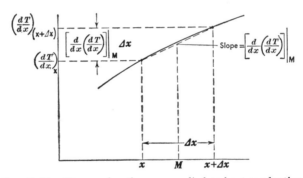

FIG. 2–10.   Mean-value theorem applied to heat conduction.

We can simplify Eq. 2–24 by canceling the terms $-kA(dT/dx)_{\text{at } x}$ and noting that

$$\frac{d}{dx}\left(\frac{dT}{dx}\right) = \frac{d^2 T}{dx^2}$$

Equation 2–24 then becomes

$$\dot{q}A\Delta x = -kA \frac{d^2 T}{dx^2}\Big|_M \Delta x$$

If we divide the above equation by $A\Delta x$ and let the size of the element approach zero as a limit, a value at M becomes a value at the point x. Since this point is a perfectly general one, the equation

$$k \frac{d^2T}{dx^2} = \dot{q} \qquad (2\text{-}25)$$

must hold at every point in the body.

A solution to Eq. 2–25 is obtained by two successive integrations. The first yields the temperature gradient

$$\frac{dT}{dx} = -\frac{\dot{q}}{k} x + C_1 \qquad (2\text{-}26)$$

and the second integration gives the temperature distribution

$$T = -\frac{\dot{q}}{2k} x^2 + C_1 x + C_2 \qquad (2\text{-}27)$$

where C_1 and C_2 are constants of integration whose values are determined by the boundary conditions. If we specify that the temperature at both faces is T_o, then the boundary conditions are

$$T = T_o \quad \text{at } x - 0 \qquad \text{and} \qquad T = T_o \quad \text{at } x = 2L$$

For the solution to satisfy these conditions we substitute them successively into Eq. 2–27 and solve for C_1 and C_2. This yields

$$T_o = C_2$$

and

$$T_o = -\frac{\dot{q}}{2k} 4L^2 + C_1 2L + T_o$$

Solving for C_1 we obtain
$$C_1 = \frac{\dot{q}L}{k}$$

Substituting these expressions for C_1 and C_2 in Eq. 2-27 yields the temperature distribution as

$$T = -\frac{\dot{q}}{2k} x^2 + \frac{\dot{q}L}{k} x + T_o \qquad (2\text{-}28)$$

or
$$T - T_o = \frac{\dot{q}L^2}{2k} \left[2\left(\frac{x}{L}\right) - \left(\frac{x}{L}\right)^2 \right]$$

Thus, the temperature distribution across the plate is a parabola with the apex at the median plane, $x = L$.

We can check this last result from another point of view. Since the system is symmetrical about the mid-plane at $x = L$, no heat can flow across this plane. This means that, at $x = L$, the temperature gradient must be zero and the temperature a maximum. Substituting $\dot{q}L/k$ for C_1 in Eq. 2–26 yields, at $x = L$

$$\frac{dT}{dx}\bigg|_{x=L} = -\frac{\dot{q}L}{k} + \frac{\dot{q}L}{k} = 0$$

as expected.

The temperature difference between the center plane and the surface is

$$(T - T_o)_{\max} = \frac{\dot{q}L^2}{2k} \tag{2–29}$$

If the plate is immersed in a fluid at T_∞ and the surface conductance at both faces is $\bar{h}_o$, then the heat generated in one half of the plate must flow continuously through the adjacent face under steady-state conditions. This condition, expressed algebraically for a unit of area, is

$$\dot{q}L = -k\frac{\partial T}{\partial x}\bigg|_{\text{at }x=0} = \bar{h}_o(T_o - T_\infty) \tag{2–30}$$

In Eq. 2–30 the first term represents the rate at which heat is generated in the plate, the second term the rate at which heat is conducted to the surface, and the third term the rate at which heat flows by convection and radiation from the surface to the surrounding medium. The temperature difference $T_o - T_\infty$ required to remove the heat from the surface is therefore

$$T_o - T_\infty = \frac{\dot{q}L}{\bar{h}_o} \tag{2–31}$$

Example 2–9. A fluid ($T_\infty = 150$ F) of low electrical conductivity is heated by a long iron plate, $\frac{1}{2}$ in. thick and 3 in. wide. Heat is generated uniformly in the plate at a rate $\dot{q} = 100,000$ Btu/hr cu ft by passing electric current through it. Determine the unit-surface conductance required to maintain the temperature of the bar below 300 F.

Solution: Disregarding the heat dissipated from the edges, Eq. 2–29 applies and the temperature difference between the mid-plane and the surface is

$$(T - T_o)_{\max} = \frac{\dot{q}L^2}{2k} = \frac{(100,000)(\frac{1}{4}/12)^2}{(2)(25)} = 0.87 \text{ F}$$

The temperature drop in the iron is so low because its thermal conductivity is high ($k = 25$ Btu/hr ft F). From Eq. 2–31 we get

$$\bar{h}_o = \frac{\dot{q}L}{T_o - T_\infty} = \frac{(100,000)(\frac{1}{4}/12)}{150} = 14 \text{ Btu/hr sq ft F}$$

Thus the minimum unit-surface conductance which will keep the temperature in the heater below 300 F is 14 Btu/hr sq ft F. *Ans.*

Long solid cylinder with uniformly distributed heat sources. A long solid circular cylinder with uniform internal heat generation may be thought of as an idealization of a real system such as an electric coil, in which heat is generated as a result of the electric current in the wire, or a cylindrical fuel element of uranium 235, in which heat is generated by nuclear fission.

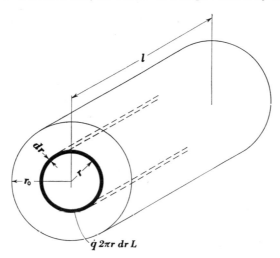

FIG. 2–11. Sketch illustrating nomenclature for heat conduction in a long circular cylinder with internal heat generation.

The energy equation for an annular element (Fig. 2–11) formed between an inner cylinder of radius r and an outer cylinder of radius $r + dr$ is

$$-kA_r \left.\frac{dT}{dr}\right|_r + \dot{q}l2\pi r dr = -kA_{r+dr} \left.\frac{dT}{dr}\right|_{r+dr} \tag{2-32}$$

where $A_r = 2\pi rl$ and $A_{r+dr} = 2\pi(r + dr)l$. Using the mean-value theorem to relate the temperature gradient at $r + dr$ to the temperature gradient at r, we obtain, after some simplifications,

$$\dot{q}r = -k\left(\frac{dT}{dr} + r\frac{d^2T}{dr^2}\right) \tag{2-33}$$

Integration of Eq. 2–33 can best be accomplished by noting that

$$\frac{d}{dr}\left(r\frac{dT}{dr}\right) = \frac{dT}{dr} + r\frac{d^2T}{dr^2}$$

and rewriting it in the form

$$\dot{q}r = -k\frac{d}{dr}\left(r\frac{dT}{dr}\right)$$

Integration then yields

$$\frac{\dot{q}r^2}{2} = -kr\frac{dT}{dr} + C_1 \qquad\qquad (2\text{–}34)$$

from which we deduce that, to satisfy the boundary condition,

$$\frac{dT}{dr} = 0 \qquad \text{at } r = 0$$

the constant of integration C_1 must be zero.   Another integration yields the temperature distribution

$$T = -\frac{\dot{q}r^2}{4k} + C_2$$

The second integration constant C_2 must satisfy the condition that the maximum temperature $T_{\max}$ occurs in the center, so that $C_2 = T_{\max}$.   The temperature distribution in a long solid cylinder can then be expressed as

$$\frac{T}{T_{\max}} = \frac{\dot{q}r_o^2}{4kT_{\max}}\left(\frac{r}{r_o}\right)^2 \qquad\qquad (2\text{–}35)$$

where r_o is the outside radius.

Example 2–10.   A sketch of a graphite-moderated reactor, typical of the type which will be used for commercial power production, is shown in Fig. 2–12.   Heat is generated at the rate of 7.2×10^6 Btu/hr cu ft in long 1-in.-OD uranium rods[2] ($k = 17$ Btu/hr ft F) which are jacketed by an annulus in which water is flowing.   For an average water temperature of 270 F and a unit-surface conductance of 1000 Btu/hr sq ft F, determine the maximum temperature of the fuel rods.

Solution: Applying Eq. 2–34,

$$-k\left.\frac{dT}{dr}\right|_{r=r_o} = \frac{\dot{q}r_o}{2} = \frac{(7.2 \times 10^6 \text{ Btu/hr cu ft})(1/12 \text{ ft})}{2}$$

$$= 3 \times 10^5 \text{ Btu/hr sq ft}$$

The rate of heat flow by conduction at the outer surface equals the rate of heat flow by convection from the surface to the water

$$2\pi r_o\left(-k\frac{dT}{dr}\right)\Big|_{r_o} = 2\pi r_o\bar{h}_o(T_{r_o} - T_{\text{water}})$$

from which

$$T_{r_o} = \frac{-k\,(dT/dr)r_o}{\bar{h}_o} + T_{\text{water}}$$

Upon substituting the data specified in the statement of the problem, we get

$$T_{r_o} = \frac{3 \times 10^5 \text{ Btu/hr sq ft}}{1 \times 10^4 \text{ Btu/hr sq ft F}} + 270 \text{ F} = 300 \text{ F}$$

[2] This value of the thermal conductivity is taken from Ref. 11.

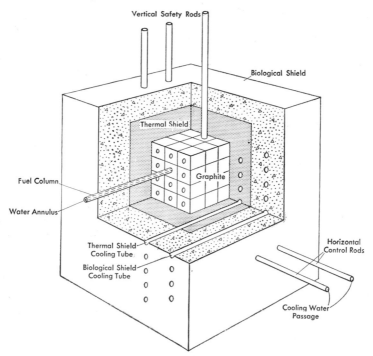

FIG. 2–12. Graphite-moderated reactor. (Reprinted from *General Electric Review*.)

and
$$T_{\max} = T_{r_o} + \frac{\dot{q} r_o{}^2}{4k} = 300 + 735 = 1035 \text{ F} \qquad \textit{Ans.}$$

The exact determination of the rate of heat conduction and temperature distribution in a nuclear pile is a complicated problem. The preceding problem only illustrates the basic idea, and for more complete information Refs. 11, 12, 14, 15, and 16 should be consulted.

2–4. HEAT TRANSFER FROM EXTENDED SURFACES

The problems considered in this section are encountered in practice when a solid of relatively small cross-sectional area protrudes from a large body into a fluid at a different temperature. Such extended surfaces have wide industrial applications as fins attached to the walls of heat-transfer equipment for the purpose of increasing the rate of heating or cooling.

Fins of uniform cross section. As a simple illustration, consider a pin fin having the shape of a rod whose base is attached to a wall at surface temperature T_s (Fig. 2–13). The fin is cooled along its surface by a fluid at temperature T_∞. The fin has a uniform cross-sectional area A, is made of a material having a uniform thermal conductivity k, and the heat-

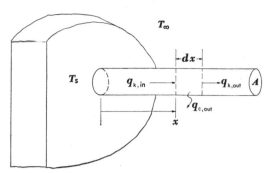

Fig. 2-13. Sketch and nomenclature for a pin fin protruding from a wall.

transfer coefficient between the surface of the fin and the fluid is $\bar{h}$. We shall assume that transverse temperature gradients are so small that the temperature at any cross section of the rod is uniform, i.e., $T = T(x)$ only. The limitations of this simplification, which reduces the problem to one-dimensional heat flow, has been investigated analytically in Ref. 10. The results of this study show that, even in a relatively thick fin, the error in a one-dimensional solution is less than one per cent.

To derive an equation for the temperature distribution, we make a heat balance for a small element of the fin. Heat flows by conduction into the left face of the element, while heat flows out of the element by conduction through the right face and by convection from the surface. Under steady-state conditions, the rate of heat flow into the element is equal to the rate of the heat flow out of the element, or

Rate of heat flow by conduction into element at x $=$ rate of heat flow by conduction out of element at $(x + dx)$ $+$ rate of heat flow by convection from surface between x and $(x + dx)$

In symbolic form, this equation becomes

$$-kA\,\frac{dT}{dx} = \left[-kA\,\frac{dT}{dx} + \frac{d}{dx}\left(-kA\,\frac{dT}{dx}\right)dx\right] + \bar{h}Pdx(T - T_\infty) \quad (2\text{--}36)$$

where P is the perimeter of the rod and Pdx represents the surface area between sections x and $(x + dx)$ in contact with the surrounding fluid. Equation 2–36 can be simplified to

$$\frac{d^2T}{dx^2} = m^2(T - T_\infty) \quad (2\text{--}37)$$

where $m^2 = \bar{h}P/kA$. Equation 2–37 is a standard form of an ordinary second-order linear differential equation whose general solution is

$$T - T_\infty = C_1 e^{mx} + C_2 e^{-mx} \quad (2\text{--}38)$$

where C_1 and C_2 are constants of integration whose values must be determined from the boundary conditions. One of the boundary conditions is $T = T_s$ at $x = 0$, the temperature at the base of the rod equals the temperature of the surface to which the rod is attached. To obtain a solution satisfying this condition, we substitute it in Eq. 2–38 and get

$$T_s - T_\infty = C_1 e^{(m)0} + C_2 e^{-(m)0} = C_1 + C_2 \tag{2-39}$$

To solve for C_1 and C_2 we need another equation, i.e., another boundary condition. The second boundary condition depends upon the nature of the problem. Since the appropriate selection of boundary conditions often causes considerable difficulty, we shall consider several cases which will assist the reader in gaining some facility in applying physical concepts to a mathematical analysis. Figure 2–14 illustrates schematically the conditions described by the three boundary conditions to be analyzed.

a) If the rod is infinitely long, its temperature will approach the temperature of the fluid as $x \to \infty$, or $T = T_\infty$ at $x \to \infty$. Substituting this condition in Eq. 2–38 yields

$$T_\infty - T_\infty = 0 = C_1 e^{m\infty} + C_2 e^{-m\infty} \tag{2-40}$$

Since the second term is zero, the boundary condition is satisfied only if $C_1 = 0$. Substituting 0 for C_1 in Eq. 2–39 gives

$$C_2 = T_s - T_\infty$$

and the temperature distribution becomes

$$T - T_\infty = (T_s - T_\infty)e^{-mx} \tag{2-41}$$

The heat-flow rate from the fin to the fluid can be obtained by two different methods. Since the heat flowing by conduction across the root of the fin must be transmitted by convection from the surface of the rod to the fluid,

$$q_{\text{fin}} = -kA \left. \frac{dT}{dx} \right|_{x=0} = \int_0^\infty \bar{h}P(T - T_\infty)dx \tag{2-42}$$

Differentiating Eq. 2–41 and substituting the result for $x = 0$ in Eq. 2–42 yields

$$q_{\text{fin}} = -kA\left[-m(T_s - T_\infty)e^{(-m)0} \right]_{x=0} = \sqrt{\bar{h}PkA}\,(T_s - T_\infty) \tag{2-43}$$

The same result is obtained by evaluating the convective heat flow from the surface of the rod

$$q_{\text{fin}} = \int_0^\infty \bar{h}P(T - T_\infty)e^{-mx}dx = \frac{\bar{h}P}{m}(T - T_\infty)e^{-mx}\Big|_0^\infty = \sqrt{\bar{h}PkA}\,(T_s - T_\infty)$$

Equations 2–41 and 2–43 are reasonable approximations of the temperature distribution and heat-flow rate in a finite fin if its length is very large compared to its cross-sectional area.

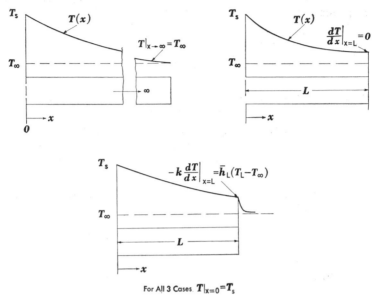

FIG. 2–14.　Schematic illustration of three boundary conditions for a pin fin.

b) If the rod is of finite length, but the heat loss from the end of the rod is neglected, or if the end of the rod is insulated, the second boundary condition requires that the temperature gradient at $x = L$ be zero, or $dT/dx = 0$ at $x = L$. Differentiating Eq. 2–38 and inserting this condition, gives

$$C_2 = C_1 e^{2mL}$$

Substituting this expression for C_2 in Eq. 2–39, we obtain

$$C_1 = \frac{T_s - T_\infty}{1 + e^{2mL}}$$

and

$$C_2 = \frac{T_s - T_\infty}{1 + e^{-2mL}}$$

The complete solution is therefore

$$T - T_\infty = (T_s - T_\infty)\left(\frac{e^{mx}}{1 + e^{2mL}} + \frac{e^{-mx}}{1 + e^{-2mL}}\right) \qquad (2\text{–}44)$$

or, in simplified dimensionless form,[3]

$$\frac{T - T_\infty}{T_s - T_\infty} = \frac{\cosh m(L - x)}{\cosh (mL)} \qquad (2\text{--}44a)$$

As L becomes infinite, Eq. 2–44 reduces to the previous solution, as would be expected.

The heat loss from the fin can be found from Eq. 2–42 by substituting the temperature gradient at the root

$$\frac{dT}{dx}\bigg|_{x\,=\,0} = (T_s - T_\infty)m \left(\frac{1}{1 + e^{2m L}} - \frac{1}{1 + e^{-2m L}}\right)$$

The above equation can be put into more convenient form by placing the final member of the right-hand side over a common denominator, and noting that

$$\frac{e^{m L} - e^{-m L}}{e^{m L} + e^{-m L}} = \tanh (mL)$$

where tanh is the hyperbolic tangent. The heat-flow rate from the rod is then found to be

$$q_{\text{rod}} = -kA \frac{dT}{dx}\bigg|_{x\,=\,0} = \sqrt{P\bar{h}kA}\,(T_s - T_\infty)\tanh (mL) \qquad (2\text{--}45)$$

c) If the end of the rod loses heat by convection, the heat flowing by conduction to the face at $x = L$ must be equal to the convection heat flow from the end section of the rod to the fluid, or

$$-k \frac{dT}{dx}\bigg|_{x\,=\,L} = \bar{h}_L(T_{x=L} - T_\infty)$$

The heat-transfer coefficient at the end face $\bar{h}_L$ is not necessarily equal to the value of $\bar{h}$ over the circumferential surface of the rod. Substituting for $T_{x=L}$ and $(dT/dx)_{x=L}$ from Eq. 2–38 we obtain

$$q_{x=L} = -k(C_1 m e^{mx} - C_2 m e^{-mx})_{x=L} = \bar{h}_L(T_{x=L} - T_\infty)$$

or
$$C_2 e^{-m L} - C_1 e^{m L} = \frac{\bar{h}_L}{km}\,(C_1 e^{m L} + C_2 e^{-m L}) \qquad (2\text{--}46)$$

Equations 2–39 and 2–46 can now be solved simultaneously to obtain the constants C_1 and C_2, just as in the previous cases. The algebra is some-

---

[3] The reduction of Eq. 2–44 to 2–44a is left as an exercise for the reader. The hyperbolic cosine, cosh for short, is defined by $\cosh x = (e^x + e^{-x})/2$.

what more involved, but the principle is the same. It is left as an exercise for the reader to show that the dimensionless temperature distribution along the fin is

$$\frac{T - T_\infty}{T_s - T_\infty} = \frac{\cosh m(L - x) + (\bar{h}_L/mk)\sinh m(L - x)}{\cosh mL + (\bar{h}_L/mk)\sinh mL} \tag{2-47}$$

and the heat-flow rate from the fin is

$$q_{\text{fin}} = \sqrt{P\bar{h}Ak}\,(T_s - T_\infty)\frac{\sinh mL + (\bar{h}_L/mk)\cosh mL}{\cosh mL + (\bar{h}_L/mk)\sinh mL} \tag{2-48}$$

It is important to check the end results of more complicated cases by reducing them to the results available for simpler cases, because this often shows up errors which might otherwise remain unnoticed. Comparing Eqs. 2–47 and 2–48 with the corresponding results for case b (i.e., the end face insulated), we note that, for $\bar{h}_L = 0$, these equations indeed reduce to those obtained previously for $(dT/dx)_{\text{at } x=L} = 0$. Only the second terms in the numerator and the denominator contain $\bar{h}_L$. These terms indicate the influence of the heat loss from the end face of the rod and modify the results obtained when the end losses were neglected.

Example 2–11. The temperature of steam flowing in a 3-in. steel pipe has been measured in the laboratory by means of a mercury-in-glass thermometer immersed in an oil-filled steel well. While a reliable pressure gauge in the line read 153 psia, the mercury thermometer indicated a temperature of 355 F. Reference to steam tables indicates that the saturation temperature of steam at 153 psia is 360 F. At first glance the thermometer reading, since it is below the saturation temperature, seems in error.

For the temperature-measuring station shown in Fig. 2–15, show that the thermometer reading is not inconsistent with the pressure reading and estimate the true temperature if the pipe-wall temperature is 200 F and the heat-transfer coefficient between the steam and the thermometer well is 50 Btu/hr sq ft F.

Solution: The thermometer well is essentially a hollow rod protruding into steam at temperature T_∞. Since heat flows from the steam along the well toward the cooler pipe walls, the thermometer does not indicate the true steam temperature, but rather the temperature at the bottom of the well. We can estimate the steam temperature by treating the thermometer well as a rod. The conduction along the glass ($k = 0.5$ Btu/hr ft F) is neglected, since it is very small compared with the heat flow along the steel well. The cross-sectional area of the fin A is $(\pi/4)[(1/2)^2 - (1/4)^2] = 0.1475$ sq in. The perimeter P is $\frac{1}{2}\pi = 1.57$ in. The thermal conductivity of steel is 25 Btu/hr ft F. Thus

$$m = \sqrt{\frac{\bar{h}P}{kA}} = \sqrt{\frac{(50)(1.57)}{(25)(0.1475)}}\,12 = 16$$

As a first approximation, we could use Eq. 2–41 with $x = \frac{1}{6}$ ft. Then,

$$T - T_\infty = (T_s - T_\infty)e^{-16/6} = (T_s - T_\infty)\,0.07$$

Solving the above equation for T_∞ with $T_s = 355$ F, we obtain $T_\infty = 360$ F.

Although this first-order correction yields a reasonable value, the boundary conditions used to obtain Eq. 2–41 are not in physical correspondence with the conditions of the well. Since heat also flows from the end of the fin, Eq. 2–47 is more nearly true. For $x = L$, we get

$$T - T_\infty = (T_s - T_\infty) \frac{1}{\cosh mL + (\bar{h}_L/mk)\sinh mL}$$

Substituting numerical values, we find

$$T - T_\infty = (T_s - T_\infty) \frac{1}{7.18 + [50/(25)(16)](7.04)} = (T_s - T_\infty)(0.124)$$

The preceding equation yields a steam temperature T_∞ of 365 F. Therefore, the steam in the pipe is actually superheated and the error in the thermometer reading was 10 F. This error could be reduced to less than 2 F by increasing the length of the thermometer well to 3 in. and inserting it at a 45-deg angle to prevent it from touching the wall.

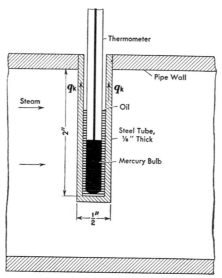

FIG. 2–15. Thermometer well for Example 2–11.

Example 2–12. Estimate the increase in heat-dissipation rate which could be obtained from a cylinder wall by using four pin-shaped fins per square inch, each having a diameter of $\frac{3}{16}$ in. and a height of 1 in. Assume that the heat-transfer coefficient between the surface of the cylinder wall or a fin and the surrounding air is 25 Btu/hr sq ft F, the cylinder wall is at 600 F, and the air at 70 F. The wall and the fins are made of aluminum.

Solution: The heat dissipation per square inch of surface, without the fin, is

$$\frac{q}{A} = \frac{25}{144}(600 - 70) = 92 \text{ Btu/hr sq in.}$$

The heat dissipation for a single fin can be estimated from Eq. 2–45. The rate of heat transfer per fin q is equal to

$$\sqrt{P\bar{h}Ak}\,(T_s - T_\infty)\tanh mL$$

where
$$P = \left(\frac{3}{16}\right) \pi \left(\frac{1}{12}\right) = 0.0492 \text{ ft}$$

$$A = \left(\frac{3}{16}\right)^2 \left(\frac{\pi}{4}\right) \left(\frac{1}{144}\right) = 0.000192 \text{ sq ft}$$

$$k = 120 \text{ Btu/hr ft F}$$

$$\sqrt{P\bar{h}Ak} = \sqrt{(0.049)(25)(0.000192)(120)} = 0.167$$

$$mL = \frac{1}{12} \sqrt{\frac{\bar{h}P}{kA}} = \frac{1}{12} \sqrt{\frac{(25)(0.0492)}{(120)(0.000192)}} = 0.192$$

so that
$$q_{\text{fin}} = (0.167)(530)(0.188) = 16.7 \text{ Btu/hr}$$

For four fins the heat-dissipation rate would be 66.8 Btu/hr. The rate of heat dissipation from the remaining wall surface would be approximately equal to the area not occupied by fins times the product of the heat-transfer coefficient and the temperature potential. On this basis, the total rate of heat transfer for the wall with fins is

$$\frac{q}{A} \simeq 67 + 92 \,(1.0 - 0.11) = 149 \text{ Btu/hr sq in.}$$

Thus we see that the use of the fins can increase the heat-dissipation rate by over 50 per cent. *Ans.*

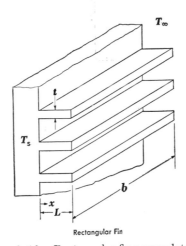

FIG. 2–16. Rectangular-fin nomenclature.

The straight rectangular fin (Fig. 2–16) can be treated by the same methods as those used for the rod. If the width of the fin b is large compared with its thickness t, then the fin perimeter is

$$P = 2(b + t) \simeq 2b$$

The cross-sectional area of the fin is $A = bt$, and

$$m = \sqrt{\frac{\bar{h}P}{kA}} \simeq \sqrt{\frac{2\bar{h}}{kt}}$$

The development of the equations for the temperature distribution and the heat flow in a rectangular fin are identical to the previous cases, and the results may be applied directly.

Tapered fin.[4]   The tapered fin (Fig. 2–17) is of practical interest because it very closely approximates the shape yielding the maximum heat flow per unit weight.   We shall base our analysis upon width b and again assume that the temperature is only a function of x.   A heat balance for a differential section of the fin between x and $x + dx$ yields

$$\frac{d}{dx}\left(kA\frac{dT(x)}{dx}\right) = \bar{h}P(T(x) - T_\infty) \qquad [\,2\text{–}36\,]$$

While A and P are constant for a rod, they are both functions of x for the tapered fin.   Upon performing the differentiation with respect to x, Eq. 2–36 becomes

$$kA(x)\frac{d^2T(x)}{dx^2} + \frac{dA(x)}{dx}k\frac{dT(x)}{dx} = \bar{h}P(x)\,[T(x) - T_\infty] \qquad (2\text{–}49)$$

We note that Eq. 2–49 is a linear second-order differential equation with *variable* coefficients.   The coefficients $kA(x)$, $k\,[dA(x)/dx]$, and $hP(x)$ are variable because their values depend on the independent variable x.

Equation 2–49 can be written in more convenient form by dividing through by kA to give

$$\frac{d^2T}{dx^2} + \frac{(dA/dx)}{A}\frac{dT}{dx} - \frac{\bar{h}P}{kA}(T - T_\infty) = 0 \qquad (2\text{–}50)$$

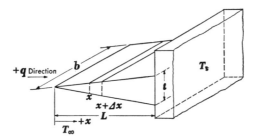

Tapered or Wedge Fin

Fig. 2–17.   Tapered-fin nomenclature.

[4] This subsection may be omitted without breaking the continuity of the presentation.

If we neglect the effect of the sides, then $P \simeq 2b$, and the cross-sectional area of the fin can be obtained by noting that the thickness of the fin at any point x is equal to $t(x/L)$ so that $A = (bt/L)x$. Substituting this expression for A in Eq. 2-50, we find that

$$\frac{d^2T}{dx^2} + \frac{1}{x}\frac{dT}{dx} - \frac{2L\bar{h}}{ktx}(T - T_\infty) = 0 \qquad \textbf{(2-51)}$$

Equation 2-51 resembles a modified Bessel equation (7), whose general form for any value of n is

$$z^2\frac{d^2y}{dz^2} + z\frac{dy}{dz} - (z^2 + n^2)y = 0 \qquad \textbf{(2-52)}$$

The solutions to this type of equation have been worked out and tabulated (see, for example, Ref. 6) in much the same fashion as the sine and cosine functions. Therefore, we shall transform Eq. 2-51 into the same form as Eq. 2-52 in order to take advantage of the available solution. For convenience, let B^2 represent the constant $2L\bar{h}/kt$ and let $y = (T - T_\infty)$. Multiplying Eq. 2-52 by x^2, we obtain

$$x^2\frac{d^2y}{dx^2} + x\frac{dy}{dx} - B^2xy = 0 \qquad \textbf{(2-53)}$$

This is almost the desired form for $n = 0$, except for the coefficient $-B^2x$ in the last term. We shall therefore try to find a variable related to x which will modify this term. Whether or not such a variable exists can be determined by a technique which has been outlined in detail by Wylie (7). In our case we can readily see that, if the coefficient of the last term B^2x is to be the square of some other variable, it must be proportional to $B\sqrt{x}$, the square root of B^2x. If we assume that this new variable, which we shall call z, is equal to a constant, C, times $B\sqrt{x}$, we obtain by differentiation the following relations:

$$z = CB\sqrt{x} \qquad \text{or} \qquad x = \frac{z^2}{C^2B^2}$$

$$\frac{dz}{dx} = \frac{CB}{2}x^{-\frac{1}{2}}$$

$$\frac{dy}{dx} = \frac{dy}{dz}\frac{dz}{dx} = \frac{dy}{dz}\frac{CB}{2}x^{-\frac{1}{2}}$$

and

$$\frac{d^2y}{dx^2} = \frac{d}{dx}\left(\frac{dy}{dz}\frac{CB}{2}x^{-\frac{1}{2}}\right) = \frac{dy}{dz}\frac{CB}{2}\left(-\frac{1}{2}x^{-\frac{3}{2}}\right) + \frac{d^2y}{dz^2}\frac{dz}{dx}\frac{CB}{2}x^{-\frac{1}{2}}$$

Substituting the preceding relations in Eq. 2–53 changes the variable from x to z and the resulting equation is

$$z^2 \frac{d^2 y}{dz^2} + z \frac{dy}{dz} - \frac{4}{C^2} z^2 y = 0 \tag{2-54}$$

This equation is identical to the modified Bessel equation of zero order $(n = 0)$ if $C^2 = 4$ or $z = 2B\sqrt{x}$. The general solution is then (7)

$$y = (T - T_\infty) = C_1 I_0(2B\sqrt{x}) + C_2 K_0(2B\sqrt{x}) \tag{2-55}$$

where C_1 and C_2 are constants of integration which must be determined from the boundary conditions, while $I_0(z)$ and $K_0(z)$ are modified zero-order Bessel functions of the first and second kind, respectively.

For convenience, selected values of $I_0(z)$ and $K_0(z)$ have been tabulated in Table 2–1.[5] It should be noted that $I_0(0) = 1$, while $K_0(0) = \infty$. To evaluate C_1 and C_2 we apply the boundary conditions. The first boundary condition is one which we have used previously, namely, that the temperature at the root of the fin is T_s. Note, however, the manner in which the coordinate system of Fig. 2–17 is set up. In this coordinate system the first boundary condition is $T = T_s$ at $x = L$.

The second boundary condition is that the temperature of the fin must be everywhere finite. At the tip of the fin $(x = 0)$, $K_0(0)$ approaches infinity and therefore the coefficient C_2 must be zero for the temperature to remain finite. Substituting these two boundary conditions in the usual manner gives the temperature distribution

$$\frac{T - T_\infty}{T_s - T_\infty} = \frac{I_0(2B\sqrt{x})}{I_0(2B\sqrt{L})} \tag{2-56}$$

The heat-flow rate from the fin is obtained by differentiating Eq. 2–56, evaluating the temperature gradient at the root $x = L$, and multiplying the result by the root area. For the purpose of differentiation we use the relation (see e.g. Ref. 7)

$$d[I_n(Cz)] = I_{n+1}(Cz)\, d(Cz)$$

so that, for $n = 0$,

$$\frac{d[I_0(2B\sqrt{x})]}{dx} = [I_1(2B\sqrt{x})]\, Bx^{-\frac{1}{2}}$$

Then, the rate of heat flow from the fin is

$$q_{fin} = kA \left. \frac{dT}{dx} \right|_{x=L} = \sqrt{2\hbar kb}\, (T_s - T_\infty) \frac{I_1(2B\sqrt{L})}{I_0(2B\sqrt{L})} \tag{2-57}$$

[5] In Ref. 6 $I_n(z)$ is written $i^{-n} J_n(ix)$ and $2/\pi\, K_n(z)$ is written $i^{n+1} H_n^{(1)}(ix)$.

TABLE 2–1

SELECTED MAGNITUDES OF BESSEL FUNCTIONS

z	$I_0(z)$	$I_1(z)$	$\frac{2}{\pi}K_0(z)$	$\frac{2}{\pi}K_1(z)$
0.0	1.0000	0.0000	Infinity	Infinity
0.2	1.0100	0.1005	1.116	3.040
0.4	1.0404	0.2040	0.7095	1.391
0.6	1.0920	0.3137	0.4950	0.8294
0.8	1.1665	0.4329	0.3599	0.5486
1.0	1.2661	0.5652	0.2680	0.3832
1.2	1.3937	0.7147	0.2028	0.2767
1.4	1.5534	0.8861	0.15512	0.2043
1.6	1.7500	1.0848	0.11966	0.15319
1.8	1.9896	1.3172	0.09290	0.11626
2.0	2.2796	1.5906	0.07251	0.08904
2.2	2.6291	1.9141	0.05683	0.06869
2.4	3.0493	2.2981	0.04470	0.05330
2.6	3.5533	2.7554	0.03527	0.04156
2.8	4.1573	3.3011	0.02790	0.03254
3.0	4.8808	3.9534	0.02212	0.02556
3.2	5.7472	4.7343	0.017568	0.02014
3.4	6.7848	5.6701	0.013979	0.015915
3.6	8.0277	6.7927	0.011141	0.012602
3.8	9.5169	8.1404	0.028891*	0.029999*
4.0	11.3019	9.7595	0.027105	0.027947
4.2	13.4425	11.7056	0.025648	0.026327
4.4	16.0104	14.0462	0.024551	0.025044
4.6	19.0926	16.8626	0.023648	0.024027
4.8	22.7937	20.2528	0.022927	0.023218
5.0	27.2399	24.3356	0.022350	0.022575
5.2	32.5836	29.2543	0.021888	0.022062
5.4	39.0088	35.1821	0.021518	0.021653
5.6	46.7376	42.3283	0.021221	0.021326
5.8	56.0381	50.9462	0.039832	0.021065
6.0	67.2344	61.3419	0.037920	0.038556
6.2	80.72	73.89	0.036382	0.036879
6.4	96.98	89.03	0.035156	0.035534
6.6	116.54	107.30	0.034151	0.034455
6.8	140.14	129.38	0.033350	0.033588
7.0	168.6	156.04	0.032704	0.032891
7.2	202.9	188.3	0.032184	0.032331
7.4	244.3	227.2	0.031765	0.031880
7.6	294.3	274.2	0.031426	0.031517
7.8	354.7	331.1	0.031153	0.031225
8.0	427.6	399.9	0.049325	0.049891
8.2	515.6	483.0	0.047543	0.047991
8.4	621.9	583.7	0.046104	0.046458
8.6	750.5	705.4	0.044941	0.045220
8.8	905.8	852.7	0.044000	0.044221
9.0	1093.6	1030.9	0.043239	0.043415
9.2	1320.7	1246.7	0.042624	0.042763
9.4	1595.3	1507.9	0.042126	0.042236
9.6	1927.	1824.	0.0417226	0.041810
9.8	2329.	2207.	0.0413962	0.041466
10.0	. . . . .	. . . . .	0.0411319	0.041187

* In the columns for $K_0(z)$ and $K_1(z)$ from this point down, the first integer indicates the number of zeros, for instance 0.028891 = 0.008891.

Example 2–13.   The installation of fins is under consideration for the purpose of increasing the heat dissipation from an air-cooled cylinder wall.   If the wall temperature is 1100 F and the heat-transfer coefficient between the solid surface and the air ($T_\infty = 100$ F) is 15 Btu/hr sq ft F, compare the effectiveness of a tapered fin with that of a straight rectangular fin on the basis of heat flow per unit weight.   Each fin is to be 1 in. thick at the base and 4 in. long and made from a stainless steel ($k = 15$ Btu/hr ft F). Also plot the temperature distribution along the fins.

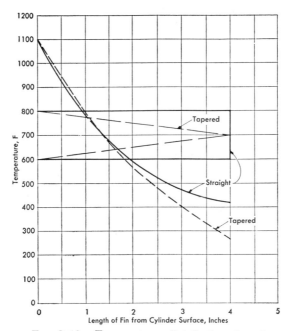

Fig. 2–18.   Temperature distribution for the tapered fin and the rectangular fin of Example 2–13.

Solution: We shall first consider each fin shape separately.

Tapered fin: From the data, we obtain

$$B = \sqrt{\frac{2L\bar{h}}{kb}} = \sqrt{\frac{(2)(4/12)(15)}{(15)(1/12)}} = \sqrt{8} = 2.83$$

From Eq. 2–56, the temperature distribution is

$$T = 100 + (1100 - 100)\frac{I_0\,(5.66\,\sqrt{x})}{I_0\,(5.66\,\sqrt{\tfrac{1}{3}})}$$

From Table 2–1 we get $I_0\,(2B\sqrt{L}) = I_0\,(3.26) = 6.05$ by interpolation and

$$T = 100 + 165\,I_0\,(5.66\,\sqrt{x})$$

The temperature distribution is plotted in Fig. 2–18.
The rate of heat flow from the fin per foot of width can be obtained from Eq. 2–57 as

$$q = \sqrt{2\bar{h}kb}\ (1100 - 100)\ \frac{I_1\ (2B\ \sqrt{\tfrac{1}{3}})}{I_0\ (5.66\ \sqrt{\tfrac{1}{3}})}$$

$$= \sqrt{(2)(15)(15)(\tfrac{1}{12})} \times 1000\ \frac{I_0\ (3.26)}{I_0\ (3.26)}$$

$$= 5050\ \text{Btu/hr ft}$$

The weight of the fin per foot of width is

$$(\rho b L/2)/\text{ft} = (490)\ \left(\frac{1}{2}\right)\ \left(\frac{1 \times 4}{144}\right) = 6.8\ \text{lb/ft}$$

Finally, the rate of heat flow per unit weight is

$$q = \frac{5050}{6.8} = 744\ \text{Btu/hr lb}_\text{m}$$

Straight rectangular fin: According to the specifications we have

$$m = \sqrt{\frac{\bar{h}P}{kA}} = \sqrt{\frac{(15)(2)}{(15)(\tfrac{1}{12})}} = 2\sqrt{6}$$

The temperature distribution is, from Eq. 2–47,

$$T = 100 + 1000\left[\frac{\cosh 2\sqrt{6}(\tfrac{1}{3} - x) + 1/2\sqrt{6}\ \sinh 2\sqrt{6}(\tfrac{1}{3} - x)}{\cosh 1.63 + 0.204\ \sinh 1.63}\right]$$

The temperature distribution along the fin is plotted in Fig. 2–18. The rate of heat flow from the fin per foot width can be found from Eq. 2–48:

$$q = 6130\ \frac{\sinh 1.63 + 0.204\ \cosh 1.63}{\cosh 1.63 + 0.204\ \sinh 1.63} = 5820\ \text{Btu/hr ft}$$

The weight of the fin is twice that of the tapered fin, i.e., 13.6 lb/ft, and the heat dissipation per unit weight for the straight fin is 428 Btu/hr lb$_\text{m}$. Hence, the tapered fin can dissipate 75 per cent more heat per unit weight than the straight fin. *Ans.*

Selection and design of fins. The selection of a suitable fin geometry requires a compromise of the cost, the weight, the available space, and the pressure drop, as well as the heat-transfer characteristics of the extended surface. Harper and Brown (10) and Gardner (9) have analyzed a variety of fin geometries, and their papers are recommended for a general treatment of the problem. The following remarks are largely based on their work.

For a plane surface of area A, the thermal resistance is $1/\bar{h}A$. The addition of fins increases the surface area, but at the same time it also introduces a conductive resistance over that portion of the original surface at which the fins are attached. The addition of fins will therefore not always increase the rate of heat transfer.

For a fin of uniform cross-sectional area, the limiting condition can be obtained by differentiating the rate of heat flow (Eq. 2–45 or Eq. 2–48) with respect to the fin length for given values of $\bar{h}$, k, P, and A and setting the result equal to zero. This operation shows that increased heat transfer can be expected by the addition of fins only if $\bar{h}A/Pk \leq 1$. In practice, however, the addition of fins is hardly ever justified unless $\bar{h}$ is less than $0.25Pk/A$.

Using the values of the average surface conductances in Table 1–2 as a guide, we can easily see that fins effectively increase the heat transfer to or from a gas, are less effective when the medium is a liquid in forced convection, but offer no advantage in heat transfer to boiling liquids or from condensing vapors. For a $\frac{1}{8}$-in.-diameter aluminum pin fin in a typical gas heater, $\bar{h}A/Pk = \bar{h}D/4k = [(20)(0.125/12)]/[(4)(115)] = 0.00045$, whereas in a water heater, for example, $\bar{h}A/Pk = [(1000)(0.125/12)]/[(4)(115)] = 0.022$. In the gas heater the fin would therefore be much more effective than in the water heater.

It is apparent from these considerations that, when fins are used, they should be placed on the side of the heat-exchange surface where the heat-transfer coefficient between the fluid and the surface is the lowest. Thin, slender, and closely spaced fins are superior to fewer and thicker fins from the heat-transfer standpoint. Obviously, fins made of materials having a high thermal conductivity are desirable.

Fins are often attached circumferentially to the outer surface of tubes. The performance of such fins can be calculated approximately by using the equations for straight fins with the area A and the perimeter P taken at a mean between the root and outer radii of such a circumferential fin. This approximation is satisfactory so long as the fin height is small compared with the base diameter. Exact methods of calculations are presented in Refs. 3, 8, 9 and 10.

To calculate the over-all conductance of a finned surface and to evaluate its thermal performance, the temperature gradient along the extended surfaces must be considered. The unfinned portion of the surface is at the wall temperature and transfers heat at 100 per cent efficiency. The portion of the surface to which the fins are attached is not directly in contact with fluid, but heat flows through it by conduction to or from the fin. The heat transfer to or from the surface of the fin is by convection, but since the temperature varies along the fin, its surface does not operate at maximum efficiency. To evaluate the thermal performance of the fin, its efficiency must therefore be known. The fin efficiency η_f is the ratio of the heat transferred across the fin surface to the heat which would be transferred if the entire surface were at the base temperature. For a fin of rectangular cross section (length L and thickness t) (see Ref. 9 and Prob. 2-26) the fin efficiency is approximately given by

$$\eta_f = \frac{\tanh\left[\sqrt{2\bar{h}/kt}\,(L + t/2)\right]}{\sqrt{2\bar{h}/kt}\,(L + t/2)} \tag{2-58}$$

whereas for circular pin fins of diameter D and length L the efficiency is

$$\eta_f = \frac{\tanh\sqrt{4L^2\bar{h}/kD}}{\sqrt{4L^2\bar{h}/kD}} \tag{2-59}$$

For circumferential fins of rectangular cross section, the approximate fin efficiency is plotted in Fig. 2-19 as a family of curves (see Ref. 9) which approach in the limiting case the behavior of the straight fin, Eq. 2-58.

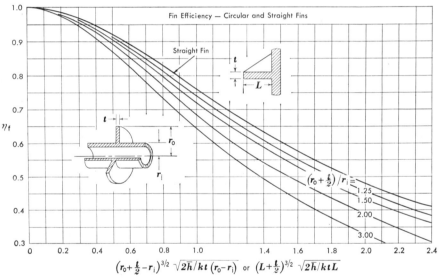

FIG. 2-19.   Efficiency of circumferential fins of rectangular cross-sectional area.

To obtain the total efficiency of a surface with fins η_t we combine the unfinned portion of the surface at 100 per cent efficiency with the surface area of the fins at η_f, or

$$A\eta_t = A - A_f + A_f\eta_f = A - A_f(1 - \eta_f) \tag{2-60}$$

where A = total heat-transfer area;

A_f = heat-transfer area of the fins.

The over-all heat-transfer coefficient U, based on the total outer surface area, for heat transfer between two fluids separated by a wall with fins can then be expressed as

$$U = \cfrac{1}{\cfrac{1}{\eta_{to}\bar{h}_o} + R_{k\ \text{wall}} + \cfrac{A_o}{\eta_{ti}A_i\bar{h}_i}} \qquad (2\text{-}61)$$

where $R_{k\ \text{wall}}$ = thermal resistance of the wall to which the fins are attached, in Btu/hr F sq ft outside surface;

A_o = total outer surface area, in sq ft;

A_i = total inner surface area, in sq ft;

η_{to} = total efficiency for outer surface;

η_{ti} = total efficiency for inner surface;

$\bar{h}_o$ = average unit conductance for outer surface, in Btu/hr sq ft F;

$\bar{h}_i$ = average unit conductance for inner surface, in Btu/hr sq ft F.

For tubes with fins on the outside only, the usual case in practice, η_{ti} is unity and $A_i = \pi D_i l$.

In the analysis presented in this chapter, details of the convection heat flow between the fin surface and the surrounding fluid have been omitted. A complete engineering analysis not only requires an evaluation of the fin performance, but must also take the interrelation between the fin geometry and the convection heat transfer into account. Problems on the convective heat transfer part of the design will be considered in later chapters.

REFERENCES

1. R. Schuman, Jr., *Metallurgical Engineering*, Vol. I, *Engineering Principles*. (Cambridge, Mass.: Addison-Wesley Publishing Company, 1952.)

2. I. Langmuir, E. Q. Adams, and S. F. Meikle, "Flow of Heat Through Furnace Walls," *Trans. Am. Electrochem. Soc.*, Vol. 24 (1913), pp. 53–84.

3. P. J. Schneider, *Conduction Heat Transfer*. (Cambridge, Mass.: Addison-Wesley Publishing Company, 1955.)

4. M. E. Barzelay, K. N. Tong, and G. F. Holloway, "Effect of Pressure on Thermal Conductance of Contact Joints," *NACA TN* 3245, May, 1955.

5. T. N. Cetinkale and M. Fishenden, "Thermal Conductance of Metal Surfaces in Contact," *General Discussion on Heat Transfer*, pp. 271–275. (London: IME; New York: ASME, 1951.)

6. E. Jahnke and F. Emde, *Tables of Functions with Formulae and Curves*, 4th ed. (New York: Dover Publications, 1945.)

7. C. R. Wylie, Jr., *Advanced Engineering Mathematics*. (New York: McGraw-Hill Book Company, Inc., 1951.)

8. M. Jakob, *Heat Transfer*, Vol. I. (New York: John Wiley & Sons, Inc., 1949.)

9. K. A. Gardner, "Efficiency of Extended Surfaces," *Trans. ASME*, Vol. 67 (1945), pp. 621–631.

10. W. P. Harper and D. R. Brown, "Mathematical Equations for Heat Conduction in the Fins of Air-Cooled Engines," *NACA Report* 158, 1922.

11.   H. A. Saller, "Uranium and its Alloys", *The Reactor Handbook*, Vol. 3, AECD-3647, p. 391. (USAEC, May, 1955.)

12.   S. Glasstone, *Principles of Nuclear Reactor Engineering.* (Princeton, N. J.: D. Van Nostrand Company, Inc., 1955.)

13.   J. R. Dietrich and D. Okrent, "Spatial Distribution of Heat Generation," *The Reactor Handbook*, Vol. 2, AECD-3646, pp. 87–121. (USAEC, May, 1955.)

14.   A. S. Thompson and O. E. Rodgers, *Thermal Power from Nuclear Reactors.* (New York: John Wiley & Sons, Inc., 1956.)

15.   C. F. Bonilla, *Nuclear Engineering.*   (New York: McGraw-Hill Book Company, Inc., 1957.)

16.   H. C. Schwenk and R. H. Shannon, *Nuclear Power Engineering* (New York: McGraw-Hill Book Company, Inc., 1957.)

PROBLEMS

2-1.   The interior of a refrigerator, having inside dimensions of $1\frac{1}{2}$-by $1\frac{1}{2}$-ft base area and 4-ft height, is to be maintained at 45 F.   The walls of the refrigerator are constructed of two $\frac{1}{8}$-in. mild-steel sheets with 3 in. of glass-wool insulation between them.   If the average heat-transfer coefficients at the inner and outer surfaces are 2.0 and 2.5 Btu/hr sq ft F respectively, *estimate* the rate at which heat must be removed from the interior to maintain the specified temperature in a kitchen at 85 F.   What will be the temperature at the outer surface of the wall?

2-2.   In a manufacturing operation, a large sheet of plastic, $\frac{1}{2}$ in. thick, is to be glued to a 1-in.-thick sheet of cork board.   To effect a bond, the glue is to be maintained at a temperature of 110 F for a considerable period of time.   This is accomplished by a radiant heat source, applied uniformly over the surface of the plastic ($k = 1.3$ Btu/hr ft F).   The exposed sides of the cork and of the plastic have a heat-transfer coefficient by convection of 2.0 Btu/hr sq ft F, and the room temperature during the operation is 70 F.   Neglecting heat losses by radiation from the sheets, estimate the rate at which heat must be supplied to the surface of the plastic to obtain the required temperature at the interface.   The thermal resistance of the glue may be neglected.   Draw the thermal circuit for the system.

2-3.   Steam having a quality of 98 per cent at a pressure of 20 psia is flowing at a velocity of 3 fps through a $\frac{3}{4}$-in. steel pipe (1.05 in. OD, 0.824 in. ID).   The heat-transfer coefficient at the inner surface, where condensation occurs, is 1000 Btu/hr sq ft F.   A dirt film at the inner surface adds a unit thermal resistance of 1.0 hr sq ft F/Btu.   Estimate the rate of heat loss per foot length of pipe if (a) the pipe is bare, (b) the pipe is covered with a 2-in. layer of 85 per cent magnesia insulation.   For both cases assume that the unit-surface conductance at the outer surface is 2.0 Btu/hr sq ft F and that the environmental temperature is 70 F.   Also estimate the change in quality per 10-ft length of pipe in both cases.

2-4.   The rate of heat flow per unit length q/L through a hollow cylinder of inside radius r_i and outside radius r_o is

$$q/L = \bar{A}\ k\ \Delta\ T/(r_o - r_i)$$

where $\bar{A} = 2\pi(r_o - r_i)/\ln(r_o/r_i)$.   Determine the per cent error in the rate of heat flow if the arithmetic mean area $\pi(r_o + r_i)$ is used instead of the logarithmic mean area $\bar{A}$ for ratios of inside to outside diameters (D_o/D_i) of 1.5, 2.0, and 3.0.   Plot the results.

2-5.   Estimate the rate of heat loss per unit length from a 2-in.-ID, $2\frac{3}{8}$-in.-OD steel pipe covered with asbestos insulation ($3\frac{3}{8}$ in. OD).   Steam flows in the pipe.   It has a quality of 99 per cent and is at 300 F.   The total thermal resistance at the inner wall is 0.015 hr sq ft F/Btu, the heat-transfer coefficient at the outer surface is 3.0 Btu/hr sq ft F, and the ambient temperature is 60 F.

2-6. To measure the thermal conductivity, two similar 1-in.-thick specimens are placed in an apparatus shown in the accompanying sketch. Electric current is supplied to the 6- by 6-in. guarded heater, and a wattmeter shows that the power dissipation is 7 watts (w). Thermocouples attached to the warmer and to the cooler surfaces show temperatures of 120 F and 80 F respectively. Calculate the thermal conductivity of the material at the mean temperature in Btu/hr ft F.

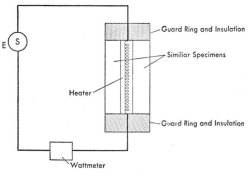

PROB. 2–6.

2-7. Estimate the rate of heat flow per sq ft area through a furnace wall consisting of an 8-in.-thick inner layer of chrome brick, a center layer of kaolin insulating brick (4 in. thick) and an outer layer of masonry brick (4 in. thick). The unit-surface conductance at the inner surface is 15 Btu/hr sq ft F and the outer-surface temperature is 150 F. The temperature of the gases inside the furnace is 3000 F. What temperatures prevail in the steady state at the inner and outer surfaces of the center layer?

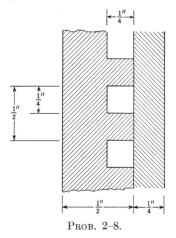

PROB. 2–8.

2-8. A composite insulating wall is made of two layers of cork (k = 0.025 Btu/hr sq ft F) as shown in the accompanying sketch. If the spaces are filled with atmospheric air, determine the total unit thermal resistance of the wall and compare it with that of a solid wall.

2–9. An electrical heater capable of generating 10,000 w/ft is to be designed. The heating element is to be a stainless steel wire, having an electrical resistivity of 32×10^{-6} ohms per square inch area per inch length. The operating temperature of the stainless steel is to be no more than 2300 F. The heat-transfer coefficient at the outer surface is expected to be no less than 300 Btu/hr sq ft F in a medium whose maximum temperature is 200 F. A transformer capable of delivering current at 9 and 12 v is available. Determine a suitable size for the wire, the current required, and discuss what effect a reduction in the heat-transfer coefficient could have. HINT: Demonstrate *first* that the temperature drop between the center and the surface of the wire is independent of the wire diameter, and determine its value.

2–10. Design the contour of a tapered fin of copper $\frac{1}{4}$ in. thick at base and 4 in. long, which will produce a linear temperature gradient.

2–11. Derive an expression for the temperature distribution in an infinitely long rod of uniform cross section within which there is uniform heat generation at the rate of 1 Btu/sec per in. length. Assume that the rod is attached to a surface at T_s and is exposed through a unit-surface conductance $\bar{h}$ to a fluid at T_∞.

2–12. A thin flat electrical heating element is covered on one side with a layer of asbestos ($\rho = 36$ lb/cu ft) 1 in. thick and on the other side with a carbon-steel plate $\frac{1}{8}$ in. thick. The heat-transfer coefficient for the fluid on the outer sides of this sandwich plate is 2 Btu/hr sq ft F and the fluid there is at 60 F. Calculate (a) the rate of heat dissipation at the heater, in watts per sq ft which will make the heater temperature 700 F under conditions of steady state, and (b) specify the temperature of the outside surface of the steel for these conditions.

2–13. Compare the rates of heat transfer per unit weight of fin material for three types of fins attached to a wall at T_{wall}: (a) a rectangular fin, 4 in. from base to tip, $\frac{1}{4}$ in. thick, and 1 ft long; (b) same as (a) except tapered from $\frac{1}{4}$ to $\frac{1}{16}$ in. (base to tip); and (c) same base area, length, and width, but the thickness is tapered to produce a linear temperature drop.

In each case consider copper with $h = 2$ Btu/hr sq ft F and $T_{\text{wall}} - T_\infty = 150$ F.

2–14. To determine the thermal conductivity of a long, solid 1-in.-diam rod, one half was inserted into a furnace while the other half was projecting into air at 80 F. After steady state had been reached, the temperatures at two points 3 in. apart were measured and found to be 258 F and 196 F respectively. The heat-transfer coefficient over the surface of the rod exposed to the air was estimated to be 4.0 Btu/hr sq ft F. What is the thermal conductivity of the rod?

2–15. A turbine blade $2\frac{1}{2}$ in. long, cross-sectional area A of 0.005 sq ft, perimeter P of 0.400 ft is made of stainless steel ($k = 15$ Btu/hr ft F). The temperature of the root T_s is 900 F. The blade is exposed to a hot gas at 1600 F, and the unit-surface conductance $\bar{h}$ is 80 Btu/hr sq ft F. Determine the temperature distribution and the rate of heat flow at the root of the blade. Assume that the tip is insulated.

2–16. In a cylindrical fuel rod of a nuclear reactor, heat is generated internally according to the equation

$$\dot{q} = \dot{q}_1 \left[1 - (r/r_o)^2 \right]$$

where $\dot{q}$ = local rate of heat generation per unit volume at r;

r_o = outside radius;

$\dot{q}_1$ = rate of heat generation per unit volume at the center line.

Calculate the temperature drop from the center line to the surface for a 1-in.-OD rod having a thermal conductivity of 15 Btu/hr ft F if the rate of heat removal from its surface is 500,000 Btu/hr sq ft.

2–17. Two long pieces of copper wire, $\frac{1}{16}$ in. in diameter, are to be soldered together end to end. If the air temperature is 80 F and the melting point of the solder is 450 F, what is the minimum rate of heat input required?   Assume that the unit-surface conductance between the surface of the wire and the ambient air is 3.0 Btu/hr sq ft F.

2–18.   Show that the temperature distribution in a long solid tube, insulated on the outside, cooled on the inside, with uniform heat generation within the solid, is given by

$$T(r) - T_o = -\frac{\dot{q}}{4k}(r^2 - r_o{}^2) + \frac{\dot{q}r_o{}^2}{2k}\ln\frac{r}{r_o}$$

2–19.   The heated aircraft wing-deicing system in the leading edge (nose section) is arranged substantially as indicated in the sketch.   That is, air heated to a temperature T_1 supplies a spanwise duct, D, and is distributed, at a rate of W lb/hr ft of span, into trapezoidal-shaped "double skin" chordwise ducting at a temperature of T_2.   Let T_a = outside air temperature; heat-transfer coefficients $\bar{h}_a$ = outside surface, $\bar{h}_2$ = inside trapezoidal duct surfaces, and $\bar{h}_1$ = inside D-duct surfaces, d = depth, $2b$ and b the widths, and L the length of the trapezoidal ducts.   Assuming that $T_1 \simeq T_2 = T_m$, derive a formula for the rate of heat transfer to the outer air per foot of span length for n trapezoidal ducts per foot.

PROB. 2–19.

2–20.   For a finite fin of cylindrical cross section, radius r_o, insulated at the end, the relation governing the heat loss is

$$q = \sqrt{2\,\bar{h}\,k\,\pi^2\,r_o{}^3}\,(T_s - T_\infty)\tanh mL$$

where $m = \sqrt{2\bar{h}/kr_o}$ and L is the length of the fin.   Find the length of such a fin that is most economical from the standpoint of the least amount of material used to give the maximum heat dissipation.   *Ans.* $L = 0.222/m$

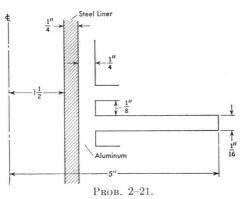

PROB. 2–21.

2–21.   An aircraft cylinder has the dimensions shown in the accompanying sketch. For an inside wall temperature of 1500 F and an $\bar{h}_c$ of 30 Btu/hr sq ft F, find the temperature distribution through the cylinder and along the fin.   For the same cylinder, fin dimensions, and spacing but with *radial* fins, find the temperature distribution. Compare the heat transfer rate with the circular fins to that with the radial fins. What assumptions or simplifications have you made in this problem?

2–22.   In practice, the end of a tapered fin will be flat, as shown in the accompanying sketch.   Find an expression for the temperature distribution and the rate of heat loss from this fin, assuming that the end is insulated.   Also, plot the temperature distribution along the fin if $T_o = 0$ F, $T_\infty = 212$ F, $b = \frac{1}{4}$ in., and $\bar{h}_c = 10$ Btu/hr sq ft F. The fin material is aluminum.

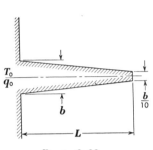
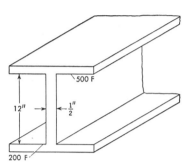

PROB. 2–22.   PROB. 2–23.

2–23.   The top of a 12-in. I beam is maintained at a temperature of 500 F, while the bottom is at 200 F.   The thickness of the web is $\frac{1}{2}$ in.   Air at 500 F is blowing along the side of the beam so that $\bar{h} = 7$ Btu/hr sq ft F.   The thermal conductivity of the steel may be assumed constant and equal to 25 Btu/hr ft F.   Find the temperature distribution along the web from top to bottom and plot the result.

2–24.   Find the temperature distribution along a wedge-shaped fin which is 3 in. wide at the base and 12 in. long.   The fin is constructed of stainless steel whose $k = 15$ Btu/hr ft F.   The base temperature is 1600 F, the ambient gases are at 400 F, and the heat-transfer coefficient between the fin and the gases is 15 Btu/hr sq ft F.   Plot the results and also determine the total rate of heat loss per foot length of the fin.

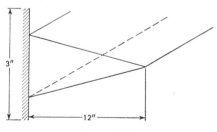

PROB. 2–24.

2–25.   The handle of a ladle used for pouring molten lead is 12 in. long.   Originally the handle was made of $\frac{3}{4}$- by $\frac{1}{2}$-in. mild-steel bar stock.   To reduce the grip temperature, it is proposed to form the handle of tubing $\frac{1}{16}$ in. thick to the same rectangular shape.   If the average unit-surface conductance over the handle surface is 2.5 Btu/hr sq ft F, estimate the reduction of the temperature at the grip in 70 F air.

2–26. Derive Eq. 2–58 in detail. Assume that tip losses are taken into account by extending the length of the pin by $t/2$, while the end of this extended pin is adiabatic ($L^1 = L + t/2$, $\partial T/\partial x = 0$ at $x = L^1$).

2–27. Derive Eq. 2–44a in detail.

2–28. Derive Eq. 2–47, showing all steps.

2–29. (a) Find the thermal resistance per sq ft of a wall constructed of 2 by 4 wooden beams on 16-in. centers, with 1-in. boards on the exterior, $\frac{1}{2}$-in. sheet rock on the interior, and rock wool insulation in the space between the studs. (b) If the inside air temperature is 70 F, the outside 40 F, and the surface heat-transfer coefficient is 2 Btu/hr sq ft F on both sides, what is the rate of heat loss per square foot? (c) If a 20-ft cubical structure has walls and roof of this resistance, what is the necessary current rating of a 110-v electric heater if it is to maintain the specified conditions?

Data: Two-by-four dimensions $= 1\frac{5}{8}$ in. x $3\frac{1}{2}$ in.
One-inch board thickness $= \frac{3}{4}$ in.
Wood conductivity $= 0.10$ Btu/hr ft F
Sheet rock conductivity $= 0.30$ Btu/hr ft F
Rock wool conductivity $= 0.03$ Btu/ft F

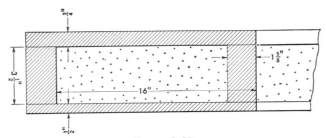

PROB. 2–29.

2–30. The addition of insulation to a cylindrical surface, such as a wire, may sometimes increase the rate of heat dissipation to the surroundings. (a) For a No. 10 wire (0.102 in. diam), what is the optimum thickness of rubber insulation ($k = 0.08$ Btu/hr ft F) if the unit-surface conductance is 3 Btu/hr sq ft F? (b) If the current-carrying capacity of this wire is considered to be limited by the insulation temperature, what per cent increase in capacity is realized by addition of the insulation?

2–31. (a) Derive an expression for the temperature rise of the center of a current-carrying wire relative to the surface as a function of the current, the diameter, and the electrical and thermal conductivities. (b) Compare the temperature differences between center and surface for No. 14 wires (0.064 in. diam) of copper and nichrome when both are carrying 15 amps. (c) Compare the surface temperature rise of these wires if the unit-surface conductance is 2 Btu/hr ft F for both.

Assume: Thermal conductivity of copper $= 220$ Btu/hr ft F
of nichrome $= 8$ Btu/hr ft F
Electrical conductivity of copper $= 1.47$ x 10^6 mho/in.
of nichrome $= 3.76$ x 10^3 mho/in.

2–32. A standard 4-in. steel pipe (ID $= 4.026$ in., OD $= 4.500$ in.) carries superheated steam at 1200 F in an enclosed space where a fire hazard exists, limiting the outer-surface temperature to 100 F. In order to minimize the insulation cost, two materials are to be used; first a high temperature insulation (relatively expensive) applied to the pipe and then magnesia (a less expensive material) on the outside.   The maximum temperature of the magnesia is to be 600 F.   The following constants are known:

Steam side coefficient	$\bar{h} = 100$	Btu/hr sq ft F
High-temperate insulation conducting	$k = 0.06$	Btu/hr ft F
Magnesia conductivity	$k = 0.045$	Btu/hr ft F
Outside heat-transfer coefficient	$\bar{h} = 2.0$	Btu/hr sq ft F
Steel conductivity	$k = 25$	Btu/hr ft F
Ambient temperature	$T_\infty = 70$	F

(a) Specify the thickness for each insulating material.   (b) Calculate the over-all conductance based on the pipe OD.   (c) What fraction of the total resistance is due (1) steam side resistance, (2) steel pipe resistance, (3) insulation (combination of the two), and (4) outside resistance?   (d) How much heat is transferred per hour, per foot length of pipe?

2–33.   Heat is transferred from water to air through a brass wall ($k = 45$ Btu/hr ft F).   The addition of rectangular brass fins, 0.03 in. thick and 1 in. long, spaced 0.5 in. apart, is contemplated.   Assuming a waterside heat-transfer coefficient of 30 Btu/hr sq ft F and an airside heat-transfer coefficient of 3 Btu/hr sq ft F, compare the gain in heat-transfer rate achieved by adding fins to (a) the waterside, (b) the airside, and (c) both sides.   (Neglect temperature drop through the wall.)

3 Two- and Three-Dimensional Steady-State Conduction

3-1. METHODS OF ANALYSIS

In the preceding chapter we dealt with problems in which the temperature and the heat flow can be treated as functions of a single variable. Many practical problems fall into this category, but when the boundaries of a system are irregular or when the temperature along a boundary is non-uniform, a one-dimensional treatment may no longer be satisfactory. In such cases the temperature is a function of two, and possibly even three, coordinates. The heat flow through a corner section where two or three walls meet, the heat conduction through the walls of a short, hollow cylinder, or the heat loss from a buried pipe are typical examples of this class of problems.

In this chapter we shall consider some methods for analyzing conduction in two- and three-dimensional systems. The emphasis will be placed on two-dimensional problems because they are less cumbersome to solve and illustrate the basic methods of analysis equally well.

Heat conduction in two- and three-dimensional systems can be treated by *analytical, graphical, analogical,* and *numerical methods.* A complete treatment of analytical solutions requires a prior knowledge of Fourier series, Bessel functions, Legendre polynomials, Laplace transform methods, and complex variable theory. A number of excellent books dealing exclusively with mathematical solutions of heat-conduction problems are available. Since most of this material is too advanced for an introductory course, it will not be presented here. We shall consider only the analytical solution of one relatively simple problem to illustrate the analytical method of approach. The other three methods will be considered in more detail because they do not require advanced mathematics and are more useful for engineering calculations where a good approximate solution is usually satisfactory, especially when it can be obtained quickly. The reader interested in additional information on mathematical solutions of heat-conduction problems should consult Refs. 1, 2, 3, and 4.

3–2. DERIVATION OF THE HEAT-CONDUCTION EQUATION

Before discussing specific problems, we shall derive the differential equation governing the temperature distribution in a body. Then, by making certain assumptions, we shall simplify this equation and reduce it to forms which are amenable to analytical, graphical, or numerical solutions.

Consider a small element of material in a solid body. The element has the shape of a rectangular parallelepiped with its edges dx, dy, and dz parallel, respectively, to the x, y, and z axes as shown in Fig. 3–1. To

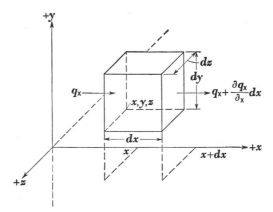

Fig. 3–1. Sketch illustrating nomenclature for the derivation of the general heat-conduction equation in Cartesian coordinates.

obtain an equation for the temperature distribution we write an energy balance for the element for a small time $d\theta$. Semantically the energy balance can be written in the form

| Heat in-flow during $d\theta$ | + | heat generated by internal sources during $d\theta$ | = | heat out-flow during $d\theta$ | + | change in internal energy during $d\theta$ | **(3–1)** |

or algebraically in the form

$$(q_x + q_y + q_z)\, d\theta + \dot{q}(dx\, dy\, dz)\, d\theta = (q_{x+dx} + q_{y+dy} + q_{z+dz})\, d\theta \\ + c\rho dT\, (dx\, dy\, dz)$$

where dT is the temperature change of the element during $d\theta$. Since the temperature T will in general vary throughout the body, it is a function of the three coordinates x, y, z as well as of time θ, i.e., $T = T(x,y,z,\theta)$.

The heat conducted into the element per unit time across the left face in the x direction, q_x, can according to Eq. 1–1 be written as

$$q_x = \left(-k\,\frac{\partial T}{\partial x}\right)dy\,dz$$

The temperature gradient is expressed as a partial derivative because T is not only a function of x, but also of y, z, and θ. By the mean-value theorem explained in Sec. 2–3, or by expanding q_x in a Taylor series about x and neglecting all but the first two terms, the corresponding rate of heat outflow across the right face at $x + dx$, q_{x+dx}, can be written

$$q_{x+dx} = \left[\left(-k\,\frac{\partial T}{\partial x}\right) + \frac{\partial}{\partial x}\left(-k\,\frac{\partial T}{\partial x}\right)dx\right]dy\,dz$$

Subtracting the heat-flow rate out of the element from the heat-flow rate into the element yields

$$q_{x+dx} - q_x = \frac{\partial\left(k\,\dfrac{\partial T}{\partial x}\right)}{\partial x}\,dx\,dy\,dz$$

and similarly for the y and z directions

$$q_{y+dy} - q_y = \frac{\partial\left(k\,\dfrac{\partial T}{\partial y}\right)}{\partial y}\,dx\,dy\,dz$$

$$q_{z+dz} - q_z = \frac{\partial\left(k\,\dfrac{\partial T}{\partial z}\right)}{\partial z}\,dx\,dy\,dz$$

Substituting these relations into the energy balance and dividing each term by $dx\,dy\,dz\,d\theta$ gives

$$\frac{\partial}{\partial x}\left(k\,\frac{\partial T}{\partial x}\right) + \frac{\partial}{\partial y}\left(k\,\frac{\partial T}{\partial y}\right) + \frac{\partial}{\partial z}\left(k\,\frac{\partial T}{\partial z}\right) + \dot{q} = c\rho\,\frac{\partial T}{\partial\theta} \qquad (3\text{–}2)$$

if the specific heat c and the density ρ are independent of temperature. If k is assumed to be uniform, Eq. 3–2 can be written

$$\frac{\partial^2 T}{\partial x^2} + \frac{\partial^2 T}{\partial y^2} + \frac{\partial^2 T}{\partial z^2} + \frac{\dot{q}}{k} = \frac{1}{a}\,\frac{\partial T}{\partial\theta} \qquad (3\text{–}3)$$

where the constant $a = k/c\rho$ is called the *thermal diffusivity* and has the units, sq ft/hr, in the engineering system. Equation 3–3 is known as the general heat-conduction equation and governs the temperature distribution and the conduction heat flow in a solid having uniform physical properties.

If the system contains no heat sources, Eq. 3–3 reduces to the *Fourier equation*

$$\frac{\partial^2 T}{\partial x^2} + \frac{\partial^2 T}{\partial y^2} + \frac{\partial^2 T}{\partial z^2} = \frac{1}{a}\frac{\partial T}{\partial \theta}$$

(3–4)

If the system is steady, but heat sources are present, Eq. 3–3 becomes the *Poisson equation*

$$\frac{\partial^2 T}{\partial x^2} + \frac{\partial^2 T}{\partial y^2} + \frac{\partial^2 T}{\partial z^2} + \frac{\dot{q}}{k} = 0$$

(3–5)

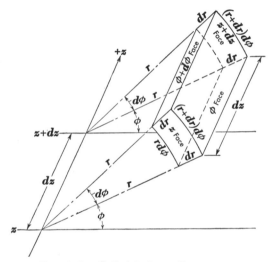

FIG. 3–2. Cylindrical coordinate system.

In the steady state the temperature distribution in a body free of heat sources must satisfy the *Laplace equation*

$$\frac{\partial^2 T}{\partial x^2} + \frac{\partial^2 T}{\partial y^2} + \frac{\partial^2 T}{\partial z^2} = 0$$

(3–6)

For one-dimensional steady heat conduction, Eq. 3–6 becomes $d^2T/dx^2 = 0$, which yields, after integration, $dT/dx = $ constant, as anticipated from Eq. 1–1 for steady one-dimensional heat conduction.

There are numerous problems in heat conduction which can be handled more conveniently in a cylindrical or spherical coordinate system. The general heat-conduction equation in the cylindrical coordinate system shown in Fig. 3–2 is

$$\frac{\partial^2 T}{\partial r^2} + \frac{1}{r}\frac{\partial T}{\partial r} + \frac{1}{r^2}\frac{\partial^2 T}{\partial \phi^2} + \frac{\partial^2 T}{\partial z^2} + \frac{\dot{q}}{k} = \frac{1}{a}\frac{\partial T}{\partial \theta} \tag{3-7}$$

The derivation of this equation is left as an exercise. However, attention is directed to the fact that the area through which heat flows into the element in the positive r direction is $r\,d\phi\,dz$ and the area through which heat flows out of the element in the r direction is $(r + dr)\,d\phi dz$. This change in area results in the term $(1/r)(\partial T/\partial r)$ in Eq. 3–7.

In the spherical coordinate system shown in Fig. 3–3, the general heat-conduction equation becomes

$$\frac{1}{r}\frac{\partial^2 (rT)}{\partial r^2} + \frac{1}{r^2 \sin \phi}\frac{\partial T}{\partial \phi}\left(\sin \phi \frac{\partial T}{\partial \phi}\right)$$

$$+ \frac{1}{r^2 \sin^2 \phi}\frac{\partial^2 T}{\partial \psi^2} + \frac{\dot{q}}{k} = \frac{1}{a}\frac{\partial T}{\partial \theta} \tag{3-8}$$

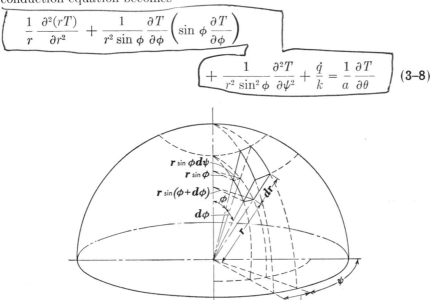

FIG. 3–3. Spherical coordinate system.

3–3. ANALYTICAL SOLUTION [1]

An analytical solution of a heat-conduction problem must satisfy the heat-conduction equation as well as the boundary conditions specified by the physical conditions of the particular problem. The classical approach to an exact solution of the Fourier equation is the separation-of-variables technique. We shall illustrate this approach by applying it to a relatively simple problem. Consider a thin rectangular plate, free of heat sources and insulated at the top and bottom surface (Fig. 3–4). For a thin plate,

[1] This section may be omitted without interrupting the continuity of the presentation.

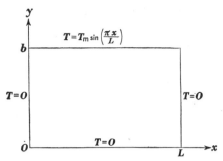

Fɪɢ. 3–4.   Rectangular adiabatic plate.

$\partial T/\partial z$ is negligible and the temperature is a function of x and y only, i.e., $T = T(x,y)$. The temperature distribution in a plate with adiabatic faces must therefore satisfy the equation

$$\frac{\partial^2 T}{\partial x^2} + \frac{\partial^2 T}{\partial y^2} = 0 \qquad (3\text{--}9)$$

if the thermal conductivity is uniform. Equation 3–9 is a linear and homogeneous partial-differential equation. This type of equation usually can be integrated by assuming a product solution for $T(x,y)$ of the form

$$T = XY \qquad (3\text{--}10)$$

where $X = X\,(x)$, a function of x only, and $Y = Y(y)$, a function of y alone. Substituting Eq. 3–10 in Eq. 3–9 yields

$$-\frac{1}{X}\frac{d^2 X}{dx^2} = \frac{1}{Y}\frac{d^2 Y}{dy^2} \qquad (3\text{--}11)$$

The variables are now separated. The left-hand side is a function of x only, while the right-hand side is a function of y alone. Since neither side can change as x and y vary, both must be equal to a constant, say λ^2. We have, therefore, the two total-differential equations

$$\frac{d^2 X}{dx^2} + \lambda^2 X = 0 \qquad (3\text{--}12)$$

and

$$\frac{d^2 Y}{dy^2} - \lambda^2 Y = 0 \qquad (3\text{--}13)$$

The general solution to Eq. 3–12 is

$$X = A\,\cos \lambda x + B\,\sin \lambda x$$

the general solution to Eq. 3–13 is

$$Y = Ce^{-\lambda y} + De^{\lambda y}$$

and therefore

$$T = XY = (A \cos \lambda x + B \sin \lambda x)(Ce^{-\lambda y} + De^{\lambda y}) \qquad \text{(3–14)}$$

where $A,B,C,$ and D are constants to be evaluated from the boundary conditions. As shown in Fig. 3–4, the boundary conditions to be satisfied are

$$T = 0 \qquad \text{at } y = 0$$

$$T = 0 \qquad \text{at } x = 0$$

$$T = 0 \qquad \text{at } x = L$$

$$T = T_m \sin \frac{\pi x}{L} \qquad \text{at } y = b$$

Substituting Eq. 3–14 for T we get from the first condition

$$(A \cos \lambda x + B \sin \lambda x)(C + D) = 0$$

from the second condition

$$A \ (Ce^{-\lambda y} + De^{\lambda y}) = 0$$

and from the third condition

$$(A \cos \lambda x + B \sin \lambda x)(Ce^{-\lambda L} + De^{\lambda L}) = 0$$

The first condition can be satisfied only if $C = -D$, and the second if $A = 0$. Using these results in the third condition, we obtain

$$(B \sin \lambda L) C \ (e^{-L} - e^{L}) = 2BC \sin \lambda L \sinh \lambda y = 0$$

To satisfy this condition, $\sin \lambda L$ must be zero or $\lambda = n\pi/L$, where $n = 1,2,3,$ etc.[2] There exists therefore a different solution for each integer n and each solution has a separate integration constant C_n. Summing these solutions, we get

$$T = \sum_{n=1}^{\infty} C_n \sin \frac{n\pi x}{L} \sin \frac{n\pi y}{L} \qquad \text{(3–15)}$$

The last boundary condition demands that, at $y = b$

$$\sum_{n=1}^{\infty} C_n \sin \frac{n\pi x}{L} \sinh \frac{n\pi b}{L} = T_m \sin \frac{\pi x}{L} \qquad \text{(3–16)}$$

[2] The value $n = 0$ is excluded because it would give the trivial solution $T = 0$.

so that only the first term in the series solution with $C_1 = T_m/\sinh(\pi b/L)$ is needed. The solution therefore becomes

$$T(x,y) = T_m \frac{\sinh(\pi y/L)}{\sinh(\pi b/L)} \sin \frac{\pi x}{L} \qquad (3\text{--}17)$$

The corresponding temperature field is shown in Fig. 3–5, where the solid lines are isotherms and the dotted lines are heat-flow lines drawn perpendicular to the isotherms.

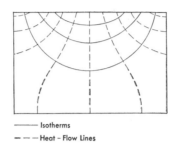

—— Isotherms

– – – Heat – Flow Lines

FIG. 3–5. Isotherms and heat-flow lines in the rectangular adiabatic plate shown in Fig. 3–4.

When the boundary conditions are not as simple as in the illustrative problem, the solution is obtained in the form of an infinite series. For example, if the temperature at the edge $y = b$ is a function of x, say $T(x,b) = F(x)$, then the solution, as shown in Ref. 1, is the infinite series

$$T = \frac{2}{L} \sum_{n=1}^{\infty} \frac{\sinh(n\pi/L)y}{\sinh n\pi(b/L)} \sin \frac{\pi n}{L} x \int_0^L F(x) \sin \frac{n\pi}{L} x \, dx \qquad (3\text{--}18)$$

which is quite laborious to evaluate quantitatively.

The separation-of-variables method can be extended to three-dimensional cases by assuming $T = XYZ$, substituting this expression for T in Eq. 3–6, separating the variables, and integrating the resulting total-differential equations subject to the given boundary conditions. Examples of three-dimensional problems are presented in Refs. 2, 8, and 20.

Analytical solutions are useful when they can be obtained. There are, however, relatively few practical problems dealing with geometries and boundary conditions which can be solved analytically without making simplifying assumptions, and even when a solution has been obtained, it is often too complicated to justify the time and effort required to evaluate it quantitatively. The main advantages of analytical solutions are the ease with which they lend themselves to parameterization and the possibility of applying them, once they are available, to similar problems.

3–4. POTENTIAL-FIELD PLOTTING

An approximate solution of the Laplace equation for a two-dimensional system can be obtained graphically by plotting the temperature field freehand. The graphical method is particularly simple in systems with isothermal boundaries, but it can also be applied to cases in which heat flows across a boundary of unknown temperature by convection or radiation from a source, or to a sink, of known temperature. For problems of the latter type, the graphical method becomes quite tedious, and analogical or numerical methods will give an answer more quickly. We shall therefore restrict the scope of the graphical method to the solution of problems with isothermal boundaries. The application of the graphical method to systems with unknown boundary temperatures is illustrated in detail in Refs. 1 and 5.

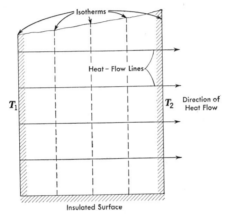

FIG. 3–6. Isotherms and heat-flow lines in a plane wall.

The object of a graphical solution is to construct a network consisting of isotherms and lines of constant-heat flow. The heat-flow lines are analogous to streamlines in a fluid-flow field, i.e., they are tangent to the direction of heat flow at any point. Consequently no heat can flow across heat-flow lines, and a constant amount of heat flows between any two of them.

The basic principles of the graphical method can be illustrated by applying it to heat conduction through a plane wall. If the temperatures T_1 and T_2 are constant over the faces of the wall, isotherms and lines of constant heat flow can be readily drawn. As shown in Fig. 3–6, the heat-flow lines run perpendicular to and the isotherms run parallel to the faces of the wall. If the heat-flow lines are equally spaced so that the same amount of heat flows in each flow tube formed between adjacent heat-flow lines, the total rate of heat flow equals the rate of heat flow per tube $\Delta\tilde{q}$ times the number of tubes N.

An inspection of the net in Fig. 3–6 shows that isotherms and heat-flow lines cross at right angles everywhere. This condition is obvious for the plane wall, but it must be satisfied, as we shall see, in any system. In fact, the basis of the graphical method is to draw, by trial and error, the isotherms and flow lines so that they are perpendicular at their points of intersection and satisfy the boundary conditions. Once such a net has been drawn, the temperature distribution and the rate of heat flow can be determined. This technique, called potential-field, or flux, plotting, will now be considered in detail.

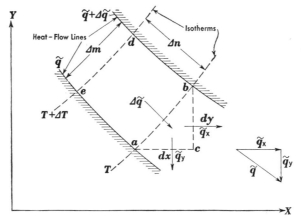

FIG. 3–7. Potential-field element.

An elementary portion of a flux plot in a system of unit thickness is shown in Fig. 3–7. The rate of heat flow in one flow tube is

$$\Delta\tilde{q} = \tilde{q}(\Delta m) \tag{3–19}$$

where $\tilde{q} = q/A$ = the rate of heat flow per unit area, or the *heat flux*, in Btu/hr sq ft;

$\Delta m1$ = area of the flow tube, in sq ft.

The change in temperature ΔT over a distance Δn perpendicular to a heat-flow line is, from Eq. 1–2

$$\Delta T = -\frac{\tilde{q}}{k}\Delta n \tag{3–20}$$

Dividing Eq. 3–19 by Eq. 3–20 gives

$$\frac{\Delta\tilde{q}}{-k\Delta T} = \frac{\Delta m}{\Delta n} \tag{3–21}$$

which shows that the ratio $\Delta m / \Delta n$ is a constant when heat flows at the same rate between any two adjacent flow lines and the temperature difference is the same between any two adjacent isotherms. Equation 3–21 indicates that, in general, a net of isotherms and heat-flow lines in a two-dimensional heat-flow region consists of small rectangles having a width Δm and a length Δn. To facilitate the graphical construction of a net, it is convenient to select $\Delta n = \Delta m$, so that the net consists of small squares. A net of square blocks is the easiest to draw by eye because any deviation is easy to detect. It is also convenient to use for numerical work because the rate of heat flow in each stream tube is related to the temperature difference between adjacent isotherms by

$$\Delta \tilde{q} = -k \Delta T \qquad (3\text{–}22)$$

irrespective of the size of the squares.

To show that isotherms and heat-flow lines intersect at right angles, we write a heat balance for the triangular element abc of Fig. 3–7. Heat is conducted into the element across the face ab at the rate $\Delta \tilde{q}$. If $\tilde{q}_x$ and $\tilde{q}_y$ are the x and y components of the heat flux $\tilde{q}$, heat is conducted out of the element at the rate $\tilde{q}_x \Delta y - \tilde{q}_y \Delta x$, where the minus sign of the second term is a result of the sign convention which specifies that the heat flow is negative when it is in the negative direction of a coordinate. As the size of the element approaches zero, the heat balance at a point x,y can be written in the form

$$d[\tilde{q}(x,y)] = \tilde{q}_x dy - \tilde{q}_y dx$$

Along a line of constant heat flow, the value of $\tilde{q}$ is constant. The differential of $\tilde{q}$ is therefore zero along a constant-heat-flow line and the slope of a constant-heat-flow line at any point is

$$\frac{dy}{dx}\bigg|_{\tilde{q}\,=\,\text{const}} = \frac{\tilde{q}_y}{\tilde{q}_x}$$

Also the temperature is a function of x and y, and a differential change in temperature may be written as

$$d[T(x,y)] = \frac{\partial T}{\partial x}\,dx + \frac{\partial T}{\partial y}\,dy$$

Along an isotherm, $dT = 0$ and the slope of an isotherm at any point is therefore

$$\frac{dy}{dx}\bigg|_{T\,=\,\text{const}} = \frac{\partial T/\partial x}{\partial T/\partial y}$$

Multiplying the numerator and the denominator by k, the slope of an iso-therm can be written as

$$\left.\frac{dy}{dx}\right|_{T\,=\,\text{const}} = -\frac{k\,(\partial T/\partial x)}{k\,(\partial T/\partial y)} = -\frac{\tilde{q}_x}{\tilde{q}_y}$$

Then, at any point of intersection between an isotherm and a heat-flow line,

$$\left.\frac{dy}{dx}\right|_{T\,=\,\text{const}} = -\left(\frac{1}{dy/dx}\right)_{\tilde{q}\,=\,\text{const}} \tag{3-23}$$

which is the condition of perpendicularity.

Except for the plane wall, the elements of a heat-flow net will not be geometrically perfect squares unless they are made infinitesimally small. In an irregularly shaped body they form so-called *curvilinear squares*. The sides of a curvilinear square intersect orthogonally, and the sums of op-posite sides are equal, or as shown in Fig. 3–7

$$\overline{ab} + \overline{de} = \overline{ae} + \overline{bd}$$

A curvilinear square in a flow field has the same physical characteristics as a true square, and Eq. 3–22 applies.

In making a flux plot, the general procedure is to divide the body into curvilinear squares by trial and error, at the same time satisfying the given boundary conditions. The problem is solved when the network satisfies the following requirements:

1. Boundary conditions.
    a. Flow lines are perpendicular to isothermal boundaries.
    b. Isotherms are perpendicular to insulated boundaries.
    c. Flow lines leading to a corner of an isothermal boundary bisect the angle between the surfaces of the boundary at the corner.
2. Isotherms and flow lines intersect each other at right angles.
3. Isotherms and flow lines form a network of curvilinear squares.
4. Diagonals of curvilinear squares bisect each other at 90 deg and bisect the corners.

A graphical solution, just as an analytic solution of a heat-conduction problem described by the Laplace equation and appropriate boundary conditions, is unique. Therefore *any* network which satisfies all of the above conditions represents the correct solution.

The rate of heat flow between isothermal boundaries can be obtained directly from the network. Each heat-flow tube may be thought of as a composite wall with equal series resistances (Sec. 1–4), and the rate of heat flow through it is, from Eq. 3–22,

$$\Delta \tilde{q} = \frac{k}{M} \, (T_2 - T_1) \tag{3-24}$$

where M is the number of curvilinear squares in the channel. Finally, for N tubes, we get

$$q = \frac{N}{M} \, k(T_2 - T_1) = Sk(T_2 - T_1) \tag{3-25}$$

where the ratio N/M, the number of flow tubes divided by the number of squares (i.e., ΔT's) in each, is called the *shape factor*, S, of the system. It should be noted that the number of flow tubes and the number of temperature increments enter only as a ratio. Hence, the size of the unit curvilinear square makes no difference in the result. If the number of either flow tubes or temperature increments is not integral, a fraction of a tube or curvilinear square must be interpolated.

Freehand flux plotting is something of an art, and no set of infallible rules can be given. However, the following general suggestions by Bewley (6) will help to reduce the amount of trial and error:

1. Note conditions of symmetry. Lines of symmetry are flow lines and divide the temperature field into compartments.
2. Select a known isotherm as a datum, and mark all known isotherms.
3. At each corner of an isothermal boundary, draw a short line bisecting the angle. All such lines are the beginnings of flow lines.
4. Tentatively extrapolate the lines of (3) to other isotherms.
5. Start isotherms in a region (if there is one) where flow lines are uniformly spaced.
6. Begin with a crude network and first find the approximate orientation of the isothermal and heat-flow lines with a minimum of erasure.
7. At first attempt it will usually be found that the flow lines cannot be made orthogonal to the isotherms and at the same time form a network of curvilinear squares. To satisfy the requirements, individual or simultaneous adjustments may have to be made in the locations of isotherms and flow lines.

After a plausible-appearing network has been drawn, it is sometimes advisable to sketch in the diagonals in order to expose errors. The diagonals should also form an orthogonal grid and bisect each other at right angles in each square. A cross, scribed on a transparent sheet, aids in checking orthogonality.

Example 3-1.   Determine (a) the shape factor and (b) the rate of heat conduction through the corner section of Fig. 3-8a.   The thermal conductivity of the material is 0.50 Btu/hr ft F, the face ABC is at 600 F, the face DEF is at 100 F and the faces CD and AF are insulated.

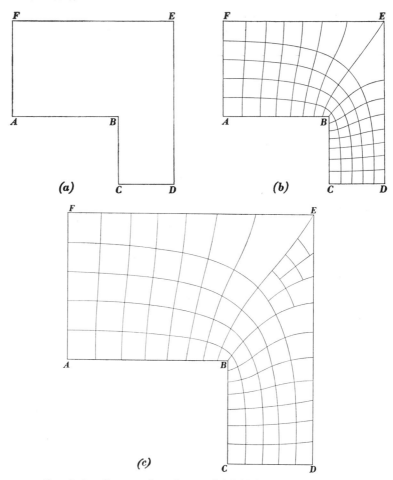

FIG. 3-8.   Construction of potential field for Example 3-1.

Solution: (a) The evolution of the flux plot is shown in Figs. 3-8b and 3-8c.   The faces AF and CD are insulated, and each of them forms, therefore, one boundary of a flow tube.   We select initially five equal temperature increments, and start the isotherms perpendicular to the two insulated faces.   Then we bisect the corners at B and E, the lines being the beginnings of flow tubes.   The first trial plot is shown in Fig. 3-8b. The blocks in the corner are not curvilinear squares, and the 200 F isotherm must be shifted upward.   This necessitates other adjustments which have been made in Fig. 3-8c.   In this plot the corner sections have been further subdivided to check the network there.   The lines form an "arrowhead" pattern which, if subdivided further, would eventually evolve into curvilinear squares.

TABLE 3–1

Conduction Shape Factor S for Various Systems

$$[q_k = Sk \, (T_1 - T_2)]$$

Description of System	Symbolic Sketch	Shape Factor S
Conduction through a homogeneous medium of thermal conductivity k between an isothermal surface and a sphere buried a distance z below		$\dfrac{2\pi D}{1 + (D/4z)}$
Conduction through a homogeneous medium of thermal conductivity k between an isothermal surface and a horizontal cylinder of length L buried with its axis a distance z below the surface		$\dfrac{2\pi L/\ln(2L/D)}{1 + \dfrac{\ln(2z/L)}{\ln(2L/D)}}$ If $D \ll z$ and $z \ll L$
Conduction through a homogeneous medium of thermal conductivity k between an isothermal surface and an infinitely long cylinder buried a distance z below		$\dfrac{2\pi}{\cosh^{-1}(2z/D)}$
Conduction through a homogeneous medium of thermal conductivity k between an isothermal surface and a vertical circular cylinder of length L		$\dfrac{2\pi L}{\ln(4L/D)}$
Horizontal thin circular disc buried far below an isothermal surface in a homogeneous material of thermal conductivity k		$4D$
Conduction through a homogeneous material of thermal conductivity k between two long parallel cylinders a distance L apart		$\dfrac{2\pi}{\cosh^{-1}\left(\dfrac{L^2 - r_1{}^2 - r_2{}^2}{2r_1 r_2}\right)}$
Conduction through two plane sections and the edge section of two walls of thermal conductivity k—inner and outer surface temperatures uniform*		$\dfrac{al}{\Delta x} + \dfrac{bl}{\Delta x} + 0.54l$
Conduction through the corner section c of three homogeneous walls of thermal conductivity k—inner and outer surface temperatures uniform*		$0.15 \, \Delta x$

* These shape factors apply only to enclosures whose inside dimensions are greater than one-fifth the wall thickness Δx. For enclosures having smaller inside dimensions see Ref. 8.

From the final plot we obtain the number of flow tubes ($N = 15$) and the number of curvilinear squares per flow tube ($M = 5$). Thus, the shape factor is

$$S = \frac{N}{M} = \frac{15}{5} = 3 \qquad\qquad Ans.$$

b) From Eq. 3–25, the rate of heat flow is

$$q = Sk \, (T_2 - T_1) = (3)(0.5)(600 - 100) = 750 \text{ Btu/hr} \qquad Ans.$$

Appropriate shape factors for some geometrical configurations of practical importance in engineering problems have been determined theoretically or experimentally (7,8,9) and are tabulated for in Table 3–1.

Example 3–2. A long 6-in.-OD pipe is buried with its center line 30 in. below the surface in soil having an average thermal conductivity of 0.20 Btu/hr ft F. (a) Determine, by means of a flux plot, the rate of heat loss per foot length of pipe if the surface temperature of the pipe is 200 F and the surface of the soil is at 40 F. (b) Compare the result with that obtained by using the appropriate shape factor from Table 3–1.

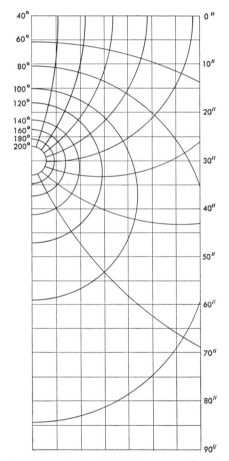

FIG. 3–9. Potential field for Example 3–2.

Solution: (a) The flux plot for this problem is shown in Fig. 3–9. Because of the symmetry, only one half of the heat-flow field has been plotted. There are 18 heat-flow tubes leading from the pipe to the surface, and each flow tube consists of 8 curvilinear squares. The shape factor is therefore $S = 18/8 = 2.25$

and the rate of heat flow is

$$q = (0.2)\ (2.25)\ (200 - 40) = 72 \text{ Btu/hr ft} \qquad Ans.$$

b) From Table 3–1,

$$S = \cfrac{2\pi}{\ln \cfrac{30 + \sqrt{30^2 - 3^2}}{3}} = \frac{2\pi}{3.0} = 2.08$$

and the rate of heat flow is

$$q = (0.2)\ (2.08)\ (160) = 66.5 \text{ Btu/hr ft} \qquad Ans.$$

The reason for the difference between the two answers is that the potential field in Fig. 3–9 has been drawn approximately with a finite number of flow lines and isotherms. The accuracy of the graphical solution can be increased by further subdividing the potential field.

3–5. ANALOGICAL METHODS

When two or more phenomena can be described mathematically by the same equation, the phenomena are said to be mathematically analogous and the variables in one system are called the *analogues* of the corresponding variables in any other systems. A simple example of such a case is the two-dimensional Laplace equation. Not only does it apply to a temperature field, but, if the symbol $T(x,y)$ is replaced by $E(x,y)$ (the potential in an electric field), the equation governing the voltage distribution in an electrical field is obtained. An examination of the respective equations

$$\frac{\partial^2 T}{\partial x^2} + \frac{\partial^2 T}{\partial y^2} = 0$$

and

$$\frac{\partial^2 E}{\partial x^2} + \frac{\partial^2 E}{\partial y^2} = 0$$

shows that the electrical potential $E(x,y)$ can be regarded as the analogue of the thermal potential T. In other words, constant-voltage lines in an electric field correspond to constant-temperature lines in a heat-flow field, and lines of electric-current flow correspond to heat-flow lines. A similar correspondence can be established between a two-dimensional potential fluid-flow field in the steady state and either of the two aforementioned phenomena. Table 3–2 illustrates the analogy.

There are many heat-flow problems for which solutions cannot be obtained analytically and for which experimental solutions in a thermal system would be too expensive or too time-consuming. It is often possible, however, to obtain experimental solutions of such problems quite simply in an analogous system and reinterpret the solution in terms of the thermal problem. The application of an experimental solution obtained in one system to an analogous system is the basis of the *experimental-analogic method*.

TABLE 3–2

Type of Flow Field	Potential Lines	Flow Lines
Heat	Constant temperature or isotherms	Heat-flow lines
Incompressible inviscid fluid	Constant velocity potential	Streamlines
Electricity	Constant voltage potential	Lines of force or electric current

There are many experimental-analogic methods by which heat-flow problems can be solved.   The fluid-flow analogy by means of Moore's fluid mapper (10), the membrane analogy (1), which is also applicable to fields with sources (11), and the various electrical analogies are all valuable analogic methods.   Schneider (1) and Jakob (4) give extensive reviews of these methods.   We shall consider in detail only the *Analog Field Plotter*, an electrical-geometrical analogue which is simple and has been more widely used on two-dimensional steady-state problems than any of the other methods.   An electrical-analogic network method which is suitable for unsteady-state problems will be presented in Chapter 5.

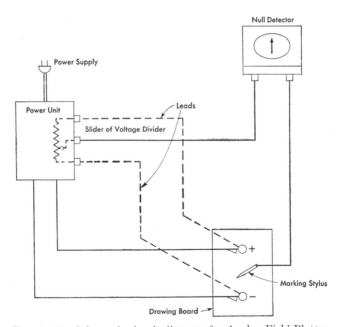

Fig. 3–10.   Schematic circuit diagram for Analog Field Plotter.

The Analog Field Plotter (12) makes use of a thin sheet (0.004 in.) of electrically conducting "Teledeltos" paper of relatively high resistivity which can be cut to a shape geometrically similar to that of the heat conductor. An electrical-current-flow pattern can be set up in the paper by means of suitably attached and energized electrodes. The resultant pattern of constant-voltage lines is detected and marked (i.e., plotted) directly on the paper by means of a searching stylus which is attached to a high-sensitivity detecting instrument. Figure 3-10 is a schematic sketch and circuit diagram of the equipment. Boundary conditions corresponding to a constant-temperature potential in the heat flow are obtained in the electrical field by applying copper wires, or highly conductive areas of silver paint, to the surface of the paper and attaching them to a direct-voltage source.

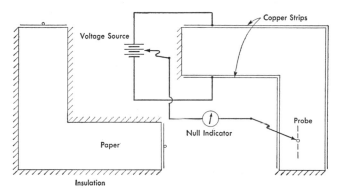

FIG. 3-11. Arrangement of the Analog Field Plotter for solving Example 3-1.

Insulated surfaces in the heat-flow field correspond to plain edges of the conducting paper. Lines of constant voltage are obtained directly by selecting a voltage level on the *null detector*, moving the stylus to maintain a zero reading on the instrument, and making small perforations in the paper while tracing the equipotential lines. The voltage level of the particular equipotential being traced is determined by the slider position chosen on the voltage-dividing potentiometer of the null detector. By selecting equal increments of voltage, adjacent lines become analogous to isotherms separated by the same temperature difference.

Since the heat-flow, or current-flow, lines are everywhere perpendicular to the potential lines, they can usually be sketched in freehand, so that the resulting network forms curvilinear squares. The flow lines can also be traced by simply reversing the insulating and conducting portions of the boundary. By selecting appropriate voltage increments, a curvilinear network is then obtained. Figure 3-11 illustrates this latter method for the corner section considered in Example 3-1.

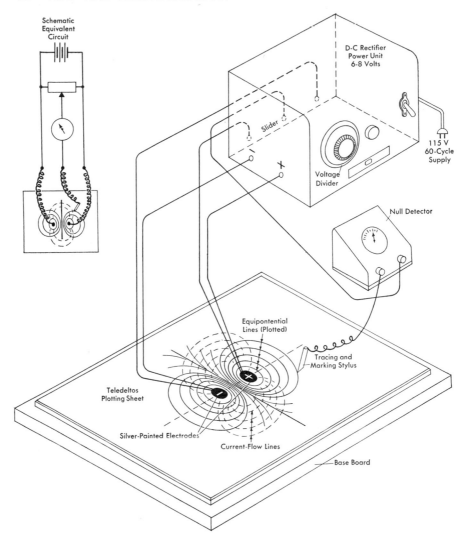

FIG. 3–12.   Arrangement of the Analog Field Plotter for solving Example 3–2.
(Courtesy of Sunshine Scientific Instrument)

The experimental setup used for determining the isotherms between the ground and the buried pipe (Example 3–2) is shown in Fig. 3–12.   Instead of painting the isothermal ground surface as a constant-voltage line, a *mirror image* of the pipe is placed into the field.   As a result of the symmetry of this arrangement, the boundary condition at the ground is automatically satisfied.   The pipes are painted on the sheet and connected to the voltage supply by copper wires as shown.   The interpretation of the resulting networks is identical to that given for the freehand flux plot, since both methods establish a network of curvilinear squares formed by constant-potential lines and flow lines.   The Analog Field Plotter is more accurate and faster, but a freehand flux plot usually gives satisfactory results.

Electrical-geometrical analogues which can account for finite thermal resistances of the boundaries, and even for variable thermal conductivities, have been used by Kayan (13,14).

In addition to the geometrical analogues of which the electric field plotter is the handiest, network analogues have been used to solve heat-transfer problems.   The latter use an equivalent "lumped" electrical circuit to simulate the thermal system.   For steady-state heat flow without heat sources or sinks, the network consists simply of resistors (Example 1–2).   They are equivalent to the fictitious heat-conducting rods which will be described in the following section, dealing with a numerical method. An interesting application of the network analogue to the determination of the temperature field in an internally cooled turbine blade is described by Ellerbrook et al. (15).

3–6. NUMERICAL RELAXATION METHOD

The relaxation method is a numerical method for solving a set of algebraic equations or a differential equation such as the heat-conduction equation.   The general method was first used by Sir Richard Southwell, in 1935, to solve framework problems; since that time, it has become a powerful tool in the solution of many other types of engineering problems. The basic principle of the method is very simple, but the speed with which a solution is obtained depends on how familiar the operator is with the many short cuts and variations which can be employed in practice.   Here we shall consider only basic features of the method and illustrate the relaxation technique by applying it to steady-state heat-transfer problems. A detailed treatment of other applications, as well as various short cuts and simplifications of the basic process, is presented in Refs. 16, 17, and 18.

Basic concepts.   The fundamental ideas of the relaxation technique can be illustrated by solving numerically the pair of algebraic equations

$$-4x + y + 56 = 0 \qquad\qquad (3\text{–}26)$$
$$x - 2y + 34 = 0$$

The solution of Eq. 3–26 could of course be obtained by determinants or by eliminating one of the unknowns in one of the equations and substituting the resulting expression in the other equation to obtain the remaining unknown.   However, as the number of equations becomes larger, the amount of labor required to solve a set of equations by these methods increases tremendously and the numerical relaxation method will save time and effort.

To obtain a solution to the problem contained in Eq. 3–26 by the relaxation method, the equations are first rewritten in the form

$$F_1 = -4x + y + 56 \qquad \textbf{(3-27)}$$
$$F_2 = x - 2y + 34$$

where F_1 and F_2 are called residuals. The objective of the numerical procedure is to reduce the values of the residuals systematically and eventually to make them zero, or as nearly zero as practicable. Those values of x and y which make the residuals in Eq. 3–27 equal to zero are the desired values, since they satisfy Eq. 3–26.

The first step in the numerical solution is to select initial values for x and y. When dealing with algebraic equations which do not represent a physical problem, it is satisfactory to take the unknowns initially equal to zero. With this choice the residuals are $F_1 = 56$ and $F_2 = 34$.

The next step in the relaxation method is to set up an *operation table* which shows the effect of a unit positive increment in the variables x and y on the residuals. For the system of Eq. 3–26 involving two equations in two unknowns, the operation table is

	ΔF_1	ΔF_2
$\Delta x = 1$	-4	1
$\Delta y = 1$	1	-2

We observe that an incremental change Δx will not only affect the residual F_1, but also F_2. Similarly, a change Δy will affect the value of F_2 as well as of F_1.

According to the basic rule of relaxation, the aim of each step of the procedure is to reduce the value of the *currently largest residual* to zero. Following this rule, we begin by changing x by $\Delta x = 14$. This reduces F_1 to zero, but leaves a residual F_2 of 48.

The actual computations are conveniently recorded in tabular form. The relaxation table for the solution of Eq. 3–26 is shown in Table 3–3.

TABLE 3–3

		F_1	F_2	
$x = 0$	$y = 0$	56	34	
$\Delta x = 14$		0	48	
	$\Delta y = 24$	24	0	
$\Delta x = 6$		0	6	
	$\Delta y = 3$	3	0	
$\Delta x = 1$		-1	1	
$x = 21$	$y = 27$	-1	1	a
$\Delta x = -0.3$		0.2	0.7	
	$\Delta y = 0.4$	0.6	-0.1	
$\Delta x = 0.1$		0.2	0.0	
$x = 20.8$	$y = 27.4$	0.2	0.0	

We observe how the residuals are relaxed in a stepwise manner.   The results of each step are recorded on consecutive lines and the reader can easily verify the details.   Following Allen's suggestions (16), the relaxation method has first been used to obtain a solution correct to the nearest whole number.   The results of these preliminary calculations are summarized in line a and checked by substituting the numerical values of x and y in Eq. 3–27.[3]   Then, the calculations are refined to obtain a solution to the first decimal place by using first-decimal increments.   Further refinements could be made in a similar manner if desired.

Short cuts.   The technique used in the preceding example could, in principle, also be applied to more complex problems.   However, with a little insight and ingenuity, considerable time and effort can be saved by modifying the basic technique.   When dealing with equations derived from a physical problem, the first modification is to start the calculations with initial values estimated from a preliminary survey of the physical aspect of the problem.   This step will be illustrated when the relaxation method is applied to heat-transfer problems.

The second short cut is called *overrelaxation*.   Instead of reducing each residual to zero, it is desirable to choose larger increments and change a negative residual to a positive one, and vice versa.   Overrelaxation is useful in all practical applications, but no general quantitative rule for the choice of the increments which will speed up the process most effectively can be given.   The selection of the best incremental changes is mostly a matter of experience, as will become apparent from the illustrative examples.

The third device requires the creation of additional operations in the operation table.   The most important of these is the *block operation*, which consists of changing each of the variables by the same amount.   The effects produced on the residuals by a *unit block operation* are obtained by adding together the changes due to the individual unit increments in the operation table.   For the illustrative example the new operation is represented by the last line in the operation table.   The unit step can be used

	ΔF_1	ΔF_2
$\Delta x = 1$	-4	1
$\Delta y = 1$	1	-2
$\Delta x = 1, \Delta y = 1$	-3	-1

at any stage but it is of particular value in the initial step of the calculation. If we add the residuals and divide the sum by the total effect of the unit block operation (-4 in our case), a block operation with a step of this

---

[3] If a mistake is discovered at this point, there is no need to repeat the calculations. One simply continues relaxing, but uses the corrected values for the residuals.

	ΔF_1	ΔF_2
$x = \quad y = 0$	56	34
$\Delta x = \Delta y = \dfrac{90}{4} \approx 22$	-10	12
$y = 6$	-4	0
$x = -1$	0	-1
$x = 21, y = 28$	0	-1

size will reduce the *net sum* of *all* the residuals to zero. This initial step substantially reduces the number of subsequent steps required to eliminate the residuals. The table above illustrates the application of the unit step in the solution of Eq. 3–26. We observe that the number of steps required to eliminate the residuals is now only four instead of the six steps necessary without the unit block operation. In addition to the modification considered here, group relaxation and multiplying factors are useful. For these and other useful hints, the reader should consult Refs. 16 and 17.

Application to heat-transfer problems. Before the relaxation method can be applied to a heat-transfer problem, or any other physical problem described by a differential equation, some preliminary steps are necessary. The purpose of these preliminary steps is to approximate the differential equation and the boundary conditions by a set of algebraic equations. This is accomplished by replacing the continuous domain by a pattern of discrete points within the domain and introducing finite-difference approximations between the points. If n points are selected, a set of n algebraic equations is obtained. It can be solved by the numerical method for the values of unknown at the n points.

The preparation of a problem for solution by the relaxation method can be accomplished mathematically or physically. In the mathematical approach the derivatives in the differential equation are simply replaced with finite-difference approximation (1,16). We shall follow here a physical approach and obtain the pertinent equations from simple heat balances.

To apply the relaxation method to a heat-conduction problem we subdivide the system into a number of small but finite subvolumes and assign a reference number to each. Then we assume that each subvolume is at the temperature corresponding to its center and replace the physical system by a network of fictitious heat-conducting rods between the centers, or *nodal points*, of the subvolumes. Now, if a thermal conductance corresponding to the conductance of the material between nodal points is assigned to each rod, the heat flow in the rod network will approximate the heat flow in the continuous system.

In the absence of heat sources or sinks within the system, the rate of heat flow toward each nodal point must equal the rate of heat flow away from it in the steady state. To satisfy this condition we set up heat balances for each nodal point, estimate nodal-point temperatures, and correct them in successive steps until the rate of heat inflow equals the rate of heat outflow at every point in the system. The details of the numerical method will be illustrated in the following examples. A one-dimensional heat-flow problem has been selected as the first example because it illustrates the basic concepts without introducing unnecessary conceptual difficulties.

One-dimensional example. Consider the circular pin fin shown in Fig. 3–13. It is 0.25 ft long and 0.05 ft in diameter. Its base is attached to a wall at 300 F, while its surface is exposed to a gas at 100 F through an average unit-surface conductance of 20 Btu/hr sq ft F. The fin is made of a stainless steel with a thermal conductivity of 10 Btu/hr ft F. The temperature distribution along the fin and the rate of heat dissipation are to be determined numerically, and the results are to be compared with the analytic solution obtained in Sec. 3–5.

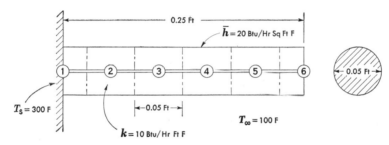

FIG. 3–13. Circular pin fin subdivided for relaxation solution.

First Step. The first step is to subdivide the system. We choose the uniform linear network shown in Fig. 3–13 with six equally spaced nodal points. This selection yields four complete subvolumes with half sub-volumes at the base and at the tip of the fin. Increasing the number of nodal points will improve the accuracy of the solution but will also increase the amount of work and time required.

Second Step. The second step consists of writing heat-balance equations for each of the nodal points. The same heat-balance equation holds for all interior points, but the nodal points at the base and at the tip (i.e., the boundary conditions) require separate analyses. For the interior point 3 (Fig. 3–14a), the heat-balance equation is simply

$$q_{k\ 2\to3} + q_{c\ \infty\to3} + q_{k\ 4\to3} = 0 \qquad (3\text{–}28)$$

where $q_{k\ 2\to3} = K_{k\ 2\text{--}3}\,(T_2 - T_3)$, the rate of heat conduction from 2 to 3;

$q_{c\ \infty\to3} = K_{c\ \infty\text{--}3}\,(T_\infty - T_3)$, the rate of heat flow by convection from the surrounding gas to the curved surface;

$q_{k\ 4\to3} = K_{k\ 4\text{--}3}\,(T_4 - T_3)$, the rate of heat conduction from 4 to 3.

The physical basis of Eq. 3–28 is analogous to Kirchhoff's first law for electrical circuits. The equation simply states that the algebraic sum of all the heat flows (or currents) at a junction point of a network equals zero in the steady state. The arrows indicate that the direction of positive heat flow is toward the nodal point 3. This, of course, does not imply that heat flows only toward point 3. If T_2, T_4 or T_∞ is less than T_3, any one of the three terms may be negative.

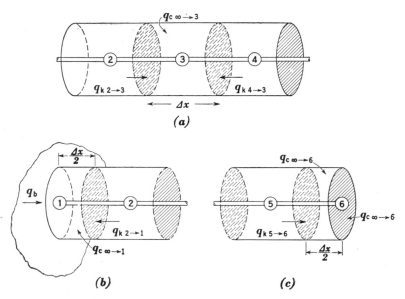

FIG. 3–14.   Sketches illustrating heat balances.

If we write the heat balance as

$$Q_3 = q_{k\ 2\to3} + q_{c\ \infty\to3} + q_{k\ 4\to3} \qquad (3\text{–}29)$$

then Q_3 is the residual at 3 which must be zero in the steady state. The residual in Eq. 3–29, Q_3, can be interpreted physically as the rate of internal energy change at point 3.

Assuming straight-line temperature distributions along the fictitious rods between nodal points, a reasonable assumption when the points are close together, the conductances can be evaluated from Eqs. 1–4 and 1–16.[4] For the circular fin we have

$$K_{k\ 2\text{–}3} = K_{k\ 4\text{–}3} = \frac{k\pi D^2}{4\Delta x} \qquad \text{and} \qquad K_{c\ \infty\text{–}3} = \bar{h}\pi D\Delta x$$

[4] In the residual Eq. 3–29, terms of the order of Δx^4 are neglected (see Ref. 19). Equation 3–29 is therefore only an acceptable approximation, when Δx^4 is small.

With these expressions for the conductances, Eq. 3–29 can be written

$$Q_3 = \frac{k\pi D^2}{4\Delta x}(T_2 - T_3) + \bar{h}\pi D\Delta x(T_\infty - T_3) + \frac{k\pi D^2}{4\Delta x}(T_4 - T_3)$$

or in simplified form as

$$Q_3' = \frac{Q}{k\pi D^2/4\Delta x} = T_2 + T_4 + \frac{4\bar{h}\Delta x^2}{kD}T_\infty - \left(2 + \frac{4\bar{h}\Delta x^2}{kD}\right)T_3$$

where the term involving T_∞ drops out if all temperatures are measured above or below T_∞, and T_∞ is taken as zero.

At the base of the fin (Fig. 3–14b) the temperature T_1 is equal to the wall temperature and remains constant.   The residual equation with $T_\infty = 0$ becomes therefore

$$Q_1' = \frac{Q}{k\pi D^2/4\Delta x} = \frac{4\Delta x}{k\pi D^2}q_b + T_2 - \left(1 + \frac{2\bar{h}\Delta x^2}{kD}\right)T_1$$

where q_b is the rate of heat conduction from the wall to the base of the fin.

At the tip of the fin, heat is transferred by convection (Fig. 3–14c) and the residual equation for point 6 is

$$Q_6' = \frac{Q}{k\pi D^2/4\Delta x} = T_5 - \left(1 + \frac{2\bar{h}\Delta x^2}{kD} + \frac{\bar{h}\Delta x^2}{kD}\right)T_3$$

Third Step.   The third step consists of collecting the residual equations for all the nodal points and evaluating the coefficients.   For the circular fin these equations are summarized below.

Point	Equation for Q'
1	$2.54\,q_b + T_2 - 240$
2	$200 + T_3 - 2.4\,T_2$
3	$T_2 + T_4 - 2.4\,T_3$
4	$T_3 + T_5 - 2.4\,T_4$
5	$T_6 + T_4 - 2.4\,T_5$
6	$T_5 - 1.3\,T_6$

The only remaining problem is that of finding the values of T_2, T_3, T_4, T_5, and T_6 which satisfy the residual equations and eliminate the residuals. Since we have a set of five equations in five unknowns, the relaxation method can be used.   Following the procedure previously outlined, we guess initial temperatures and set up a *relaxation pattern* corresponding to the operation table.   The relaxation pattern for the fin is shown in Table 3–4, which includes, in the last line, the changes produced by a unit block.

Because T_1 is fixed, there is no relaxation pattern at point 1.   However, once the temperatures have been calculated, the rate of heat flow

TABLE 3–4

RELAXATION PATTERN

	$\Delta Q_1'$	$\Delta Q_2'$	$\Delta Q_3'$	$\Delta Q_4'$	$\Delta Q_5'$	$\Delta Q_6'$
$\Delta T_2 = 1$	+1	−2.4	+1	....	....	....
$\Delta T_3 = 1$	...	+1	−2.4	+1	....	....
$\Delta T_4 = 1$	...	....	+1	−2.4	+1	....
$\Delta T_5 = 1$	...	....	....	+1	−2.4	+1
$\Delta T_6 = 1$	...	....	....	....	+1	−1.3
$\Delta T_2 = \Delta T_3 = \ldots = \Delta T_6 = 1$	...	−1.4	−0.4	−0.4	−0.4	−0.3

through the base of the fin can be determined by substituting the numerical value of T_2 into the residual equation for point 1.

The numerical solution is carried out in Table 3–5. The temperature distribution assumed initially is shown in the first line. A thorough physical understanding of the problem and past experience with similar problems will assist the operator in selecting reasonable values for the unknown temperatures to start with, but any initial guess is acceptable. The residuals corresponding to the initial temperatures are recorded in the second line. Since the residuals are predominantly negative, a block operation is applied as a first step to reduce the net total of all the residuals

TABLE 3–5

RELAXATION TABLE USING OVERRELAXATION AND INITIAL BLOCK RELAXATION

	T_1 (fixed)	Q_2	T_2	Q_3	T_3	Q_4	T_4	Q_5	T_5	Q_6	T_6	Line
Initial temperature distribution (assumed)	200		150		110		80		50		30	1
Residuals		−50		−34		−32		−10		+11		2
Block −40			−40		−40		−40		−40		−40	3
		+6		−18		−16		+6		+23	+20	4
								+26	+12	−3		5
					−10	−4		−2.8		+9		6
		−4			+6	−14	−6					7
					0	+0.4		−8.8			+8	8
			−1					−0.8		−1.4		9
		−1.6			−1	+0.4		−0.8		−1.4		10
$T-T_\infty$	200		109		60		34		22		18	11
Check		260		143		82		52		22		
		−261.6		−144		−81.6		−52.8		−23.4		
		−1.6		−1		+0.4		−0.8		−1.4		
Block −2			−2		−2		−2		−2		−2	
		+1.2		−0.2		−0.4		0.0		−0.8		12
$T-T_\infty$(relaxation)	200		107		58		32		20		16	13
$T-T_\infty$(analytical)	200		107		58		32		18		15	14

to zero and to distribute the residuals more uniformly. The appropriate size of the block, rounded off to the nearest whole number, is

$$\Delta T = \frac{-50 -34 -32 -10 +11}{-1.4 -0.4 -0.4 -0.4 -0.3} = \frac{115}{2.4} \simeq 40$$

The values of the new residuals are recorded on line 4. The largest residual is now at point 6. We change T_6 by $+20$, using some over-relaxation to speed up the convergence. The new values of the residuals resulting from the increase in T_6 are recorded on line 5. The next temperature correction, an increase in T_5 by $+12$, is also recorded on line 5 to save space.

The subsequent steps of the relaxation process are shown in the table and the reader can verify them by himself. In line 10 all of the residuals are listed, and in line 11 the temperatures at each of the nodal points are recorded. These temperatures are obtained by adding the temperature adjustments made during the relaxation process to the initial temperatures. Then the residuals in line 10 are checked by substituting the temperatures from line 11 in the residual equations. In line 12 a unit block operation of -2 is carried out, and the final results are recorded in line 13. For comparison, the temperature distribution $T_{(x)} - T_\infty$ calculated from Eq. 2–47 is shown in the last line. The agreement is within 2 F.

The rate of heat flow to the fin is

$$q_b = \frac{T_2 - 240}{2.54} = \frac{107 - 240}{2.54} = 52.3 \text{ Btu/hr}$$

from the first residual equation, whereas the rate of heat flow calculated from the analytic solution, i.e., Eq. 2–48, is 49.5 Btu/hr, a difference of about 6 per cent.

In practice the relaxation method is not used when an analytic solution is available. The error in the final result can therefore not be determined directly. One way of checking the accuracy of the answer is to repeat the calculations with successively smaller subdivisions until there are no further changes in the numerical results. For additional information on the accuracy of relaxation solutions, Refs. 1 and 19 are recommended.

Two-dimensional systems. The relaxation method can readily be extended to two- and also to three-dimensional systems. Consider a two-dimensional system such as a solid of constant thickness b (Fig. 3–15). Subdivide the system into *squares* so that each subvolume has the dimensions $\Delta l \Delta l b$, and select the center of each subvolume as a nodal point. Replacing the material between nodal points by fictitious rods having the same conductance as the actual material, a steady-state heat balance on an interior point such as 0,

$$q_{1\rightarrow0} + q_{2\rightarrow0} + q_{3\rightarrow0} + q_{4\rightarrow0} = 0$$

can be expressed as a residual equation in the form

$$Q_0 = K_{k\ 1-0}(T_1 - T_0) + K_{k\ 2-0}(T_2 - T_0)$$
$$+ K_{k\ 3-0}(T_3 - T_0) + K_{k\ 4-0}(T_4 - T_0) \qquad (3\text{-}30)$$

where Q_0 is the residual which must be zero in the steady state and

$$K_{k\ 1-0} = \frac{k(\Delta lb)}{\Delta l} = kb = K_{k\ 2-0} = K_{k\ 3-0} = K_{k\ 4-0}$$

Since Δl, the size of the subvolume, cancels, it is evident that, for square subdivisions, the numerical value of the conductance is independent of

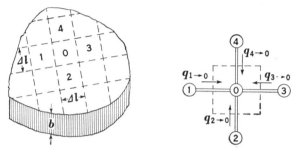

FIG. 3–15.   Relaxation network for interior nodal
point in a two-dimensional system.

the actual size of the squares.   The residual equation for an interior point can therefore be written

$$Q_0' = \frac{Q_0}{kb} = T_1 + T_2 + T_3 + T_4 - 4T_0 \qquad (3\text{-}31)$$

In the process of subdividing a two-dimensional system it is usually convenient to start by selecting a square network of nodes.   Interior points are then surrounded by full squares of material, but the nodal points at the edges have less material associated with them.   Thus, while Eq. 3–31 applies to all interior points, the residual equations for nodal points at a boundary depend on the geometry as well as the particular boundary conditions.   Several typical cases will be considered to illustrate the technique of setting up residual equations for points at a boundary.

a) Nodal point at an isothermal boundary (Fig. 3–16a).   Since $T_2 = T_4 = T_0$, heat can only flow along the fictitious rod between 3 and 0 and from the outside to 0.   Thus,

$$Q_0' = \frac{Q_0}{kb} = \bar{q}\,\frac{\Delta l}{k} + T_3 - T_0$$

3-9. By me
10 Btu/hr ft F)

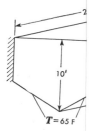

$T = 65$ F

3-10. Deter
at 300 F placed e
The outside dian
3-11. Sugge:
dition in a model
3-12. Calcul
4-in.-OD pipe at
Btu/hr ft F) 4 f
9 in., center to ce
3-13. Calcul
surface.
3-14. Derive
3-15. Deterr
the accompanyin
thickness. Assur
the symmetry of

3-16. A turbi
P of 0.40 ft is made
T_w, is 900 F. The

3
of th
107,
2.5, (
and t
at po
havir

3-:

(a)
steady
one sh
infinity
for the
the rat
dicular

are iden
with a r
if a coal
imation
tions ca
(20). I
sequent
the valu
residual
equatior
tempera

the desir
ture colu
of heat f
stituting
which, (
examples

Examp
per foot ol
that the i
and the th

Solutio
which is s

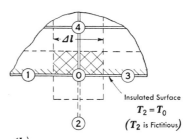

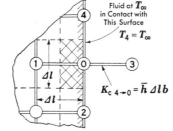

$\vec{q}$ $q_{3\to0}$ Δl

$\dfrac{\Delta l}{2}$

Isothermal Surface

(a) Nodal Point at an Isothermal Boundary $T_2 = T_0 = T_4$

Insulated Surface

$T_2 = T_0$

$(T_2$ is Fictitious$)$

(b) Nodal Point at an Insulated Surface

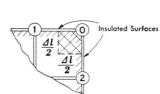

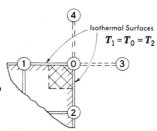

Fluid at T_∞ in Contact with This Surface

$T_4 = T_\infty$

Δl

$K_{c\,4\to0} = \bar{h}\,\Delta l\,b$

(c) Nodal Point at Surface in Contact with a Fluid

Isothermal Surfaces

$T_1 = T_0 = T_2$

(d) Nodal Point in Exterior Corner Between Isothermal Surfaces

Insulated Surfaces

$\dfrac{\Delta l}{2}$ $\dfrac{\Delta l}{2}$

(e) Nodal Point at an Exterior Corner Between Insulated Surfaces

Fluid at T_∞ in Contact with These Surfaces

$T_1 = T_2 = T_\infty$

$K_{c\,1\to0} = K_{c\,2\to0} = \bar{h}\,\Delta l\,b/2$

(f) Nodal Point at an Exterior Corner in Contact with a Fluid

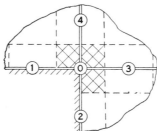

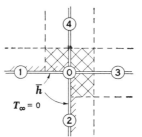

(g) Nodal Point at an Interior Corner Between Insulated Surfaces

$\bar{h}$

$T_\infty = 0$

(h) Nodal Point at an Interior Corner whose Surfaces are in Contact with a Fluid at $T_\infty = 0$

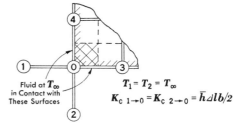

Fig. 3-16. Sketches illustrating heat balances for nodal points at boundaries of a two-dimensional system.

wh
vol

hea
eve
i.e.

cor
sut
equ

(F
it.

3–
eac

a f
res

(It
tic

(F

wi

3–4
materi;

3–5
rate q_r
shown
residua
to redu

3–6.
ground
heat of
ground-
length (

3–7.
structur
at -34
duct he

3–8.

tance $\bar{h}$ is 80 Btu/hr sq ft F. Using the network shown in the accompanying sketch, estimate the temperature distribution and the rate of heat transfer by the relaxation method and compare your results with those obtained analytically in Sec. 2–5 or Prob. 2–15. Assume that the tip is insulated.

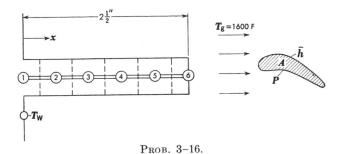

PROB. 3–16.

3–17. Show that for a semi-infinite plate of width L, having the boundary condition for $T\ (x, y)$

$$T\ (0, y) - T_1 = 0$$
$$T\ (L, y) - T_1 = 0$$
$$T\ (x, \infty) - T_1 = 0$$
$$T\ (x, 0) - T_1 = (T_2 - T_1)$$

the temperature distribution is

$$\frac{T - T_1}{T_2 - T_1} = \frac{4}{\pi}\left[e^{-(\pi/L)y} \sin \frac{\pi}{Lx} + \frac{1}{3} e^{-(3\pi/L)y} \sin \frac{3\pi}{L} x + \cdots \right]$$

For $T_1 = 0$ and $T_2 = 100$ F, plot isotherms of 25, 50, and 75 F.

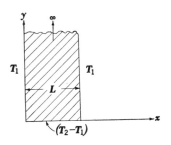

PROB. 3–17.

3–18. The temperatures at points 1, 2, 3, 4, 5, 6, and 7 in a corner cross section of the wall shown in plan view are given in the sketch. The lower surface is insulated, the left surface is exposed through a unit-surface conductance of 5 Btu/hr sq ft F to a fluid at $T_\infty = 90$ F. The thermal conductivity of the wall material is 1 Btu/hr sq ft F/ft and the distance between nodal points is 1 in. Using the relaxation method (a) compute the residual at point 5, (b) compute the residual at point 2.

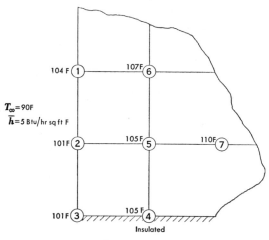

PROB. 3–18.

3–19.   A 6-in.-tall mild steel wedge, 1 in. on the top, 3 in. on the bottom, 5 ft long, is used as a footing for a high temperature vessel (900 F).   The wedge is insulated along the sloping sides.   Estimate the heat loss from the vessel through the wedge if the bottom of the wedge is at 300 F.

4 Conduction of Heat in the Unsteady State

4–1. TRANSIENT AND PERIODIC HEAT FLOW

In the preceding chapters we dealt only with problems involving steady-state heat conduction. However, before steady-state conditions can be reached, some time must elapse after the heat-transfer process is initiated to allow the transient conditions to disappear. For instance, when we determined the rate of heat flow through the furnace wall in Sec. 2–1, we did not consider the period during which the furnace was starting up and the temperatures of the interior, as well as those of the walls, were slowly increasing. We simply assumed that this period of transition had passed and that steady-state conditions had been established. In Sec. 2–3 where we determined the temperature distribution in an electrically heated wire, we also neglected the warming-up period. Yet we know that when we turn on a toaster, it takes some time before the resistance wires attain maximum temperature, although heat generation starts instantaneously when the current begins to flow.

Transient heat conduction is also important in the equalization of temperatures in boiler drums during pressure-raising and reducing periods. When the pressure is raised, the water temperature increases and the interior surface temperature of the drum is raised. It takes a finite period of time before the heat flow reaches the outer surface and equalizes the temperatures. To prevent excessive thermal stresses during the transient period it is necessary to restrict the rate at which the pressure rises in the drum. Similarly, during pressure-reducing periods, the transient heat flow process dictates the rate of pressure reduction in thick-walled boiler drums.

Another type of unsteady-heat-flow problem encountered in engineering involves periodic variations of temperature and heat flow. Periodic heat flow is of importance in internal-combustion engines, air-conditioning, instrumentation, and process contol. For example, at the end of a hot day the atmospheric air becomes cooler, and yet the temperatures inside stone buildings remain quite high for several hours after sundown. In the morning, even though the atmosphere has already become warm, the air inside the buildings will remain comfortably cool for several hours. The

reason for this phenomenon is the existence of a time lag before temperature equilibrium between the inside of the building and the outdoors can
be reached.   Another typical example is the periodic heat flow through
the walls of engines which are heated only during a portion of their cycle
of operation.   After the engine has warmed up and operates in the steady
state, the temperature at any point in the wall undergoes cyclic variations
with time.   While the engine is warming up, transient heat flow phenomena
are superimposed on the cyclic variations.

In this chapter we shall consider a number of heat-transfer problems
in which either periodic or transient temperature variations are of primary
concern.   We shall first analyze problems which can be simplified by assuming that the temperature is only a function of time and is uniform
throughout the system at any instant.   In subsequent sections of this
chapter we shall consider various methods for solving practical problems
of unsteady heat flow when the temperature depends not only on the
time, but also varies in the interior of the system.   Throughout this
chapter we shall not be concerned with the mechanisms of heat transfer by
convection or radiation.   Where these modes of heat transfer affect the
boundary conditions of the system, an appropriate value for the unit-surface
conductance will simply be specified.

4–2. TRANSIENT HEAT FLOW IN SYSTEMS WITH NEGLIGIBLE INTERNAL RESISTANCE

Even though there are no materials in nature that possess an infinite
thermal conductivity, many transient heat-flow problems can be readily
solved with acceptable accuracy by assuming that the internal conductive
resistance of the system is so small that the temperature within the system
is substantially uniform at any instant.   This simplification is justified
when the external thermal resistance between the surface of the system
and the surrounding medium is so large compared to the internal thermal
resistance of the system that it controls the heat-transfer process.

A measure of the relative importance of the thermal resistance within
a solid body is the ratio of the external to the internal resistance.   This
ratio can be written in dimensionless form as $\bar{h}L/k_s$, the *Biot number*,
where $\bar{h}$ is the average unit-surface conductance, L is a significant length
dimension obtained by dividing the volume of the body by its surface
area, and k_s is the thermal conductivity of the solid body.   In bodies
whose shape resembles a plate, a cylinder, or a sphere, the error introduced by the assumption that the temperature at any instant is uniform
will be less than 5 per cent when the internal resistance is less than 10 per
cent of the external surface resistance, i.e., when $\bar{h}L/k_s < 0.1$.

A typical example of this type of transient heat flow is the cooling of
a small metal casting or a billet in a quenching bath after its removal from

a hot furnace.   Suppose that the billet is removed from the furnace at a uniform temperature T_o and is quenched so suddenly that we can approximate the environmental temperature change by a step.   Designate the time at which the cooling begins as $\theta = 0$, assume that the heat-transfer coefficient $\bar{h}$ remains constant during the process, and that the bath temperature T_∞ at a distance far removed from the billet does not vary with time.   Then, in accordance with the assumption that the temperature within the body is substantially constant at any instant, an energy balance for the billet over a small time interval $d\theta$ is

$$\text{The change in internal energy of the billet during } d\theta = \text{the net heat flow from the billet to the bath during } d\theta$$

or

$$-c\rho V dT = \bar{h}A_s(T - T_\infty)d\theta \qquad (4\text{-}1)$$

where c = the specific heat of the billet, in Btu/lb F;
 ρ = density of the billet, in lb/cu ft;
 V = volume of the billet, in cu ft;
 T = average temperature of the billet, in F;
 A_s = surface area of the billet, in sq ft;
 dT = temperature change during $d\theta$.

The minus sign in Eq. 4–1 indicates that the internal energy decreases when $T > T_\infty$.   The variables T and θ can be readily separated and, for a differential time interval $d\theta$, Eq. 4–1 becomes

$$\frac{dT}{T - T_\infty} = \frac{d(T - T_\infty)}{(T - T_\infty)} = -\frac{\bar{h}A_s}{c\rho V}\, d\theta \qquad (4\text{-}2)$$

where it is noted that $d(T - T_\infty) = dT$, since T_∞ is constant.   With an initial temperature of T_o and a temperature at time θ of T as limits, integration of Eq. 4–2 yields

$$\ln \frac{T - T_\infty}{T_o - T_\infty} = -\frac{\bar{h}A_s}{c\rho V}\, \theta$$

or

$$\frac{T - T_\infty}{T_o - T_\infty} = e^{-(\bar{h}A_s/c\rho V)\theta} \qquad (4\text{-}3)$$

The quantity $(c\rho V/\bar{h}A_s)$ has the dimension of time and is called the *time constant*.   Its value is indicative of the rate of response of a single capacity system to a sudden change in the environmental temperature.   When $\theta = (c\rho V/\bar{h}A_s)$ the temperature difference $(T_o - T)$ reaches 62.3 per cent of the initial potential difference $(T_o - T_\infty)$.

Equation 4–3 describes the temperature-time history of the cooling billet. It is similar to the equation describing the voltage-time history in an electrical system consisting of a capacitor C_e and resistance R_e in series (Fig. 4-1).   When the switch S in this system is suddenly opened, the condenser begins to discharge and the voltage difference $E - E_\infty$ decreases.

Cooling Billet   Discharging Condenser

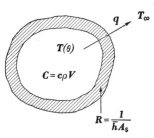

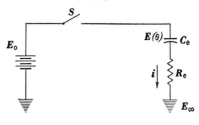

$$q = \frac{T - T_\infty}{R} = -C\frac{dT}{d\theta}$$

$$\frac{T - T_\infty}{T_o - T_\infty} = e^{-(1/CR)\theta}$$

$\theta = 0$ when billet is immersed in fluid and heat begins to flow.

$$i = \frac{E - E_\infty}{R_e} = -C_e\frac{dE}{d\theta}$$

$$\frac{E - E_\infty}{E_o - E_\infty} = e^{-(1/C_eR_e)\theta}$$

$\theta = 0$ when switch S is opened and the condenser begins to discharge.

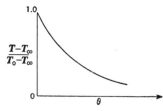

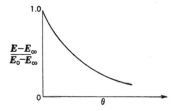

Thermal Circuit

Heat Flow q (Btu/hr)
Thermal Capacity
    $C = c\rho V$ (Btu/F)
Thermal Resistance
    $R = 1/\hbar A s$ (F hr/Btu)
Thermal Potential $(T - T_\infty)$ (F)

Electrical System

Current Flow i (amps)
Electrical Capacity C_e (farads)

Electrical Resistance R_e (ohms)

Electrical Potential $(E - E_\infty)$ (volts)

FIG. 4-1.   Analogy between cooling billet and discharging condenser.

The current i flowing from the condenser through the electrical resistance R_e is related to the voltage difference by

$$i = \frac{E - E_\infty}{R_e} = -\frac{dQ_e}{d\theta} = -C_e\frac{dE}{d\theta} \qquad (4\text{-}4)$$

where C_e = capacitance of the condenser, in farads;
    Q_e = charge of the condenser, in coulombs;
    E_∞ = ground potential.

Separating the variables in Eq. 4–4 and integrating yields

$$\frac{E - E_\infty}{E_o - E_\infty} = e^{-(1/R_e C_e)\theta} \qquad (4\text{--}5)$$

where E_o is the voltage at $\theta = 0$, i.e., when the switch is opened. We see that the potential in the electrical system, as the potential in thermal system, decays exponentially with time. In fact, if $1/C_e R_e$ is numerically equal to $\bar{h} A_s / c\rho V$, both potentials will decay at the same rate and the two systems will be analogous.

The analogy between the electrical system and the thermal system is illustrated in Fig. 4–1. We note that $1/\bar{h} A_s$ is the thermal resistance R at the surface of the billet, $c\rho V$ is equivalent to a *lumped thermal capacitance* C of the billet in the sense that it indicates the amount of internal energy which must be removed from the billet for each unit change of its temperature potential. The opening of the switch in the electrical system corresponds to the exposure of the billet to the colder environment, because both processes initiate flow of energy—current from the condenser in the electrical system, and heat from the billet in the thermal system.

Example 4–1. Determine the temperature response of a $\frac{1}{32}$-in.-diam copper wire originally at 300 F when suddenly immersed in (a) water ($\bar{h} = 15$ Btu/hr sq ft F) at 100 F; (b) air ($\bar{h} = 2$ Btu/hr sq ft F) at 100 F.

Solution: From Table A–1 in Appendix III we obtain

$$k_s = 216 \text{ Btu/hr ft F}$$
$$c = 0.091 \text{ Btu/lb F}$$
$$\rho = 558 \text{ lb/cu ft}$$

The surface area A_s and volume V of the wire are

$$A_s \text{ per inch length} = \pi D = 8.18 \times 10^{-3} \text{ sq ft/in.}$$
$$V \text{ per inch length} = \pi D^2/4 = 5.32 \times 10^{-5} \text{ cu ft}$$

The Biot modulus is

$$\frac{\bar{h} D}{4 k_s} = \frac{(15)(1/32)/12}{(4)\,216} \ll 0.1 \text{ for water}$$

Hence, the internal resistance may be neglected and Eq. 4–3 applies. From the data and the properties we have

$$C = c\rho V = 2.72 \times 10^{-4} \text{ Btu/F}$$

$$R = \frac{1}{\bar{h} A_s} = \frac{61.4 \text{ F hr/Btu, for air}}{8.18 \text{ F hr/Btu, for water}}$$

The temperature response is given by Eq. 4–3, and we get

$$T(\theta) = 100 + 200 e^{-\theta/RC} \qquad \text{F}$$

The results are plotted in Fig. 4–2. We note that the time required for the temperature difference between the wire and surroundings to reach one-half of the initial temperature difference is 42 sec in air, but only 5.6 sec in water.   *Ans.*

A thermocouple of $\frac{1}{32}$-in. diameter would therefore lag considerably if it were used to measure rapid changes in air temperature, and it would be advisable to use wire of the smallest available diameter to reduce this lag.

The results of the preceding analysis can be expressed conveniently in terms of dimensionless parameters. Let $V/A_s = L$, where L is a significant length dimension for the body, and multiply the numerator and

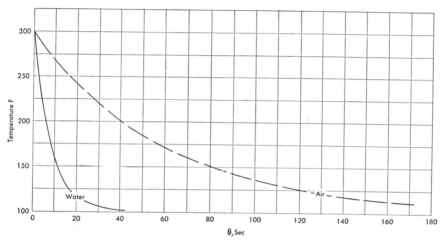

FIG. 4–2.   Cooling of wire in air and water.

the denominator of the exponent $\bar{h}\theta/c\rho L$ by Lk_s. Separating the resulting expression into two dimensionless groups gives

$$\frac{\bar{h}\theta Lk_s}{c\rho L^2 k_s} = \left(\frac{\bar{h}L}{k_s}\right)\left(\frac{k_s}{\rho c}\frac{\theta}{L^2}\right) = (\text{Bi})\,(\text{Fo})$$

and Eq. 4–3 becomes

$$\frac{T - T_\infty}{T_o - T_\infty} = e^{-(\text{Bi})(\text{Fo})} \tag{4-6}$$

where Fo is the *Fourier modulus*, $a\theta/L^2$ and a, the thermal diffusivity, denotes the combination of physical properties $k_s/c\rho$. The results can best be plotted in terms of dimensionless numbers as shown in Fig. 4–3.

Example 4–2.   Determine the time required for a small aluminum casting to be heated in a furnace to 950 F by gases at 2200 F if the casting is put into the oven at 60 F. The significant length of the casting V/A_s is $\frac{1}{2}$ ft and the unit-surface conductance $\bar{h}$ between the casting surface and the gases is 15 Btu/hr sq ft F.

Solution: First we determine the Biot modulus, using an average value for k_s from Table A–1,

$$\bar{h}L/k_s = (15)(0.5/130) = 0.0577$$

Since this is less than 0.1, we neglect the internal resistance and use Fig. 4–3. The temperature ratio is

$$(T - T_\infty)/(T_o - T_\infty) = (950 - 2200)/(60 - 220) = 0.584$$

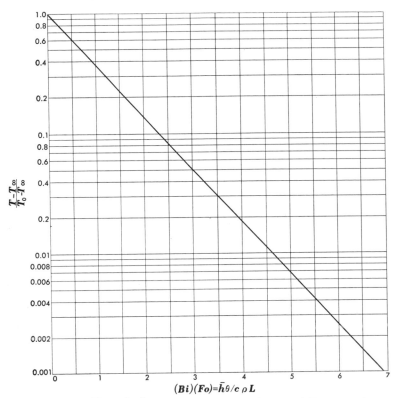

Fɪɢ. 4–3.   Dimensionless temperature ratio $(T - T_\infty)/(T_o - T_\infty)$ vs. product of Biot and Fourier moduli (Bi)(Fo).

From Fig. 4–3 we get Bi Fo = 0.5.   From Table A–1, $a = 3.70$ sq ft/hr at an average temperature of 500 F, and therefore

$$\theta = 0.5 \, [(0.5)(130)/(3.7)(15)] = 0.585 \text{ hr}$$

The time required to heat the casting from 60 F to 950 F is thus roughly 0.585 hr.   *Ans.*

For some problems the change in the internal energy of the system during a given time interval must be determined.   From Eq. 4–1 the instantaneous rate of heat flow at any time θ is

$$q = c\rho V \frac{dT}{d\theta}$$

From Eq. 4–3 the instantaneous rate of temperature change is

$$\frac{dT}{d\theta} = (T_\infty - T_o) \frac{\bar{h} A_s}{c_\rho V} e^{-(\bar{h}A_s/c_\rho V)}$$

and we get

$$\frac{q}{\bar{h}A_s(T_\infty - T_o)} = e^{-(\bar{h}A_s/c_\rho V)\theta} = e^{-\text{BIFo}} \tag{4-7}$$

Integrating Eq. 4–7 between $\theta = 0$ and $\theta = \theta$ yields Q, the amount of heat transferred in the time interval θ, which equals the change in internal energy of the system, or

$$\frac{Q}{\bar{h}A_s(T_\infty - T_o)} = \int_0^\theta e^{-(\bar{h}A_s/c_\rho V)\theta}d\theta = 1 - e^{-(\bar{h}A_s/c_\rho V)\theta} \tag{4-8}$$

The same general method can also be used to estimate the temperature-time history and the internal energy change of a well-stirred fluid in a metal container when the entire system is suddenly immersed in a fluid and heated or cooled by the surrounding medium.   If the walls of the container are so thin that their heat capacity is negligible, the temperature-time history of the fluid is

$$\frac{T - T_\infty}{T_o - T_\infty} = e^{-(UA_s/c_\rho V)} \tag{4-3}$$

where UA_s is the transmittance between the fluid and the surrounding medium and c and ρ are the specific heat and the density of the fluid respectively.

The lumped capacity method of analysis can also be applied to composite systems or bodies.   It leads to a set of n simultaneous linear equations for n composite layers.   For example, if the walls of the container have a substantial thermal capacitance $(c_\rho V)_1$, the unit thermal conductance at A_1, the outer surface of the container, is $\bar{h}_1$, the unit thermal conductance at A_2, the inner surface of the container, is $\bar{h}_2$, and the thermal capacitance of the fluid in the container is $(c_\rho V)_2$, the temperature-time history of the fluid $T(\theta)$ is obtained by solving simultaneously the equations

$$-(c_\rho V)_2 \frac{dT}{d\theta} = \bar{h}_2 A_2 (T - T_c)$$

$$-(c_\rho V)_1 \frac{dT}{d\theta} = \bar{h}_1 A_1 (T_c - T_\infty) - \bar{h}_2 A_2 (T - T_c)$$

where T_c is the temperature of the walls of the container.   The temperature time history of the fluid in the container, when the entire system, originally at T_o, is suddenly immersed in a medium at temperature T_∞, is

$$\frac{T - T_\infty}{T_o - T_\infty} = \frac{K_1 e^{-\theta/K_1} - K_2 e^{-\theta/K_2}}{K_1 - K_2}$$

where K_1 and K_2 are obtained by solving the equations

$$K_1 + K_2 = \frac{(C\rho V)_1}{\bar{h}_1 A_1} + \frac{(C\rho V)_2}{\bar{h}_2 A_2} + \frac{(C\rho V)_2}{\bar{h}_1 A_1}$$

$$K_1 K_2 = \frac{(C\rho V)_1}{\bar{h}_1 A_1} \frac{(C\rho V)_2}{\bar{h}_2 A_2}$$

simultaneously. The details of this derivation and the construction of the thermal circuit are left as an exercise (see Prob. 4–23).

4–3. PERIODIC HEAT FLOW IN SYSTEMS WITH NEGLIGIBLE INTERNAL RESISTANCE[1]

The preceding analysis has been limited to transient heat flow in systems where the ambient temperature remains constant. There exist, however, many problems in which the temperature of the medium surrounding the system varies with time. For example, there are batch processes in the chemical industry where the temperature of a chemical compound in a container must periodically follow a specified time schedule. The temperature changes of the material in the container are usually induced by heating or cooling the environment. Even if the compound is well stirred, it cannot immediately respond to the variation in the environmental temperature, as a result of its finite thermal capacity. To obtain the desired temperature-time schedule it is therefore necessary to initiate changes in the environmental temperature early enough to allow for the time lag in the system. Other typical examples of periodic-heat-flow problems are encountered in the design of a thermostatic temperature-control unit for a building which is continuously exposed to cyclic temperature variations and the design of the temperature-sensing element of a transducer used in the control and programming of high-vaccum processes such as the purification of vitamins.

The equation describing the temperature-time history of a system exposed to periodic temperature fluctuations is identical to the one derived for a constant ambient temperature. For a differential time interval $d\theta$ we can write Eq. 4–1 in the form

$$c\rho V \, dT = \bar{h} A_s (T_\infty - T) d\theta \qquad\qquad \textbf{[4–1]}$$

but since T_∞ now varies with time, i.e., $T_\infty = T_\infty(\theta)$, we cannot simply

---

[1] This section may be omitted without breaking the continuity of the presentation.

separate the variables. To obtain the temperature-time history of a system subjected to a variable environmental temperature we collect the terms containing the system temperature T on the left-hand side. This yields

$$\frac{dT(\theta)}{d\theta} + \frac{\bar{h}A_s}{\rho c V} \, T(\theta) = \frac{\bar{h}A_s}{\rho c V} \, T_\infty(\theta) \qquad \textbf{(4-9)}$$

a linear nonhomogeneous equation with constant coefficients. The general solution of Eq. 4–9 for a specified variation of T_∞ (θ) will be composed of the sum of two parts. The first part, called the *particular integral*, satisfies the complete equation and contains no arbitrary constants. Physically, the particular integral is the temperature-time history of the system after the transient phenomena have disappeared. In problems in dynamics and electric-circuit theory, this portion of the solution is often called the steady-state solution. Steady state in periodic phenomena means that the cyclic variations of the system will not change with time. The steady-state response of the system temperature T is caused and sustained by the environmental temperature T_∞, which acts as the driving potential and will generally be of the same form. If the periodic steady state is a cyclic variation of T_∞, then the temperature of the system T will also be cyclic. For example, if T_∞ is sinusoidal, the steady-state response of T will also be sinusoidal.

The second part of the solution, called the *complementary function*, makes the left-hand side of Eq. 4–9 equal to zero. It contains the constants of integration whose values must be obtained from the initial or boundary conditions and represents physically the transient response of the system temperature. The transient response arises because of a lack of initial equilibrium and will decay exponentially as when T_∞ is constant.

In summary, the complete solution to Eq. 4–9 consists of two parts:

$$T = T_{ss} + T_t \qquad \textbf{(4-10)}$$

where T_{ss} means the steady-state part and T_t means the transient part of the system temperature T. It should be noted that the boundary conditions and the initial conditions must always be applied to the complete solution, $T = T_{ss} + T_t$, and never to the transient part alone.

Example 4–3. Compare the temperature-time response of a bare iron-constantan thermocouple with that of a mercury-in-glass thermometer when these instruments are used to measure the temperature-time history of a gas whose temperature is a sinusoidal function of time, θ, i.e., $T_\infty = (100 + 50 \sin 2\pi\theta)$ F. Assume that the over-all heat-transfer coefficient for both instruments is equal to 5 Btu/hr sq ft F. The thermocouple is $\frac{1}{32}$ in. in diameter with 2 in. of length immersed. The thermometer is idealized by a mercury cylinder 1 in. long and $\frac{1}{4}$ in. in diameter. The initial temperature of both instruments is 60 F.

Solution: The transient response is obtained by solving Eq. 4–9 for the complementary function. Setting the left-hand side of Eq. 4–9 equal to zero, we obtain the homogeneous equation

$$\frac{dT}{d\theta} + \frac{\bar{h}A_s}{c_\rho V} T = 0$$

After separating the variables and integrating, the solution is found to be

$$T_t = C_1 e^{-(\bar{h}A_s/c_\rho V)\theta} \tag{4–11}$$

In order to find the steady-state response we must obtain the particular integral. Since the driving potential (i.e., the bath temperature) is sinusoidal, the response also must be sinusoidal. In addition, the driving potential contains a constant term, and therefore the response also must contain a constant. We recall that, when the solutions to linear differential equations are superposed (i.e., simply added), the sum also is a solution. By means of this fact we can construct the type of equation which meets the required conditions, as

$$T_{ss} = C_2 \sin 2\pi\theta + C_3 \cos 2\pi\theta + C_4 \tag{4–12}$$

This expression must satisfy Eq. 4–9 if it is a solution. Hence, we take the derivative of Eq. 4–12

$$\frac{dT_{ss}}{d\theta} = 2\pi C_2 \cos 2\pi\theta - 2\pi C_3 \sin 2\pi\theta$$

and substitute Eqs. 4–11 and 4–12 into Eq. 4–9, the original expression for T. If we let $m = \bar{h}A_s/c_\rho V$, we obtain, after collecting terms,

$$(2\pi C_2 + mC_3) \cos 2\pi\theta + (mC_2 - 2\pi C_3) \sin 2\pi\theta + mC_4$$
$$= m100 + m50 \sin 2\pi\theta \tag{4–13}$$

This can be an identity for all values of time θ only if the coefficients of like terms on each side of the equation are equal and we have

$$2\pi C_2 + mC_3 = 0 \quad \text{from the cosine terms}$$
$$mC_2 - 2\pi C_3 = 50m \quad \text{from the sine terms}$$
$$C_4 = 100 \quad \text{from the constant term}$$

Solving these equations for C_2 and C_3 simultaneously, we obtain

$$C_2 = \frac{50}{1 + (2\pi/m)^2} \quad \text{and} \quad C_3 = -\frac{(2\pi/m)50}{1 + (2\pi/m)^2}$$

The steady-state temperature response is therefore

$$T_{ss} = 100 + \frac{50}{1 + (2\pi/m)^2} \sin 2\pi\theta - \frac{(2\pi/m)50}{1 + (2\pi/m)^2} \cos 2\pi\theta \tag{4–14}$$

Terms such as $C_2 \sin 2\pi\theta - C_3 \cos 2\pi\theta$ can be combined by using the relation

$$C_2 \sin 2\pi\theta - C_3 \cos 2\pi\theta = \sqrt{C_2^2 + C_3^2} \left(\frac{C_2}{\sqrt{C_2^2 + C_3^2}} \sin 2\pi\theta - \frac{C_3}{\sqrt{C_2^2 + C_3^2}} \cos 2\pi\theta \right)$$

If we now construct a right triangle with $\sqrt{C_2^2 + C_3^2}$ as the hypotenuse and C_2 and C_3

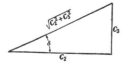

as the sides, we get $C_2/\sqrt{C_2^2 + C_3^2} = \cos \delta$ and $C_3/\sqrt{C_2^2 + C_3^2} = \sin \delta$. But since $\sin (A - B) = \sin A \cos B - \cos A \sin B$, we get $C_2 \sin 2\pi\theta - C_3 \cos 2\pi\theta = \sqrt{C_2^2 + C_3^2} \sin (2\pi\theta - \delta)$ where δ is equal to the $\tan^{-1} (C_3/C_2)$.

Combining the last two terms of Eq. 4–14 in this manner and adding T_t from Eq. 4–11 gives

$$T = 100 + \frac{50}{1 + (2\pi/m)^2} \sqrt{1 + (2\pi/m)^2} \sin(2\pi\theta - \delta) + C_1 e^{-m\theta} \quad (4\text{-}15)$$

where $\delta = \tan^{-1}(2\pi/m)$ and represents the time lag in the temperature response of the instruments.

The constant of integration C_1 can now be evaluated from the initial condition, i.e., $T = 60$ F at $\theta = 0$. Substituting this condition into Eq. 4–15 yields

$$T_{\theta=0} = 60 = 100 + \frac{50}{\sqrt{1 + (2\pi/m)^2}} \sin(-\delta) + C_1 \quad (4\text{-}16)$$

Making use of the trigonometric identity for $\sin \delta$ we obtain

$$C_1 = \frac{100\pi/m}{1 + (2\pi/m)^2} - 40 \quad (4\text{-}17)$$

Finally, the expression for the temperature-time history of the instrument is

$$T = \left[\frac{100\pi/m}{1 + (2\pi/m)^2} - 40\right] e^{-m\theta} + \frac{50}{\sqrt{1 + (2\pi/m)^2}} \sin(2\pi\theta - \delta) + 100 \quad (4\text{-}18)$$

To obtain the time lag δ in units of time we first find the time required for the system to go through one complete cycle. In the problem under consideration, the bath or the steady-state response of the instruments will complete one cycle each hour (i.e., $2\pi\theta$ increases by 2π radians as θ increases by one). The time lag δ in hours is therefore obtained by dividing the lag in radians by the number of radians corresponding to a unit increase of time, which is 2π radians in this case.

In order to plot the results, we determine the numerical value of m for the instruments. By definition we have

$$m = \frac{\bar{h}A_s}{c\rho V} = \frac{\bar{h}}{c\rho} \frac{\pi DL}{(\pi/4)D^2L} = \frac{4\bar{h}}{c\rho D}$$

For the thermometer, using physical properties of mercury

$$\rho = 849 \text{ lb/cu ft}$$
$$c = 0.0325 \text{ Btu/lb F}$$
$$D = 0.021 \text{ ft} \qquad m = 35.2 \text{ hr}^{-1}$$

For the thermocouple, using properties of iron as an approximation

$$\rho = 475 \text{ lb/cu ft}$$
$$c = 0.12 \text{ Btu/lb F}$$
$$D = 0.0026 \text{ ft} \qquad m = 135 \text{ hr}^{-1}$$

The final equations for the temperature response of the thermometer and thermocouple are respectively within slide-rule accuracy

$$T_{\text{meter}} = 100 + 49.3 \sin(2\pi\theta - 10.3) - 31.35\, e^{-35.2}$$
$$T_{\text{couple}} = 100 + 50 \sin(2\pi\theta - 2.7) - 37.7\, e^{-135\theta}$$

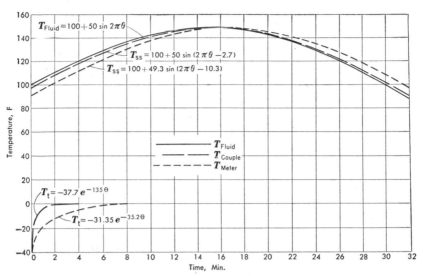

FIG. 4–4. Transient and steady-state response of the thermocouple and the thermometer in Example 4–3.

These results are plotted in Figs. 4–4 and 4–5. In the graphs of Fig. 4–4, the steady-state and the transient response are plotted separately. We note that the transient response of the thermometer is considerably slower—it takes about 6 min to die out—than that of the thermocouple. This is not unexpected since the time constant of the thermometer is 1.7 min, while the time constant of the thermocouple is less than one half of a minute. The steady-state lag of the thermometer is nearly a minute, while the thermocouple lags less than five seconds behind the temperature of the bath. The reason for this behavior is the large thermal capacitance of the mercury thermometer, which makes this type of instrument unsuitable when high sensitivity and fast response are desired.

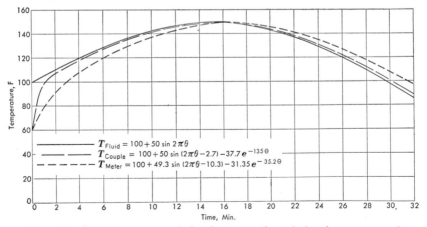

FIG. 4–5. Initial response of the thermocouple and the thermometer of Example 4–3 when immersed suddenly in a sinusoidally varying medium.

The preceding technique can be extended to arbitrary kinds of periodic temperature variations, since nearly any periodic function of time can be expressed in terms of a series of sine and cosine terms of the form

$$T_\infty(\theta) = \frac{A_0}{2} + A_1 \cos \frac{2\pi}{\theta_0} \theta + A_2 \cos \frac{4\pi}{\theta_0} \theta + \dots$$

$$+ B_1 \sin \frac{2\pi}{\theta_0} \theta + B_2 \sin \frac{4\pi}{\theta_0} \theta + \dots \qquad (4\text{-}19)$$

Once the temperature variation in Eq. 4–9 is expressed in this form, a solution can be obtained by algebraic addition of the solutions corresponding to each term of the series. The type of series shown in Eq. 4–19 is called a Fourier series. It can be written more compactly as

$$T_\infty(\theta) = \frac{A_0}{2} + \sum_{n=1}^{\infty} A_n \cos \frac{2\pi n}{\theta_0} \theta + B_n \sin \frac{2\pi n}{\theta_0} \theta \qquad (4\text{-}20)$$

or in the equivalent form,

$$T_\infty(\theta) = \frac{A_0}{2} + \sum_{n=1}^{\infty} C_n \cos \left(\frac{2\pi n}{\theta_0} \theta - \beta_n \right) \qquad (4\text{-}21)$$

where $\dfrac{A_0}{2}$ = mean temperature, T_{avg};

θ_0 = period of the first harmonic or fundamental component;

$C_n = \sqrt{A_n^2 + B_n^2}$ = the temperature amplitude of the nth harmonic;

$\beta_n = \tan^{-1}(B_n/A_n)$, the phase angle of the nth harmonic;

n = positive integers 1,2,3,etc.

The solution of Eq. 4–9 can be written compactly as

$$T(\theta) = T_{avg} + \sum_{n=1}^{\infty} \frac{T_{avg}}{\sqrt{1 + \left(\dfrac{2\pi n}{\theta_0} m \right)^2}} \cos \left(\frac{2\pi n}{\theta_0} \theta - \beta_n - \delta_n \right) + Ce^{-m\theta} \qquad (4\text{-}22)$$

where C is a constant whose value depends on the initial conditions and δ_n is the lag of the nth harmonic in the response. It should be noted that the coefficient $T_{avg}/\sqrt{1 + [(2\pi n/\theta_0)m]^2}$, often called the *amplitude ratio*, decreases rapidly for higher harmonics, i.e., if n is large. Therefore, the higher harmonics of the ambient-temperature variation have little or no effect on the system temperature, $T(\theta)$. The analogy to problems dealing with electrical or mechanical vibrations is apparent and may assist in the analysis of the thermal problems.

4–4. TRANSIENT HEAT FLOW IN AN INFINITE PLATE[2]

In Sec. 4–2 we discussed analytic methods for solving a class of transient-heat-flow problems which could be simplified by neglecting the thermal resistance within the system and treating the thermal capacity of the entire system as a lumped parameter. The mathematical description of this type of problem leads to ordinary differential equations. For simple shapes this approach is satisfactory when the Biot modulus is less than 0.1. Systems having a Biot modulus larger than 0.1 could be analyzed by means of graphical or numerical methods described in Secs. 4–6 and 4–7, but, for several cases of practical importance, solutions are available in the form of charts which are based on exact solutions and reduce the amount of labor and time required for the analysis. The material in this section serves as an introduction to the mathematical methods for solving the general heat-conduction equation and it will also foster an understanding of the technique for using the charts presented in Sec. 4–5.

The equations describing the temperature distribution in a solid having a finite thermal conductivity were derived in Sec. 3–2. These equations are partial-differential equations because the temperature is a function of time as well as location. A detailed treatment of the methods for solving the general heat-conduction equation is beyond the scope of this book, and for an extensive treatment reference may be made to the books by Schneider (1), Carslaw and Jaeger (2), and Jacob (3). Only one of the simplest cases which can be handled essentially with the tools of ordinary differential equations will be solved here.

To illustrate the analytic method of solving transient-heat-conduction problems, consider a large flat plate of thickness L having, under steady-state conditions, a uniform temperature T_o. One side of the plate is insulated and the other side is in contact with a fluid. At some instant, the temperature of the fluid is suddenly raised from T_o to T_∞. Heat begins to flow from the fluid to the plate, and we are to determine the rate of heat flow and the temperature distribution in the plate at arbitrary values of time.

The solution to this problem has numerous practical applications. For example, the walls of an uncooled rocket motor are suddenly exposed to hot gases when the propellants are ignited, and the operating time of the motor is limited by the resulting thermal stresses and the temperature rise at the inner wall. To predict the permissible time of operation it is necessary to know the temperature-time history in the shell of the rocket.

---

[2] This section may be omitted without breaking the continuity of the presentation.

Since heat losses from the outer surface are generally so small that one may assume the surface is insulated, the boundary conditions conform approximately to the problem under consideration if the wall thickness is small compared to the motor diameter.   Another example is the vulcanization of tires.   The tire is placed in a mold, steam is admitted to both sides, and the surfaces are maintained at an elevated temperature until the central layer has been heated to a specified temperature.   This system also meets the specifications of the problem at hand if it is recognized that uniform and equal temperatures on both sides of a wall (or a geometry which approximates it) result in a temperature profile which is symmetrical about the center plane.   Thus the temperature gradient at the center must be zero, and this is exactly the boundary condition for the insulated face.

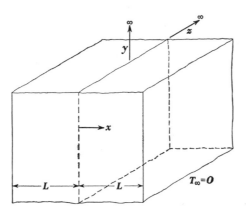

FIG. 4–6.   Nomenclature for transient
heat flow in an infinite plate.

Figure 4–6 is a schematic diagram of the system to be analyzed.   For simplicity we shall choose as a datum the temperature of the fluid to which the surface of the slab is exposed at $\theta = 0$.   This simply means that we measure all temperatures in degrees above (or below) the temperature of the fluid, and $T_\infty = 0$.   Since the slab is assumed very long in the y and z direction, the temperature will be uniform in any yz plane at a specified value of x.   Then, the general heat-conduction equation, in the absence of heat sources and sinks, reduces to

$$\frac{1}{a}\frac{\partial T}{\partial \theta} = \frac{\partial^2 T}{\partial x^2} \qquad 0 \le x \le L \qquad (4\text{–}23)$$

The thermal diffusivity a, which appears in all unsteady-heat-conduction problems is a property of the material, and the time rate of temperature change depends on its numerical value.   Qualitatively we observe that, in a material that combines a low thermal conductivity with a large specific heat per unit volume, the rate of temperature change will be slower than in a material that possesses a large thermal diffusivity.

Since the temperature T must be a function of time θ and distance x, we begin by assuming a product solution, i.e., multiply one function which only depends on time, Θ (θ), by another function which only depends on distance, $X(x)$. The nature of these functions is not known at this point, but will be determined as we proceed.

Thus, if

$$T(x,\theta) = X(x)\Theta(\theta) \tag{4-24}$$

it follows that

$$\frac{\partial T}{\partial \theta} = X \frac{\partial \Theta}{\partial \theta} \quad \text{and} \quad \frac{\partial^2 T}{\partial x^2} = \Theta \frac{\partial^2 X}{\partial x^2}$$

Substituting these partial derivatives into Eq. 4–23, yields

$$\frac{1}{a} X \frac{\partial \Theta}{\partial \theta} = \Theta \frac{\partial^2 X}{\partial x^2} \tag{4-25}$$

We can now separate the variables, i.e., bring all functions which depend on x to one side of the equation and all functions which depend on θ to the other. By dividing both sides of Eq. 4–25 by $X\Theta$, we obtain

$$\frac{1}{a\Theta} \frac{\partial \Theta}{\partial \theta} = \frac{1}{X} \frac{\partial^2 X}{\partial x^2} \tag{4-26}$$

Now observe that the left-hand side is a function of θ only and, therefore, is independent of x. Similarly, the right-hand side is a function of x only and will not change as θ varies. Since neither side can change as θ and x vary, both sides are equal to a constant which we shall call μ. Hence, we have two ordinary and linear differential equations with constant coefficients

$$\frac{d\Theta(\theta)}{d\theta} = a\mu\Theta(\theta) \tag{4-27}$$

and

$$\frac{d^2 X}{dx^2} = \mu X(x) \tag{4-28}$$

The general solution for Eq. 4–27 is

$$\Theta(\theta) = C_1 e^{a\mu\theta}$$

If μ were a positive number, the temperature of the slab would become infinitely high as θ increased, which is absurd. Therefore, we must reject the possibility that $\mu > 0$. If μ were zero, then we would find that the function expressing the time dependence of the temperature in the slab would be a constant. Again, this possibility must be rejected because it would not be consistent with the physical conditions of the problem.   We therefore conclude that μ must be a negative number, and for convenience we let $\mu = -\lambda^2$.   The time-dependent function, then, becomes

$$\Theta(\theta) = C_1 e^{-a\lambda^2\theta} \tag{4-29}$$

Next we direct attention to the equation involving x (Eq. 4–28).   Its general solution can be written in terms of a sinusoidal function.   Since this is a second-order equation, there must be two constants of integration in the solution.   In convenient form, the solution to the equation

$$\frac{\partial^2 X(x)}{\partial x^2} = -\lambda^2 X(x)$$

can be written as

$$X(x) = C_2 \cos \lambda x + C_3 \sin \lambda x \tag{4-30}$$

Returning now to the original product solution as expressed by Eq. 4–24, the temperature, as a function of distance and time in the slab, is given by

$$\begin{aligned} T(x,\theta) &= C_1 e^{-a\lambda^2\theta}(C_2 \cos \lambda x + C_3 \sin \lambda x) \\ &= e^{-a\lambda^2\theta}(A \cos \lambda x + B \sin \lambda x) \end{aligned} \tag{4-31}$$

where $A = C_1 C_2$ and $B = C_1 C_3$, both A and B being constants which must be evaluated from the boundary and initial conditions.   In addition we must also determine the value of the constant λ in order to complete the solution.

The boundary and initial conditions, stated in symbolic form, are:

1. At $x = 0$, $\partial T/\partial x = 0$.
2. At $x = L$, $-(\partial T/\partial x) = (\bar{h}/k_s)(T_{x\,=\,L} - 0)$.
3. At $\theta = 0$, $T = T_o$ (initial condition).

In order to meet boundary condition 1, we take the partial derivative of $T(x,\theta)$ with respect to x and set the resulting expression equal to zero, which gives

$$\left.\frac{\partial T}{\partial x}\right|_{x\,=\,0} = e^{-a\lambda^2\theta}\,(-A\lambda \sin \lambda x + B\lambda \cos \lambda x)\Big|_{x\,=\,0} = 0$$

Now $\sin 0 = 0$, but the second term in the bracket, involving the $\cos 0$ can be zero only if $B = 0$.   The solution for $T(x,\theta)$ becomes, therefore,

$$T(x,\theta) = e^{-a\lambda^2\theta}A \cos \lambda x \tag{4-32}$$

In order to satisfy the second boundary condition, namely that the heat flow by conduction at the interface must be equal to the heat flow by convection, the equality

$$-\frac{\partial T}{\partial x}\bigg|_{x=L} = e^{-a\lambda^2\theta}\, A\lambda \,\sin \lambda L = \frac{\bar{h}}{k_s}\,(T_{x=L} - 0) = \frac{\bar{h}}{k_s}\, e^{-a\lambda^2\theta}\, A \cos \lambda L$$

must hold for all values of θ, which gives

$$\frac{\bar{h}}{k_s}\cos \lambda L = \lambda \sin \lambda L$$

or
$$\cot \lambda L = \frac{k_s}{\bar{h} L}\,\lambda L = \text{Bi } \lambda L \qquad\qquad (4\text{–}33)$$

Equation 4–33 is transcendental, and there are an infinite number of values of λ which will satisfy it.   Mathematicians refer to these values of

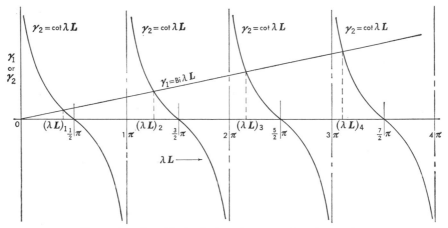

Fig. 4–7.   Graphical solution of transcendental equation.

λ as *characteristic values* or *Eigenwerte*. The simplest way to determine the numerical values of λ is to plot $\cot \lambda L$ and Bi λL against λL.   The values of λ at the points of intersection of these curves are the characteristic values and will satisfy the second boundary condition.   Figure 4–7 is a plot of these curves, and if $L = 1$ we read off the first few characteristic values as $\lambda_1 = 0.86\text{Bi}$, $\lambda_2 = 3.43\text{Bi}$, $\lambda_3 = 6.44\text{Bi}$, etc.   The value $\lambda = 0$ is disregarded because it leads to the trivial solution $T = 0$ (see Eq. 4–32).

A particular solution of Eq. 4–32 corresponds to each value of λ.   Of course, the constant A must be evaluated for each value of λ.   Therefore, we shall adopt a subscript notation to identify the correspondence between A and λ.   For instance, A_1 corresponds to λ_1 or, in general, A_n to λ_n.   The complete solution is formed as the sum of the solutions corresponding to each characteristic value, or

$$T(x,\theta) = \sum_{n=1}^{\infty} e^{-a\lambda_n^2\theta} A_n \cos \lambda_n x \tag{4-34}$$

Each term of this infinite series contains a constant. These constants are evaluated by substituting the initial condition, i.e., the initial temperature distribution, into Eq. 4–34. For our problem, we have

$$T(x,0) = T_o = \sum_{n=1}^{\infty} A_n \cos \lambda_n x \tag{4-35}$$

It can be shown that the characteristic functions, $\cos \lambda_n x$, are orthogonal between $x = 0$ and $x = L$ and therefore[3]

$$\int_0^L \cos \lambda_n x \cos \lambda_m \, x dx = 0 \qquad \text{if } m \neq n$$
$$\neq 0 \qquad \text{if } m = n \tag{4-36}$$

where λ_m may be any characteristic value of λ. To obtain a particular value of A_n, we multiply both sides of Eq. 4–35 by $\cos \lambda_m x$ and integrate between 0 and L. In accordance with Eq. 4–36, all terms on the right-hand side disappear except the one involving the square of the characteristic function, $\cos \lambda_n x$, and we obtain

$$\int_0^L T_o(\cos \lambda_n x) dx = A_n \int_0^L (\cos^2 \lambda_n x) dx$$

From standard integral tables (12) we get

$$\int_0^L \cos^2 \lambda_n x dx = \frac{1}{2}x + \frac{1}{2\lambda_n} \sin \lambda_n x \cos \lambda_n x \int_0^L = \frac{L}{2} + \frac{1}{2\lambda_n} \sin \lambda_n L \cos \lambda_n L$$

and

$$\int_0^L \cos \lambda_n x dx = \frac{1}{\lambda_n} \sin \lambda_n L$$

[3] This can be verified by performing the integration which yields

$$\int_0^L \cos \lambda_n x \cos \lambda_m x dx = \frac{\lambda_n \sin L\lambda_n \cos L\lambda_m - \lambda_m \sin L\lambda_m \cos L\lambda_n}{2L(\lambda_m^2 - \lambda_n^2)}$$

when $m \neq n$. However, from Eq. 4–33 we have

$$\frac{\cot \lambda_m L}{\lambda_m} = \frac{k}{h} = \frac{\cot \lambda_n L}{\lambda_n}$$

or $\qquad \lambda_n \cos \lambda_m L \sin \lambda_n L = \lambda_m \cos \lambda_n L \sin \lambda_m L$

Therefore, the integral is zero when m $\neq$ n.

whence the constant A_n is

$$A_n = \frac{2\lambda_n}{L\lambda_n + \sin \lambda_n L \cos \lambda_n L} \frac{T_o \sin \lambda_n L}{\lambda_n}$$

$$= \frac{2T_o \sin \lambda_n L}{L\lambda_n + \sin \lambda_n L \cos \lambda_n L} \qquad (4\text{-}37)$$

As an illustration of the general procedure outlined above, let us determine A_1 when $\bar{h} = 1$, $k_s = 1$, and $L = 1$. From the graph of Fig. 4–7, the value of λ_1 is 0.86 radians or 49.2 deg. Then we have

$$A_1 = T_o \frac{2 \sin 49.2}{1 \times 0.86 + \sin 49.2 \cos 49.2} = T_o \frac{2 \times 0.757}{0.86 + 0.757 \times 0.653} = 1.12T_o$$

Similarly, we obtain

$$A_2 = -0.152T_o \quad \text{and} \quad A_3 = 0.046T_o$$

We note that the series converges rapidly and, for Bi $= 1$, three terms represent a fairly good approximation for practical purposes.

To express the temperature in the slab in terms of conventional dimensionless moduli, we let $\lambda_n = \delta_n/L$. The final form of the solution, obtained by substituting Eq. 4–37 into Eq. 4–32, is then

$$\frac{T(x,\theta)}{T_o} = \sum_{n=1}^{\infty} e^{-\delta_n{}^2(\theta a/L^2)} 2 \frac{\sin \delta_n \cos(\delta_n x/L)}{\delta_n + \sin \delta_n \cos \delta_n} \qquad (4\text{-}38)$$

We note that the time dependence is now contained in the dimensionless Fourier modulus, Fo $= \theta a/L^2$. Furthermore, if we write the second boundary condition in terms of δ_n, we obtain from Eq. 4–33

$$\cot \delta_n = \frac{k_s}{\bar{h}L} \delta_n \qquad (4\text{-}39)$$

or

$$\delta_n \tan \delta_n = \frac{\bar{h}L}{k_s} = \text{Bi}$$

We observe that δ_n is a function only of the dimensionless Biot modulus, Bi $= \bar{h}L/k_s$. Hence the temperature $T(x,\theta)$ can be fully expressed in terms of the three dimensionless quantities, Fo $= \theta a/L^2$, Bi $= \bar{h}L/k_s$, and x/L.

It is not difficult to determine also the internal energy change of the slab. At any instant θ, the rate of heat flow per unit area from the fluid to the surface of the slab is given by

$$\frac{q}{A} = -k_s \left. \frac{\partial T}{\partial x} \right|_{x=L}$$

If we let dQ represent the heat flow per unit area during a time interval $d\theta$, we can write

$$dQ = -k_s \left. \frac{\partial T}{\partial x} \right|_{x = L} d\theta \qquad (4\text{-}40)$$

The temperature gradient can be obtained by differentiating Eq. 4–38 with respect to x for a given value of θ, or

$$\left. \frac{\partial T}{\partial x} \right|_{x = L} = -\frac{2T_o}{L} \sum_{n=1}^{\infty} e^{-\delta_n{}^2 \text{Fo}} \frac{\delta_n \sin^2 \delta_n}{\delta_n + \sin \delta_n \cos \delta_n} \qquad (4\text{-}41)$$

Substituting Eq. 4–41 into Eq. 4–40 and integrating between the limits of $\theta = 0$ and θ gives the change in internal energy of the slab during the time θ, which is equal to the amount of heat Q absorbed by (or removed from) the slab. After some algebraic simplification, we obtain

$$Q = 2T_oLc\rho \sum_{n=1}^{\infty} (1 - e^{-\delta_n{}^2\text{Fo}}) \frac{\sin^2 \delta_n}{\delta_n{}^2 + \delta_n \sin \delta_n \cos \delta_n} \qquad (4\text{-}42)$$

In order to make Eq. 4–42 dimensionless, we note that $c\rho LT_o$ represents the initial internal energy per square foot of the slab relative to the datum, $T_\infty = 0$. If we denote $c\rho LT_o$ by Q_o, we get

$$\frac{Q}{Q_o} = \sum_{n=1}^{\infty} \frac{2 \sin^2 \delta_n}{\delta_n{}^2 + \delta_n \sin \delta_n \cos \delta_n} (1 - e^{-\delta_n{}^2\text{Fo}}) \qquad (4\text{-}43)$$

The temperature distribution and the amount of heat transferred at any time may be determined from Eqs. 4–38 and 4–43 respectively. The final expressions are in the form of infinite series. These series have been evaluated, and the results are available in the form of charts. The use of the charts for the problem treated in this section as well as for other cases of practical interest will be taken up in the following section. A complete understanding of the methods by which the mathematical solutions have been obtained, although helpful, is not necessary for using the charts.

4–5. CHARTS FOR TRANSIENT HEAT CONDUCTION

For transient heat conduction in several simple shapes, subject to boundary conditions of practical importance, the temperature distribution and the heat flow have been calculated and the results are available in the form of charts or tables (1,2,3,9,10,11). In this section we shall illustrate the application of some of these charts to typical problems of transient heat conduction in solids having Biot moduli larger than 0.1. The charts

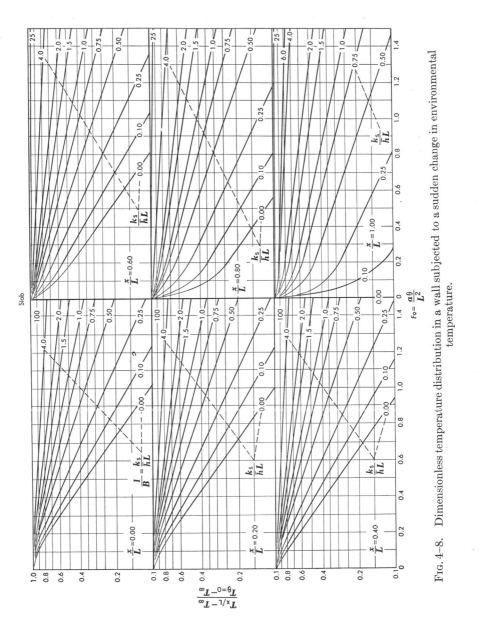

Fɪɢ. 4–8.   Dimensionless temperature distribution in a wall subjected to a sudden change in environmental temperature.

presented here have been taken from Refs. 9 and 10, and for details of the mathematical solutions, the original references should be consulted.

Flat plate. The first series of charts (Figs. 4–8 and 4–9) apply to a large flat plate of thickness $2L$. Initially the temperature of the plate is uniform at T_o. At some instant of time which will be designated as $\theta = 0$, the plate is immersed in a fluid at T_∞. If T_∞ is larger than T_o, heat begins to flow from the fluid to the plate. The rate of heat flow depends on the temperature difference $T_\infty - T_o$, the unit-surface conductance $\bar{h}$ between the plate and the fluid, the physical properties of the plate, and the plate thickness. The temperature distribution and the internal energy in the plate at any instant are functions of the same variables. The functional relationships, derived in the preceding section, are given by

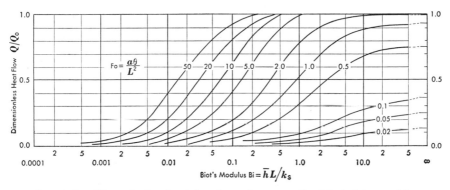

Fig. 4–9. Dimensionless heat flow to or from a wall subjected to a sudden change in environmental temperature.

Eqs. 4–38 and 4–43 respectively in terms of dimensionless parameters. The numerical results are presented in Figs. 4–8 and 4–9. In Fig. 4–8 the dimensionless temperature ratio $(T_{x/L} - T_\infty)/(T_{\theta=0} - T_\infty)$ is plotted against Fo, the Fourier modulus $a\theta/L^2$. There are six separate graphs for depth ratios x/L of 0, 0.2, 0.4, 0.6, 0.8, and 1.0, where x is the distance from the central plane as shown in Fig. 4–6. The upper left-hand graph $(x/L = 0)$ shows the temperature at the center plane where $\partial T/\partial x = 0$. The graph in the lower right-hand corner applies to the surface of the slab in contact with the fluid.

The constant parameter for each of the dimensionless temperature-time curves is the reciprocal of the Biot modulus, i.e., $k_s/\bar{h}L$. The curves labeled $k_s/\bar{h}L = 0$ are for an infinite surface conductance, that is, a sudden change in the temperature at the face $x = L$. An inspection of the graph for $x/L = 1$ shows that the temperature at the face $x = L$ is equal to T_∞ at $\theta \gg 0$. For small values of the Biot modulus, say $\bar{h}L/k_s < 0.1$, there is little difference between the temperatures at $x = L$ and $x = 0$ at any time.

For such cases the assumption that a uniform temperature prevails through-out the body does not introduce a serious error, and the simplified analysis presented in Sec. 4–2 may be used. The justification for this assumption is now substantiated for one system by the results of an exact analysis.

Figure 4–9 is a plot of Q/Q_o vs. the Biot modulus for various values of Fo. Here Q represents the total change in internal energy per unit area, i.e., the amount of heat transferred per unit area in the time interval be-tween $\theta = 0$ and $\theta = \theta$ in Btu per square foot; Q_o represents the initial internal-energy per unit area relative to the fluid temperature T_∞, i.e., $c\rho L(T_o - T_\infty)$. A positive value of Q indicates, therefore, that heat is transferred from the wall to the fluid, while a negative value of Q shows that the direction of heat flow is into the slab.

Example 4–4. A concrete wall, 1 ft thick and originally at 100 F, is suddenly exposed on one side to a hot gas at 1600 F. If the heat-transfer coefficient on the hot side is 5 Btu/hr sq ft F and the other side is insulated, determine (a) the time required to raise the temperature at the insulated face of the slab to 500 F, (b) the temperature distri-bution in the wall at that instant, and (c) the heat transferred to the wall per square foot of surface area.

Solution: (a) From Table A–1 of properties we get

$$k_s = 0.54 \text{ Btu/hr ft F}$$
$$c = 0.20 \text{ Btu/lb F}$$
$$\rho = 144 \text{ lb/cu ft}$$
$$a = 0.0187 \text{ sq ft/hr}$$

We note that the insulated face corresponds to the center plane in a slab of thickness $2L$, since $\partial T/\partial x = 0$ for both at $x = 0$. The temperature ratio at the insulated face is

$$\left. \frac{T - T_\infty}{T_o - T_\infty} \right|_{\text{at } x\, =\, 0} = \frac{500 \text{ F} - 1600 \text{ F}}{100 \text{ F} - 1600 \text{ F}} = 0.733$$

and the reciprocal of the Biot modulus is

$$\frac{k_s}{hL} = \frac{0.54}{(5)(1)} / = 0.108$$

From the chart of Fig. 4–8, $a\theta/L^2 \big|_{\text{at } x\, =\, L} = 0.25$ under these conditions, and there-fore $\theta = 0.25 \times 1/0.0187 = 13.3$ hr.   *Ans.*

b) The temperature distribution in the slab at this instant is determined from the graphs for the various depth ratios as shown below.

x/L	0.2	0.4	0.6	0.8	1.0
$\dfrac{T - T_\infty}{T_o - T_\infty}$	0.7	0.65	0.5	0.32	0.12
$T_\infty - T$	1050	975	750	480	265

The temperatures at various distances from the insulated face are tabulated below.

x (ft)	0	0.2	0.4	0.6	0.8	1.0
Temp (F)	500	550	625	850	1120	1335

Ans.

c) The heat transferred to the wall during the process can be obtained from Fig. 4–9. For $\bar{h}L/k_s$ equal to 9.25, Q/Q_o at $a\theta/L^2 = 0.25$ is about 0.5. Thus, we find that

$$Q = c_\rho L\,(T_o - T_\infty)\,(0.5) = (0.2)\,(144)\,(1)\,(100 - 1600)\,(0.5) = -21{,}600 \text{ Btu} \quad Ans.$$

The minus sign indicates that the heat flow is into the wall and that the internal energy of the wall increased during the process. A positive answer would of course indicate the opposite conditions.

Long cylinder and sphere. In addition to the plane wall, solutions are also available in chart form for the infinitely long cylinder and the sphere. The mathematical solutions may be obtained by the same method of approach that was used in Sec. 4–4 for the slab, namely by assuming a product solution and separating the variables. The basic differential equations to be solved are

$$\frac{\partial T}{\partial \theta} = a\left(\frac{\partial^2 T}{\partial r^2} + \frac{1}{r}\frac{\partial T}{\partial r}\right) \text{ for a long cylinder} \tag{4–44}$$

$$\frac{\partial T}{\partial \theta} = a\left(\frac{\partial^2 T}{\partial r^2} + \frac{2}{r^2}\frac{\partial T}{\partial r}\right) \text{ for a sphere} \tag{4–45}$$

The initial and the boundary conditions for which the solutions to Eqs. 4–44 and 4–45 have been evaluated are described as follows:

1. The initial temperature distribution in the cylinder or the sphere is uniform and equal to T_o, i.e., at $\theta = 0$, $T = T_o$.
2. At time $\theta = 0$, the cylinder or the sphere is exposed to a fluid whose temperature is T_∞. This temperature is used as the datum above or below which changes in temperature are measured.
3. The unit-surface conductance, $\bar{h}$, between the surface of the body and the fluid is uniform and does not change with time.

The charts of Figs. 4–10 and 4–12 show the dimensionless temperature ratios $(T_{r/r_o} - T_\infty)/(T_{\theta=0} - T_\infty)$ as a function of the Fourier modulus $a\theta/r_o^2$ for various values of $k_s/\bar{h}r_o$, the reciprocal of the Biot modulus; T_{r/r_o} is the temperature at time θ at the location r/r_o. As for the slab, there are six separate graphs for depth ratios r/r_o of 0, 0.2, 0.4, 0.6, 0.8, and 1.0, where r_o is the outside radius and r the radial distance from the center.

The ratios of the total amount of heat transferred during the process to the initial internal energy are plotted in Fig. 4–11 for the cylinder and in

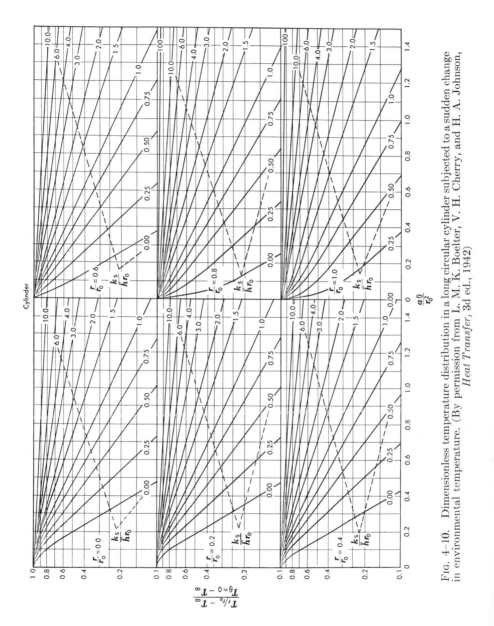

Fig. 4–10.   Dimensionless temperature distribution in a long circular cylinder subjected to a sudden change in environmental temperature. (By permission from L. M. K. Boelter, V. H. Cherry, and H. A. Johnson, *Heat Transfer*, 3d ed., 1942)

Fig. 4–13 for the sphere against the Biot modulus at various values of the Fourier modulus. The initial energy stored is measured with respect to T_∞ and is defined as $Q_o = c\rho\pi r_o^2(T_o - T_\infty)$ per unit length of the cylinder and as $Q_o = c\rho \frac{4}{3} \pi r_o^3(T_o - T_\infty)$ for the sphere.

The use of these charts is illustrated in the following example.

Example 4–5. In California the problem of preventing the freezing of oranges during cold nights is of considerable economic importance. Heat is transferred from the oranges by radiation and convection to the cold environment. To reduce the heat transfer by radiation to the cold sky and to warm the surrounding air, oil heaters, or smudge pots, are used. These devices generate a smoky haze which reduces the radiant

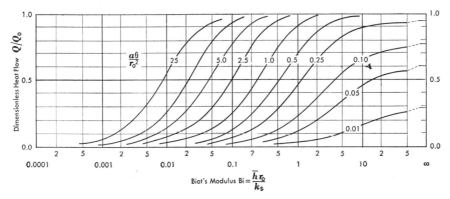

FIG. 4–11.   Dimensionless heat flow to or from a long circular cylinder subjected to a sudden change in environmental temperature. (By permission from U. Grigull, "Die Grundgesetze der Wärmeübertragung," *Springer Verlag*, 3d ed., Berlin: 1955)

heat loss and also heats the air. To specify the heating requirements, it is necessary to estimate the temperature at the center of a 4-in.-diam orange originally at 65 F when exposed to an environment at an effective temperature of 25 F for a period of 6 hr. The over-all surface conductance is estimated to be 2 Btu/hr sq ft F. Since the juice of an orange consists largely of water, the physical properties of water given in Table A–3 may be used.

Solution: We shall assume that the exposure to the cold air is quite sudden and use Fig. 4–12. The Biot modulus is

$$\frac{\bar{h}r_o}{k} = \frac{(2 \text{ Btu/hr sq ft F})(2 \text{ in.})}{(0.33 \text{ Btu/hr ft F})(12 \text{ in./ft})} = 1.0$$

and hence we cannot neglect the internal resistance. The Fourier modulus is,

$$\frac{a\theta}{r_o^2} = \frac{(0.005 \text{ sq ft/hr})(6 \text{ hr})(144 \text{ sq in. /sq ft})}{2^2 \text{ sq in.}} = 1.08$$

In Fig. 4–12 we obtain from the graph for $r/r_o = 0$ the temperature ratio

$$\frac{T - T_\infty}{T_o - T_\infty} = 0.10$$

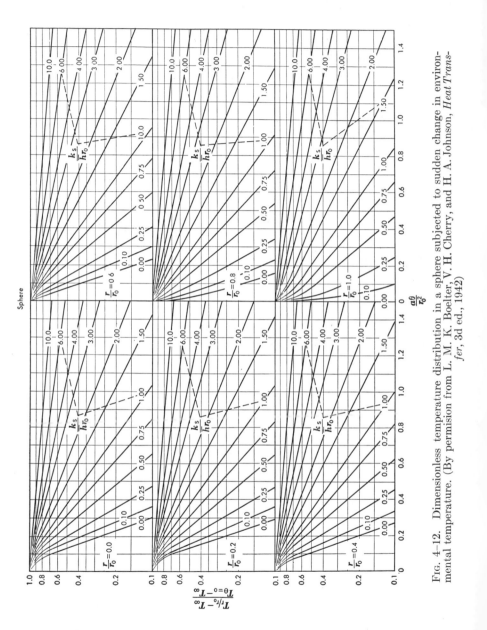

FIG. 4–12. Dimensionless temperature distribution in a sphere subjected to sudden change in environmental temperature. (By permission from L. M. K. Boelter, V. H. Cherry, and H. A. Johnson, *Heat Transfer*, 3d ed., 1942)

whence the temperature at the center is

$$T = (0.10)(65{-}25) + 25 = 28 \text{ F}$$

It appears, therefore, that the frost will penetrate the fruit.

An inspection of Figs. 4–8, 4–10, and 4–12 shows that a change in the surface of environmental temperature may not affect the interior of the body for some time after the temperature change originally occurred. There are numerous practical problems where one is only interested in the temperature distribution and the heat flow during the initial stages of a process or where the body is so large that the temperature at the interior is not affected by the temperature changes at the surface. In such cases it is often found that the charts of Figs. 4–8 to 4–13 cannot be read to a

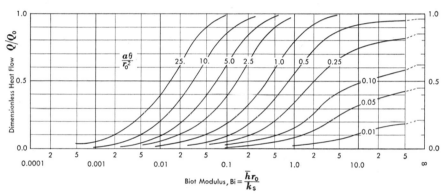

FIG. 4–13.   Dimensionless heat flow to or from a sphere subjected to a sudden change in environmental temperature. (By permission from U. Grigull, "Die Grundgesteze der Wärmeübertragung," *Springer Verlag*, 3d ed., Berlin: 1955)

sufficient degree of accuracy.   However, Boelter (9) and Heisler (11) have prepared special charts for short-time heating or cooling to supplement Figs. 4–8 to 4–13.

Semi-infinite body.   If the temperature in the interior of a slab does not change during a process, the temperature distribution near the surface is identical to that in an infinitely thick slab and we have a so-called semi-infinite solid.   For transient heat conduction in a semi-infinite solid (Fig. 4–14), solutions are available in the form of charts subject to the following initial and boundary conditions.

1. The temperature distribution in the body is originally uniform at T_o.
2. At time $\theta = 0$, the face of the semi-infinite solid is brought in contact with a fluid at T_∞.
3. The unit-surface conductance $\bar{h}$ over the face $x = 0$ is constant and uniform.

These boundary conditions are also valid for a wall of finite thickness, or for a long rod which is insulated around its circumference when $L/2\sqrt{\theta a}$ is larger than 0.5; they are approximately correct for cylinders and spheres as long as the depth to which the heat conduction has penetrated is small compared with the radius of curvature.

We shall first consider the special case of one-dimensional transient heat conduction in a semi-infinite solid with no thermal resistance at the surface. This assumption simplifies the problem because, at $\theta = 0$, the

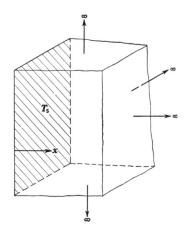

FIG. 4–14.   Sketch illustrating nomenclature for semi-infinite slab.

temperature change occurs directly at the surface, i.e., $T_{x=0} = T_\infty$ for $\theta \geqslant 0$.

For this case[4] the solution to Eq. 4–23 becomes

$$\frac{T - T_\infty}{T_o - T_\infty} = G\left(\frac{x}{\sqrt{a\theta}}\right) \tag{4-46}$$

where $G(x/2\sqrt{a\theta})$ is the Gaussian error integral defined as

$$G\left(\frac{x}{2\sqrt{a\theta}}\right) = \frac{2}{\pi} \int_0^{x/2\sqrt{a\theta}} e^{-\beta^2} d\beta \tag{4-47}$$

In Fig. 4–15, $G(x/2\sqrt{a\theta})$ is plotted against $x/2\sqrt{a\theta}$, and the curve may be used for convenience in computation. The variable $x/2\sqrt{a\theta}$ is a dimensionless quantity. If a is in sq ft/hr, θ must be expressed in hours and x in feet.

The instantaneous rate of heat flow at the surface can be readily ob-

[4] For details of the solution, see Refs. 1, 2, or 3.

tained from Eq. 4–46 by evaluating the temperature gradient at the surface, or

$$q = -k_sA\frac{\partial T}{\partial x}\bigg|_{x=0} = -k_sA\frac{T_o - T_\infty}{\sqrt{\pi a\theta}}e^{-x^2/4a\theta}\bigg|_{x=0}$$

$$= k_sA\frac{T_\infty - T_o}{\sqrt{\pi a\theta}} \qquad (4\text{–}48)$$

The total change in internal energy of the slab during the process from $\theta = 0$ to $\theta = \theta$ is

$$Q = \int_0^\theta q\,d\theta = \int_0^\theta k_sA\frac{T_\infty - T_o}{\sqrt{\pi a}}\theta^{-\frac{1}{2}}\,d\theta = 2k_sA(T_\infty - T_o)\sqrt{\frac{\theta}{\pi a}} \qquad (4\text{–}49)$$

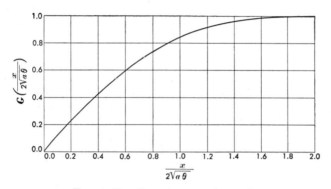

FIG. 4–15.   Gaussian error integral.

Example 4–6.   In the installation of underground water pipes, it is important to determine the depth to which a change in surface temperature is felt during a 12-hr period.   If the original soil temperature is 40 F and the surface temperature suddenly drops to 25 F, determine the depth to which the freezing temperature penetrates. Assume that the soil is dry and $a = 0.012$ sq ft/hr.

Solution: For the dimensionless temperature ratio we have

$$\frac{T - T_\infty}{T_o - T_\infty} = \frac{32\ F - 25\ F}{40\ F - 25\ F} = 0.467$$

From Fig. 4–15 we find that

$$G\left(\frac{x}{2\sqrt{a\theta}}\right) = 0.467$$

when

$$\frac{x}{2\sqrt{a\theta}} = 0.44$$

Solving for x, we get

$$x = 2\sqrt{(0.012)} \ (12) \ 0.44 = 0.334 \text{ ft}$$

Thus, freezing will not occur if the pipe is more than 4 in. below the surface.   *Ans.*

For a finite value of the surface conductance at the face of a semi-infinite slab, the solution to Eq. 4–23 is shown in Fig. 4–16 where the temperature ratio $(T - T_\infty)/(T_o - T_\infty)$ is plotted against a *local Biot modulus* $\bar{h}x/k_s$, where x *is the distance from the face.* The constant parameter for each of the curves is Θ, the dimensionless time parameter $(\bar{h}/k_s)^2 \, a\theta$, often called the *boundary Fourier modulus.* The use of this chart is illustrated by the following example.

Example 4–7. A cylindrical combustion chamber (10 in. ID) has a refractory lining of 1-in. thickness on the inside to protect the exterior shell. In order to determine the thermal stress, it is necessary to obtain the temperature distribution in the lining 1 min after initiation of combustion. The following data are given:

$$\begin{aligned}
T_\infty &= 3000 \text{ F} \\
\bar{h} &= 40 \text{ Btu/hr sq ft F} \\
a &= 0.020 \text{ sq ft/hr} \\
k &= 0.6 \text{ Btu/hr ft F} \\
T_o &= 100 \text{ F}
\end{aligned}$$

Solution: The time period of interest is short and the radius of curvature of the refractory wall is large compared to the wall thickness. We therefore treat the system as a semi-infinite slab. For $\theta = 1/60$, the boundary Fourier modulus is

$$\frac{\bar{h}^2 a\theta}{k_s^2} = \frac{(40)^2(0.02)}{(0.6)^2(60)} = 1.48$$

For this value of the time parameter, the temperature at various values of x can be found from Fig. 4–16. The results are tabulated below.

| x (in.) | 0.0 | 0.2 | 0.4 | 0.6 | 0.8 | 1.0 |
$\bar{h}x/k_s$	0.0	1.11	2.22	3.33	4.44	5.55
$\dfrac{T - T_\infty}{T_o - T_\infty}$	0.38	0.7	0.9	0.97	1.0	1.0
$T - T_\infty$	1100	2040	2610	2810	2900	2900
T (F)	1900	960	390	190	100	100

The temperature distribution permits an analysis of the thermal stress due to the differential expansion of the lining.

Two- and three-dimensional bodies. The problems considered in this section have so far been limited to one-dimensional heat flow. Since many practical problems involve heat flow in two- and three-dimensional systems, we shall now show how solutions for one-dimensional problems can be combined to yield solutions of certain two- and three-dimensional transient systems. As an example, consider the heating of a long rectangular bar (Fig. 4–17a) initially at a uniform temperature T_o. At

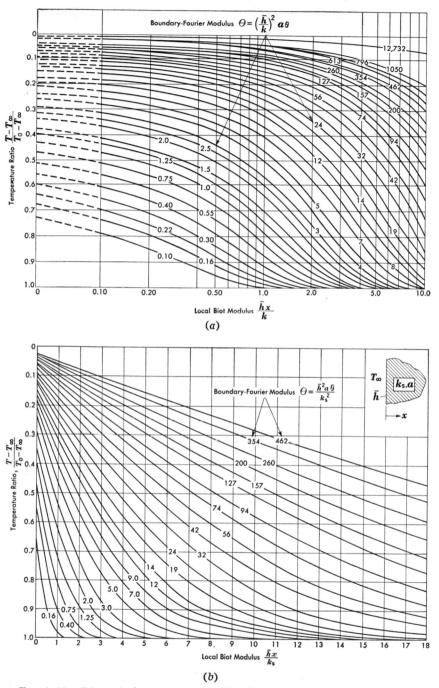

FIG. 4–16. Dimensionless temperature distribution in a semi-infinite slab subjected to a sudden change in environmental temperature. (By permission from L. M. K. Boelter, V. H. Cherry, and H. A. Johnson, *Heat Transfer*, 3d ed., 1942)

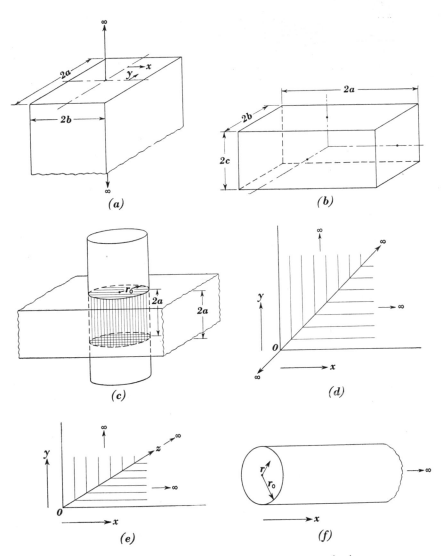

(a) Co-ordinate system for infinitely long rectangular bar.
(b) Co-ordinate system for brick-shaped body.
(c) Co-ordinate system for finite cylinder.
(d) Co-ordinate system for quarter-infinite body.
(e) Co-ordinate system for eighth-infinite body.
(f) Co-ordinate system for semi-infinite cylinder.

FIG. 4–17. Sketches illustrating two- and three-dimensional systems amenable to product solutions.

time $\theta = 0$, the rod is placed into an environment at a temperature T_∞. The unit-surface conductance over both of the longer sides is $\bar{h}_a$, over both of the shorter sides, $\bar{h}_b$.

If we compare this problem with the heating of a large plate of width $2b$, it is physically obvious that the heat flow from the shorter sides accelerates the heating. It can be shown (see, for example, Refs. 1 and 2) that the effect of the shorter sides on the solution for an infinitely long plate of width $2b$ can also be expressed in the form of a product solution. In other words, to obtain the temperature-time history of the rectangular bar we need only multiply the dimensionless temperature ratios for two infinite plates, one $2b$, the other $2a$ wide. Symbolically we write

$$\left(\frac{T - T_\infty}{T_0 - T_\infty}\right)_{\text{bar}} = \left(\frac{T - T_\infty}{T_0 - T_\infty}\right)_{2a \text{ plate}} \left(\frac{T - T_\infty}{T_0 - T_\infty}\right)_{2b \text{ plate}} \qquad \textbf{(4-50)}$$

where the temperature ratios at the respective locations for any point in the system may be taken from Fig. 4–8 at *corresponding time parameters*. The Biot moduli are of course different for the two infinite plates from which the solution to the rectangular bar is formed.

Example 4–8. In the design of fire-fighting equipment it is necessary to know how long wooden beams can be exposed to fire before they ignite. The beams are long, 2 by 4 in. in cross section, and initially at a uniform temperature of 60 F. The physical properties of the wood are as follows:

$$\rho = 50 \text{ lb/cu ft}$$
$$c = 0.6 \text{ Btu/lb F}$$
$$k = 0.2 \text{ Btu/hr ft F}$$

At the instant the fire breaks out, the beams are exposed to gases at 1200 F and the unit-surface conductance is 3.0 Btu/hr sq ft F over all of the faces. Estimate the time elapsed before the wood reaches the ignition temperature of 800 F.

Solution: The dimensionless temperature ratio when $T = 800$ F is

$$\frac{T - T_\infty}{T_0 - T_\infty} = \frac{800 \text{ F} - 1200 \text{ F}}{60 \text{ F} - 1200 \text{ F}} = 0.35$$

According to Eq. 4–50, the temperature ratio for this rectangular beam equals the product of the temperature ratios for two large plates, one of them 4 in., the other, 2 in. thick, or

$$\frac{T - T_\infty}{T_0 - T_\infty} = 0.35 = \left(\frac{T - T_\infty}{T_0 - T_\infty}\right)_{\text{4-in. plate}} \left(\frac{T - T_\infty}{T_0 - T_\infty}\right)_{\text{2-in. plate}}$$

To obtain the time required for the temperature to reach 800 F we use the charts of Fig. 4–8. The surface will reach 800 F first and therefore the graphs for $x/L = 1$ apply. The solution, however, cannot be obtained directly, but requires some trial and error. We assume various values of time, use Fig. 4–8 to determine the temperature ratios for each of the plates, and multiply these ratios. The value of θ at which the product equals 0.35 is the desired answer.

Assuming $\theta = 0.5$ hr, $a\theta/L^2$ of the wider plate is

$$\frac{a\theta}{L^2} = \frac{k\theta}{c\rho L^2} = \frac{(0.2 \text{ Btu/hr ft F})(0.5 \text{ hr})(12^2 \text{ sq in./sq ft})}{(0.6 \text{ Btu/lb F})(50 \text{ lb/cu ft})(2^2 \text{ sq in.})} = 0.12$$

and since $k/\bar{h}L$ is equal to 0.4, we have

$$\left(\frac{T - T_\infty}{T_o - T_\infty}\right)_{\text{4-in. plate}} = 0.48$$

from the graph for $x/L = 1.0$ in Fig. 4–8. Similarly, for the other plate ($L = 1$ in.) we find at $\theta = 0.5$

$$\left(\frac{T - T_\infty}{T_o - T_\infty}\right)_{\text{2-in. plate}} = 0.27$$

Then the temperature ratio for the wooden beam at $\theta = 0.5$ is

$$\frac{T - T_\infty}{T_o - T_\infty} = (0.27)(0.48) = 0.13$$

Since this is less than 0.35, the assumed value of θ is too large. Repeating the calculations for $\theta = 0.10$, we find that the surface temperature reaches 800 F during this time. *Ans.*

It is suggested that the reader fill in the remaining steps and verify the answer.

The extension of the product solution to a brick-shaped solid (Fig. 4–17b) leads to

$$\left(\frac{T - T_\infty}{T_o - T_\infty}\right)_{\text{brick}} = \left(\frac{T - T_\infty}{T_o - T_\infty}\right)_{2a \text{ plate}} \left(\frac{T - T_\infty}{T_o - T_\infty}\right)_{2b \text{ plate}} \left(\frac{T - T_\infty}{T_o - T_\infty}\right)_{2c \text{ plate}}$$

$$(4\text{–}51)$$

For a cylinder of finite length (Fig. 4–17c) the dimensionless temperature ratio is obtained by forming the product of the temperature ratios for an infinite cylinder and an infinite plate of a width equal to the length of the cylinder, or

$$\left(\frac{T - T_\infty}{T_o - T_\infty}\right)_{\text{cyl } 2a \text{ long}} = \left(\frac{T - T_\infty}{T_o - T_\infty}\right)_{\text{infinite cyl}} \left(\frac{T - T_\infty}{T_o - T_\infty}\right)_{2a \text{ plate}} \qquad (4\text{–}52)$$

When using the above product solutions, it should be noted that, to satisfy the boundary conditions of the one-dimensional problems to which the charts apply, the coordinates of a two- or three-dimensional system must lie along the axes of symmetry and intersect at the center of the body.

In a similar manner the solution for the semi-infinite body can be used to build up solutions for a quarter-infinite body (Fig. 4–17d), an eighth-infinite body (Fig. 4–17e) and a semi-infinite cylinder (Fig. 4–17f). Using the notation of Fig. 4–17 the respective solutions are

$$\left(\frac{T - T_\infty}{T_o - T_\infty}\right)_{x, y} = \left(\frac{T - T_\infty}{T_o - T_\infty}\right)_x \left(\frac{T - T_\infty}{T_o - T_\infty}\right)_y \qquad (4\text{–}53)$$

for a quarter-infinite body (an edge bounded by two planes),

$$\left(\frac{T - T_\infty}{T_o - T_\infty}\right)_{x,\,y,\,z} = \left(\frac{T - T_\infty}{T_o - T_\infty}\right)_x \left(\frac{T - T_\infty}{T_o - T_\infty}\right)_y \left(\frac{T - T_\infty}{T_o - T_\infty}\right)_z \quad \textbf{(4-54)}$$

for an eighth-infinite body (a corner bounded by three planes), and

$$\left(\frac{T - T_\infty}{T_o - T_\infty}\right)_{r,\,x} = \left(\frac{T - T_\infty}{T_o - T_\infty}\right)_r \left(\frac{T - T_\infty}{T_o - T_\infty}\right)_x \quad \textbf{(4-55)}$$

for a semi-infinite cylinder of outer radius r_o.

4-6. GRAPHICAL METHOD

In this section we shall take up a graphical method for solving unsteady-heat-conduction problems. This technique, known as the *Schmidt plot*, requires only the simplest mathematics, but its accuracy depends on the number of approximations used in the solution. The Schmidt method is very flexible and yields practical solutions to problems which have such complicated boundary conditions that they could not be handled conveniently by analytical methods.

Plane wall. As an illustration of this method, consider an infinitely thick wall having a plane face whose temperature is constant at T_s. The temperature distribution at a certain time $\theta = 0$ is represented by the heavy dashed line in Fig. 4-18. We shall find the temperature distribution and the heat-flow rate into the wall as a function of time by means of the Schmidt plot.

First, we divide the wall into layers, each of them Δx thick, and label the cross-sectional planes between layers by integers as shown in Fig. 4-18. Then we replace the continuous curve representing the temperature distribution at $\theta = 0$ by short straight lines between sectional planes 1, 2, 3, etc., each line having a slope closely approximating the temperature gradient at the center of the layer. It is obvious from an inspection of Fig. 4-18 that the representation of the temperature curve can be made more exact by using smaller Δx subdivisions. Since a temperature difference exists, heat will flow from the higher to the lower temperature at a rate proportional to the temperature gradient. In the first layer the average initial temperature gradient is $(T_s^o - T_1^o)/\Delta x$ and in the second layer it is $(T_1^o - T_2^o)/\Delta x$. During a time interval $\Delta\theta$, heat is therefore conducted from the surface to cross-sectional plane 1 and also from plane 1 to plane 2. The amount of heat flowing *toward* plane 1 is greater than the amount of heat flowing *from* the same plane, as seen from an inspection of the respective temperature gradients. The difference between the heat flow to and the heat flow from cross-sectional plane 1 changes the internal energy in a layer ab extending $\Delta x/2$ to the left and to the right of plane 1. Writing an energy balance for the time interval $\Delta\theta$ on the basis of a unit area, the semantic expression is

Heat flow toward sectional plane 1 during $\Delta\theta$	$-$	heat flow from sectional plane 1 during $\Delta\theta$	$=$	change in internal energy in layer ab during $\Delta\theta$

and the algebraic expression is

$$k \frac{T_s^0 - T_1^0}{\Delta x} \Delta\theta - k \frac{T_1^0 - T_2^0}{\Delta x} \Delta\theta = c\rho\Delta x(T_1^1 - T_1^0) \qquad \text{(4–56)}$$

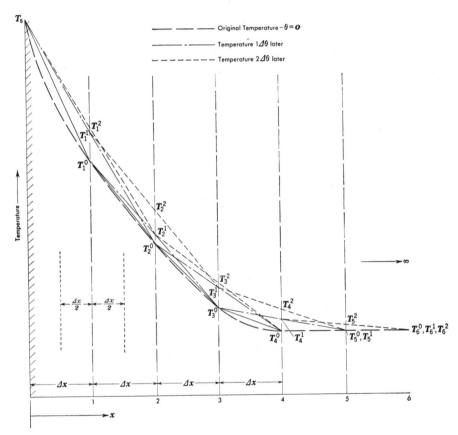

FIG. 4–18. Schmidt plot in an infinitely thick wall.

where the superscript indicates the time and the subscript the location (e.g., T_1^1 is the temperature at the plane 1 after a time interval equal to one $\Delta\theta$ has elapsed).   Dividing each term of Eq. 4–56 by $k\Delta\theta/2\Delta x$ yields

$$\frac{T_s^0 - T_2^0}{2} - T_1^0 = (T_1^1 - T_1^0) \frac{c\rho\Delta x^2}{2k\Delta\theta} \qquad \text{(4–57)}$$

We now select for convenience Δx and $\Delta \theta$ so that

$$\frac{\Delta x^2}{2a\Delta\theta} = \frac{c\rho\Delta x^2}{2k\Delta\theta} = 1 \qquad (4\text{-}58)$$

With this relationship, Δx is fixed by the choice of $\Delta\theta$, and vice versa. When Eq. 4–57 is now solved for $T_1{}^1$, the temperature at plane 1 after a time interval $\Delta\theta$ has elapsed, $T_1{}^0$ disappears and we have

$$T_1{}^1 = \frac{T_s{}^0 - T_2{}^0}{2} \qquad (4\text{-}59)$$

We see that the choice of Δx and $\Delta\theta$ in accordance with Eq. 4–58 has eliminated $T_1{}^0$ in Eq. 4–57, and the new temperature $T_1{}^1$ is simply equal to the arithmetic mean of the temperatures in the planes on each side of section 1. Consequently, if we draw a straight line connecting $T_s{}^0$ and $T_2{}^0$, its intersection with section 1 is the temperature $T_1{}^1$ at sectional plane 1 after a time interval $\Delta\theta$ has elapsed.

In the same manner it can be shown that the temperature in any plane at a time $(t + 1)\Delta\theta$ is the arithmetic mean of the temperatures in the planes on each side of it at $t\,\Delta\theta$, or

$$T_n{}^{t+1} = \frac{T_{n-1}{}^t + T_{n+1}{}^t}{2} \qquad (4\text{-}60)$$

where the superscript t refers to the number of time intervals $\Delta\theta$ and the subscript n to location. Figure 4–18 illustrates the graphical construction by which the approximate temperature distributions at times $1\Delta\theta$ and $2\Delta\theta$ are obtained. It is interesting to note that the effect of the higher surface temperature is not felt at section 6 until $3\Delta\theta$'s have elapsed.

The rate of heat flow per unit area into the slab at any instant $(q/A)^t$ can be obtained from the slope of the temperature gradient between the surface and section 1, that is

$$\left(\frac{q}{A}\right)^t = k\frac{T_s{}^t - T_1{}^t}{\Delta x} \qquad (4\text{-}61)$$

From a mathematical point of view, the Schmidt plot is a step-by-step solution of the unsteady conduction equation in one dimension,

$$\frac{1}{a}\frac{\partial T}{\partial \theta} = \frac{\partial^2 T}{\partial x^2} \qquad [4\text{-}23]$$

Equation 4–60 can be obtained from Eq. 4–23 by writing the latter as a finite difference equation (i.e., for finite $\Delta\theta$ and Δx), or

$$\frac{1}{a}\frac{\Delta_\theta T}{\Delta\theta} = \frac{\Delta_x{}^2 T}{\Delta x^2} \qquad (4\text{-}62)$$

where the subscripts θ and x indicate whether the time θ or the location x is the variable effecting the change in T.   If we again adopt the subscript and superscript notation to indicate time and location, we can write the left-hand side of Eq. 4–62 as

$$\frac{1}{a}\frac{\Delta_\theta T}{\Delta\theta} = \frac{1}{a}\frac{T_n^{t+1} - T_n^{t}}{\Delta\theta} \tag{4-63}$$

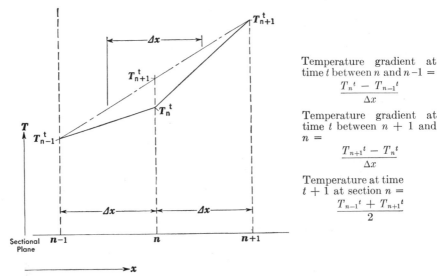

Temperature gradient at time t between n and $n-1$ =
$$\frac{T_n^{t} - T_{n-1}^{t}}{\Delta x}$$

Temperature gradient at time t between $n + 1$ and n =
$$\frac{T_{n+1}^{t} - T_n^{t}}{\Delta x}$$

Temperature at time $t + 1$ at section n =
$$\frac{T_{n-1}^{t} + T_{n+1}^{t}}{2}$$

FIG. 4–19.   Second derivative by finite difference method.

The second derivative of T with respect to x is actually the change of the slope $\Delta T/\Delta x$ with distance x at a given time.   This can be expressed in finite difference form (Fig. 4–19) as

$$\frac{\Delta_x^2 T}{\Delta x^2} = \frac{\Delta_x\left(\dfrac{\Delta T}{\Delta x}\right)}{\Delta x} = \frac{\dfrac{T_{n+1}^{t} - T_n^{t}}{\Delta x} - \dfrac{T_n^{t} - T_{n-1}^{t}}{\Delta x}}{\Delta x} \tag{4-64}[5]$$

Substituting Eqs. 4–63 and 4–64 into Eq. 4–62 yields

$$\frac{1}{a}\frac{T_n^{t+1} - T_n^{t}}{\Delta\theta} = \frac{T_{n+1}^{t} - 2T_n^{t} + T_{n-1}^{t}}{\Delta x^2} \tag{4-65}$$

If we now select the time interval $\Delta\theta$ or the distance Δx in accordance with Eq. 4–58, the above expression reduces to Eq. 4–60.

Example 4–9.   Determine the thickness of asbestos required to protect a large safe against fire.   For an initial temperature of 100 F, the temperature at the inner surface

[5] For a discussion of the errors incurred in the solution of Eq. 4–23 by graphical or numerical methods, see Ref. 1.

should remain below 300 F for 1 hr after the exterior temperature is suddenly raised to 1500 F. The asbestos is to be placed between two steel plates of $\frac{1}{16}$-in. thickness. The effects of corners may be neglected. Average physical properties pertinent to the system are listed below (see Tables A–1 and A–2).

Asbestos

$k = 0.087$ Btu/hr ft F

$c = 0.25$ Btu/lb F

$\rho = 36$ lb/cu ft

Steel

$k = 26$ Btu/hr ft F

Solution: Since the steel plate has a thermal conductivity about 300 times greater than that of the asbestos and is also relatively thin, it offers no appreciable resistance to the heat flow and has only a small thermal capacity. Therefore, we need only to analyze the temperature-time history in the asbestos. We first divide the asbestos wall into five equal layers, the number of layers being arbitrarily selected. The layer thickness will be evaluated from Eq. 4–58 after the number of time intervals required for the inner surface to reach 300 F has been found.

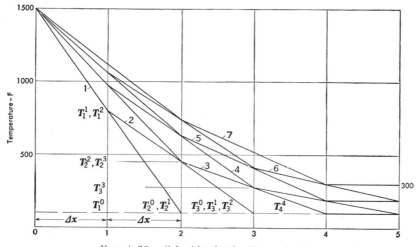

FIG. 4–20. Schmidt plot for Example 4–9.

The graphical construction of the Schmidt plot is shown in Fig. 4–20. A straight line between section 0 and 2 yields the approximate temperature at plane 1 after $\Delta\theta$ has elasped. The next step consists of connecting T_1^1 and T_3^1 by a straight line which yields T_2^2. It should be noted that in this problem, as in any other problem in which the initial temperature throughout the body is constant, the temperature at any plane separating two adjacent layers changes only during alternate periods.

After four periods have elapsed, the temperature at the inner surface begins to rise. The temperature in the interior of the safe will be assumed to be equal to the temperature at the inner wall surface. This boundary condition demands that the temperature gradient at the inner surface be zero. Accordingly, we find the temperature at the inner surface at the end of the fifth time interval by constructing a horizontal line from T_4^4.

If the construction is continued in this manner, after the end of the seventh time interval the temperature at the inner surface is seen to reach almost 300 F.   To meet the specifications seven $\Delta\theta$'s must therefore equal 1 hr, or

$$\Delta\theta = \frac{1}{7}\ \mathrm{hr}$$

Substituting this value for $\Delta\theta$ and the numerical constants for the asbestos properties c, ρ, and k in Eq. 4–58 yields

$$\Delta x^2 = \frac{2k\Delta\theta}{c\rho} = (2)(0.087/7)(0.25)(36) = 0.00276\ \mathrm{sq\ ft}$$

Hence, the thickness of one layer is 0.0475 ft and the total thickness of asbestos required for 1-hr protection is five times that value, or about $2\frac{7}{8}$ in.   *Ans.*

In the foregoing example it was assumed that the surface temperature does not vary with time.   The more usual condition, however, is one where the surface of a wall is in contact with a fluid whose temperature is either constant or a known function of time.   The graphical method can easily be extended to permit solution of these cases.   The boundary condition for this type of problem can be stated as follows.   *At any instance, the heat flowing by convection from the fluid to the surface must be equal to the heat flowing by conduction from the surface toward plane 1.*   We can express this boundary condition symbolically as

$$\left.\frac{q}{A}\right|_{\mathrm{at}\ x\,=\,0} = \bar{h}(T_\infty - T_o) = -k_s\left.\frac{\partial T}{\partial x}\right|_{\mathrm{at}\ x\,=\,0} \tag{4–66}$$

where q/A is the rate of heat flow per unit area; $\bar{h}$, the unit-surface conductance; k_s, the thermal conductivity of the solid; T_∞, the fluid temperature far away from the surface; T_o, the surface temperature and $(\partial T/\partial x)|_{\mathrm{at}\ x\,=\,0}$, the temperature gradient at the surface.

In the graphical solution, the boundary condition expressed by Eq. 4–66 can be handled very simply by writing it in the form of a difference equation as

$$\left(\frac{\partial T}{\partial x}\right)_o^t = \frac{T_o{}^t - T_\infty{}^t}{k_s/\bar{h}} \tag{4–67}$$

Equation 4–67 states that, at any time $t\Delta\theta$, the temperature gradient at the surface $(\partial T/\partial x)_o{}^t$, must be equal to the temperature difference between the surface and the fluid, $T_o{}^t - T_\infty{}^t$, divided by $k_s/\bar{h}$.   The fraction $k_s/\bar{h}$ has the dimensions of length and $(T_o{}^t - T_\infty{}^t)/(k_s/\bar{h})$ is therefore equivalent to a temperature gradient.   In the graphical construction we simply extend the solid by the distance $k_s/\bar{h}$ and draw the temperature curve as a continuous straight line between the temperature at plane 1 through the surface of the solid to the temperature of the fluid $T_\infty{}^t$ at a distance $k_s/\bar{h}$ from the surface.   The extension of the wall represents physically the thermal resistance between the surface and the fluid.   It should be noted that this resistance is not combined with a thermal capacity. The fictitious distance $k_s/\bar{h}$ is therefore not subdivided in the construction of the temperature lines.[6]

To clarify this point we shall draw an electrical circuit analogous to the thermal circuit under consideration. In Fig. 4–21 each layer of the slab is represented by a capacity C_e and resistances $R_e/2$ on each side of it. The resistance R_s between the first layer and the voltage supply corresponds to the thermal resistance between the fluid and the solid surface. The voltage potential E_∞ is analogous to the difference between the fluid and the original slab-temperature. Closing the switch in the electrical system is analogous to exposing the slab to a fluid at temperature T_∞.

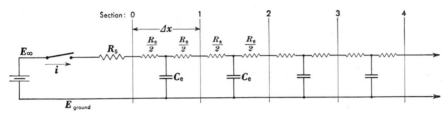

FIG. 4–21.   Analogous electrical circuit for a wall subdivided into finite sections.

The flow of current is analogous to the flow of heat, and the charging of the condensers corresponds to increasing the internal energy stored in the finite layers of the slab. Electrical networks similar to the one shown in Fig. 4–21 have been used in practice to obtain solutions to a variety of transient-heat-transfer problems. For a detailed description of the construction and application of these so-called *thermal analyzers* see Refs. 4, 5, 6, and 15.

Example 4–10.   A steel casting (k_s = 10 Btu/hr ft F, a = 0.48 sq ft/hr) having the shape of a large plate 12 in. thick is to be heat-treated in an air furnace. The casting, originally at 100 F, is suddenly put into the furnace where the temperature is 3000 F. If the unit-surface conductance is 25 Btu/hr sq ft F, determine the time required for the center to reach 700 F. Neglect end effects.

Solution: The plate is first divided into 12 layers, each having a thickness of 1 in. The thermal resistance at the surface is then represented by an extension of the plate thickness by a distance of

$$\frac{k}{\bar{h}} = \frac{10 \text{ Btu/hr ft F}}{25 \text{ Btu/hr sq ft F}} \, 12 \frac{\text{in.}}{\text{ft}} = 4.8 \text{ in.}$$

The steps of the graphical solution are shown in Fig. 4–22. To start the construction, a straight line is drawn between the fluid temperature at a plane 4.8 in. from the surface and the temperature of the casting at plane 1. This line is taken as the tempera-

---

[6] Some refinements for handling the conditions at the solid-fluid interface have been suggested by Jakob (3). However, if the solid is divided into sufficiently thin sections, the method presented here is satisfactory in practice.

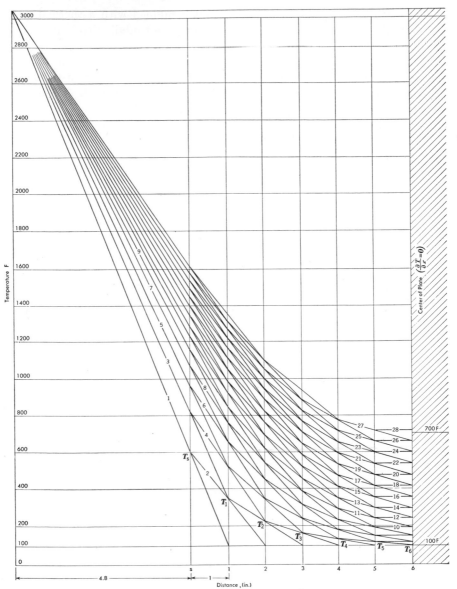

FIG. 4–22. Schmidt plot for Example 4–10.

ture distribution at time $\Delta\theta$ after the casting has been put into the furnace. Because of the symmetry, only the left half of the plate is considered, and the temperature planes 5 and 7 are identical. Accordingly, the temperatures in the center, i.e., plane 6, are determined by connecting corresponding points in planes 5 and 7. For example, the temperature in the center after 11 $\Delta\theta$'s have elapsed is found by connecting the points representing the temperatures in planes 5 and 7 after 10 $\Delta\theta$'s have elapsed.

In accordance with Eq. 4–58, the time increment between steps is

$$\Delta\theta = \frac{\Delta x^2}{2a} = \frac{12 \text{ sq in.}}{(2)(0.48 \text{ sq ft/hr})} \frac{1}{144} \frac{\text{sq ft}}{\text{sq in.}} = 0.00724 \text{ hr}$$

The integers on the individual lines in Fig. 4–22 indicate the number of $\Delta\theta$'s which have elapsed.   The time required for the center to reach 700 F is about $28\Delta\theta$'s or 12 min.   *Ans.*

As another illustration of the Schmidt method we shall apply the technique to a problem where the boundary condition varies with time. The general approach used in this case can be extended to problems involving periodic variation of the environmental temperature.

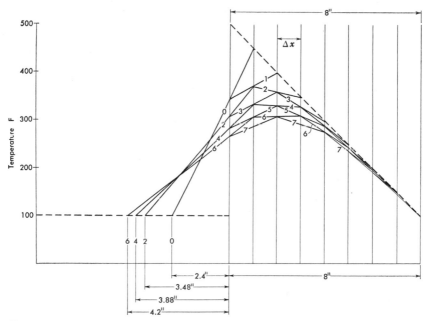

FIG. 4–23.   Schmidt plot for time dependent boundary condition—Example 4–11.

Example 4–11.   A large plastic plate, 8 in. thick, is exposed to a hot environment on one side and a cold environment on the other.   The temperature distribution under steady-state conditions is a straight line, as shown in Fig. 4–23 by heavy dashes.   The temperature on the hot side is suddenly reduced to 100 F and the heat-transfer coefficient on this side depends upon the temperature difference between the surface and the fluid, as given by the expression

$$\bar{h} = 2.0 + 0.02 \, (T_s - T_\infty)$$

Determine the temperature-time history in the plate if $k_s = 2.0$ Btu/hr ft F and $a = 0.003$ sq ft/hr.

Solution: In this problem the boundary condition varies with time.   Therefore, we shall change the resistance at the surface with time.   This can be done conveniently by preparing a table which can be completed as the construction of the Schmidt plot progresses. In this table we shall record the time in terms of $\Delta\theta$'s elapsed, the surface temperature (read from the plot), the heat-transfer coefficient, and the effective surface resistance. By dividing the wall into eight layers, $\Delta x = 1$ in. $= 0.0833$ ft and, from Eq. 4–58, $\Delta\theta = 1.16$ hr. The fictitious surface resistance is $k/\bar{h}$ as in the previous example. The first six steps of the solution are shown in Fig. 4–23 and the following table.

$\Delta\theta$	T_s(F)	$T_s - T_\infty$ (F)	$\bar{h}\left(\dfrac{\text{Btu}}{\text{hr sq ft F}}\right)$	$\dfrac{k}{\bar{h}} \times 12$ (in.)
0	500	400	10	2.4
2	345	245	6.9	3.48
4	310	210	6.2	3.88
6	285	185	5.7	4.2

Composite walls.[7] The graphical method can also be extended to problems in transient heat flow through composite walls. This type of problem is rather difficult to solve analytically, and we shall therefore develop the graphical technique in detail.

In the basic equation for unidimensional transient heat flow

$$\frac{\partial T}{\partial \theta} = \frac{k}{\rho c}\frac{\partial^2 T}{\partial x^2}$$

the variable x can be replaced by ζ where

$$\zeta = \frac{x}{k} \quad \text{and} \quad \Delta\zeta = \frac{\Delta x}{k}$$

Using ζ instead of x, the heat-conduction equation becomes

$$\frac{\partial T}{\partial \theta} = \frac{1}{k\rho c}\frac{\partial^2 T}{\partial \zeta^2}$$

In finite-difference form, which is suitable for the graphical method, this equation is

$$\frac{\Delta_\theta T}{\Delta\theta} = \frac{1}{k\rho c}\frac{\Delta_\zeta^2 T}{\Delta\zeta^2}$$

Using the subscript notation and repeating the development of Eq. 4–65 we obtain

$$T_n{}^{t+1} = \frac{2\Delta\theta}{k\rho c\Delta\zeta^2}\left(\frac{T_{n+1}{}^t + T_{n-1}{}^t}{2}\right) \tag{4-68}$$

[7] The rest of this section may be omitted without breaking the continuity of the presentation.

The reason for changing the variable x to ζ is to avoid any discontinuity in the graphical construction at the interface between the slabs I and II.   At this interface, we must have continuity of heat flow, that is,

$$\left(-k\frac{\Delta T}{\Delta x}\right)_{\mathrm{I}} = \left(-k\frac{\Delta T}{\Delta x}\right)_{\mathrm{II}} \tag{4-69}$$

Clearly, if k_{I} is not equal to k_{II}, there will be a discontinuity in the temperature gradient.   This inconvenience has been overcome by changing the variables.   If we use ζ instead of x in Eq. 4–69, the boundary condition at the interface becomes

$$\left(\frac{\Delta T}{\Delta \zeta}\right)_{\mathrm{I}} = \left(\frac{\Delta T}{\Delta \zeta}\right)_{\mathrm{II}} \tag{4-70}$$

Hence, we simply divide each slab into equal increments of $\Delta\zeta$ and then use the Schmidt technique in the same manner as before.   That is, we select $\Delta\theta$ so that

$$\frac{2\Delta\theta}{k\rho c\Delta\zeta^2} = 1 \tag{4-71}$$

In order that the $\Delta\theta$ increments in both materials be the same, we must also satisfy the requirement that

$$\frac{\Delta\theta_{\mathrm{I}}}{\Delta\theta_{\mathrm{II}}} = 1 = \frac{k\rho c(\Delta\zeta)_{\mathrm{II}}^2}{k\rho c(\Delta\zeta)_{\mathrm{I}}^2} \tag{4-72}$$

or

$$\frac{\Delta\zeta_{\mathrm{I}}}{\Delta\zeta_{\mathrm{II}}} = \sqrt{\frac{(k\rho c)_{\mathrm{II}}}{(k\rho c)_{\mathrm{I}}}}$$

In terms of Δx, the above relation is

$$\frac{\Delta x_{\mathrm{I}}}{\Delta x_{\mathrm{II}}} = \sqrt{\frac{a_{\mathrm{I}}}{a_{\mathrm{II}}}} \tag{4-73}$$

Example 4–12.   A special type of combustion chamber intended for repeated short-time operations consists of an interior layer of alumina refractory $\frac{1}{4}$ in. thick and an outer layer of stainless steel 1.0 in. thick.   The following properties are given.

Refractory (r)	Steel (s)
$k_r = 2$ Btu/hr ft F	$k_s = 10$ Btu/hr ft F
$a_r = 0.05$ sq ft/hr	$a_s = 0.20$ sq ft/hr

There is no external cooling, and the walls will fail if the refractory reaches a temperature of 3000 F or the steel a temperature of 1600 F.   If the heat-transfer coefficient between the hot gases and the inner lining is 15 Btu/hr ft F, determine the total time of operation possible if the initial temperature is 100 F and the combustion gases reach 5000 F almost instantaneously after ignition.

Solution: From Eq. 4–73 we have

$$\frac{\Delta x_s}{\Delta x_r} = \sqrt{\frac{a_s}{a_r}} = \sqrt{4} = 2$$

If we arbitrarily divide the refractory wall into five equal parts ($\Delta x = 0.05$ in./(12 in./ft) $= 0.00417$ ft), the Δx for the steel will be $0.00417 \times 2.0 = 0.00834$ ft and there will be 10 layers in 1.0 in.   However the actual width of each layer in the plot will be $\Delta x/k$,

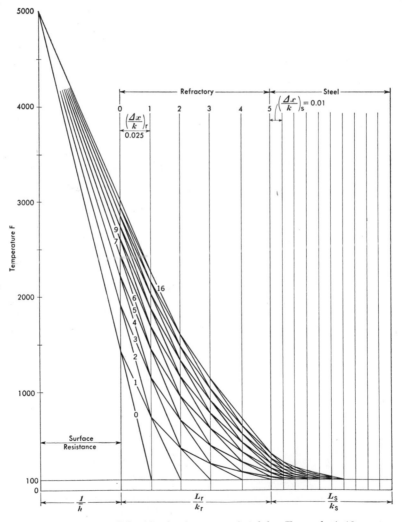

FIG. 4–24.   Schmidt plot for composite slab—Example 4–12.

and a convenient way to lay out the slices is to begin with a slab of refractory $L_r/k_r =$ 0.25/2 = 0.125 units thick and a steel slab $L_s/k_s =$ 1.0/10 = 0.10 units thick and divide these into 5 and 10 layers respectively as shown in Fig. 4–24. Now the problem is to describe the boundary condition between the gas and the refractory. Neglecting contact resistance this boundary condition can be written as

$$q = k\frac{\Delta T}{\Delta x}\bigg|_{\text{at }x\,=\,0} = \frac{\Delta T}{\Delta \zeta}\bigg|_{\text{at }\zeta\,=\,0} = \bar{h}(T_{\zeta=0} - T_\infty) = \frac{T_{\zeta=0} - T_\infty}{1/\bar{h}}$$

Thus, using the ζ coordinate system, the surface resistance is represented by an extension of the refractory equal to $1/\bar{h}$ units. Then, if the temperature curve is continued at the slope equal to that at the surface, (i.e., at $\zeta = 0$), it will reach the gas temperature a distance $1/\bar{h}$ from the surface. The details of the solution are illustrated in Fig. 4–24.

We begin the construction at time 0 by drawing a straight line between the edge of the extended refractory at 5000 F and plane 1 at 100 F. Then we find the new temperatures and continue in the usual manner. The numbers on the lines indicate the time in terms of $\Delta\theta$'s elapsed. We note that the surface temperature will reach 3000 F after 16 $\Delta\theta$'s. At this time the steel has only reached a temperature of 600 F, from which we conclude that the critical design parameter is the refractory.

To determine $\Delta\theta$ we use Eq. 4–71

$$\Delta\theta = \frac{k\rho c\Delta\zeta^2}{2} = \frac{\Delta x^2}{2a_r}\left(3600\,\frac{\text{sec}}{\text{hr}}\right) = 0.625 \text{ sec}$$

Hence, the safe operating time for the liner will be 16 $\Delta\theta$'s = 10 sec.   *Ans.*

If the liner were replaced by a material of similar conductivity, specific heat, and density, but capable of withstanding 3500 F, the operating time could be more than doubled. If the refractory could withstand 3800 F, the steel would reach a temperature of 1600 F before the liner would fail.

Long cylinder. The Schmidt method can also be applied to long solid or hollow cylinders. If the wall of a hollow cylinder is thin, it is usually satisfactory to treat it as a plate, but for long solid circular cylinders or thick-walled hollow cylinders, Eq. 4–44 must be used. The equation

$$\frac{\partial T}{\partial \theta} = a\left(\frac{\partial^2 T}{\partial r^2} + \frac{1}{r}\frac{\partial T}{\partial r}\right) \qquad [4\text{–}44]$$

can be transformed into a finite-difference equation, similar to Eq. 4–60, if we let

$$\eta = \ln r \qquad (4\text{–}74)$$

so that

$$\frac{d\eta}{dr} = \frac{1}{r} \qquad (4\text{–}75)$$

Using Eq. 4–75, the temperature gradient is then written as

$$\frac{\partial T}{\partial r} = \frac{\partial T}{\partial \eta}\frac{d\eta}{dr} = \frac{1}{r}\frac{\partial T}{\partial \eta}$$

and the second derivative of T with respect to r as

$$\frac{\partial^2 T}{\partial r^2} = \frac{\partial}{\partial r}\left(\frac{\partial T}{\partial r}\right) = \frac{\partial}{\partial r}\left(\frac{1}{r}\frac{\partial T}{\partial \eta}\right) = \frac{\partial}{\partial \eta}\left(\frac{1}{r}\frac{\partial T}{\partial \eta}\right)\frac{d\eta}{dr}$$

Differentiating the last term yields

$$\frac{\partial^2 T}{\partial r^2} = \left[\frac{1}{r}\frac{\partial^2 T}{\partial \eta^2} + \frac{\partial T}{\partial \eta}\frac{\partial(1/r)}{\partial \eta}\right]\frac{1}{r} \tag{4-76}$$

If we now use Eq. 4–74 to write

$$r = e^{\eta} \quad \text{or} \quad \frac{1}{r} = e^{-\eta}$$

and

$$\frac{\partial}{\partial \eta}\left(\frac{1}{r}\right) = \frac{\partial}{\partial \eta}\left(e^{-\eta}\right) = -e^{-\eta} = -\frac{1}{r}$$

and then replace $-1/r$ in Eq. 4–76 by $(\partial/\partial\eta)\,(1/r)$, we obtain

$$\frac{\partial^2 T}{\partial r^2} = \frac{1}{r^2}\frac{\partial^2 T}{\partial \eta^2} - \frac{1}{r^2}\frac{\partial T}{\partial \eta} \tag{4-77}$$

Substituting Eq. 4–77 for $\partial^2 T/\partial r^2$ in Eq. 4–44 yields

$$\frac{\partial T}{\partial \theta} = a\left(\frac{1}{r^2}\frac{\partial^2 T}{\partial \eta^2}\right) \tag{4-78}$$

since the terms $(1/r^2)\,(\partial T/\partial\eta)$ cancel. Finally, Eq. 4–78 is written in finite-difference form as

$$\frac{T_n{}^{t+1} - T_n{}^t}{\Delta\theta} = \frac{a}{r^2}\left(\frac{T_{n+1}{}^t + T_{n-1}{}^t - 2T_n{}^t}{\Delta\eta^2}\right)$$

or

$$T_n{}^{t+1} - T_n{}^t = \frac{2a\Delta\theta}{(r\Delta\eta)^2}\left(\frac{T_{n+1}{}^t + T_{n-1}{}^t}{2} + T_n{}^t\right) \tag{4-79}$$

Selecting $\Delta\theta$ or $r\Delta\eta$ so that

$$\frac{2a\Delta\theta}{(r\Delta\eta)^2} = 1 \tag{4-80}$$

yields the equation

$$T_n{}^{t+1} = \frac{T_{n+1}{}^t + T_{n-1}{}^t}{2} \tag{4-81}$$

which is identical to the expression derived previously for a slab (Eq.

4–60). The graphical construction for the cylinder is therefore the same as that for a wall or a slab. However, instead of layers of equal Δx thickness, Eq. 4–80, the Schmidt rule for the cylinder, prescribes constant increments of $r\Delta\eta$. Since according to Eq. 4–75 $\Delta\eta = \Delta r/r$, we see that each partition of a cylinder for a Schmidt plot has to be $\Delta r/r$ thick. A mean radius for each section is sufficiently accurate in practice. If the initial temperature is not uniform, it must be plotted on a scale corresponding to the $\Delta\eta$ increment, that is, on a logarithmic scale, in accordance with Eq. 4–74.

Example 4–13.   A fluid at 300 F bulk temperature is flowing through an 18–8 stainless-steel, type 347, pipe of 1 in. ID and $2\frac{1}{2}$ in. OD. Initially the temperature at the outer surface of the pipe is 100 F and steady-state conditions prevail. The unit-surface conductance at the inner pipe surface is 250 Btu/hr sq ft F.

If the fluid is suddenly heated, and its temperature increases linearly at the rate of 100 F/sec, determine the temperature distribution in the pipe 6 sec after the heating of the fluid is initiated.

Average physical properties for the stainless-steel pipe are

$$k_s = 10.5 \text{ Btu/hr ft F}$$
$$a_s = 0.197 \text{ sq ft/hr}$$

Solution: The pipe is first divided into six annular sections of $\Delta r = \frac{1}{8}$ in. The corresponding values of $\Delta\eta$ and their calculations are shown in Table 4–1.

TABLE 4–1

Section No.	Inner Radius (in.)	Outer Radius (in.)	Mean Radius (in.)	Mean Radius (ft.)	$\Delta\eta = \Delta r/r$
1	0.500	0.625	0.563	0.0494	0.222
2	0.625	0.750	0.688	0.0573	0.182
3	0.750	0.875	0.813	0.0678	0.154
4	0.875	1.000	0.938	0.0782	0.133
5	1.000	1.125	1.063	0.0886	0.118
6	1.125	1.250	1.188	0.0990	0.105
					0.914

The equivalent resistance at the inner boundary is calculated from the boundary conditions

$$q = \bar{h}(2\pi r_i)(T_\infty - T_o) = 2\pi r_i \left(k \frac{\partial T}{\partial r}\right)_{r = r_i}$$

or

$$\frac{q}{A} = \bar{h}(T_\infty - T_o) = k_s \left(\frac{\partial T}{\partial \eta} \frac{\partial \eta}{\partial r}\right)_{r = r_i} = \frac{k_s}{r_i} \frac{\partial T}{\partial \eta}$$

Following the procedure used previously for the slab, we get at $r = r_i$

$$\frac{\partial T}{\partial \eta} = \frac{T_\infty - T_o}{k/\bar{h}r_i}$$

The distance corresponding to $k/\bar{h}r_i$ is

$$\frac{(10.5 \text{ Btu/hr ft F})(12 \text{ in./ft})}{(250 \text{ Btu/hr sq ft F})(0.5 \text{ in.})} = 1.0$$

The time increment is calculated from Eq. 4–80, or

$$\Delta\theta = \frac{\Delta r^2}{2a} = \frac{(0.125/12)^{12} \text{ sq ft}}{(2)(0.197 \text{ sq ft/hr})} 3600 \text{ sec/hr} = 1.0 \text{ sec}$$

The solution of the problem is the Schmidt plot shown in Fig. 4–25. The accuracy could be improved by selecting smaller time increments.   *Ans.*

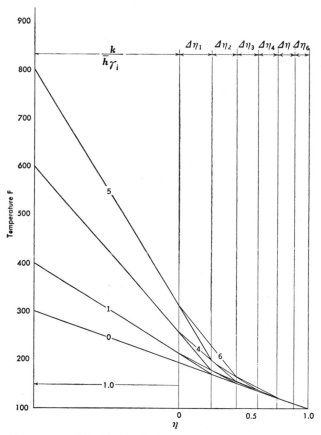

Fig. 4–25.   Schmidt plot for hollow cylinder—Example 4–13.

4–7. NUMERICAL METHOD

The graphical method for solving unsteady heat conduction problems is widely used in industry because it gives a running picture of the changing temperature distribution; its details can be delegated to relatively untrained

personnel, and mistakes—if they occur—are quickly discovered. However, for precise computations, especially when variations of physical
properties with temperature are important, a numerical method should be
used instead of the graphical method. Numerical methods for solving
transient heat conduction problems are treated in detail by Dusinberre (8)
and Schneider (1). We shall consider only the basic elements of the
simplest method. For a detailed discussion of the stability, convergence,
and accuracy of numerical methods, the reader should consult Refs. 1, 13,
and 14.

As shown in the preceding section, Eq. 4–65 is the one-dimensional
transient-heat-conduction equation in finite-difference form. It can also
be written in the form

$$T_n{}^{t+1} = \overline{\Theta} \left[T_{n+1}{}^t + T_{n-1}{}^t + \left(\frac{1}{\overline{\Theta}} - 2 \right) T_n{}^t \right] \tag{4-82}$$

where
$$\overline{\Theta} = k\Delta\theta / c\rho\Delta x^2$$

Equation 4–82 can be used to predict the temperature at section n at time
$(t + 1)\Delta\theta$ from the temperatures at sections $n - 1$, n, and $n + 1$ at time
$t\Delta\theta$.

Theoretically, any value of $\overline{\Theta}$ between 0 and $\frac{1}{2}$ could be selected for
this calculation, but values larger than $\frac{1}{2}$ violate the first law of thermodynamics, as can be seen from Eq. 4–82. In practice, although smaller
values of $\overline{\Theta}$ improve the accuracy, $\overline{\Theta}$ is usually set equal to $\frac{1}{2}$ because this
choice reduces the amount of labor in the computations. With $\overline{\Theta}$ equal
to $\frac{1}{2}$, the numerical method is equivalent to the graphical method, so that
the techniques for handling convection boundary conditions, composite
structures, and cylindrical systems are identical to those described in
Sec. 4–6. However, as shown in Example 4–14, selection of half volumes
at surfaces is necessary for a complete correspondence between the results
of the numerical and graphical methods.

Example 4–14. Determine numerically the temperature distribution in the asbestos
insulation of the safe described in Example 4–9 one hour after the surface temperature
has been raised suddenly from 100 to 1500 F.

Solution: We begin the solution by dividing the asbestos into five equal slices of
thickness $\Delta x = 0.0475$ ft, with half slices at the two surfaces. Selecting $\overline{\Theta} = \frac{1}{2}$, the
time increment in each step of the calculation is

$$\Delta\theta = \Delta x^2 \overline{\Theta} / a = (0.0475)^2 \, (\tfrac{1}{2}) / 0.0079 = 0.143 \text{ hr}$$

The details of numerical solution are illustrated in Table 4–2. The reader should
verify the individual steps and compare his intermediate results with those obtained
previously by the graphical method, whose final results are listed in the last line of the

TABLE 4–2

NUMERICAL SOLUTION FOR EXAMPLE 4–14

θ (hr)	1	2	3	4	5	6
0	1500	100	100	100	100	100
0.143	1500	800	100	100	100	100
0.286	1500	800	450	100	100	100
0.429	1500	975	450	275	100	100
0.572	1500	975	625	275	187.5	100
0.715	1500	1062.5	625	406.25	187.5	187.5
0.858	1500	1062.5	734.375	406.25	286.375	187.5
1.00	1500	1117.1725	734.375	510.00	286.375	286.375
Graphical results	1500	1110	730	508	290	290

table.   The accuracy of the graphical solution was obviously limited by the small scale used in the construction of the temperature curves.

REFERENCES

1.   P. J. Schneider, *Conduction Heat Transfer*.   (Cambridge, Mass.: Addison-Wesley Publishing Company, 1955.)

2.   H. S. Carslaw, and J. C. Jaeger, *Conduction of Heat in Solids*.   (Oxford: Clarendon Press, 1947.)

3.   M. Jakob, *Heat Transfer*, Vol. I.   (New York: John Wiley & Sons, Inc., 1949.)

4.   V. Paschkis and M. D. Baker, "A Method for Determining Unsteady State Heat Transfer by Means of an Electrical Analogy," *Trans. ASME*, Vol. 64 (1942), pp. 105–112.

5.   C. B. Neel, Jr., "An Investigation Utilizing an Electrical Analogue of Cyclic De-Icing of a Hollow Steel Propeller with an External Blade Shoe," *NACA TN* 2852, 1952.

6.   D. I. Lawson and J. H. McGuire, "The Solution of Transient Heat Flow Problems by Analogous Electrical Networks," *Proc. (A) Inst. Mech. Engrs.*, Vol. 167, No. 3 (1953), pp. 275–287.

7.   G. A. Hawkins and J. T. Agnew, "The Solution of Transient Heat Conduction Problems by Finite Differences," *Eng. Bull. Res. Series* 98, Purdue Univ., 1947.

8.   G. M. Dusinberre, *Numerical Analysis of Heat Flow*.   (New York: McGraw-Hill Book Company, Inc., 1949.)

9.   L. M. K. Boelter, V. H. Cherry, and H. A. Johnson, *Heat Transfer*, 3d ed. (Berkeley: University of California Press, 1942.)

10.   H. Gröber, S. Erk, and U. Grigull, *Grundgesetze der Wärmeübertragung*, 3d ed. (Berlin: Springer-Verlag, 1955.)

11.   M. P. Heisler, "Temperature Charts for Induction and Constant Temperature Heating," *Trans. ASME*, Vol. 69 (1947), pp. 227–236.

12.   B. O. Peirce, *A Short Table of Integrals*.   (Boston: Ginn & Company, 1929.)

13.   G. Leppert, "A Stable Numerical Solution for Transient Heat Flow," *J. Am. Soc. Naval Engrs.*, Vol. 65 (1953), pp. 741–752.

14.   C. M. Fowler, "Analysis of Numerical Solutions of Transient Heat Flow Problems," *Quart. Appl. Math.*, Vol. 3 (1945), pp. 361–376.

15.   M. Jakob and G. A. Hawkins, *Elements of Heat Transfer*, 3d ed. (New York: John Wiley & Sons, Inc., 1957.)

PROBLEMS

4-1. Derive the conduction equation for an infinitely long cylinder in the unsteady state without heat generation in cylindrical coordinates starting with an energy balance.

4-2. A copper wire, $\frac{1}{32}$ in. OD, 2 in. long, is placed in an air stream whose temperature rises as $T_{air} = (50 + 25\theta)$ F, where θ is the time in seconds. If the initial temperature of the wire is 50 F, determine its temperature after 2 sec, 10 sec, and 1 min. The unit-surface conductance between the air and the wire is 7 Btu/hr sq ft F.

4-3. In the vulcanization of tires, the carcass is placed into a jig, and steam at 300 F is admitted suddenly to both sides. If the tire thickness is 1 in. and the initial temperature 70 F, estimate the time required for the central layer to reach 270 F.

4-4. The temperature distribution in a 6-in.-thick magnesite wall ($k = 2.2$ Btu/hr ft F, $a = 0.06$ sq ft/hr) is linear, 500 F on the hot side and 100 F on the cold side. At time zero the air temperature on the hot side is suddenly reduced to 100 F. The heat-transfer coefficient between the slab and the air is a function of the temperature difference given by

$$\bar{h} = 2.0 + 0.01 \, (T_{surface} - T_{air}) \qquad \text{Btu/hr sq ft F}$$

Determine by means of the numerical method and the Schmidt method the time required to cool the hot side to 200 F.   *Ans.* ~ 1 hr

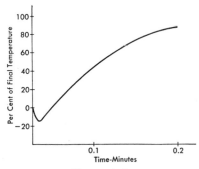

PROB. 4-5.

4-5. The metal bulb of a mercury-filled expansion thermometer is suddenly dipped into a hot fluid. The resulting temperature record is shown in the accompanying sketch. Explain the initial dip with reference to the heat-transfer characteristics of the system as well as the physical properties of the materials involved.

4-6. A large steel plate (thermal diffusivity of 0.5 sq ft/hr and thermal conductivity of 25 Btu/hr ft F) is 1 in. thick. At zero time it begins to receive heat on one side at the rate of 30,000 Btu/hr sq ft while the other side is exposed to a fluid at 0 F through a unit-surface conductance of 1000 Btu/hr sq ft F. If the initial temperature of the entire plate is 100 F, determine by the numerical method the temperature at the midplane after 5 sec.

4-7. A thin-wall cylindrical vessel (3 ft in diam) is filled to a depth of 4 ft with water at an initial temperature of 60 F. The water is well stirred by a mechanical agitator. Estimate the time required to heat the water to 120 F if the tank is suddenly immersed into oil at 220 F. The over-all heat-transfer coefficient between the oil and the water is 50 Btu/hr sq ft F, and the effective heat-transfer-surface area is 45 sq ft.

4-8. A cylindrical mild-steel billet, 1 in. OD, 3 in. long, initially at 1000 F is cooled in a large vessel filled with oil at 200 F. The average unit-surface conductance between the oil and the steel during cooling is 100 Btu/hr sq ft F. Determine the time required to cool (a) the center of the billet and (b) the surface of the billet to 500 F.

4–9. Estimate the time required to heat the center of a 5-lb roast in a 400 F oven to 300 F. State your assumptions carefully and compare your results with cooking instructions in a standard cookbook.

4–10. To determine the heat-transfer coefficient between a heated steel ball and cooler ground or crushed mineral solids experimentally, a series of SAE 1040 steel balls were heated to a temperature of 700 C and the center temperature-time history of each was measured with a thermocouple while it was cooling in a bed of crushed iron ore which was placed in a steel drum, rotating horizontally at about 30 rpm. For a 2-in.-diam ball, the time required for the temperature difference between the ball center and the surrounding ore to decrease from 500 to 250 C was found to be 64, 67, and 72 sec respectively in three different test runs. Determine the average unit-surface conductance between the ball and the ore. Compare the results obtained by assuming the thermal conductivity to be infinite with those obtained by taking the internal thermal resistance of the ball into account. *Ans.* $\sim$ 54 Btu/hr sq ft F

4–11. A fireproof safe is to be constructed. Its walls consist of two $\frac{1}{16}$-in. steel sheets with a layer of asbestos board between them. Using the chart for a slab, estimate the thickness of asbestos required to give 1 hr of fire protection on the basis that, for an outside temperature of 1500 F, the inside temperature is not to rise above 250 F during this period. The heat-transfer coefficient at the exterior surface is 5 Btu/hr sq ft F.

4–12. A large slab of 1-ft-thick steel armor plate ($k = 10$ Btu/hr ft F, $a = 0.12$ sq ft/hr) is initially at a uniform temperature of 1300 F. One surface is maintained at 1300 F while air is blown over the other surface at a velocity which gives rise to an average heat-transfer coefficient of 20 Btu/hr sq ft F. The temperature of the air varies with time as $T_\infty = (600 - 10\theta)$ F, where θ is in minutes. Determine the surface temperature at the distribution after 1 hr has elapsed.

4–13. A long 2-ft-OD solid steel ($k = 12$ Btu/hr ft F) cylindrical billet at 60 F room temperature is placed in an oven where the temperature is 500 F. If the average unit-surface conductance is 3 Btu/hr sq ft F, estimate the time required for the center temperature to increase to 450 F by (a) using the appropriate chart, (b) dividing the solid into *two* equal lumped thermal capacities with appropriate thermal resistances between them. Also (c) determine the instantaneous surface heat fluxes when the center temperature is 450 F.

4–14. Repeat Prob. 4–13a, but assume that the billet is only 4 ft long with the average unit-surface conductance at both ends equal to 6 Btu/hr sq ft F.

4–15. A large billet of steel originally at a temperature of 500 F is placed in a

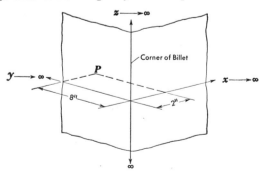

PROB. 4–15.

radiant furnace where the surface temperature is held at 2200 F.   Assuming the billet infinite in extent, compute the temperature at point P shown in the accompanying sketch after 25 min has elapsed.   The average steel properties are: $k = 23$ Btu/hr ft F, $\rho = 460$ lb$_m$/cu ft, and $c = 0.12$ Btu/lb$_m$ F. $Ans.$ 1904 F

4–16.   Estimate the depth in moist soil at which the annual temperature variation will be 10 per cent of that at the surface.

4–17.   A slab of material having a thermal diffusivity of 0.05 sq ft/hr is 2 in. thick and of relatively large breadth and width.   The slab is being held at a mean temperature of 1000 F in a gas stream having a mean temperature of 1000 F.   The gas temperature is controlled by an on-off controller which produces an essentially triangular gas-temperature variation of 25 F amplitude and 10-min period.   Presuming the film conductance to be 20 Btu/hr sq ft and the heat transfer to be convective only, comment on the adequacy of the control system if the slab temperature should not depart from the mean value of 1000 F by more than 5.0 F at any point in the slab.

4–18.   It is desired to anneal a disk of plate glass 8 in. in diam by 1 in. thick to remove stresses in the disk in preparation for optical grinding.   If the disk was originally at 75 F throughout, how long must it remain in an oven so that every part of the disk is at least 750 F?   The air temperature in the oven is 770 F and $\bar{h} = 1.6$ Btu/sq ft F.

4–19.   A 6-in.-diam pipe projects vertically into the earth.   For a point sufficiently deep so that the heat flow is essentially two-dimensional, determine the time required, after a sudden rise of pipe temperature from the 50 F ground temperature to a value of 100 F, for the temperature of the ground 1 ft from the surface of the pipe to increase to 55 F.   Plot the rate of heat flow from the pipe surface as a function of the time.

4–20.   The thermometer well, described in Example 2–11, is subjected to a sudden temperature rise of 100 F.   Derive the equation describing the response of the thermometer, lumping the heat capacity of the well and the thermometer separately.   For a unit-surface conductance at the outer surface of the well of 12 Btu/hr sq ft F and a thermal resistance between the inner surface of the well and the mercury thermometer of 0.01 hr sq ft F/Btu, plot the response of the thermometer as a function of time.

4–21.   The heat-transfer coefficients for the flow of 80 F air over a $\frac{1}{2}$-in.-diam sphere are measured by observing the temperature-time history of a copper ball of the same dimension.   The temperature of the copper ball ($c = 0.09$ Btu/lb F, $\rho = 558$ lb/cu ft) was measured by two thermocouples, one located in the center, the other near the surface.   Both of the thermocouples registered, within the accuracy of the recording instruments, the same temperature at a given instant.   In one test run the initial temperature of the ball was 150 F and in 1.15 min the temperature decreased by 20 F.   Calculate the heat-transfer coefficient for this case.

4–22.   You are asked to heat and cool a glass bar 1 by 1 by 3 in.   The bar is first to be placed in a deep freeze where the temperature is -100 F, and the heat-transfer coefficient is 2 Btu/hr sq ft F.   Then the bar is to be placed in a hot box where the temperature is 165 F and the heat-transfer coefficient is 2 Btu/hr sq ft F.   The bar is to be removed whenever the temperature at the center reaches -65 F or 120 F respectively.   If the cycling is to be repeated 100 times, how long will the test take?

4–23.   Derive in detail the equation for the temperature-time history of a fluid in a container whose walls have a substantial thermal capacity when the entire system is suddenly immersed in a fluid at T_∞.

4–24.   A spherical stainless steel vessel at 200 F contains 100 lb$_m$ of water at the same temperature.   If the entire system is suddenly immersed in ice water, determine (a) the time required for the water in the vessel to cool to 60 F, and (b) the temperature of the walls of the vessel at that time.   Assume that:

1. The unit-surface conductance at the inner surface is 3 Btu/hr sq ft F.

2. The unit-surface conductance at the outer surface is 4 Btu/hr sq ft F.

3. The wall of the vessel is 1 in. thick.

4–25. Water, while flowing through a pipe, is heated by steam condensing on the outside of the pipe. (a) Assuming the over-all conductance is constant along the pipe, derive an expression for the temperature as a function of pipe length. (b) For a unit conductance of 100 Btu/hr sq ft F based on the inside diam of 2 in., steam temperature of 220 F, and a water flow rate of 500 lb_m/min, what length will be required to raise the temperature of the water from 60 F to 150 F? (c) What will be the final water temperature if the pipe length is made twice that calculated in (b)?

Ans. (b) $L = 7.91$ ft, (c) 189.4 F

4–26. A thin-wall jacketed tank, heated by condensing steam at 14.7 psia, contains 200 lb of agitated water (assume uniform water temperature). The heat-transfer area of the jacket is 10 sq ft and the over-all conductance $U =$ Btu/hr sq ft F based on that area. Determine the heating time required for an increase in temperature from 60 to 140 F.

Ans.   18 min

4–27. A 3-lb aluminum household iron has a 20 watt heating element. The surface area is 0.5 sq ft. The ambient temperature is 70 F and the surface heat-transfer coefficient is 2.0 Btu/hr sq ft F (assumed constant). How long after the iron is plugged in will its temperature reach 220 F?

4–28. A long, slender metal rod of length L is attached at its base to a wall at 0 F. The curved surface of the rod is insulated. The end of the rod is in contact with a fluid at 0 F, where the unit-surface conductance at the interface $\bar{h}$ is constant and uniform. If the initial temperature in the rod is given by $T(x,\theta) = f(x)$, show that the temperature distribution after time θ is

$$T\,(x,\,\theta) = \sum_{n=1}^{\infty} C_n e^{-(\lambda_n{}^2\ \theta/a)} \sin \lambda_n x$$

where

$$C_n = \frac{2\lambda_n L}{(\lambda_n L - \sin \lambda_n\ L \cos \lambda_n L)_L} \int_0^L f\,(x) \sin \lambda_n x dx$$

Calculate the temperature at the end ($x = L$) of a 0.1 in. diam, 2-in.-long stainless-steel rod as a function of time, if the initial temperature distribution is linear, with 100 F at the end, and $\bar{h} = 10$ Btu/hr sq ft F at the end.

4–29. A turnip (assume spherical) weighing 1 lb is dropped into water boiling at atmospheric pressure. If the initial temperature of the turnip is 62 F, how long does it take to reach 197 F at the center? Assume that:

$$\bar{h}_c = 300 \text{ Btu/hr sq ft F} \qquad\qquad c_p = 0.95 \text{ Btu/lb F}$$
$$k = 0.3 \text{ Btu/hr ft F} \qquad\qquad \rho = 65 \text{ lb/cu ft}$$

4–30. Two gas streams are passed alternately for a duration of 5 min each over the surface of a steel plate. The one stream is hot (1000 F), the other cold (100 F), but for both streams $\bar{h} = 5$ Btu/hr sq ft F. Determine the temperature variation with time of the plate surface if the imposed free stream temperature variation is approximated by the Fourier series (θ is in min).

$$T_\infty = 100 + \frac{900}{\pi}\left[(\pi/2) + 2\left(\sin\frac{\pi\theta}{5} + \frac{1}{3}\sin\frac{3\pi\theta}{5} + \frac{1}{5}\sin\frac{5\pi\theta}{5} + \ldots\right)\right]$$

4–31. A long wooden rod 1 in. OD is placed at 100 F into an airstream at 1500 F. The unit-surface conductance between the rod and air is 5 Btu/hr sq ft F. If the ignition temperature of the wood is 800 F, $\rho = 50$ lb/cu ft, $k = 0.1$ Btu/hr ft F, and $c = 0.6$ Btu/lb F, determine the time between initial exposure and ignition of the wood.

5 Heat Transfer
by Radiation

5-1. THERMAL RADIATION

The transfer of heat by radiation is only one of numerous electromagnetic phenomena. The term "radiation" is applied generally to all kinds of processes which transmit energy by means of electromagnetic waves. The entire gamut of such waves is subdivided into classes according to wavelength or frequency and also according to application. Figure 5-1 illustrates the electromagnetic spectrum, which ranges from electric waves of long wavelength and low frequency to cosmic rays of extremely short wavelength and high frequency.

The true nature of radiation and its transport mechanism have not been completely established to date. Some radiation phenomena can be described in terms of the wave theory and others by the quantum theory, but neither theory completely explains all of the experimental observations. It is known, however, that radiation travels in free space with the speed of light, V_l, and does not require an intervening medium for its propagation. The transfer of energy takes place in the form of small but finite energy units known as quanta. The frequency of radiation ν_r depends entirely on the nature of its source; i.e., a metal bombarded by high-frequency electrons emits X-rays, a metal conductor emits electric waves when a high-frequency current passes through it, and a body of any kind at any temperature emits thermal radiation. The wavelength of radiation λ is defined as the ratio of the propagation velocity to the frequency, i.e.,

$$\lambda = \frac{V_l}{\nu_r} \tag{5-1}$$

The unit of wavelength which will be used in this chapter is the micron. One micron, or μ, is 10^{-6} m or 3.94×10^{-5} in.

A qualitative explanation of the mechanism by which radiant energy is transferred may be given in terms of the wave theory. In the process of emitting radiation, a body converts a part of its internal energy into electromagnetic waves, which are a form of energy. These waves move through space until they strike another body, where a part of their energy is absorbed and reconverted into internal energy. The emission of radiation causes a decrease of the internal energy in the emitting body and, unless heat is generated within that body, as for example in the sun, or the body receives heat from another source, its temperature will decrease. Only when the rate at which a body generates or receives heat equals the rate of energy emission will its temperature remain constant.

All bodies continuously emit radiation to which we are exposed at all times. Our senses, however, are able to detect radiation only if its wavelength falls within the spectrum region between 0.1 to 100μ. Radiation in this wavelength range causes appreciable heating of the receiving body, and within the narrow band from 0.38 to 0.76μ, it also affects the optical nerve as light.

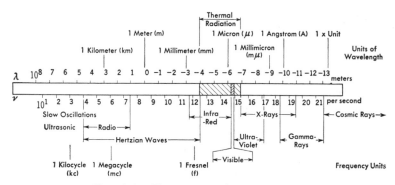

Fig. 5–1.   Electromagnetic-wave spectrum.

In this chapter we shall only be concerned with *thermal radiation*, that is, radiation emitted by bodies by virtue of their temperature. For practical purposes the radiation of importance in heat-transfer calculations is limited to wavelengths ranging from 0.1 to 100μ. The total amount of radiation emitted by a body per unit area and time, called the *total emissive power E*, depends on the temperature and the characteristics of the surface of the body. At any particular temperature the quantity of radiation emitted per unit wavelength is different at the various wavelengths. For an ideal radiator, i.e., one which emits the maximum possible radiation at a given temperature, the distribution of emissive power with wavelength is shown in Fig. 5–2 for different temperatures. These curves are called *spectroradiometric curves:* the height determines the amount of radiation emitted per unit time and area at a particular wavelength, and the area under the curve is the total amount of radiation emitted over all of the wavelengths. We can see from these curves that the major portion of radiation is emitted within a relatively narrow band to both sides of the wavelength at which the emissive power is a maximum.   One can therefore characterize the quality of the radiation in terms of the wavelength at which maximum emission occurs.   For instance, the sun, whose effective surface temperature is approximately 10,000 F, emits over 90 per cent of its total radiation between 0.1 and 3μ, while a body at 2000 F emits most of its radiation between 1 and 20μ.   This explains in part why a greenhouse is warm inside even when the outside air is cool.   Glass permits radiation at the wavelength of the sun to pass, but it is opaque to radiation in the wavelength range emitted by the interior of the greenhouse.   Thus solar radiation may enter, but once it has been absorbed, it cannot leave the greenhouse.

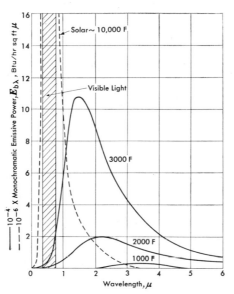

FIG. 5–2. Spectral distribution of monochromatic emissive power for an ideal radiator or black body at various temperatures.

5–2. ABSORPTION, REFLECTION, AND TRANSMISSION OF RADIATION

When radiation impinges on a body, it is partially absorbed, partially reflected, and partially transmitted, as indicated in Fig. 5–3.   The relation between the absorbed, reflected, and transmitted energy is

$$\alpha + \rho + \tau = 1 \tag{5-2}$$

where α = absorptivity, i.e., the fraction of the incident radiation absorbed by the body;

ρ = reflectivity, i.e., the fraction of the incident radiation reflected from the surface of the body;

τ = transmissivity, i.e., the fraction of the incident radiation transmitted through the body.

The majority of solid materials encountered in practice absorb practically all of the radiation in a very thin surface layer, less than 0.05 in. in depth.

Bodies which do not transmit radiation are called *opaque*, and for these Eq. 5–2 reduces to

$$\alpha + \rho = 1 \qquad (5\text{--}3)$$

Glass and rock salt and other inorganic crystals are examples of exceptions among the solids because, unless very thick, they are to a certain degree

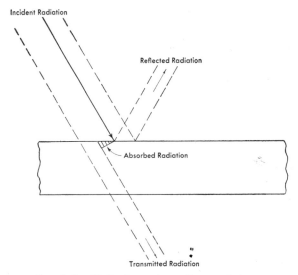

Fig. 5–3.   Reflection, absorption, and transmission of radiation.

transparent to radiation of certain wavelengths.   Many liquids and all gases are also transparent.

The reflection of radiation may either be *regular* or *diffuse*.   If a surface is highly polished and smooth, the reflection of radiation will be similar to the reflection of a light beam, that is, the angle of incidence will be equal to the angle of reflection.   This is called a regular reflection.   Most materials used in industrial practice are "rough" because their surfaces have asperities which are large compared with one wavelength.   The reflection of radiation from a rough surface occurs practically indiscriminately in all directions and is called diffuse.   A diffuse-reflecting surface can be defined as one which reflects with the same spatial energy distribution as a *black body* (Sec. 5–3).   For most practical situations the reflection may be treated as though it were completely diffuse.

The relative magnitudes of α, ρ, and τ depend not only on the material, its thickness, and its surface finish, but vary also with the wavelength of the radiation.   The numerical evaluation of these properties will be taken up in Sec. 5–5 for opaque bodies and in Sec. 5–10 for gases.

5–3. KIRCHHOFF'S LAW AND THE BLACK BODY

Like the ideal gas, the black body is a theoretical concept which can only be approximated in practice.   A black body, or ideal radiator, may be defined either as a body which absorbs all radiation incident upon it and reflects or transmits none or as a radiator which emits at any specified temperature the maximum possible amount of thermal radiation at all wavelengths.   The black body is used as a standard with which the radiation characteristics of other bodies are compared.

The concept of a black body can be clarified by considering a simple experiment.   Suppose that two small bodies B_1 and B_2 of surface areas A_1 and A_2 are placed in a large evacuated enclosure which is perfectly insulated from its surroundings.   Radiation will be exchanged between the bodies and the walls of the enclosure until equilibrium is attained and both bodies and the walls have reached the same temperature.   Then the rate at which each body emits radiation must equal the rate at which it absorbs radiation. If G is the rate at which radiant energy from the walls falls on each of the bodies, α_1 and α_2 are the absorptivities, and E_1 and E_2 the emissive powers of B_1 and B_2 respectively, an energy balance yields

$$A_1 \, G \, \alpha_1 = A_1 \, E_1 \quad \text{and} \quad A_2 \, G \, \alpha_2 = A_2 \, E_2$$

from which

$$\frac{E_1}{\alpha_1} = \frac{E_2}{\alpha_2} = \frac{E}{\alpha}$$

Kirchhoff's Law

for any body.

This relation is known as Kirchhoff's law.   It states that, at thermal equilibrium, the ratio of the emissive power of a surface to its absorptivity is the same for all bodies.   Since according to Eq. 5–2 the absorptivity is limited to values between 0 and 1, Kirchhoff's law places an upper limit on the emissive power of a body.   The maximum emissive power occurs when α has its maximum value of unity, a condition which applies precisely to a black body.   Thus, a black body is also an ideal radiator and its emissive power will be designated by the subscript b, as E_b.   The emissive power of other bodies is less than that of the black body, and the ratio E/E_b is called the emissivity ϵ of the body.   From Kirchhoff's law, the ratio E/E_b is also equal to the absorptivity, since $\alpha_b = 1$.   Hence we see that, *at thermal equilibrium, the absorptivity and the emissivity of a body are equal.* For the black body both are equal to unity.

A black body can be approached in practice by a cavity such as a hollow sphere whose interior surface is maintained at a uniform temperature. If a small hole is provided in the wall of the sphere, any radiation entering through it is partly absorbed and partly reflected diffusely at the interior surface. The reflected radiation, as shown schematically in Fig. 5–4, will not immediately escape from the cavity but will first strike repeatedly the interior surface. Each time it strikes, a part of it is absorbed; when the original radiation beam finally reaches the hole again and escapes, it has been so weakened by repeated reflection that the energy leaving the cavity is negligible. This is true regardless of the surface and composition of the wall of the cavity. Thus, a small hole in the walls surrounding a large

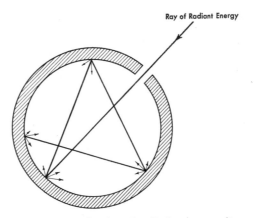

Fig. 5–4. Reflection of radiation in a cavity.

cavity acts like a black body because practically all the radiation incident upon it is absorbed.

In a similar manner, the radiation emitted by the interior surface of a cavity is absorbed and reflected many times and eventually fills the cavity uniformly. If a black body at the same temperature as the interior surface is placed into the cavity, it receives radiation uniformly, i.e., it is irradiated isotropically. The black body absorbs all of the incident radiation and, since the system consisting of the black body and the cavity is at a uniform temperature, the rate of emission of radiation by the body must equal its rate of irradiation. Otherwise there would be a net transfer of energy as heat between two bodies at the same temperature in an isolated system, an obvious violation of the second law of thermodynamics. Denoting the rate at which radiant energy from the walls of the cavity is absorbed by the black body, i.e., the *black-body irradiation,* by G_b and the rate at which the black body emits energy by E_b, we thus obtain $G_b = E_b$.   This means that the irradiation in a cavity whose walls are at a temperature T is equal to the emissive power of a black body at the same temperature.   A small hole in the wall of a cavity will not disturb this condition appreciably, and the radiation escaping from it will therefore have black-body characteristics. Since this radiation is independent of the nature of the surface, it follows that the emissive power of a black body depends only on its temperature.

A quantitative relationship between the temperature and the total emissive power of a black body was obtained by the Austrian physicist, Stefan, in 1879.   He deduced empirically from experimental data obtained earlier by the scientist, Tyndall, that the energy radiated by a black body is proportional to the fourth power of its absolute temperature, or

$$E_b = \sigma T^4 \tag{5-4}$$

Measurements obtained by different observers (1) give an average of 0.1714 $\times$ 10^{-8} for the constant of proportionality σ if E_b is in Btu per hour per square foot and T in *degrees Fahrenheit absolute* (i.e., degrees Rankine).   The fourth-power law was later also derived from thermodynamical considerations by Boltzmann, and Eq. 5-4 is commonly known as the Stefan-Boltzmann law.

The emissive power determined from the Stefan-Boltzmann equation represents the total radiant energy emitted by a black body in all directions of a half space per unit area and time over the entire wavelength spectrum. It does not reveal the distribution of energy in the spectrum.   A relationship which shows how the emissive power is distributed among the different wavelengths was derived by Max Planck, in 1900, by means of his quantum theory.   If $E_{b\lambda}$ is the emissive power of a black body at the wavelength λ, so that $E_{b\lambda} \, d\lambda$ is the radiant power emitted from a black surface per unit area in the wavelength interval $d\lambda$, Planck's law can be expressed as

$$E_{b\lambda} = \frac{C_1 \lambda^{-5}}{e^{C_2/\lambda T} - 1} \tag{5-5}$$

where $E_{b\lambda}$ = monochromatic emissive power of a black body in Btu/hr sq ft μ;

$\quad\lambda$ = wavelength, in μ;

$\quad T$ = temperature of the body, in deg F abs;

$\quad e$ = Napierian base of logarithms;

$\quad C_1$ = 1.1870 $\times$ 10^8 Btu μ^4/sq ft hr;

$\quad C_2$ = 2.5896 $\times$ 10^4 Rμ.

The monochromatic emissive power for various temperatures of black bodies is plotted in Fig. 5-2 as a function of wavelength.   At temperatures of engineering interest, the emissive power is appreciable over wavelengths from 0.3 to at least 50μ. The wavelength at which the monochromatic emissive power is a maximum shifts with increasing temperature to shorter wavelengths. The relationship between the wavelength λ_{max} at which $E_{b\lambda}$ is a maximum and the absolute temperature is given by Wien's displacement law (1) as

$$\lambda_{max} T = 5215.6 \ \mu \ \mathrm{R} \tag{5-6}$$

The visible range of wavelengths extends only over a narrow region from about 0.4 to 0.7μ, shown as a shaded band in Fig. 5–2. Only a very small amount of the total energy falls into this range of wavelengths at temperatures below 1200 F. At higher temperatures, the amount of radiant energy within the visible range increases and the human eye begins to detect the radiation. The sensation produced on the retina and transmitted to the optical nerve depends on the temperature, a phenomenon which is still used to estimate the temperatures of metals during heat treatment. At about 1300 F an amount of radiant energy sufficient to be observed is emitted at wavelengths between 0.6 to 0.7μ, and an object at that temperature glows with a dull-red color. As the temperature is further increased, the color changes to bright red and yellow, becoming nearly white at about 2400 F. At the same time also, the brightness increases because more and more of the total radiation falls within the visible range.

To obtain the Stefan-Boltzmann equation from Planck's law it is necessary to multiply the right-hand side of Eq. 5–5 by a differential wavelength $d\lambda$ and integrate it between the limits $\lambda = 0$ and $\lambda = \infty$. The total area under any one of the curves of Fig. 5–2 represents the total energy radiated by a black body at the indicated temperature and is numerically equal to σT^4, or

$$\int_0^\infty E_{b\lambda} \, d\lambda = \sigma T^4 \tag{5-7}$$

There are, however, many problems which require an estimate of the energy radiated at a specified wavelength or within a finite band of wavelengths. Numerical computations for such cases are facilitated by the auxiliary curves shown in Figs. 5–5, 5–6, and 5–7 (2). If we divide the monochromatic emissive power of a black body $E_{b\lambda}$ by its maximum monochromatic emissive power at the same temperature $E_{b\lambda \ max}$, we obtain

$$\frac{E_{b\lambda}}{E_{b\lambda \ max}} = \frac{C_1}{\lambda^5(e^{C_2/\lambda T} - 1)} \frac{\lambda_{max}{}^5(e^{C_2/\lambda_{max}T} - 1)}{C_1}$$

$$= \left(\frac{5215.6}{\lambda T}\right)^5 \left(\frac{e^{4.965} - 1}{e^{25896/\lambda T} - 1}\right) \tag{5-8}$$

Since the right-hand side is now a unique function of λT, we can plot $E_{b\lambda}/E_{b\lambda\,max}$ vs. λT as shown in Fig. 5-5. We obtain $E_{b\lambda\,max}$ by combining Eqs. 5-5 and 5-6, or

$$E_{b\lambda\,max} = \frac{C_1 T^5}{5215.6^5(e^{C_2/5215.6} - 1)} = 2.161 \times 10^{-13} \, T^5 \; \text{Btu/hr sq ft } \mu \qquad \text{(5-9)}$$

A plot of $E_{b\lambda\,max}$ vs. T is shown in Fig. 5-6. To determine $E_{b\lambda}$ at a given temperature T, we calculate $E_{b\lambda\,max}$ from Eq. 5-9 or read $E_{b\lambda\,max}$ from Fig. 5-6, calculate λT for the desired wavelength, read $E_{b\lambda}/E_{b\lambda\,max}$ from Fig. 5-5, and multiply the result by $E_{b\lambda\,max}$.

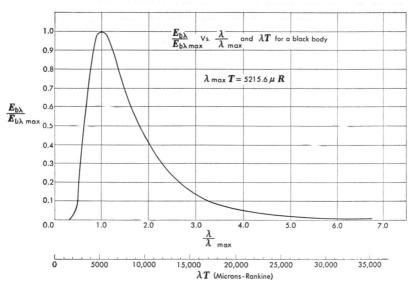

FIG. 5-5. Ratio of monochromatic emissive power to maximum monochromatic emissive power at λ_{max} as a function of λT.

The black-body emissive power over a specified wavelength range can be obtained either from Fig. 5-7 where the ratio of

$$\int_0^\lambda E_{b\lambda} \, d\lambda \Big/ \int_0^\infty E_{b\lambda} \, d\lambda$$

is plotted vs. λT or from Table A-4 where this ratio is tabulated as a function of λT. The procedure is illustrated in the following example.

Example 5-1. Silica glass transmits 92 per cent of the incident radiation in the wavelength range between 0.35 and 2.7μ and is opaque at longer and shorter wavelengths. Estimate the per cent of solar radiation which the glass will transmit. The sun may be assumed to radiate as a black body at 10,000 R.

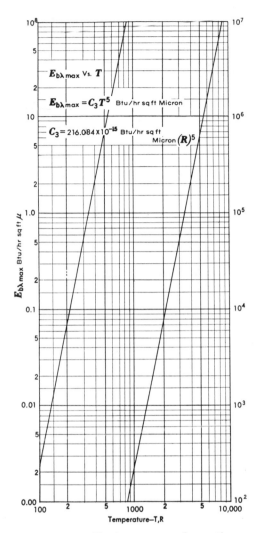

Solution: For the wavelength range within which the glass is transparent, $\lambda T = 3500$ at the lower limit and 27,000 at the upper limit. From Fig. 5–7 or Table A–4 we find

$$\frac{\int_0^{0.35} E_{b\lambda}\,d\lambda}{\int_0^\infty E_{b\lambda}\,d\lambda} = 0.6 \text{ per cent}$$

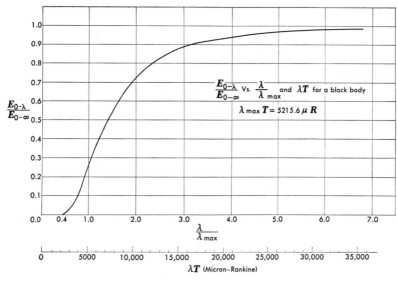

FIG. 5–7. Fraction of total emissive power in spectral region between $\lambda = 0$ and λ as a function of λT.

and
$$\frac{\displaystyle\int_0^{2.7} E_{b\lambda}d\lambda}{\displaystyle\int_0^{\infty} E_{b\lambda}d\lambda} = 96.9 \text{ per cent}$$

Thus 96.3 per cent of the total radiant energy incident upon the glass from the sun is in the wavelength range between 0.35 and 2.7μ and 88.5 per cent of the solar radiation is transmitted through the glass. $Ans.$

5–4. RADIATION INTENSITY AND TOTAL EMISSIVE POWER

In the preceding sections we have only considered the total radiation emitted by a black body in all directions. This condition may be visualized by placing a hemispherical surface over a surface element dA_1, as shown in Fig. 5–8. The hemisphere will then intercept all of the radiation beams

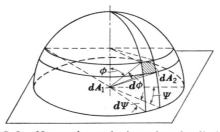

FIG. 5–8. Nomenclature for intensity of radiation.

emitted from the surface element, but only from directly above it will dA_1 be seen without distortion. When viewed from a point on the hemisphere displaced by the angle ϕ from the normal to the surface, the element dA_1 will appear as the projected area $dA_1 \cos \phi$.

To determine the radiant heat per unit time emitted by dA_1 which reaches an area dA_2 on the surrounding hemisphere of radius r, we introduce a term called *intensity*. The intensity of radiation I from dA_1 in space is defined as the radiant energy propagated in a particular direction area per unit solid angle and per unit of area dA_1 as projected on a plane perpendicular to the direction of propagation. Referring to Fig. 5–8, the intensity is so defined that the rate of radiant heat flow from dA_1 to dA_2 is

$$dq_{1\rightarrow 2} = I \cos \phi \, dA_1 \, dA_2/r^2 \qquad (5\text{--}10)$$

Noting that dA_2/r^2 is the *solid angle* $d\omega_1$ subtended by dA_2 at dA_1 and that $dA_1 \cos \phi$ is the effective area seen from dA_2, i.e., the projected area dA_{1p} in the direction ϕ, we see that

$$I = dq_{1\rightarrow 2}/dA_{1p} \, d\omega_1 \qquad \text{Btu/hr sq ft steradian}$$

For a diffuse surface the intensity is constant and does not vary with the emission angle ϕ. Such a surface therefore obeys Lambert's cosine law, and we can relate the intensity to the emissive power by integrating the radiation intercepted by an elemental area dA_2 over the half space represented by the surface of the hemisphere, or

$$E = \int_{A_2} \int I \cos \phi \, \frac{dA_2}{r^2} \qquad (5\text{--}11)$$

where dA_2/r^2 is the solid angle $d\omega_1$ subtended by dA_2 at dA_1, since a solid angle is by definition numerically *the area subtended on a sphere of unit radius,* or, for a sphere of radius r, the intercepted area divided by r^2. From Fig. 5–8 we see that

$$d\omega_1 = \frac{(r \sin \phi)d\psi(rd\phi)}{r^2} = \sin \phi \, d\psi d\phi$$

Substituting this relation for $d\omega_1$ in Eq. 5–11 we obtain

$$E = I \int_0^{2\pi} d\psi \int_0^{\pi/2} \sin \phi \cos \phi \, d\phi$$

which yields on integration

$$E = \pi I \qquad (5\text{--}12)$$

Thus, the total emissive power of a diffuse surface is π times its intensity.

5–5. RADIATION FROM REAL SURFACES

Radiation from real surfaces differs in several aspects from black-body radiation. According to Kirchhoff's law, a real surface always radiates less than a black body at the same temperature. If the ratio of the monochromatic emissive power of a body to the emissive power of a black body at the same wavelength, i.e., if it is constant over the entire wavelength spectrum, the body is said to be *gray* and its emissive power E_g is given by

$$E_g = \epsilon_g \sigma T^4 \quad \text{Btu/hr sq ft} \qquad (5\text{–}13)$$

The shape of a spectroradiometric curve for a gray surface is similar to that of a black surface at the same temperature, but the height is reduced

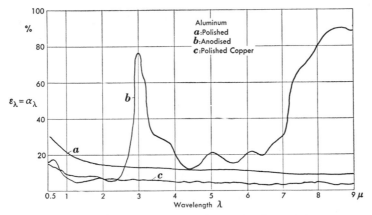

FIG. 5–9. Variation of monochromatic absorptivity or emissivity with wavelength for an electrical conductor. (According to W. Sieber, Ref. 3)

by the numerical value of the emissivity. For the purpose of heat-transfer calculations, surfaces are usually regarded as gray even though the characteristics of most surfaces deviate from gray-body specifications. Sieber (3) measured the reflectivity of several materials over a range of wavelengths and found that their values change with wavelength. From these measurements the absorptivity and the emissivity can be calculated from Eq. 5–3 and Kirchhoff's law. The results are shown in Figs. 5–9 and 5–10, which illustrate the variation of the monochromatic absorptivity α_λ with wavelength. The curve for polished aluminum is characteristic of good electrical conductors and shows that the emissivity decreases with increasing wavelength. Electric nonconductors generally exhibit the opposite trend, as illustrated by the emissivity curves for white clay and white tiles. The emissivity of nonconductors generally increases in a more or less irregular manner with increasing wavelength.

In addition to its variation with wavelength, the emissivity of many bodies also has directional properties which do not conform to Lambert's cosine law. This is illustrated in Figs. 5–11 and 5–12, where the directional emissivities ϵ_ϕ of several substances are plotted in polar diagrams. For surfaces whose radiation intensity follows Lambert's cosine law and depends only on the projected area, the emissivity curves would be semicircles. The measurements of Schmidt and Eckert (4) show that, for nonconductors such as wood, paper, and oxide films, the emissivity decreases at large values of the emission angle ϕ, whereas for polished metals, the opposite trend is observed. For example, the emissivity of polished chromium, which is widely used as a radiation shield, is as low as 0.06 in the normal

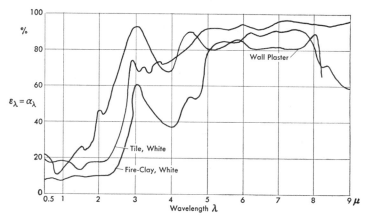

Fig. 5–10. Variation of monochromatic absorptivity or emissivity with wavelength for an electrical nonconductor. (According to W. Sieber, Ref. 3)

direction but increases to 0.14 when viewed from an angle ϕ of 80 deg. Experimental data on the directional variation of emissivity are scant, and until more information becomes available a satisfactory approximation for engineering calculations is to assume for polished metallic surfaces a mean value of $\epsilon/\epsilon_n = 1.2$ and for nonmetallic surfaces $\epsilon/\epsilon_n = 0.96$, where ϵ is the average emissivity through a hemispherical solid angle of 2π steradians and ϵ_n is the emissivity in the direction of the normal to the surface.

For heat-transfer calculations an average emissivity or absorptivity for the wavelength band in which the bulk of the radiation is emitted or absorbed is required. The wavelength band of interest depends on the temperature of the body from which the radiation originates, as pointed out in Sec. 5–1. If the distribution of the monochromatic emissivity is known, the emissive power of the body can be obtained by plotting the product $\epsilon_\lambda E_{b\lambda}$ vs. λ over the wavelength range in which appreciable emis-

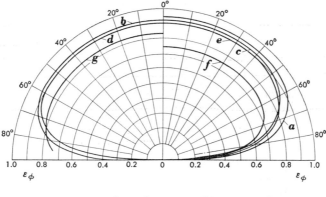

a wet ice   b wood   c glass   d paper
e clay   f copper oxide   g aluminum oxide

FIG. 5–11   Directional variation of emissivity for several electrical nonconductors. (By permission from E. Schmidt and E. Eckert, "Über die Richtungsverteilung der Wärmestrahlung," *Forsch. Gebiete Ingenieurwesen*, Vol. 6, 1935)

sion occurs at a given temperature and measuring the area under the curve. An average emissivity for each temperature can be obtained by dividing this area by the area under the spectroradiometric curve of a black body at the same temperature.   The total average emissivity at a given temperature is thus given by

$$\epsilon = \int_0^\infty \epsilon_\lambda E_{b\lambda} d\lambda \bigg/ \int_0^\infty E_{b\lambda} d\lambda$$

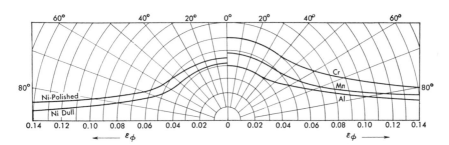

FIG. 5–12. Directional variation of emissivity for several metals. (By permission from E. Schmidt and E. Eckert, "Über die Richtungsverteilung der Wärmestrahlung," *Forsch. Gebiete Ingenieurwesen*, Vol. 6, 1935)

The total average absorptivity α for a surface receiving radiation can be obtained similarly by evaluating the fraction

$$\alpha = \int_0^\infty \alpha_\lambda E_{b\lambda} d\lambda \Big/ \int_0^\infty E_{b\lambda} d\lambda$$

The numerical evaluation of this integral may be simplified by noting that the denominator is equal to σT^4. Changing the variable of integration from λ to λT yields

$$\alpha = \int_0^\infty \alpha_\lambda \frac{E_{b\lambda}}{\sigma T^5} d (\lambda T)$$

The quantity $(E_{b\lambda}/\sigma T^5)$ is tabulated as a function of λT in Table A–4 of the Appendix. As shown by Dunkle (2), if a curve of α_λ vs. λ is available, α can be evaluated numerically by taking suitable increments of λT, tabulating the individual products $\alpha_\lambda (E_{b\lambda}/\sigma T^5)\Delta(\lambda T)$, and finally summing them.

Sieber (3) evaluated the total average absorptivity for several materials at 70 F, and his results are shown graphically in Fig. 5–13. We observe that the absorptivity of aluminum, representative of all electrical conductors, increases with increasing temperature, whereas the absorptivity of nonconductors has the opposite trend.

According to Kirchhoff's law, the absorptivity of a surface equals its emissivity at thermal equilibrium. For gray bodies α_λ and ϵ_λ are constant over the entire wave spectrum; consequently $\alpha = \epsilon$ irrespective of the tempera-

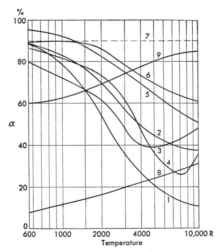

(1) White fire clay   (4) Wood   (7) Roof shingles
(2) Asbestos   (5) Porcelain   (8) Aluminum
(3) Cork   (6) Concrete   (9) Graphite

Fig. 5–13. Variation of average absorptivity with temperature for several materials. (According to W. Sieber, Ref. 3)

tures of the emitter and receiver.   It is important to note, however, that, when ϵ varies with wavelength, this relation only holds at a given temperature or at a given wavelength.   In practice a body usually emits the bulk of its radiation at wavelengths which are different from those at which it receives radiation.   Therefore the average values of ϵ and α are not necessarily the same, and to evaluate ϵ and α for a real body correctly one should choose α corresponding to the wavelength or the temperature at which the radiation striking the body was emitted and ϵ corresponding to the actual temperature of the body.

Example 5–2. A small body at 100 F is placed in a large heating oven whose walls are maintained uniformly at 2000 F.   The average absorptivity of the body at 100 F varies with the temperature of the emitter as shown in the table below.

Temperature (F)	100 F	1000 F	2000 F
Absorptivity, α	0.8	0.6	0.5

Estimate the rate at which radiant energy is (a) absorbed by and (b) emitted from the body per unit surface area.

Solution: (a) The radiation incident upon the body is characterized by the temperature of the oven walls, and the absorptivity of the body for this radiation is 0.5. Thus 50 per cent of the incident black-body radiation is absorbed, and the rate of energy absorption G is

$$G = 0.5 \times 0.173 \times 10^{-8} \times 2460^4 = 3.16 \times 10^5 \text{ Btu/hr sq ft} \qquad Ans.$$

b) Emission occurs at a temperature of 100 F and the average emissivity of the body is therefore equal to 0.8, the absorptivity at 100 F.   The emissive power is equal to

$$E = 0.8 \times 0.173 \times 10^{-8} \times 560^4 = 13.7 \text{ Btu/hr sq ft} \qquad Ans.$$

The net rate of heat transfer by radiation equals the rate at which energy is absorbed by the body minus the rate at which it emits energy.   In this problem the rate of emission is negligible compared to the rate of absorption because the temperature of the body is very low.   However, as the body becomes warmer it will emit more and more radiation.   Its temperature will approach that of the oven walls and eventually its rate of emission will be the same as its rate of absorption of energy, so that the absorptivity will equal the emissivity at the equilibrium temperature.

Table 5–1 lists average values for the emissivity of several materials at specified temperatures.[1]   It will be noted that clean and polished metal surfaces usually have low values of emissivity, whereas many other surfaces which find application in engineering have emissivities in excess of 0.85

[1] A survey of the literature reveals wide variances in the reported results. The values listed in Table 5–1 were selected from several references and deviations from these values can be expected in practice since many factors influence the emissivity and absorptivity of a surface. An experimental technique for the accurate measurement of the spectral emissivity has been developed recently and is described in Ref. 29.

TABLE 5-1

EMISSIVITIES OF VARIOUS SURFACES

MATERIAL	WAVELENGTH AND AVERAGE TEMPERATURE				
	9.3μ 100 F	5.4μ 500 F	3.6μ 1000 F	1.8μ 2500 F	0.6μ Solar
Metals					
Aluminum					
Polished	0.04	0.05	0.08	0.19	∼0.3
Oxidized	0.11	0.12	0.18		
24-ST weathered	0.4	0.32	0.27		
Surface roofing	0.22				
Anodized (at 1000 F)	0.94	0.42	0.60	0.34	
Brass					
Polished	0.10	0.10			
Oxidized	0.61				
Chromium					
Polished	0.08	0.17	0.26	0.40	0.49
Copper					
Polished	0.04	0.05	0.18	0.17	
Oxidized	0.87	0.83	0.77		
Iron					
Polished	0.06	0.08	0.13	0.25	0.45
Cast, oxidized	0.63	0.66	0.76		
Galvanized, new	0.23	....	....	0.42	0.66
Galvanized, dirty	0.28	....	....	0.90	0.89
Steel plate, rough	0.94	0.97	0.98		
Oxide	0.96	....	0.85	....	0.74
Molten	....	....	....	0.3–0.4	
Magnesium	0.07	0.13	0.18	0.24	0.30
Molybdenum filament	....	....	∼0.09	∼0.15	∼0.2*
Silver					
Polished	0.01	0.02	0.03	....	0.11
Stainless steel					
18–8, polished	0.15	0.18	0.22		
18–8, weathered	0.85	0.85	0.85		
Steel tube					
Oxidized	....	0.80			
Tungsten filament	0.03	....	....	∼0.18	0.35†
Zinc					
Polished	0.02	0.03	0.04	0.06	0.46
Galvanized sheet	∼0.25				
Building and Insulating Materials					
Asbestos paper	0.93	0.93			
Asphalt	0.93	....	0.9	...	0.93
Brick					
Red	0.93	....	....	....	0.7
Fire clay	0.9	....	∼0.7	∼0.75	
Silica	0.9	....	∼0.75	0.84	
Magnesite refractory	0.9	....	....	∼0.4	
Enamel, white	0.9				
Marble, white	0.95	....	0.93	....	0.47
Paper, white	0.95	....	0.82	0.25	0.28
Plaster	0.91				

Unless you use the bare material the important emissity is the covering (Paint) and not the material under it.

TABLE 5-1 (Continued)

MATERIAL	WAVELENGTH AND AVERAGE TEMPERATURE				
	9.3μ 100 F	5.4μ 500 F	3.6μ 1000 F	1.8μ 2500 F	0.6μ Solar
Roofing board.	0.93				
Enameled steel, white.	....	....	....	0.65	0.47
Asbestos cement, red.	....	....	....	0.67	0.66
Paints					
Aluminized lacquer.	0.65	0.65			
Cream paints.	0.95	0.88	0.70	0.42	0.35
Lacquer, black.	0.96	0.98			
Lampblack paint.	0.96	0.97	....	0.97	0.97
Red paint.	0.96	....	....	....	0.74
Yellow paint.	0.95	....	0.5	....	0.30
Oil paints (all colors).	~0.94	~0.9.			
White (ZnO).	0.95	....	0.91	....	0.18
Miscellaneous					
Ice.	~0.97‡				
Water.	~0.96				
Carbon					
T-carbon, 0.9 per cent ash.	0.82	0.80	0.79		
Filament.	~0.72	....	....	0.53	
Wood.	~0.93				
Glass.	0.90	....	....	....	(Low)

* At 5000 F.
† At 6000 F.
‡ At 32 F.
SOURCE: Refs. 11, 15–18.

and are therefore excellent absorbers as well as emitters of radiation. It is also apparent that the visual color bears no resemblance to the definition of a black body. For example ice, which appears white to our eyes, absorbs nearly all radiation in the long-wavelength range.

5–6. HEAT EXCHANGE BY RADIATION BETWEEN BLACK SURFACES

So far we have examined the emission and absorption of radiation by various surfaces without considering the net heat flow between them. To evaluate the net exchange of radiation or net heat flow between two or more bodies it is necessary to determine the fraction of the total emission from each of the radiating surfaces which reaches, and is absorbed by, the others. If only black surfaces are involved, all of the incident radiation is absorbed and we only need to consider the geometric relation between the surfaces.

Figure 5–14 shows the surfaces of two black bodies separated by a medium which does not absorb radiation appreciably (e.g., air). To determine the fraction of the energy leaving surface A_1 that strikes surface A_2, consider first the two differential surfaces dA_1 and dA_2. If the distance between them is r, then $dq_{1\to2}$, the rate at which radiation from dA_1 is received by dA_2, is, from Eq. 5–10, given by

$$dq_{1\to2} = I_1 \cos\phi_1 \, dA_1 \, d\omega_{1\text{-}2} \qquad (5\text{--}14)$$

where
$I_1 =$ intensity of radiation from dA_1;
$dA_1 \cos\phi_1 =$ projection of area element dA_1 as seen from dA_2;
$d\omega_{1\text{-}2} =$ solid angle subtended by receiving area dA_2 with respect to center point of dA_1.

The subtended angle $d\omega_{1\text{-}2}$ is equal to the projected area of the receiving

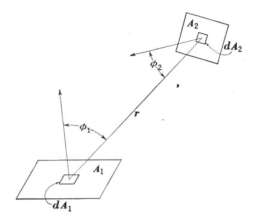

FIG. 5–14. Geometrical shape-factor notation.

surface in the direction of the incident radiation divided by the square of the distance between dA_1 and dA_2, or, using the nomenclature of Fig. 5–14,

$$d\omega_{1\text{-}2} = \cos\phi_2 \, \frac{dA_2}{r^2} \qquad (5\text{--}15)$$

Substituting Eqs. 5–10 and 5–15 for $d\omega_{1\text{-}2}$ and I_1 respectively in Eq. 5–14 yields

$$dq_{1\to2} = E_{b1} \, dA_1 \left(\frac{\cos\phi_1 \cos\phi_2 \, dA_2}{\pi r^2} \right) \qquad (5\text{--}16)$$

where the term in parentheses is equal to the fraction of the total radiation emitted from dA_1 that is intercepted by dA_2. By analogy, the fraction of the total radiation emitted from dA_2 that strikes dA_1 is

$$dq_{2\to1} = E_{b2} \, dA_2 \left(\frac{\cos\phi_2 \cos\phi_1 \, dA_1}{\pi r^2} \right) \qquad (5\text{--}17)$$

so that the net rate of radiant heat transfer between dA_1 and dA_2 is

$$dq_{1 \rightleftarrows 2} = (E_{b1} - E_{b2}) \frac{\cos \phi_1 \cos \phi_2 \, dA_1 dA_2}{\pi r^2} \qquad (5\text{-}18)$$

To determine $q_{1 \rightleftarrows 2}$, the net rate of radiation between the entire surfaces A_1 and A_2, we simply integrate the fraction in the preceding equation over both surfaces and obtain

$$q_{1 \rightleftarrows 2} = (E_{b1} - E_{b2}) \int_{A_1} \int_{A_2} \frac{\cos \phi_1 \cos \phi_2 \, dA_1 dA_2}{\pi r^2} \qquad (5\text{-}19)$$

The double integral is conveniently written in shorthand notation either as $A_1 F_{1\text{-}2}$ or $A_2 F_{2\text{-}1}$, where $F_{1\text{-}2}$ is called the shape factor evaluated on the basis of area A_1 and $F_{2\text{-}1}$ is called the shape factor evaluated on the basis of A_2. Physically $F_{1\text{-}2}$ represents the fraction of the total radiant energy leaving A_1 which is intercepted by A_2 and $F_{2\text{-}1}$ the fraction of energy reaching A_1 from A_2. The equality

$$A_1 F_{1\text{-}2} = A_2 F_{2\text{-}1} \qquad (5\text{-}20)$$

is known as the reciprocity theorem. Substituting Eq. 5–20 for the double integral in Eq. 5–19 shows that the basic relation for the net rate of heat flow by radiation between any two black bodies may be written as

$$q_{1 \rightleftarrows 2} = (E_{b1} - E_{b2}) F_{1\text{-}2} A_1 = (E_{b1} - E_{b2}) F_{2\text{-}1} A_2 \qquad (5\text{-}21)$$

Inspection of Eq. 5–21 reveals that the net rate of heat flow between two black bodies can be determined by evaluating the radiation from either one of the surfaces to the other surface and replacing its emissive power by the difference of the emissive powers of the two surfaces. Since the end result is independent of the choice of the emitting surface, one selects that surface whose shape factor can be determined more easily. For example, the shape factor $F_{1\text{-}2}$ for any surface A_1 completely enclosed by another surface is unity. In general, however, the determination of a shape factor for any but the most simple geometric configuration is rather complex. The technique is illustrated in Example 5–3.

Example 5–3. Determine the geometric shape factor for a very small disk A_1 and a large parallel disk A_2 located a distance L directly above the smaller one, as shown in Fig. 5–15.

Solution: From Eq. 5–19 the geometric shape factor is

$$A_1 F_{1\text{-}2} = \int_{A_1} \int_{A_2} \frac{\cos \phi_1 \cos \phi_2}{\pi r^2} \, dA_1 dA_2$$

but since A_1 is very small the shape factor is given by

$$A_1 F_{1\text{-}2} = \frac{A_1}{\pi} \int_{A_2} \frac{\cos \phi_1 \cos \phi_2}{r^2} \, dA_2$$

From Fig. 5–15, $\cos \phi_1 = \cos \phi_2 = L/r$, $r = \sqrt{\rho^2 + L^2}$, and $dA_2 = \rho d\psi d\rho$. Substituting these relations, we obtain

$$A_1 F_{1\text{-}2} = \frac{A_1}{\pi} \int_0^a \int_0^{2\pi} \frac{L^2}{(\rho^2 + L^2)^2} \rho d\rho d\psi$$

which can be integrated directly to yield

$$A_1 F_{1\text{-}2} = \frac{A_1 a^2}{a^2 + L^2} = A_2 F_{2\text{-}1} \qquad\qquad Ans.$$

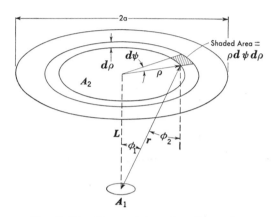

FIG. 5–15. Nomenclature for the evaluation of the shape factor between a small disk and a large disk located parallel directly above.

The preceding example shows that the determination of a shape factor by evaluating the double integral of Eq. 5–19 is generally very tedious.[2] Fortunately the shape factors for a large number of geometrical arrangements have been evaluated and a majority of them can be found in Refs. 5, 6, 7, and 8. A selected group of practical interest is summarized in Table 5–2 and Figs. 5–16, 5–17, 5–18, and 5–19. The data from the graphical solutions of cases 7 and 10 can be extended by simple arithmetical addition and subtraction of shape factors to permit the evaluation of a shape factor for geometrical arrangements which can be built up from these elementary cases. The technique is illustrated in the following example.

Example 5–4. A room 12 ft on one side by 24 ft on the other has a ceiling height of 12 ft. Determine the shape factor of the floor with respect to a small window of area A_1 located in the ceiling 6 ft from two walls.

[2] Mechanical devices which perform the double integration indicated by Eq. 5–19 are described in Refs. 6 and 7. With their aid, shape factors for odd configurations can be determined quite simply and accurately.

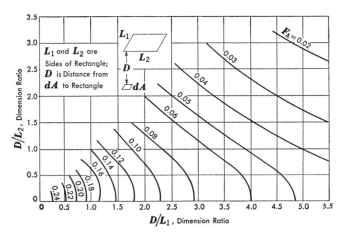

FIG. 5–16. Shape factor for a surface element and a rectangular surface parallel to it. (By permission from H. C. Hottel, "Radiant Heat Transmission," *Mechanical Engineering*, Vol. 52, 1930)

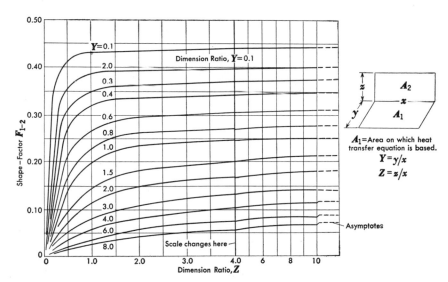

FIG. 5–17. Shape factor for adjacent rectangles in perpendicular planes. (By permission from H. C. Hottel, "Radiant Heat Transmission," *Mechanical Engineering*, Vol. 52, 1930)

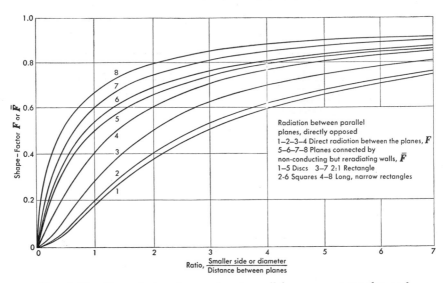

FIG. 5–18. Shape factors for equal and parallel squares, rectangles, and disks. The curves labeled 5, 6, 7, and 8 allow for continuous variation in the side-wall temperatures from top to bottom. (By permission from H. C. Hottel, "Radiant Heat Transmission," *Mechanical Engineering*, Vol. 52, 1930)

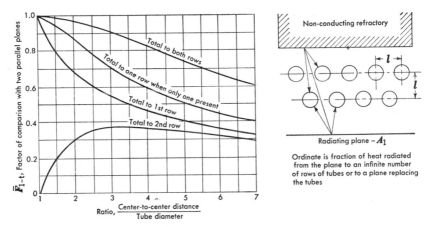

FIG. 5–19. Shape factor for a plane and one or two rows of tubes above and parallel to it. (By permission from H. C. Hottel, "Radiant Heat Transmission," *Mechanical Engineering*, Vol. 52, 1930)

Solution: If the floor is divided into four rectangles, two 6 by 6 ft each and two 6 by 18 ft each, then each rectangle meets the condition of the graphical solution presented in Fig. 5–16. The shape factor of the entire floor area will be the sum of the shape factors for each of the rectangles. The dimensionless ratios D/L_1 and D/L_2 for each of the smaller rectangles are $12/6 = 2.00$. From Fig. 5–16 the shape factor

TABLE 5–2

GEOMETRIC SHAPE FACTORS FOR USE IN EQS. 5–21 AND 5–28

Surfaces Between Which Radiation Is Being Interchanged	Shape Factor, $F_{1\text{-}2}$
1. Infinite parallel planes.	1
2. Body A_1 completely enclosed by another body, A_2. Neither of the bodies can see any part of itself.	1
3. Surface element dA (A_1) and rectangular surface (A_2) above and parallel to it, with one corner of rectangle contained in normal to dA.	See Fig. 5–16
4. Element dA (A_1) and parallel circular disk (A_2) with its center directly above dA. (See Example 5-3.)	$a^2/(a^2 + L^2)$
5. Two parallel and equal squares, rectangles or disks of width or diameter D, a distance L apart.	See Fig. 5–18
6. Two parallel disks of unequal diameter, distance L apart with centers on same normal to their planes, smaller disk A_1 of radius a, larger disk of radius b.	$\dfrac{\pi}{2}\left[L^2 + a^2 + b^2 - \sqrt{(L^2 + a^2 + b^2) - 4a^2b^2} \right]$
7. Two rectangles in perpendicular planes with a common side.	See Fig. 5–17
8. Radiation between an infinite plane A_1 and one or two rows of infinite parallel tubes in a parallel plane A_2 if the only other surface is a refractory surface behind the tubes.	See Fig. 5–19

for one section is about 0.06. For each of the larger rectangles $D/L_1 = 0.66$, $D/L_2 = 2.0$, and, from Fig. 5–16, the shape factor between the window and one of the larger rectangles is 0.10. The shape factor for the entire floor is therefore 0.32. Thus, 32 per cent of the total emissive power from the window will strike the floor, and $A_1F_{1\text{-}2} = A_2F_{2\text{-}1} = 0.32\ A_1$. $2 \times \cdot 06 = \cdot 12$ *Ans.*
$2 \times \cdot 10 = \cdot 20$
$\cdot 32$

The net radiation from a surface A_i in a black-body enclosure consisting of several surfaces can be evaluated by a simple extension of Eq. 5–21. Since the radiation exchange between A_i and any one of the n surrounding surfaces is not affected by the presence of the other surfaces, the net rate of heat flow from A_i is

$$q_{i\text{ net}} = \sum_{k=1}^{k=n} A_i F_{ik}(E_{b_i} - E_{bk}) \tag{5–22}$$

If the surface A_i is convex so that none of the radiation emitted by it can strike it directly, all of the radiation emitted from A_i is intercepted by the n surrounding surfaces of the enclosure. The shape factors based on the surface A_i must therefore obey the relation

$$\sum_{k=1}^{k=n} F_{ik} = 1 \qquad\qquad (5\text{--}22a)$$

An inspection of Eq. 5–22 shows that there is also an analogy between heat flow by radiation and the flow of electric current. If the black-body emissive power E_b is considered to act as a potential and the shape factor $A_i F_{ik}$ as the conductance between two nodes at potentials E_{bi} and E_{bk}, then the resulting net flow of heat $q_{i\ \text{net}}$ is analogous to the flow of electric current in an analogous network. As examples, networks for black-body enclosures consisting of three and four heat-transfer surfaces are shown in

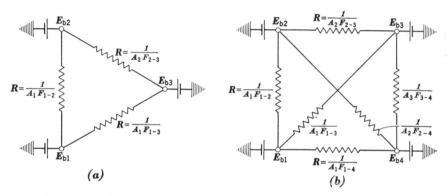

(a)   (b)

FIG. 5–20. Equivalent networks for radiation in black-body enclosures consisting of three and four surfaces.

Fig. 5–20. The numerical solution for cases involving four or more surfaces is most easily accomplished by actually constructing an equivalent electric network and measuring the current flow. Analytic methods of solution can be found in Refs. 9 and 10.

5–7. RADIATION BETWEEN BLACK SURFACES IN THE PRESENCE OF RERADIATING SURFACES

A reradiating surface is a surface which diffusely reflects and emits radiation at the same rate at which it receives radiation. Under steady-state conditions the refractory walls of industrial furnaces can usually be treated as reradiating surfaces. The interior surfaces of these walls receive heat by convection as well as radiation and lose heat to the outside by conduction through the walls. In practice, however, the heat flow by radiation is so much larger than the difference between the heat flow

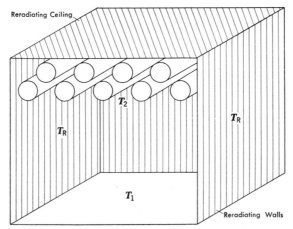

FIG. 5–21. Simplified sketch of a furnace.

by convection to and the heat flow by conduction from the surface that the walls act essentially as reradiators.

A simplified sketch of a pulverized-fuel furnace is shown in Fig. 5–21. The floor is assumed to be at a uniform temperature T_1 radiating to a nest of oxidized-steel tubes at T_2 which fill the ceiling of the furnace. The side walls are assumed to act as reradiators at *a uniform temperature* T_R. If we neglect radiation between the tubes and the ceiling and assume that the floor and the tubes are black, the equivalent network representing the radiation exchange between the floor and the tubes in the presence of the reradiating walls is that shown in Fig. 5–22. A part of the radiation emitted from A_1 goes directly to A_2, while the rest strikes A_R and is reflected from there. Of the reflected radiation, a part is returned to A_1, a part to A_2, and the rest to A_R for further reflection. However, since the refractory wall must get rid of all the incident radiation either by reflection or reradiation, its emissive power will act in the steady state like a floating potential whose actual value, i.e., its emissive power and temperature, depends only on the relative values of the conductances between E_R and E_{b1} and E_R and E_{b2}. Thus, the net effect of this rather complicated radia-

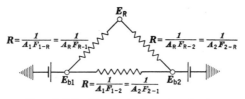

FIG. 5–22. Equivalent network for radiation between two black bodies in a reradiating enclosure.

tion pattern can be represented in the equivalent network by two parallel heat-flow paths between A_1 and A_2, one having an effective conductance of $A_1 F_{1\text{-}2}$, the other having an effective conductance equal to $1/(1/A_1 F_{1\text{-}R} + 1/A_2 F_{2\text{-}R})$. The net heat flow by radiation between a black heat source and a black heat sink in such a simple furnace is then equal to

$$q_{1 \rightleftharpoons 2} = A_1(E_{b1} - E_{b2}) \left(F_{1\text{-}2} + \frac{1}{1/F_{1\text{-}R} + A_1/A_2 F_{2\text{-}R}} \right) \quad \textbf{(5–23)}$$

If neither of the surfaces can see any part of itself, $F_{1\text{-}R}$ and $F_{2\text{-}R}$ can be eliminated by using Eqs. 5–20 and 5–22a. This yields after some simplification

$$q_{1 \rightleftharpoons 2} = A_1\sigma(T_1{}^4 - T_2{}^4) \frac{A_2 - A_1 F_{1\text{-}2}{}^2}{A_1 + A_2 - 2A_1 F_{1\text{-}2}} = A_1 \bar{F}_{1\text{-}2}(E_{b1} - E_{b2}) \quad \textbf{(5–23a)}$$

The details of this derivation are left as an exercise (see Prob. 5–33).

5–8. HEAT FLOW BY RADIATION BETWEEN GRAY SURFACES

In the preceding two sections, radiation between black surfaces was considered. The assumption that a surface is black simplifies heat-transfer calculations because all of the incident radiation is absorbed. In practice one may generally neglect reflection without introducing serious errors if the absorptivity of the radiating surfaces is larger than 0.9. There are, however, numerous problems involving surfaces of low absorptivity and emissivity, especially in installations where radiation is undesirable. For example, the inner walls of a thermos bottle are silvered in order to reduce the heat flow by radiation. Also, thermocouples for high-temperature work are frequently surrounded by radiation shields to reduce the difference between the indicated temperature and the temperature of the medium to be measured.

If the radiating surfaces are not black, the analysis becomes exceedingly difficult unless the surfaces are considered to be gray. The analysis in this section is limited to gray surfaces which follow Lambert's cosine law and reflect diffusely. The radiation from such surfaces can be treated conveniently in terms of the *radiosity J*, which is defined as the rate at which radiation leaves a given surface per unit area. The radiosity is the sum of radiation emitted, reflected, and transmitted, but for opaque bodies which transmit no radiation, the radiosity can be defined symbolically as

$$J = \rho G + \epsilon E_b \quad \textbf{(5–24)}$$

where J = radiosity, in Btu/hr sq ft;

$\quad G$ = irradiation or radiation per unit time incident on unit surface area, in Btu/hr sq ft;

E_b = black-body emissive power, in Btu/hr sq ft;
ρ = reflectivity;
ϵ = emissivity.

The net rate at which radiation is leaving a gray surface per unit area and time is equal to the difference between the radiosity and the irradiation, that is

$$\frac{dq_{net}}{dA} = J - G \qquad (5\text{--}25)$$

For a gray surface, ρ is constant and $\rho + \epsilon = 1$. The irradiation G can therefore be eliminated from Eq. 5–25, and we get

$$\frac{dq_{net}}{dA} = \frac{\epsilon}{\rho} E_b - \frac{1-\rho}{\rho} J = \frac{\epsilon}{\rho} (E_b - J) \qquad (5\text{--}26)$$

If the irradiation is uniformly distributed over the surface, the net rate of radiation leaving a surface A is obtained by integrating Eq. 5–26, and we have

$$q_{net} = \frac{\epsilon}{\rho} A(E_b - J) \qquad (5\text{--}27)$$

In terms of an equivalent circuit q_{net} in Eq. 5–27 can be interpreted as the rate of heat flow between two nodes E_b and J connected by a resistance equal to $\rho/\epsilon A$.

The effect of the system geometry on the net radiation between two gray surfaces A_i and A_k emitting radiation at the rate J_i and J_k respectively is the same as for similar black surfaces. It can therefore be expressed in terms of the geometric shape factor defined by Eq. 5–19 and the direct radiation exchange between any two opaque and diffuse surfaces A_i and A_k is given by the rate equation

$$q_{i \rightleftarrows k} = (J_i - J_k) A_i F_{i\text{-}k} = (J_i - J_k) A_k F_{k\text{-}i} \qquad (5\text{--}28)$$

Equations 5–27 and 5–28 provide the basis for determining the net rate of radiant heat transfer between gray bodies in a gray enclosure by means of an equivalent network. It should be noted, however, that, according to the condition preceding Eq. 5–27, a heat-transfer surface is that portion of an area which is not only at a constant temperature but is also uniformly irradiated. With this stipulation the effect of the reflectivity and emissivity can be taken into account by connecting a *black-body potential node E_b,* to each of the nodal points in the network by means of a *finite conductance* $A\epsilon/\rho$. In the case of a black body $(A\epsilon/\rho)$ is infinite since $\rho_b = 0$. In Fig. 5–23 the equivalent networks for radiation in an enclosure consisting of two and four gray bodies are shown. We can see from these networks that the potential nodes of the corresponding black-enclosure network become floating potential nodes which acquire an equilibrium potential equal to the surface radiosity J.

Some two-component gray enclosures, such as two parallel and infinite plates, concentric cylinders of infinite height, and concentric spheres, are of considerable practical interest. For these systems each component surface is uniformly irradiated and the network reduces to a single line of resistances

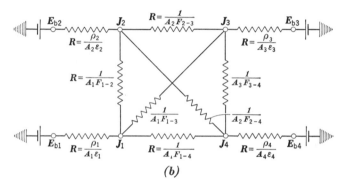

Fig. 5–23.   Equivalent networks for radiation in gray enclosures.   (a) Two gray-body surfaces.   (b) Four gray-body surfaces.

in series as shown in Fig. 5–23.   *The equivalent conductance for use in Eq. 5–21 is given by*

$$A_1 \mathfrak{F}_{1\text{-}2} = \frac{1}{\rho_1/A_1\epsilon_1 + 1/A_1 + \rho_2/A_2\epsilon_2} \tag{5–29}$$

where A_1 is the smaller surface and $\mathfrak{F}_{1\text{-}2}$ is *the gray-body shape factor* which is often written $F_A F_E$, the product of the geometric shape factor F_A and a factor F_E that allows for the departure of the surface from black-body conditions.

For radiation between two parallel flat plates, the gray-body shape factor reduces to $\mathfrak{F}_{1\text{-}2} = 1/(1/\epsilon_1 + 1/\epsilon_2 - 1)$ if end effects are neglected. For a small gray body in black surroundings we obtain $A_1 \mathfrak{F}_{1\text{-}2} = A_1\epsilon_1$ according to Eq. 5–29.

Example 5–5.   Liquified oxygen (boiling temperature, -297 F) is to be stored in a spherical container of 1-ft diam.   The system is insulated by an evacuated space between the inner sphere and a surrounding 1.5-ft-ID concentric sphere. Both spheres are made of aluminum ($\epsilon = 0.03$), and the temperature of the outer sphere is 30 F. Estimate the rate of heat flow by radiation to the oxygen in the container.

Solution: From Eq. 5–29 the equivalent conductance is

$$A_1 \mathfrak{F}_{1\text{-}2} = 1 \Big/ \left(\frac{\rho_1}{\pi D_1{}^2 \epsilon_1} + \frac{1}{\pi D_1{}^2} + \frac{\rho_2}{\pi D_2{}^2 \epsilon_2} \right)$$

but since $\qquad\qquad \rho_1 = 1 - \epsilon_1 \qquad$ and $\qquad \rho_2 = 1 - \epsilon_2$

we get $\qquad\qquad A_1 \mathfrak{F}_{1\text{-}2} = \pi \Big/ \left[\frac{0.97}{0.03} + 1 + \frac{0.97}{(0.3)(2.25)} \right] = 0.066$

The absolute temperatures are

$$T_1 = 460 - 297 = 163 \text{ R}$$
$$T_2 = 460 + 30 = 490 \text{ R}$$

The rate of heat flow to the oxygen is then, according to Eq. 5–21,

$$q_{1 \rightleftarrows 2} = A_1 \mathfrak{F}_{1\text{-}2} (E_{b1} - E_{b2}) = (0.066)(0.1714)(4.9^4 - 1.63^4) = 6.55 \text{ Btu/hr} \qquad Ans.$$

The radiant heat flow between a gray heat source and a gray heat sink in an enclosure consisting of reradiating surfaces can also be solved without

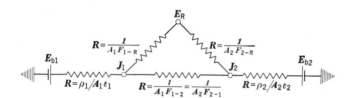

Fig. 5–24. Equivalent network for radiation between two gray bodies in a reradiating enclosure.

difficulty by means of the equivalent circuit. According to Eqs. 5–27 and 5–28, it is only necessary to replace E_{b1} and E_{b2}, the potentials used in Sec. 5–7 for black surfaces, by J_1 and J_2 and connect the new potentials by the resistances $\rho_1/\epsilon_1 A_1$ and $\rho_2/\epsilon_2 A_2$ respectively to the black-body potentials E_{b1} and E_{b2}. The resulting network is shown in Fig. 5–24, and from it we see that the total conductance between E_1 and E_2 is now

$$A_1 \mathfrak{F}_{1\text{-}2} = \frac{1}{\dfrac{\rho_1}{\epsilon_1 A_1} + \dfrac{\rho_2}{\epsilon_2 A_2} + \dfrac{1}{A_1 \left[F_{1\text{-}2} + 1/(1/F_{1\text{-}R} + A_1/A_2 F_{2\text{-}R}) \right]}} \qquad (5\text{--}30)$$

where the denominator of the last term is the conductance for the black-body network given by Eq. 5–23. The expression for the conductance can be recast into the more convenient form

$$A_1 \mathfrak{F}_{1\text{-}2} = \frac{1}{\dfrac{1}{A_1}\left(\dfrac{1}{\epsilon_1}-1\right)+\dfrac{1}{A_2}\left(\dfrac{1}{\epsilon_2}-1\right)+\dfrac{1}{A_1 \bar{F}_{1\text{-}2}}} \tag{5–31}$$

where $A_1 \bar{F}_{1\text{-}2}$ is the total conductance for the black-body network, equal to the denominator of the last term in the original expression. The equation for the net radiant heat transfer per unit time between two gray surfaces in the presence of reradiating surfaces at uniform temperature can then also be written

$$q_{1 \rightleftarrows 2} = A_1 \mathfrak{F}_{1\text{-}2}\, \sigma\,(T_1{}^4 - T_2{}^4) \tag{5–32}$$

Example 5–6. A muffle-type furnace has a floor 16 by 16 ft made of refractory material ($\epsilon = 0.7$). Two staggered rows of 3-in.-OD tubes on 6-in. centers are placed about 10 ft above and parallel to the floor. The floor is at an average temperature of 1640 F, and the tubes, made of oxidized steel, are at 540 F. The side walls and the ceiling are made of refractory and may be assumed to act as reradiating surfaces. Determine the rate of radiant heat transfer from the floor to the tubes.

Solution: We assume that the floor and the tubes behave as gray bodies having emissivities of 0.7 and 0.8 respectively. If we further assume that the reradiating surfaces are at a uniform temperature, the shape factor between the floor, acting as the heat source, and the tubes, which constitute the heat sink, can be obtained from Eq. 5–31. However, to evaluate the shape factor it is first necessary to determine an "effective" emissivity for the tubes. Since some of the radiation reflected from the first row of tubes will be absorbed by the second row, the effective emissivity is higher than 0.8. We can determine the effective emissivity by considering the radiation between the tubes and the refractory ceiling and a parallel black surface A_1 placed just below the tubes. If A_1 is at the same temperature as the tubes, we have

$$A_1\, \mathfrak{F}_{1\text{-}t}\, T_1{}^4 = A_t\, \mathfrak{F}_{t\text{-}1}\, T_t{}^4$$

where the subscript t refers to the tubes. From Fig. 5–19 for a ratio of center-to-center distance to tube diameter of 2, the shape factor $\bar{F}_{1\text{-}t}$ between A_1 and the tube-ceiling combination is 0.97. Substituting this value for $\bar{F}_{1\text{-}2}$ in Eq. 5–31 gives

$$A_t \mathfrak{F}_{t\text{-}1} = A_1 \mathfrak{F}_{1\text{-}t} = A_1 \Big/ \left[\left(\frac{1}{1}-1\right)+\frac{(16)(16)}{(16)(3\pi/12)(32)(2)}\left(\frac{1}{0.8}-1\right)+\frac{1}{0.97}\right] = 0.90 A_1$$

Thus, the tubes emit 90 per cent of black-body radiation and may be replaced by a plane A_1 having an emissivity of 0.9. The actual system can then be simplified to radiation between two 16- by 16-ft rectangles, A_1 and A_2, separated by 10 ft of reradiating walls. Equation 5–31 now applies and, using Fig. 5–18 to obtain $\bar{F}_{1\text{-}2}$, we get

$$A_1 \mathfrak{F}_{1\text{-}2} = \frac{A_1}{\left(\dfrac{1}{0.7}-1\right)+\left(\dfrac{1}{0.9}-1\right)+\dfrac{1}{0.65}} = 0.48 A_1$$

for an emissivity of 0.7 for the floor. The net radiation rate between the floor and the tubes, according to Eq. 5–32, is therefore

$$q_{\text{net}} = (16)\,(16)\,(0.48)\,(0.174)\,(21^4 - 10^4) = 3.96 \times 10^6 \text{ Btu/hr} \qquad Ans.$$

5–9. RADIATION COMBINED WITH CONVECTION AND CONDUCTION

In the preceding sections of this chapter we have considered radiation as an isolated phenomenon. Energy exchange by radiation is the predominant heat-flow mechanism at high temperatures because the rate of heat flow depends on the fourth power of the absolute temperature. In most practical problems, however, convection and conduction can not be neglected, and in this section we shall consider problems which involve two or all three modes of heat flow simultaneously.

To include radiation in a thermal network involving convection and conduction it is convenient to define a unit thermal radiative conductance, or radiant-heat-transfer coefficient, $\bar{h}_r$ as

$$\bar{h}_r = \frac{q_r}{A_1(T_1 - T_2')} = \mathfrak{F}_{1\text{-}2}\left[\frac{\sigma(T_1{}^4 - T_2{}^4)}{T_1 - T_2'}\right] \tag{5-33}$$

where A_1 = area upon which $\mathfrak{F}_{1\text{-}2}$ is based, in sq ft;

$T_1 - T_2'$ = a reference temperature difference, in F, in which T_2' may be chosen equal to T_2 or any other convenient temperature in the system;

$\bar{h}_r$ = radiant-heat-transfer coefficient, in Btu/hr sq ft F.

The reason for using a radiant-heat-transfer coefficient, similar to the convective-heat-transfer coefficient, is that the rate of heat flow becomes then linearly dependent on the temperature difference and can be incorporated directly in a thermal network for which the temperature is the driving potential. A knowledge of the value of $\bar{h}_r$ is also essential in determining the over-all conductance $\bar{h}$ for a surface to or from which heat flows by convection and radiation, since according to Eq. 1–25

$$\bar{h} = \bar{h}_c + \bar{h}_r \tag{1-25}$$

If $T_2 = T_2'$ the bracket in Eq. 5–33 is called the *temperature factor* F_T, and

$$\bar{h}_r = \mathfrak{F}_{1\text{-}2}\,F_T \tag{5-33a}$$

Values of F_T for ordinary Fahrenheit temperatures are given in Fig. 5–25. The use of these curves is illustrated in the following example.

Example 5–7. A hot-air duct having an outside diameter of 9 in. and a surface temperature of 200 F is located in a large room whose walls are at 70 F. The air in the room is at 80 F and the heat-transfer coefficient for free convection between the duct and the air is 1 Btu/hr sq ft F. Estimate the rate of heat transfer per foot of duct if (a) the duct is bare tin ($\epsilon = 0.1$) and (b) the duct is painted with white lacquer ($\epsilon = 0.9$).

Solution: (a) The duct may be considered as a small gray body in black surroundings and, from Eq. 5–29, $A_1\,\mathfrak{F}_{1\text{-}2} = A_1\,\epsilon_1$. From Fig. 5–25 we have $F_T = 1.5$, and

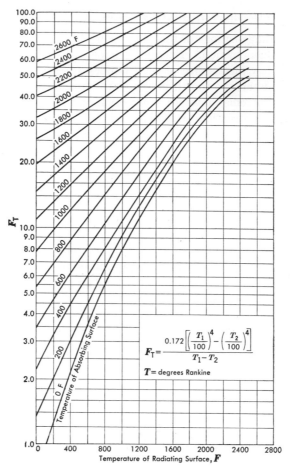

Fig. 5–25. Temperature factor, F_T, as a function of temperature in degrees Fahrenheit.

therefore $\bar{h}_r = 1.5\ \epsilon_1$. The thermal network is shown in Fig. 5–26. We note that there are two heat-flow paths in parallel but the lower temperature potentials are not equal. The total heat-flow rate is given by

$$q_{\text{total}} = q_r + q_b = A_1\ 1.5\ \epsilon_1\ (T_1 - 70) + A_1\ \bar{h}_c\ (T_1 - 80)$$

For the bare duct the total heat-flow rate is found to be 326 Btu/hr ft of which 14 per cent is due to radiation.   *Ans.*

b) If the duct were painted, the total rate of heat flow would increase to 698 Btu/hr ft, of which the contribution of radiation represents 60 per cent.   *Ans.*

Example 5–8. A butt-welded thermocouple (Fig. 5–27a) having an emissivity of 0.8 is used to measure the temperature of a transparent gas flowing in a large duct whose walls are at a temperature of 440 F. The temperature indicated by the thermocouple is 940 F. If the convective-heat-transfer coefficient between the surface of the couple and the gas $\bar{h}_c$ is 25 Btu/hr sq ft F, estimate the *true* gas temperature.

Solution: The temperature of the thermocouple is below the gas temperature because the couple loses heat by radiation to the wall. Under steady-state conditions the rate of heat flow by radiation from the thermocouple junction to the wall equals the rate of heat flow by convection from the gas to the couple. We can write this heat balance as

$$q = \bar{h}_c \, A_T \, (T_G - T_T) = A_T \, \epsilon \, \sigma \, (T_T{}^4 - T_{\text{wall}}{}^4)$$

where A_T is the surface area, T_T the temperature of thermocouple, and T_G the temperature of the gas. Substituting the data of the problem we obtain

$$\frac{q}{A_T} = 0.8 \times 0.1714 \left[\left(\frac{1400}{100}\right)^4 - \left(\frac{900}{100}\right)^4 \right] = 4410 \text{ Btu/hr sq ft}$$

and the true gas temperature is

$$T_G = \frac{q}{\bar{h}_c} + T_T = \frac{4410}{25} + 940 = 1116 \text{ F} \qquad \qquad Ans.$$

In systems where heat is transferred simultaneously by convection and radiation, it is frequently not possible to determine the radiant-heat-transfer

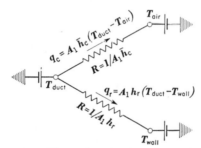

FIG. 5–26. Thermal network for Example 5–7.

coefficient directly. Since the temperature factor F_T contains the temperatures of the radiation emitter and the receiver, it can be evaluated only when both of these temperatures are known. If one of the temperatures depends on the rate of heat flow, that is, if one of the potentials in the network is "floating," one must assume a value for the floating potential and then determine if that value will satisfy continuity of heat flow in the steady state. If the rate of heat flow to the potential node is not equal to the rate of heat flow from the node, another temperature must be assumed. The trial-and-error process is continued until the energy balance is satisfied. The general technique is illustrated in the next example.

Example 5–9. Determine the correct gas temperature in Example 5–8 if the thermocouple had been shielded by a thin cylindrical radiation shield having an inside diameter four times as large as the outer diameter of the thermocouple. Assume that the convective-heat-transfer coefficient of the shield is 20 Btu/hr sq ft F on both sides and that the emissivity of the shield, made of stainless steel 3–16, is 0.3 at 1000 F.

Solution: A sketch of the physical system is shown in Fig. 5–27a. Heat flows by convection from the gas to the thermocouple and its shield. At the same time, heat flows by radiation from the thermocouple to the inside surface of the shield, is conducted through the shield, and flows by radiation from the outer surface of the shield to the walls of the duct. If we assume that the temperature of the shield is uniform (that is, if we neglect the thermal resistance of the conduction path because the shield is very thin), the thermal network is as shown in Fig. 5–27b. The temperature of the duct wall T_w and the temperature of the thermocouple T_T are known, while the temperatures of

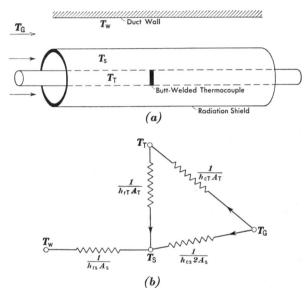

(a)

(b)

Fig. 5–27.   Physical system and thermal network for Example 5–9.

the shield T_s and of the gas T_G must be determined.   The latter two temperatures are floating potentials.   A heat balance on the shield can be written as

$$\begin{matrix} \text{Rate of heat flow from} \\ T_G \text{ and } T_T \text{ to } T_s \end{matrix} = \begin{matrix} \text{rate of heat flow} \\ \text{from } T_s \text{ to } T_w \end{matrix}$$

or

$$\bar{h}_{cs}\, 2A_s\, (T_G - T_s) + \bar{h}_{rT}\, A_T\, (T_T - T_s) = \bar{h}_{rs}\, A_s\, (T_s - T_w)$$

A heat balance on the thermocouple yields

$$\bar{h}_{cT}\, A_T\, (T_G - T_T) = \bar{h}_{rT}\, A_T\, (T_T - T_s)$$

where the nomenclature is given in the sketch.   Taking A_T as unity, A_s equals 4 and we obtain from Eq. 5–29

$$A_T \mathfrak{F}_{T-s} = \cfrac{1}{\cfrac{1-\epsilon_T}{A_T \epsilon_T} + \cfrac{1}{A_T} + \cfrac{1-\epsilon_s}{A_s \epsilon_s}} = \cfrac{1}{\cfrac{0.2}{0.8} + 1 + \cfrac{0.7}{4 \times 0.3}} = 0.547$$

and

$$A_s\, \mathfrak{F}_{s-w} = A_s\, \epsilon_s = (4)\,(0.3) = 1.2$$

Assuming a shield temperature of 900 F, we have, according to Eq. 5–33,

$$\bar{h}_{rT} A_T = A_T \mathfrak{F}_{T\text{-}s} F_T = (0.547)(18.1) = 9.85$$

and

$$\bar{h}_{rs} A_s = A_s \mathfrak{F}_{s\text{-}w} F_T = (1.2)(11.4) = 12.5$$

Substituting these values into the first heat balance permits the evaluation of the gas temperature and we get

$$T_G = \frac{\bar{h}_{rs} A_s (T_s - T_w) - \bar{h}_{rT} A_T (T_T - T_s)}{\bar{h}_{cs} \times 2A_s} + T_s$$

$$= \frac{5750 - 581}{(20)(2)(4)} + 900 = 932 \text{ F}$$

Since the temperature of the gas can not be less than that of the thermocouple, the assumed shield temperature was too low. Repeating the calculations with a new shield temperature of 930 F yields $T_G = 970$ F. We now substitute this value to see if it satisfies the second heat balance and get:

Heat flow rate by convection *to* thermocouple $= 25 A_T (970 - 940) = 750$ Btu/hr

Net heat flow rate by radiation *from* thermocouple $= h_{rT} A_T (T_T - T_s) = 203$ Btu/hr

Since the rate of heat flow to the thermocouple exceeds the rate of heat flow from the thermocouple, our assumed shield temperature was too high. Repeating the calculations with an assumed shield temperature of 923 F yields a gas temperature of 966 F, which satisfies the heat balance on the thermocouple. *Ans.*

The details of this calculation are left as an exercise to the reader. (See Prob. 5–34.)

A comparison of the results in Examples 5–8 and 5–9 shows that the indicated temperature of the unshielded thermocouple differs from the true gas temperature by 176 F, while the shielded couple reads only 26 F less than the true gas temperature. A double shield would reduce the temperature error to less than 10 F for the conditions specified in the example.

5–10. RADIATION FROM GASES, VAPORS, AND FLAMES

In this section we shall consider some basic concepts of radiation from gases and flames. A comprehensive treatment of this subject is beyond the scope of this text, and the reader should consult Refs. 9, 11, and 12 for details of the theoretical background and complete calculation techniques.

Many of the common gases and gas mixtures, such as O_2, N_2, H_2, dry air, etc. have symmetrical molecules and are practically transparent to thermal radiation: they neither emit nor absorb appreciable amounts of radiant energy at temperatures of practical interest. On the other hand, radiation of heteropolar gases and vapors such as CO_2, H_2O, SO_2, CO, NH_3, hydrocarbons, and alcohols is of importance in heat-transfer equipment. We shall restrict our consideration here to H_2O and CO_2. Not only are they the most important of the gases in furnaces, but they also illustrate the basic principles of gas radiation in general.

Whereas solids radiate at all wavelengths over the entire spectrum, gases emit and absorb radiation only between narrow regions of wavelength called bands. Figure 5–28 shows these bands for CO_2 and H_2O. The radiation bands for CO_2 lie between $\lambda = 2.36$ and 3.02 μ, $\lambda = 4.01$ and 4.80 μ, and $\lambda = 12.5$ and 16.5 μ; those for H_2O lie between $\lambda = 2.24$ and 3.27 μ, $\lambda = 4.8$ and 8.5 μ, and $\lambda = 12$ and 25 μ. Assuming black-body radiation within the bands, the radiation from all three CO_2 bands at 200, 1000, and 2000 C is 12, 10.5, and 6 per cent respectively of the total radiant black-body energy emitted at corresponding temperatures. Water vapor at the same temperatures emits 67, 46, and 24 per cent respectively of black-body radiation. We observe that the intensity of gas radiation increases less rapidly with temperature than the intensity of black-body radiation. The reason for this behavior is that, at higher temperatures, the maximum

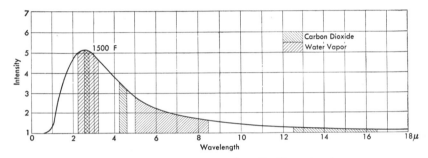

FIG. 5–28. Emission bands of carbon dioxide and water vapor.

intensity of the spectroradiometric curve shifts toward shorter wavelengths and thereby reduces the percentage of black-body radiant energy falling within the radiation bands of the gases.

Gas radiation differs from solid-body radiation in another respect. The emission and absorption of radiant energy are essentially surface phenomena for a solid body, but in calculating the radiation emitted or absorbed by a gas layer, its thickness, pressure, and shape as well as its surface area must be taken into account. When monochromatic radiation at an intensity $I_{\lambda 0}$ passes through a gas layer of thickness L, the radiant-energy absorption in a differential distance dx is governed by the relation

$$dI_{\lambda x} = - k_\lambda' I_{\lambda x} \, dx \qquad (5\text{–}34)$$

where $I_{\lambda x}$ = intensity at a distance x;

$\qquad k_\lambda'$ = monochromatic absorption coefficient, a proportionality constant whose value depends on the pressure and temperature of the gas.

Integration between the limits $x = 0$ and $x = L$ yields

$$I_{\lambda L} = I_{\lambda 0} \, e^{-k_\lambda' L} \qquad (5\text{–}35)$$

where $I_{\lambda L}$ is the intensity of radiation at L. The difference between the intensity of radiation entering the gas at $x = 0$ and the intensity of radiation leaving the gas layer at $x = L$ is

$$I_{\lambda 0} - I_{\lambda L} = I_{\lambda 0} (1 - e^{-k'_\lambda L}) \qquad (5\text{–}36)$$

the amount of energy absorbed by the gas. The quantity in the parentheses represents the absorptivity of the gas $\alpha_{G\lambda}$ at the wavelength λ, or, according to Kirchhoff's law, also the emissivity at the wavelength λ, $\epsilon_{G\lambda}$. To obtain effective values of the emissivity or absorptivity, a summation over all of the radiation bands is necessary. We observe that, for large values of L, i.e., for thick layers, gas radiation approaches black-body conditions within the wavelengths of its bands.

For gas bodies of finite dimensions, however, the effective absorptivity or emissivity depends on the shape and the size of the gas body, since radiation is not confined to one direction. The precise method of calculating the effective absorptivity or emissivity is quite complex (9,13,14), but for engineering calculations an approximate method developed by Hottel (9) yields results of satisfactory accuracy. Hottel evaluated the emissivities of a number of gases at various temperatures and pressures and presented the results of his calculations in graphs similar to those shown in Figs. 5–29 and 5–30. The graphs apply strictly only to a system in which a hemispherical gas mass of radius L radiates to an element of surface located at the center of the base of a hemisphere. However, for shapes other than hemispheres, an effective beam length can be calculated. Table 5–3 lists the constants by which the characteristic dimensions of several simple shapes are to be multiplied to obtain an equivalent mean hemispherical beam length L for Figs. 5–29 and 5–30. For rough calculations, L can be taken as $3.4 \times$ volume/surface area.

The curves in Figs. 5–29 and 5–30 give the emissivity of water vapor and carbon dioxide at a total pressure p_T of 1 atmosphere (atm) as functions

TABLE 5–3
Average Lengths of Radiant Beams in Various Gas Shapes

Shape	L
1. Sphere	$\frac{2}{3} \times$ diameter
2. Infinite cylinder	$1 \times$ diameter
3. Space between infinite parallel planes	$1.8 \times$ distance between planes
4. Cube	$\frac{2}{3} \times$ side
5. Space outside infinite bank of tubes with centers on equilateral triangles; tube diameter equals clearance	$2.8 \times$ clearance
6. Same as (5) except tube diameter equals one-half clearance	$3.8 \times$ clearance

SOURCE: Ref. 14.

of the temperature, in degrees Fahrenheit, and the product of the partial pressure of the gas p, in atmospheres, and the hemispherical beam length of the body of the gas L, in feet. The effects of the actual values of total pressures on the emissivity of CO_2 and both total and partial pressures on the emissivity of water vapor are accounted for by means of the auxiliary charts in Figs. 5–31 and 5–32 which give correction factors to the curves in Figs. 5–29 and 5–30.[3] For carbon dioxide the emissivity obtained from

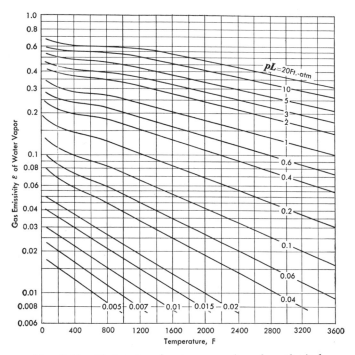

Fig. 5–29. Emissivity of water vapor for a hypothetical system at 1 atmosphere total pressure and 0 partial pressure. (By permission from H. C. Hottel and R. S. Egbert, "Radiant Heat Transmission from Water Vapor," *AIChE Trans.*, Vol. 38, 1942)

Fig. 5–30 at one atmosphere must be multiplied by the correction factor C_p from Fig. 5–32 to compensate for the broadening of the absorption bands with total pressure. For water vapor the correction procedure is illustrated in Example 5–10.

Example 5–10. Determine the emissivity of water vapor at 2000 F at a partial pressure p of 0.1 atm when the total pressure p_T is 2 atm and the equivalent hemispherical beam length of the gas body is 5 ft.

[3] Charts similar to those shown for CO_2 and H_2O are available in Ref. 9 for a number of other gases.

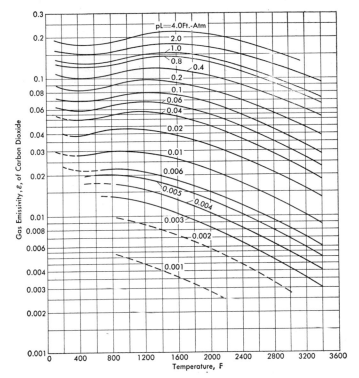

FIG. 5-30. Emissivity of carbon dioxide measured experimentally at 1 atmosphere total pressure. (By permission from H. C. Hottel and R. B. Egbert, "Radiant Heat Transmission from Water Vapor," *AIChE Trans.*, Vol. 38, 1942)

Solution: From Fig. 5-29 we obtain the emissivity reduced to $p = 0$. For pL equal to 0.5, $\epsilon_G = 0.125$ at a temperature of 2000 F. From the curves of Fig. 5-31, $C_p = 1.45$ at $(p + p_T)/2 = 1.05$. The effective emissivity is therefore 0.181.   *Ans.*

When both CO_2 and H_2O are present, the emissivity can be estimated by adding the emissivities of the two constituents. The value obtained by a simple addition is slightly too large because some of the absorption bands of these two gases overlap. A correction may be applied as shown by Hottel (9), but the error incurred by simple addition of emissivities is not appreciable.

To calculate the rate of heat flow by radiation between a nonluminous gas at T_G and the walls of a black-body container at T_w we evaluate the absorptivity α_G at the temperature T_w and the emissivity ϵ_G at the temperature T_G. The net rate of radiant heat flow is the difference between the emitted and absorbed radiation, or

$$q_r = \sigma A_G(\epsilon_G T_G{}^4 - \alpha_G T_w{}^4) \tag{5-37}$$

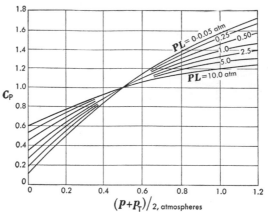

FIG. 5–31. Factor C_p for correcting emissivity of water vapor to values of p and p_T other than 0 and 1 atmosphere. (By permission from H. C. Hottel and R. B. Egbert, "Radiant Heat Transmission from Water Vapor," *AIChE Trans.*, Vol. 38, 1942)

Example 5–11. Flue gas at 2000 F containing 5 per cent water vapor flows at atmospheric pressure through a 2-ft-square flue made of refractory brick. Estimate the rate of heat flow per foot length from the gas to the wall if the inner-wall surface temperature is 1850 F and the average unit-surface convective conductance is 2 Btu/hr sq ft F.

Solution: The rate of heat flow from the gas to the wall by convection is

$$q_c = \bar{h}_c A \ (T_{\text{gas}} - T_{\text{wall}})$$
$$= (2) \ (4) \ (2 \times 1) \ (150) \ = 2400 \text{ Btu/ft length}$$

To determine the rate of heat flow by radiation, we calculate first the effective beam length, or

$$L = \frac{3.4 \times \text{volume}}{\text{surface area}} = \frac{(3.4)(4)}{8} = 1.7 \text{ ft}$$

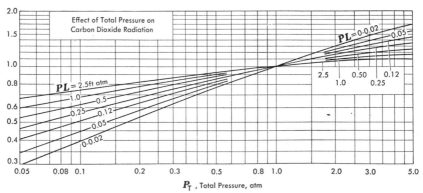

FIG. 5–32. Factor C_p for correcting emissivity of CO_2 at 1 atmosphere total pressure to emissivity at p_T atmosphere.

The product of partial pressure and L is

$$pL = (0.05)\ (1.7) = 0.085$$

From Fig. 5–29, for $pL = 0.085$ and $T_G = 2000$, we find $\epsilon_G = 0.035$. Similarly, we find $\alpha_G = 0.039$ at $T_w = 1850$ F. The pressure correction is negligible since $\overline{C}_p \simeq 1$ according to Fig. 5–31. Assuming that the brick surface is black, the net rate of heat flow from the gas to the wall by radiation is

$$q_r = 0.172 \times 8 \left[0.035 \left(\frac{24.6}{100}\right)^4 - 0.039 \left(\frac{23.1}{100}\right)^4 \right] = 2340 \text{ Btu/hr}$$

The total heat flow from the gas to the duct is therefore 4740 Btu/hr. It is interesting to note that the small amount of moisture in the gas contributes about one-half of the total heat flow.   *Ans.*

The calculation of the radiant heat flow between a gas and its enclosure becomes considerably more complicated when the enclosure surface is not black and reflects a part of the incident radiation. The reader is referred to Refs. 9, 10, and 30 for an analysis of such problems. An approximate answer may be obtained when the emissivity of the enclosure is larger than 0.7 by multiplying the radiant heat flow calculated from Eq. 5–32 by $(\epsilon_s + 1)$, where ϵ_s is the emissivity of the enclosure surface.

5–11. SOLAR, TERRESTRIAL, AND ATMOSPHERIC RADIATION

Nearly all sources of energy used by man for heating and power generation have been derived from the sun. However, those which are most easily utilized, as for example, coal and oil, have undergone changes which have substantially increased their concentration. Solar radiation is at present not used directly for industrial purposes because its concentration is relatively low. In recent years, however, industrial interest in the utilization of solar radiation, especially for heating homes and distilling fresh water from sea water, has increased considerably because the world demand for food and energy has risen so rapidly that, within the near future, available supplies are expected to become increasingly scarce and expensive. Solar radiation is also an important factor in the evaluation of heating or cooling requirement for aircraft, missiles, and buildings.

Calculations of solar radiation. The rate at which solar energy impinges on a surface of unit area placed normal to the sun at the outer fringes of the earth's atmosphere, the so-called *solar constant*, is about 442 Btu/hr sq ft (19). The rate at which solar radiation reaches the earth is, however, substantially less than 442 Btu/hr sq ft because part of the radiation is absorbed and scattered as it passes through the 90-mile-thick layer of air, water vapor, carbon dioxide, and dust which envelops the earth. The amount of solar radiation received by a surface on the earth depends on the location, the time of day, the time of year, the weather, and the tilt of the surface.

The diminution of the solar radiation by the earth's atmosphere depends on the length of the path, which in turn depends on the position of the sun. The radiant energy incident upon a surface on the earth placed normal to the rays of the sun G_n can be estimated (20) from the equation

$$G_n = G_o \tau_a{}^m \tag{5-38}$$

where G_o = solar constant;

   m = *relative air mass*, defined as the ratio of the actual path length to the shortest possible path;

   τ_a = transmission coefficient for unit air mass.

The value of τ_a is slightly less in the summer than in the winter because the atmosphere contains more water vapor during the summer. It also varies with the condition of the sky, ranging from 0.62 on a clear day to 0.81 on a cloudy one. A mean value of 0.7 is generally considered acceptable for most purposes.

The value of m depends on the position of the sun given by the *zenith distance z*, the angle between the zenith and the direction of the sun. Assuming that the thickness of the atmosphere is negligible compared to the radius of the earth, the relative air mass is equal to secant z. This relation is sufficiently accurate for z between 0 and 80 deg, and beyond this angle solar radiation is almost negligible.

If the receiving surface is not normal to the direction of the sun, the incident radiation per unit area G_i will be reduced by the cosine of i, the angle between the sun direction and the surface normal, or

$$G_i = G_n \cos i \tag{5-39}$$

If the receiving surface is horizontal, as in a solar evaporator, then $\cos i = \cos z$.

The determination of the angle between the sun direction and the surface normal requires a knowledge of the sun's position in the sky relative to an observer on the surface. The sun's position[4] depends on at least two simultaneous motions because the earth revolves in the ecliptic plane once every 365.25 days around the sun's ecliptic axis and spins at the same time like a gyroscope around its own celestial axis, which is tilted 23.5 deg with respect to the ecliptic axis, at the rate of $(\pi/12)$ radians/hr.

When the sun is viewed from the earth (see Fig. 5-33), the zenith angle varies with the latitude of the location, the time of day, and the solar declination. The latitude of a location, ϕ, can be obtained from an atlas or

[4] For more detailed information about celestial and terrestrial coordinates as well as conventional methods of measuring the azimuth and the latitude with a transit, see Chapter 17 of *Elementary Surveying* by R. C. Brinker and W. C. Taylor, International Textbook Company, 3d ed., 1955.

a globe. The time of day is expressed in terms of the *hour angle*, *h*, which indicates the apparent rotation of the celestial sphere about the earth's axis. In other words, it is the angle through which the earth must turn to bring the meridian of a particular location directly under the sun. The hour angle is measured in degrees westward from local noon (i.e., from the south meridian). As a result of the earth's rotation, *h* varies from zero at local noon to a maximum at sunrise or sunset. The maximum value of *h* depends on the latitude and the solar declination, δ_s. The latter can be

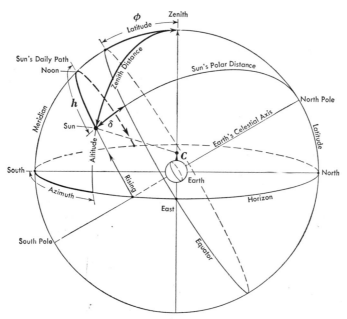

FIG. 5–33. Celestial sphere and sun's coordinates relative to observer on earth at point *C*.

obtained directly for any day of the year from an ephemeris.[5] It can be shown (e.g., Ref. 21) that the equation

$$\cos z = \sin \phi \sin \delta_s + \cos \phi \cos \delta_s \cos h \qquad (5\text{–}40)$$

relates the zenith angle to the terrestrial coordinates. Combining Eqs. 5–39 and 5–40 gives the rate at which radiant energy is received at a horizontal surface, the *local insolation*, as

$$G_i = G_n (\sin \phi \sin \delta_s + \cos \phi \cos \delta_s \cos h) \qquad (5\text{–}41)$$

[5] The *American Ephemeris and Nautical Almanac* is published yearly and may be obtained from the Superintendent of Documents, Washington, D. C.

The amount of solar radiation received during a 24-hr period, obtained by integration of the equation $dQ = G_i \, d\theta$ between sunrise and sunset, is

$$Q = \frac{24}{\pi} G_o \sin \phi \sin \delta_s \, (H - \tan H) \qquad (5\text{--}42)$$

where H is the total hour angle traversed by the sun between noon (zero) and sunrise or sunset. Its value can also be obtained from the ephemeris.

For a surface which is tilted (Fig. 5–34) at an angle ψ degrees to the horizontal and whose normal faces α degrees westward (measured along the horizon from the south meridian), the normal solar irradiation G_n can be divided into two components respectively perpendicular to and parallel to the tilted surface. Only the perpendicular component G_i impinges on the surface. The ratio of the effective radiation component to the normal intensity is given by

$$\frac{G_i}{G_n} = \cos i = \cos |z - \psi| - \sin z \sin \psi + \sin z \sin \psi \cos |A - \alpha| \qquad (5\text{--}43)$$

where A, the azimuth of the sun, is $\sin^{-1} [\cos \delta_s \sin h / \cos (90 - z)]$. Brown and Marco (22) have prepared the graphs shown in Fig. 5–35 from which the values of the pertinent angles in Eq. 5–43 can be obtained for the hours from 6 A.M. to 6 P.M. for various northern latitudes. They recommend that the curves for a solar azimuth A of 30 deg be used for latitudes from 25 to 35 deg and the curve for A of 45 deg be used for 40 to 50 deg latitude. When local and sun times do not coincide, a correction of 1 hr

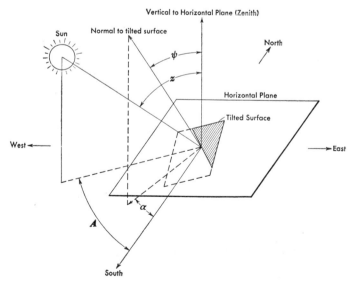

FIG. 5–34. Definition of solar and surface angles for Eq. 5–43.

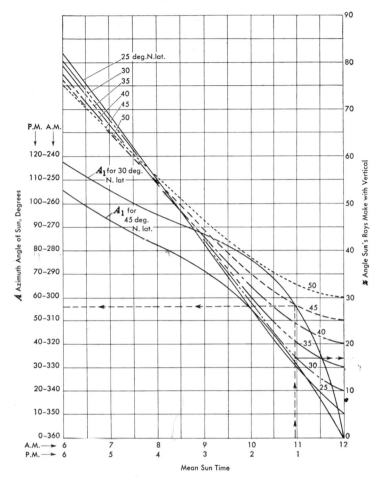

Fig. 5–35. Solar angles for the period from May to August in northern latitudes. (By permission from A. I. Brown and S. M. Marco, *Introduction to Heat Transfer*, 2d ed. New York: McGraw-Hill Book Company, Inc., 1951)

for every 15 deg of longitude by which the location departs from the standard meridian should be applied.

Equilibrium temperature. The total amount of radiant energy received by a body on the earth is the sum of the direct radiation from the sun and the diffuse radiation scattered from the atmosphere. The latter may amount to only 10 per cent of the total direct radiation reaching a horizontal surface on a bright sunny day; in partly cloudy weather it may amount to 50 per cent, while on completely overcast days it comprises the total radiation. The diffuse radiation is relatively independent of the geometry of the receiver.

If the body is up in the sky, as for example an airplane, or is tilted so that it can "see" the earth's surface, it also receives terrestrial radiation.

The net rate of heat flow to or from a body, q_{net}, can be calculated from the equation

$$q_{net} = q_s + q_a + q_t + q_c + q_k - q_r \qquad (5\text{--}44)$$

where q_s = portion of the direct solar radiation absorbed;

q_a = portion of the atmospheric radiation absorbed;

q_t = portion of the terrestrial radiation absorbed;

q_r = radiation emitted;

q_k = net conduction to the body;

q_c = net convection to the body.

The equilibrium temperature attained by a surface in the open can be calculated from Eq. 5–39 by setting the right-hand side equal to zero.

The fraction of the incident radiation absorbed by a surface depends on the value of its absorption coefficient, which is in turn a function of the spectral distribution of the incoming energy. The spectral distribution of solar radiation is shown in Table 5–4. While 99 per cent of the solar energy is contained between 0.25 and 3.0 μ, the terrestrial and emitted radiation, on the other hand, fall largely in the long-wavelength portion of the spectrum.

TABLE 5–4

SPECTRAL DISTRIBUTION OF SOLAR ENERGY, NORMAL SOLAR
IRRADIATION, AND TRANSMISSION COEFFICIENT

	m					
	0	1	2	3	4	5
Ultraviolet 0.29–0.40 μ	7.2*	4.3*	2.7*	1.5*	1.1*	0.6*
Visible 0.4–0.7 μ	40.8*	45.2*	44.3*	47.6*	40.4*	38.1*
Above 0.8 μ	52.0*	50.5*	53.0*	55.8*	58.5*	61.3*
Normal solar irradiation, G_n Btu/sq ft hr	442	310	248	203	170	143
Transmission coefficient	....	0.702	0.748	0.771	0.788	0.799

* In per cent of the total radiation within the wavelength range shown in the first column.
SOURCE: Parry Moon, "Solar Radiation Curves for Engineering Use," *J. Franklin Inst.*, Vol. 230 (1940), pp. 583–618, with correction for more recent value of the solar constant from Ref. 15.

Figure 5–36 shows the results of some measurements made by Gier and Dunkle (23). We observe that surfaces having large absorptivities in the solar-wavelength range reach substantially higher equilibrium temperatures than surfaces with low absorptivities. The lowest equilibrium temperatures are obtained by white paints which are *selective emitters*.

They are poor absorbers (i.e., good reflectors) for the spectral range of solar radiation, but good absorbers, and consequently also good emitters, in the spectral range associated with relatively low temperatures. Since these paints emit more radiation than, for example, aluminum, an equally good reflector of solar energy, their equilibrium temperatures are lower than those attained by the metal surface. This property can be used to advantage on roofs of houses in a sunny climate, where it is desirable to

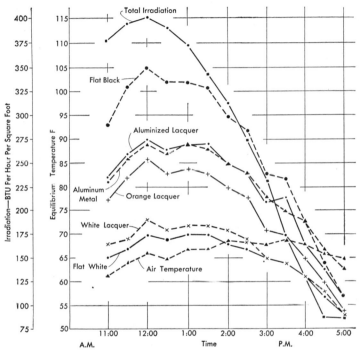

Fig. 5–36. Equilibrium temperatures of various surfaces. (Courtesy of Professors R. V. Dunkle and J. T. Gier, Ref. 23)

keep the roof temperature as low as possible for the comfort of the occupants.

Example 5–12. Calculate the equilibrium temperature of a polished-aluminum surface at 2 P.M. on a clear day. The surface faces southwest, is inclined 15 deg with the horizontal, is located at 30 deg north latitude at a longitude where the local time is 1 hr ahead of sun time. The atmosphere is at 50 F and the unit convective surface conductance is 2.0 Btu/hr sq ft F. Conduction effects may be neglected.

Solution: The direct solar radiation incident on the surface is calculated from Eqs. 5–38 and 5–43, where, for the specified conditions,

$$\alpha = 45 \text{ deg (southwest direction)}$$
$$\psi = 15 \text{ deg}$$

$$A = 56 \text{ deg (from Fig. 5–35 at 1 p.m.)}$$
$$z = 17 \text{ deg (from Fig. 5–35 at 1 p.m. sun time)}$$

The irradiation on a square foot of surface placed normal to the sun is, from Eq. 5–38,

$$G_n = G_o \, \tau_o{}^m = (442) \, (0.7^{\sec 17}) = 305 \text{ Btu/hr sq ft}$$

From Eq. 5–43 we have

$$\cos i = \cos |17 - 15| - \sin 17 \sin 15 + \sin 17 \sin 15 \cos |56 - 45|$$
$$= 0.999 - (0.297 \times 0.259) + (0.297 \times 0.259 \times 0.97)$$
$$= 0.997$$

The irradiation is found from Eq. 5–39:

$$G_i = G_n \cos i = (305) \, (0.997) = 304 \text{ Btu/hr sq ft}$$

The absorptivity of polished aluminum for solar radiation is about 0.3 (Table 5–1). The rate of heat absorption is thus

$$q_s = \alpha \text{ solar } G_i = (0.3) \, (304) = 91.2 \text{ Btu/hr sq ft}$$

On a sunny day the atmospheric radiation is about 10 per cent of the direct solar radiation or

$$q_a = (0.1) \, (91.2) = 9.12 \text{ Btu/hr sq ft}$$

Since the surface can not see any part of the earth, we have

$$q_t = 0$$

The rate at which the surface emits radiation is given by

$$q_r = \epsilon \sigma T_s{}^4 = (0.04)(0.172)(T_s/100)^4$$

where ϵ is taken at a temperature of 100 F from Table 5–1. The rate of heat flow by convection to the surrounding air is

$$q_c = \bar{h}_c \, (T_s - T_\infty) = 2.0 \, [T_s - (460 + 50)]$$

Equilibrium is established when the surface temperature has reached a value at which the rate of heat flow to the surface equals the rate of heat flow from the surface, that is, when $q_{net} = 0$ in Eq. 5–44. Then we have

$$q_s = q_r + q_c$$

or
$$103.3 = 6.88 \times 10^{-11} \, T_s{}^4 + 2T_s - 1020$$

This equation is solved by trial and error for the equilibrium surface temperature and we get $T_s = 97$ F.   *Ans.*

Nocturnal radiation. Whereas in the daytime, atmospheric radiation consists largely of reflected solar energy, measurements of nocturnal radiation taken on cold clear nights indicate that the effective sky temperature is at that time of the order of 410 Rankine (-50 F) (11). This accounts for the freezing of water during the night even when the atmospheric temperature is above 32 F. The low sky temperature is also responsible for the freezing of oranges in California.

Utilization of solar energy. Any direct utilization of solar radiation for heating systems or power production requires equipment capable of collecting and storing the energy at a sufficiently high temperature. The equipment suggested or used can be divided into three general classes: flat-plate collectors, concentrators, and solar thermoelectric generators. The first two types of device use solar radiation to heat a working substance, while the last type converts solar radiant energy into electrical energy by photoelectric cells of the photovoltaic type, or by thermoelectric means. A solar battery has been developed and is used by the Bell Telephone Company (24) to furnish power to telephone lines in some rural areas where maintenance of ordinary batteries is very expensive. A summary of calculations and experimental results for solar thermoelectric generators is given in Ref. 25.

The simplest type of flat-plate solar-radiation collector consists of a metal plate above which layers of air are trapped between glass plates. Equilibrium temperatures for various arrangements of such collectors are shown in Table 5-5. The trapped air acts as an insulator, reducing the

TABLE 5-5

EQUILIBRIUM TEMPERATURES FOR FLAT-PLATE AND
MIRROR ABSORBERS IN 80 F ATMOSPHERE

TYPE OF ABSORBER	INCIDENT RADIATION (BTU/HR SQ FT)	
	200	300
Flat-plate		
1 glass cover...............	186	225
2 glass covers..............	207	253
3 glass covers..............	228	282
Mirrors		
Concentration 5 times.....	400	520
Concentration 10 times.....	630	830
Concentration 20 times.....	1015	1360

convection loss from the collecting surface. The glass plates, being opaque to the long-wavelength radiation emitted by the collecting surface, reduce radiation losses. For efficient operation, the exposed surface is painted black, preferably with a substance which has a high absorptivity in the 0.3- to 2.0-μ wavelength range and a low emissivity in the 5- to 10-μ range. Such a surface has been produced by depositing thin black metallic films on a copper surface (26). Below the metal plate which absorbs the solar radiation, the medium to be heated is circulated in thermal contact with the plate. It has been calculated (20) that, under favorable weather conditions, steam at over 100 pounds per square inch (psi) pressure can be produced in such a collector. According to preliminary estimates (20), this type of collector operating in solar weather similar to that prevailing in Texas can attain equilibrium temperatures of the order of 250 to 300 F and yield on a yearly basis an average work output of 77 kw per acre of collecting surface. However, the cost of power production would be approximately three times the present power cost by more conventional means.

Where high temperatures are desired, some form of concentrating collector must be used. Many different combinations of mirrors and lenses have been proposed, and some arrangements have actually been used for solar engines and furnaces. The advantage of concentration is that the area from which heat losses occur is less than the area receiving radiant energy, and the heat losses are proportionately reduced with an increase in equilibrium temperature. Figure 5–37 shows a conical-mirror arrange-

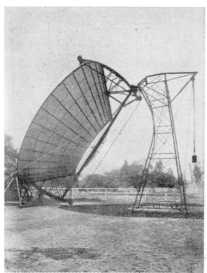

Fig. 5–37.   Solar motor.   (Courtesy C. F. Holder, Ref. 27)

ment used, in 1900, by A. G. Eneas (27) to generate steam at 150 psi. With a mirror surface of about 700 sq ft, a steam engine was driven for which an output of 10 horsepower (hp) was claimed.

The most important practical application of solar energy today is in solar furnaces (28). In these furnaces, parabolic reflectors concentrate the heat flux available at the site on a small area. Temperatures as high as 6000 R can be maintained in an object placed at focal point. Solar furnaces are therefore important tools for high-temperature research, especially in experiments where contamination by flames, combustion products, electrodes, and refractory fragments must be avoided.

The practical aspects involved in utilizing solar energy have recently been discussed in detail at two symposia, one held in Wisconsin, in 1953, and the other in Arizona, in 1955. The papers presented at these symposia have been published (25,26), and the reader who wishes to pursue this subject further is referred to them.

REFERENCES

1. N. W. Snyder, "A Review of Thermal Radiation Constants," *Trans. ASME*, Vol. 65 (1954), pp. 537–540.
2. R. V. Dunkle, "Thermal-Radiation Tables and Applications," *Trans. ASME*, Vol. 65 (1954), pp. 549–552.
3. W. Sieber, "Zusammensetzung der von Werk-und Baustoffen Zurückgeworfenen Wärmestrahlung," *Z. Tech. Physik*, Vol. 22 (1941), pp. 130–135.
4. E. Schmidt and E. Eckert, "Über die Richtungsverteilung der Wärmestrahlung von Oberflächen," *Forsch. Gebiete Ingenieurw.*, Vol. 6 (1935), pp. 175–183.
5. H. C. Hottel, "Radiant Heat Transmission Between Surfaces Separated by Non-Absorbing Media," *Trans. ASME*, FSP-53-19b, Vol. 53 (1931), pp. 265–271.
6. H. C. Hottel, "Radiant Heat Transmission," *Mech. Eng.*, Vol. 52 (1930), pp. 699–704.
7. D. C. Hamilton and W. R. Morgan, "Radiant-Interchange Configuration Factors," *NACA TN* 2836, December, 1952.
8. F. W. Hutchinson, *Industrial Heat Transfer*. (New York: The Industrial Press, 1952.)
9. H. C. Hottel, Chapter 2 of *Heat Transmission* (by W. C. McAdams), 3d ed. (New York: McGraw-Hill Book Company, Inc., 1954.)
10. A. K. Oppenheim, "The Network Method of Radiation Analysis," *ASME Paper* 54-A75, 1954.
11. M. Fischenden and O. A. Saunders, *The Calculation of Heat Transmission*. (London: His Majesty's Stationery Office, 1932.)
12. S. Chandrasekhar, *Radiative Transfer*. (Oxford: Clarendon Press, 1950.)
13. H. C. Hottel, "Heat Transmission by Radiation from Non-Luminous Gases," *Trans. Am. Inst. Chem. Engrs.*, Vol. 19 (1927), pp. 173–205.
14. H. C. Hottel and R. B. Egbert, "Radiant Heat Transmission from Water Vapor," *Trans. Am. Inst. Chem. Engrs.*, Vol. 38 (1942), pp. 531–565.
15. F. A. Brooks, "Solar Energy and Its Use for Heating Water in California," *Bull.* 602, Col. of Agric., Univ. of Calif., 1936.
16. N. W. Snyder, J. T. Gier, and R. V. Dunkle, "Total Normal Emissivity Measurements on Aircraft Materials Between 100 and 800 F," *ASME Paper* 54-A-189, 1954.
17. H. Schmidt and E. Furthman, "Üeber die Gesamtstrahlung fester Köerper," *Mitt. K. W. Inst. Eisenforsch*, Abh. 109, Dusseldorf, 1928.
18. W. H. McAdams, *Heat Transmission*, 3d ed. (New York: McGraw-Hill Book Company, Inc., 1954.)
19. F. S. Johnson, "The Solar Constant," *J. of Meteorology*, Vol. 11 (1954), pp. 431–439.
20. H. Heywood, "Solar Energy: Past, Present and Future Applications," *Engineering*, Vol. 176 (1956), pp. 377–380.
21. W. J. Humphreys, *Physics of the Air*. (New York: McGraw-Hill Book Company, Inc., 1940.)
22. A. I. Brown and S. M. Marco, *Introduction to Heat Transfer*, 2d ed. (New York: McGraw-Hill Book Company, Inc., 1951.)
23. J. T. Gier and R. V. Dunkle, "Selective Spectral Characteristics of Solar Collectors," *Trans. Tuscon Conference on Applied Solar Energy*, Vol. 2, 1957.
24. Anonymous, "Sun Powered Telephone Lines," *Mech. Eng.*, Vol. 77 (1955), p. 989.

25. M. Telkes, "Solar Thermoelectric Generators," *Solar Energy Research,* edited by F. Daniels and J. A. Duffie. (Madison, Wis.: University of Wisconsin Press, 1955.)

26. H. Tabor, "Selective Radiation," *Trans. Tuscon Conference on Applied Solar Energy,* Vol. 2, 1957.

27. C. F. Holder, "Solar Motors," *Scientific American,* Vol. 84 (new series) (1901), p. 169.

28. G. Benveniste and N. K. Hiester, "The Solar Furnace," *Mech. Eng.,* Vol. 78 (1956), pp. 915–920.

29. J. T. Gier, R. V. Dunkle, and J. T. Bevans, "Measurement of Absolute Spectral Reflectivity from 1.0 to 15.0 Microns," *J. Opt. Soc.,* Vol. 44 (1954), pp. 558–562.

30. B. Gebhart, "Unified Treatment for Thermal Radiation Processes—Gray, Diffuse Radiators and Absorbers," *ASME Paper* 57-A-34, 1957.

PROBLEMS

5–1. For an ideal radiator (hohlraum) with a 4-in.-diam opening, located in black surroundings at 60 F, calculate for hohlraum temperatures of 212 F and 1040 F, (a) the net heat-transfer rate, in Btu/hr; (b) the wavelength at which the emission is a maximum, in microns; (c) the monochromatic emission at λ_{max}, in Btu/hr sq ft μ; (d) the wavelengths at which the monochromatic emission is 1 per cent of the maximum value.

Ans. (a) 19.5, 747; (b) 7.72, 3.46; (c) 30, 1652; and (d) 2.54 and 50.8, 1.14 and 22.8

5–2. A tungsten filament is heated to 5000 R. At what wavelength is the maximum amount of radiation emitted? What fraction of the total energy is in the visible range (0.4 to 0.75 microns)? Assume that the filament radiates as a gray body.

5–3. The radiant-heating ceiling of a 12- by 20-ft room is 8 ft from the floor and is maintained at 110 F while the room air is 50 F. Assuming both surfaces are black, estimate the net rate of heat transfer per square foot of floor surface at 80 F, located (a) in the center of the room, (b) in the corner of the room. *Ans.* 18.5, 7.1 Btu/hr sq ft

5–4. Calculate the equilibrium temperature of a thermocouple in a large air duct if the air temperature is 2000 F, the duct-wall temperature 500 F, the emissivity of the couple 0.5, and the convective-heat-transfer coefficient, $\bar{h}_c$, is 20 Btu/hr sq ft F.

5–5. Repeat Prob. 5–4 with the addition of a radiation shield ($\epsilon = 0.9$, $\bar{h}_c = 20$ Btu/hr sq ft F).

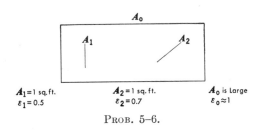

$A_1 = 1$ sq. ft. $A_2 = 1$ sq. ft. A_0 is Large
$\varepsilon_1 = 0.5$ $\varepsilon_2 = 0.7$ $\varepsilon_0 \approx 1$

PROB. 5–6.

5–6. Derive an equation for the net rate of radiant heat transfer from surface 1 in the system shown in the accompanying sketch. Assume that each surface is at a uniform temperature.

5–7. Show that the moon would appear as a disk if its surface were perfectly diffuse.

5–8. Two 5-ft-square and parallel flat plates are 1 ft apart. Plate A_1 is maintained at a temperature of 1540 F and A_2 at 460 F. The emissivities are 0.5 and 0.8. Considering the surroundings black at 0 R and including multiple interreflections, determine

(a) the net radiant exchange and (b) the heat input required by surface A_1 to maintain its temperature.

5–9. A series of surfaces, insulated to prevent heat loss from the underside, are placed in the sunlight. Estimate the equilibrium temperature for each of several surfaces with the sun at zenith for a clear atmosphere, an air temperature of 70 F, a relative humidity of 100 per cent, and a convective-heat-transfer coefficient of 3 Btu/sq ft hr F. The materials are (a) polished aluminum, (b) polished silver, (c) white (ZnO) painted surface, and (d) lamp-black painted surface.

5–10. Show that $A_1\mathfrak{F}_{1\text{-}2}$ for two parallel planes of equal area connected by re-radiating walls at a constant temperature is:

$$A_1\mathfrak{F}_{1\text{-}2} = A_1 \left(\frac{1 + F_{1\text{-}2}}{2} \right)$$

Compare the results from this problem with the curves in Fig. 5–18, where allowance is made for a continuous variation in the temperature of the reradiating walls.

5–11. Determine the steady-state temperatures of two radiation shields placed in the evacuated space between two infinite planes at temperatures of 540 F and 40 F. The emissivities of all surfaces are 0.8.

5–12. A rectangular flat water tank is placed on the roof of a house with its lower portion perfectly insulated. A sheet of glass whose transmission characteristics are tabulated below is placed $\frac{1}{4}$ in. above the water surface. Assuming that the average incident solar radiation is 200 Btu/hr sq ft, calculate the equilibrium water temperature for a water depth of 6 in. if the unit-convective conductance at the top of the glass is 1.5 Btu/hr sq ft F and the surrounding air temperature is 70 F. Disregard interreflections.

τ_λ of glass   0   for wavelength from 0 to 0.35 μ
                            0.92 for wavelength from 0.35 to 2.7 μ
                            0   for wavelength larger than 2.7 μ

ρ_λ of glass   0.08 for all wavelengths

5–13. Derive an expression for the geometric shape factor $F_{1\text{-}2}$ for a rectangular surface A_1, 1 by 20 ft, placed parallel to and centered 5 ft above a 20-ft-square surface A_2.

5–14. Calculate the net radiant-heat-transfer rate if the two surfaces in Prob. 5–13 are connected by a refractory surface of 500-sq-ft area and A_1 is at 540 F and A_2 is at 40 F. What is the refractory surface temperature?

5–15. A black sphere (1 in. diam) is placed in a large infrared heating oven whose walls are maintained at 700 F. The temperature of the air in the oven is 200 F and the heat-transfer coefficient for convection between the surface of the sphere and the air is 5 Btu/hr sq ft F. Estimate the *net rate of heat flow* to the sphere when its surface temperature is 100 F.

5–16. The irradiation received at a point on the earth's surface was found to be 394 Btu/hr sq ft. If the transmissibility (i.e., the per cent of the emitted radiation which reaches the receiver) of the earth's atmosphere is about 82 per cent, the distance from the earth to the sun is 93,000,000 miles, and the diameter of the sun is 433,000 miles, estimate the temperature of the sun. The emissivity of the sun may be taken as unity.

5–17. Two concentric spheres, 8 and 12 in. in diam, with the space between them evacuated, are to be used to store liquid air (− 220 F) in a room at 68 F. If the surfaces of the spheres have been flashed with aluminum and the liquid air has a latent heat of vaporization of 90 Btu/lb, determine the number of pounds of liquid air evaporated per hour.

5–18. A 2-ft-square section of panel heater is installed in the corner of the ceiling of a room having a 9- by 12-ft floor area with an 8-ft ceiling. If the surface of the heater, made from oxidized iron, is at 300 F and the walls and the air of the room are at 68 F in the steady state, determine (a) the rate of heat transfer to the room by radiation; (b) the rate of heat transfer to the room by convection ($\bar{h}_c \simeq 2$ Btu/hr sq ft F); (c) the cost of heating the room at 1 cent per kwhr in cents per hour.

5–19. A 2-ft-radius hemisphere (1000 F surface temperature) is filled with a gas mixture at 500 F and 3-atm pressure containing 6.67 per cent CO_2 and water vapor at 5 per cent relative humidity. Determine the emissivity and absorptivity of the gas.

5–20. Estimate the net rate of radiant heat flow to the gas in Prob. 5–19.

5–21. A ladle of molten iron at 2600 F is 12 in. in diam at the surface of the metal. Neglecting heat losses through the fire-clay body of the ladle, calculate the rate of cooling due to radiation from the surface to atmospheric air at 70 F in deg Fahrenheit per min (F/min). The ladle holds 600 lb and the heat capacity of the molten iron is 0.28 Btu/lb$_m$ F.

5–22. A gas leaving a lime kiln contains 20 per cent CO_2 and 80 per cent N_2 and O_2. This gas flows through a square duct, 6 by 6 in. at the rate of 0.4 lb/sq ft sec. The average temperature of the inside surface of the duct is 800 F, and the emissivity is 0.9. The gas enters the duct at 2000 F, leaves at 1000 F, and has an average specific heat of 0.28 Btu/lb F. The heat-transfer coefficient by convection is 1.5 Btu/hr sq ft F. (a) How long must the duct be to cool the gas to 1000 F? (b) What percentage of heat lost is transferred by radiation? (c) If the velocity of the gas were doubled and the average temperature and length of duct kept the same, what would be the temperature of the gas leaving? (When the velocity is doubled, $\bar{h}_c$ will increase to 2.6 Btu/hr sq ft F.) (*Courtesy of the American Institute of Chemical Engineers.*)

5–23. An inside room of a house, 24 ft square with a 12-ft ceiling, is to be heated by means of a panel-heating installation located in the ceiling. The ceiling is painted with an oil paint and heated uniformly by hot-water pipes imbedded in it. The floor is made of oak and is to be maintained at 80 F. To maintain comfort in the room it is necessary to transfer radiant heat between the ceiling and the floor at the rate of 6000 Btu/hr. (a) Determine the required ceiling temperature, (1) neglecting the side walls, and (2) assuming that the side walls are nonconducting, but reradiating. (b) Determine the temperature of the side walls for case (2). (c) Estimate the rate of heat flow by convection to the room for case (2) if the air temperature is 86 F and the unit-surface conductance for free convection is 1.0 Btu/hr sq ft F. (d) Estimate the total heat loss from the heater per hour.

5–24. A metal plate is placed in the sunlight. The incident radiant energy G is 250 Btu/hr sq ft. The air and the surroundings are at 50 F. The heat-transfer coefficient by free convection from the upper surface of the plate is 3 Btu/hr sq ft F. The plate has an average emissivity of 0.9 at solar wavelengths and 0.1 at long wavelengths. Neglecting conduction losses on the lower surface, determine the equilibrium temperature of the plate.   *Ans.* $\simeq$ 121 F

5–25. Liquid nitrogen at − 321 F is stored in a spherical vacuum bottle having an inside container diameter of 5 in. and an outer diameter of 5½ in. The facing surfaces are silvered to produce an emissivity of 0.05. Neglecting the end effects at the mouth of the bottle, determine the rate of heat gain when the ambient temperature is 70 F. (Assume the surfaces are at the same temperature as the adjacent fluids.)
     Ans. 2.24 Btu/hr

5–26. One hundred pounds of carbon dioxide are stored in a high-pressure cylinder 10 in. in diam (OD), 4 ft long and ½ in. thick. The cylinder is fitted with a safety rupture diaphragm designed to fail at 2000 psia (with the specified charge, this pressure will be reached when the temperature increases to 120 F). During a fire, the cylinder is completely exposed to the irradiation from flames at 2000 F (ϵ = 1.0). For the specified conditions, c_v = 0.60 Btu/lb F for CO_2. Neglecting the convective heat transfer, determine the time the cylinder may be exposed to this irradiation before the diaphragm will fail if the initial temperature is 70 F and (a) the cylinder is bare oxidized steel (ϵ = 0.79), (b) the cylinder is painted with aluminum paint (ϵ = 0.30).

Ans. (a) 0.47 min, (b) 1.24 min

5-27. A large slab of steel 4 in. thick has in it a 4-in.-diam hole, with axis normal to the surface. Considering the sides of the hole to be black, specify the rate of heat loss from the hole. The plate is at 1000 F, the surroundings at 80 F. *Ans.* 1,110 Btu/hr

5-28. A thermocouple is used to measure the temperature of a flame in a combustion chamber. If the flame temperature is 1400 F and the walls of the chamber are at 800 F, what is the error in the thermocouple reading due to radiation to the walls? Assume all surfaces are black and the convection coefficient is 100 Btu/hr sq ft F on the thermocouple. *Ans.* 168 F

5-29. If the thermocouple of Prob. 5–28 is enclosed by a thin cylindrical shield $\frac{1}{4}$ in. in diam placed with its axis in the direction of the flow, what will be the error in the thermocouple reading? Assume the shield is black and long enough to allow neglect of end effects. Also, the thermocouple surface is negligible compared to the shield surface. *Ans.* 32 F

5-30. A small sphere (1 in. diam) is placed in a large heating oven whose walls are at 2000 F. The emissivity of the sphere is equal to 0.4 − 0.0001 T, where T is the surface temperature in F. When the surface temperature of the sphere is 1000 F, determine (a) the total irradiation received *by* the walls of the oven *from* the sphere, (b) the net heat transfer by radiation between the sphere and the walls of the oven, and (c) the radiant-heat-transfer coefficient.

5-31. Repeat Prob. 5–30, but assume that the oven cavity is a 1-ft cube filled with air containing 3 per cent water vapor.

5-32. A 1-in.-diam cylindrical refractory crucible for melting lead is to be built for thermocouple calibration. An electrical heater immersed in the metal is shut off at some temperature above the melting point. The fusion-cooling curve is obtained by observing the thermocouple emf as a function of time. Neglecting heat losses through the wall of the crucible, estimate the cooling rate (Btu/hr) for the molten lead surface (melting point 621.2 F, surface emissivity 0.8) if the crucible depth above the lead surface is (a) 1 in., (b) 5 in. Assume that the emissivity of the refractory surface is unity and the surroundings are at 70 F. (c) Noting that the crucible would hold about 0.2 lb of lead for which the heat of fusion is 10 Btu/lb, comment on the suitability of the crucible for the purpose intended.

5-33. Derive Eq. 5–23a from Eq. 5–23, filling in all the steps in detail. Also show that the temperature of the reradiating surface T_R is

$$T_R = \left(\frac{A_1 F_{1R} T_1^4 + A_2 F_{2R} T_2^4}{A_1 F_{1R} + A_2 F_{2R}} \right)^{\frac{1}{4}}$$

5-34. Fill in the remaining steps of the trial-and-error solution in Example 5–9.

5-35. The overhanging eaves on the south side of a house are designed to shade its entire glass wall. (a) If the eaves are 10 ft from the ground, how far should they overhang to shade the wall on May 10 at 12:00 noon? What will be the effect of these eaves at 4:00 o'clock on the same day? Latitude is 34 N. (b) If the solar transmissivity of the glass wall is 0.85, how much solar energy is supplied to the room per hour at 12:00 noon on January 10? Assume the glass wall area is 120 sq ft.

5-36. The radiant section of a small thermal-cracking combustion chamber has a volume of 3200 cu ft and a total surface of 2000 sq ft. A single-row tube-curtain of 4 in. schedule 40 pipes on 7-in. centers covers 760 sq ft of the wall. When the furnace is fired with gas of composition $(CH_2)_x$ at a rate of 2000 lb/hr, an Orsat analysis shows that 13 per cent CO_2 are present. Estimate the rate of heat transfer to the tubes under these conditions, using the simplest furnace model that can be justified.

Additional data:

Tube emissivity = 0.9.

Fuel heating value = 250,000 Btu/lb-mole of C.

Mean molar heat capacity of combustion products = 8.2 Btu/lb-mole F.

Mean radiating gas temperature is 200 F above the bridge-wall gas-temperature.

Air and fuel enter at 60 F.

5-37. Derive an expression for the net rate of heat transfer between a small gray sphere of area A_1, emissivity ϵ_1, and temperature T_1, and a small flat disk radiating from both sides (area A_2, emissivity ϵ_2, and temperature T_2). These two bodies are separated by a distance, large compared to the area of either, and are enclosed in the center of a very large, well-insulated chamber with black walls.

5-38. Show that (a) $(E_{b\lambda})_1/(E_{b\lambda})_2 = T_2{}^5/T_1{}^5$, and (b) $E_{b\lambda}/T^5 = f(\lambda T)$. Also, for $\lambda T = 10,000$ R $- \mu$, (c) calculate $E_{b\lambda}/T^5$ and check your result with Table A-4.

5-39. Compute the average emissivity of anodized aluminum at 200 F and 1200 F from the spectral curve in Fig. 5-9. Assume $\epsilon_\lambda = 0.8$ for $\lambda > 9\mu$.

6 Fundamentals of Convection

6–1. THE CONVECTIVE-HEAT-TRANSFER COEFFICIENT

In the preceding chapters, attention has been focused on heat transfer by conduction and radiation. In an effort to simplify the work and to emphasize the methods for calculating heat transfer by conduction and radiation, an effort has been made to eliminate, as much as possible, problems related to heat transfer by convection. In spite of this effort, it is apparent from the illustrative examples that there are hardly any practical problems which can be solved without a knowledge of the mechanisms by which heat is transferred between the surface of a solid conductor and the surrounding medium. In our work so far we simply specified the unit convective surface conductance at the solid fluid interface and did not investigate the details of the transfer mechanism. We evaluated the rate of heat transfer by convection between a solid boundary and a fluid by means of the equation

$$q_{\text{surface to fluid}} = A \, \bar{h}_c \, (T_s - T_\infty) \qquad [1\text{--}13]$$

The convection equation in this form seems quite simple. The simplicity is misleading, however, because Eq. 1–13 is a definition of the average unit thermal convective conductance $\bar{h}_c$ rather than a law of heat transfer by convection. The convective-heat-transfer coefficient is actually a complicated function of the fluid flow, the thermal properties of the fluid medium, and the geometry of the system. Its numerical value is in general not uniform over a surface, and depends also on the location where the fluid temperature T_∞ is measured.

Although Eq. 1–13 is generally used to determine the rate of heat flow by convection between a surface and the fluid in contact with it, this relation is inadequate to explain the convective-heat-flow mechanism. A meaningful analysis which will eventually lead to a quantitative evaluation of the convective-heat-transfer coefficient must start with a study of the dynamics of the fluid flow. In this and the following chapters we shall follow this line of approach and investigate the influence of flow conditions, fluid properties, and boundary shapes on the convective-heat-transfer coefficient.

6–2. ENERGY TRANSPORT MECHANISM AND FLUID FLOW

The transfer of heat between a solid boundary and a fluid takes place by a combination of conduction and mass transport. If the boundary is at a higher temperature than the fluid, heat flows first by conduction from the solid to fluid particles in the neighborhood of the wall. The energy thus transmitted increases the internal energy of the fluid and is carried away by the motion of the fluid. When the heated fluid particles reach a region at a lower temperature, heat is again transferred by conduction from warmer to cooler fluid.

Since the convective mode of energy transfer is so closely linked to the fluid motion, it is necessary to know something about the mechanism of fluid flow before the mechanism of heat flow can be investigated. One of the most important aspects of the hydrodynamic analysis is to establish whether the motion of the fluid is *laminar* or *turbulent*.

In laminar, or streamline, flow, the fluid moves in layers, each fluid particle following a smooth and continuous path. The fluid particles in each layer remain in an orderly sequence without passing one another. Soldiers on parade provide a somewhat crude analogy to laminar flow. They march along well-defined lines, one behind the other, and maintain their order even when they turn a corner or pass an obstacle.

In contrast to the orderly motion of laminar flow, the motion of fluid particles in turbulent flow rather resembles a crowd of commuters in a railroad station during the rush hour. The general trend of the motion is from the gate toward the train, but superimposed upon this motion are the deviations of individuals according to their instantaneous direction and their ability to pass the less agile members of the crowd. Yet if one could obtain a statistical average of the motion of a large number of individuals, it would be steady and regular. The same applies to fluid particles in turbulent flow. The path of any individual particle is zigzag and irregular, but on a statistical basis the over-all motion of the aggregate of fluid particles is regular and predictable.

When a fluid flows in laminar motion along a surface at a temperature different from that of the fluid, heat is transferred only by molecular conduction within the fluid as well as at the interface between the fluid and the surface. There exist no turbulent mixing currents or eddies by which energy stored in fluid particles is transported across streamlines. Heat is transferred between fluid layers by molecular motion on a submicroscopic scale.

In turbulent flow, on the other hand, the conduction mechanism is modified and aided by innumerable eddies which carry lumps of fluid across the streamlines. These fluid particles act as carriers of energy and transfer energy by mixing with other particles of the fluid. An increase in the rate of mixing (or turbulence) will therefore also increase the rate of heat flow by convection.

The fluid motion can be induced by two processes. The fluid may be set in motion as a result of density differences due to a temperature variation in the fluid. This mechanism is called *free,* or *natural, convection.* The motion observed when a pot of water is heated on a stove or the motion of air in the desert on a calm day after sunset are examples of free convection. When the motion is caused by some external agency, such as a pump or a blower, we speak of *forced convection.* The cooling of an automobile radiator by the air blown over it by the fan is an example of forced convection. (The term "radiator" is obviously poorly chosen because the heat flow is *not* primarily by radiation; "convector" would be a more appropriate term.)

6-3. BOUNDARY-LAYER FUNDAMENTALS

When a fluid flows along a surface, irrespective of whether the flow is laminar or turbulent, the particles in the vicinity of the surface are slowed down by virtue of viscous forces. The fluid particles adjacent to the surface stick to it and have zero velocity relative to the boundary.[1] Other fluid particles attempting to slide over them are retarded as a result of an interaction between faster- and slower-moving fluid, a phenomenon which gives rise to shearing forces. In laminar flow the interaction, called viscous shear, takes place between molecules on a submicroscopic scale. In turbulent flow an interaction between lumps of fluid on a macroscopic scale, called turbulent shear, is superimposed on the viscous shear.

The effects of the viscous forces originating at the boundary extend into the body of the fluid, but a short distance from the surface the velocity of the fluid particles approaches that of the undisturbed free stream. The fluid contained in the region of substantial velocity change is called the *hydrodynamic boundary layer.* The thickness of the boundary layer has been defined as the distance from the surface at which the local velocity reaches 99 per cent of the external velocity u_∞.

The concept of a boundary layer was introduced by the German scientist, Prandtl, in 1904. The boundary layer essentially divides the flow field around a body into two domains: a thin layer covering the surface of the body where the velocity gradient is great and the viscous forces are large, and a region outside this layer where the velocity is nearly equal to the free-stream value and the effects of viscosity are negligible. By means of the boundary-layer concept, the equations of motion, usually called the Navier-Stokes equations, can be reduced to a form in which

---

[1] This is strictly true only when the mean free path of the molecules is small compared to the boundary-layer thickness. In rarefied gases the molecules may slide or slip along a surface.

they can be solved; the effects of viscosity on the flow can be determined; and the frictional drag along a surface can be calculated. The boundary-layer concept is also of great importance, as we shall see, to an understanding of convective heat transfer.

The shape of the velocity profile within the boundary layer depends on the nature of the flow. Consider, for example, the flow of air over a flat plate, placed with its surface parallel to the stream. At the leading edge of the plate ($x = 0$ in Fig. 6–1), only the fluid particles in immediate contact with the surface are slowed down, while the remaining fluid continues at the velocity of the undisturbed free stream in front of the plate. As the fluid proceeds along the plate, the shearing forces cause more and more of the fluid to be retarded, and the thickness of the boundary layer increases. The growth of the boundary layer and typical velocity profiles at various stations along the plate are shown in Fig. 6–1.

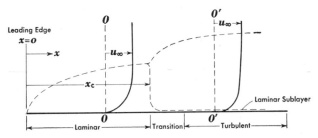

Fig. 6–1. Velocity profiles for laminar and turbulent boundary layers in flow over a flat plate. (Vertical scale enlarged for clarity.)

The velocity profiles near the leading edge are representative of laminar boundary layers. However, the flow within the boundary layer remains laminar only for a certain distance from the leading edge and then becomes turbulent. We do not know enough about the mechanism of transition to predict precisely when the transition will occur, but the phenomenon leading to the growth of disturbances in a laminar boundary layer can be described (see Ref. 1 for details). There are always small disturbances and waves in a flowing fluid, but as long as the viscous forces are large they will prevent disturbances from growing. As the laminar boundary layer thickens, the ratio of viscous forces to inertia forces decreases, and eventually a point is reached at which disturbances will no longer decay, but will grow with time. Then the boundary layer becomes unstable and the transition from laminar to turbulent flow begins. Eddies and vortexes form and destroy the laminar regularity of the boundary-layer motion. Quasi-laminar motion persists only in a thin layer in the immediate vicinity of the surface. This portion of a generally turbulent boundary layer is called the *laminar sublayer*. The region between the laminar sublayer and the completely turbulent portion of the boundary layer is called the *buffer layer*. The structure of the flow in a turbulent boundary layer is shown schematically on an enlarged scale in Fig. 6–2.

The distance from the leading edge at which the boundary layer becomes turbulent is called the critical length x_c (Fig. 6–1). This distance is usually specified in terms of a dimensionless quantity called the local critical Reynolds number $u_\infty \rho x_c / \mu$, which is an indication of the ratio of inertial to viscous forces at which disturbances begin to grow. Experimental results have shown that the point of transition depends on the surface contour, the surface roughness, the disturbance level, and even on the heat transfer. When the flow is calm and no disturbances occur, laminar flow can persist in the boundary layer at Reynolds numbers as high as 5×10^6. If the surface is rough, or disturbances are intentionally introduced into the flow, as for example by means of a grid, the flow may become turbulent at

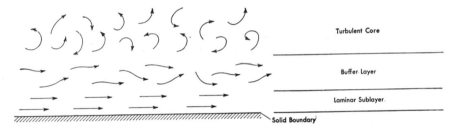

Turbulent Core

Buffer Layer

Laminar Sublayer

Solid Boundary

FIG. 6–2. Structure of a turbulent flow field near a solid boundary.

Reynolds numbers as low as 8×10^4. Under average conditions, the flow over a flat plate becomes turbulent at a distance from the leading edge x_c where the local Reynolds number $u\rho x_c / \mu$ is approximately equal to 5×10^5.

In view of the difference in the flow characteristics, the frictional forces as well as the heat transfer are governed by different relations in laminar and turbulent boundary layers. Also the limiting conditions under which the flow will follow a given contour, and the boundary-layer theory can be applied, depends on whether the flow is laminar or turbulent.

Even when the contour of the surface over which the fluid flows is curved, the flow in the boundary layer is, at least qualitatively, similar to the flow in the boundary layer on a flat plate. The contour of the body becomes very important, however, in the determination of the point at which the boundary layer separates from the surface. The separation of flow occurs mainly because the kinetic energy of the fluid in the boundary layer is dissipated by viscosity within the layer. As long as the main stream is accelerating, the external pressure is decreasing along the direction of flow and the forces at the edge of the boundary layer oppose the retardation of the fluid by the wall shear. On the other hand, when the flow is decelerating, as for example in a low-speed diffuser, the external pressure as well as the shearing forces tend to decelerate the fluid. A local reversal of the flow in the boundary layer will then occur when the kinetic energy of the fluid in the boundary layer can no longer overcome the adverse pressure gradient. Near this point the boundary layer separates as shown in Fig. 6–3. Beyond the point of separation, the flow near the surface consists of highly irregular eddies and vortexes and cannot be treated by boundary-layer theory.

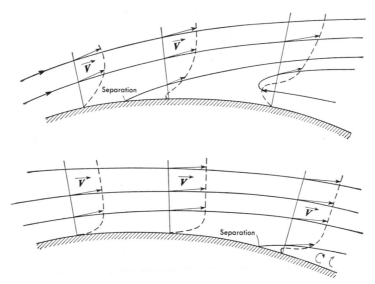

Fig. 6–3. Sketches illustrating separation of boundary layer. (*top*) Streamlines and flow pattern near separation point of laminar boundary layer. (*bottom*) Streamlines and flow pattern near separation point of turbulent boundary layer.

A more advanced boundary-layer theory allows us to calculate the point at which the flow separates from the surface (1). Generally speaking, a turbulent boundary layer will not separate as easily as a laminar boundary layer because the kinetic energy of the fluid particles is larger in a turbulent layer. In flow over a streamlined object, separation takes place near the rear, if it occurs at all. In flow over bluff objects, on the other hand, separation occurs nearer to the front. The problem of separation is too complicated to be taken up in detail here, and the reader interested in additional information on this subject should consult Refs. 1, 27, and 28 of the bibliography at the end of this chapter.

6–4. THE NUSSELT MODULUS

From the description of the mechanism of convective energy transport, we recall that both conduction and mass transport play a role. Since the thermal conductivity of fluids, except for liquid metals, is relatively small, the rapidity of the energy transfer depends largely on the mixing motion of the fluid particles.

When the fluid velocity and the turbulence are small, the transport of energy is not aided materially by mixing currents on a macroscopic scale. On the other hand, when the velocity is large and the mixing between warmer and colder fluid contributes substantially to the energy transfer, the conduction mechanism becomes less important. Consequently, to transfer heat by convection through a fluid at a given rate, a larger tem-

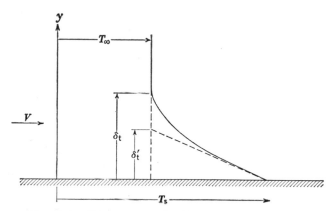

Fig. 6–4. Temperature distribution in a turbulent boundary layer for a fluid flowing over a heated plate.

perature gradient is required in a region of low velocity than in a region of high velocity.

Applying these qualitative observations to heat transfer from a solid wall to a fluid in turbulent flow, we can roughly sketch the temperature profile. In the immediate vicinity of the wall, heat can only flow by conduction because the fluid particles are stationary relative to the boundary. We naturally expect a large temperature drop in this layer. As we move further away from the wall, the movement of the fluid aids in the energy transport and the temperature gradient will be less steep, eventually, leveling out in the main stream. For air flowing turbulently over a flat plate, the temperature distribution shown in Fig. 6–4 illustrates these ideas qualitatively.

The foregoing discussion suggests a method for evaluating the rate of heat transfer between a solid wall and a fluid. Since at the interface (i.e., at $y = 0$) heat flows only by conduction, the rate of heat flow can be calculated from the equation

$$q_{\text{surface}\rightarrow\text{fluid}} = -k_f A \frac{\partial T}{\partial y}\bigg|_{y=0} \qquad (6\text{--}1)$$

This approach has indeed been used, but for engineering purposes the concept of the convective-heat-transfer coefficient is much more convenient. In order not to lose sight of the physical picture, we shall relate the heat-transfer coefficient defined by Eq. 1–13 to the temperature gradient at the wall.   Equating Eqs. 6–1 and 1–13 we obtain

$$q_{\text{surface}\rightarrow\text{fluid}} = -k_f A \frac{\partial T}{\partial y}\bigg|_{y=0} = \bar{h}_c A (T_s - T_\infty) \qquad (6\text{--}2)$$

Since the magnitude of the temperature gradient in the fluid will be the same regardless of the reference temperature, we can write $\partial T = \partial (T - T_s)$. Introducing a significant length dimension of the system L to specify the geometry of the object from which heat flows, we can write Eq. 6–2 in dimensionless form as

$$\frac{\bar{h}_c L}{k_f} = \frac{\dfrac{\partial T}{\partial y}\bigg|_{y=0}}{\dfrac{(T_s - T_\infty)}{L}} = \frac{\partial \left(\dfrac{T_s - T}{T_s - T_\infty}\right)}{\partial \left(\dfrac{y}{L}\right)}\Bigg|_{y=0} \qquad (6\text{--}3)$$

The combination of the convective-heat-transfer coefficient $\bar{h}_c$, the significant length L, and the thermal conductivity of the fluid k_f in the form $\bar{h}_c L/k_f$ is called the Nusselt modulus, or *Nusselt number*, Nu.   The Nusselt number is a dimensionless quantity.

Inspection of Eq. 6–3 shows that the Nusselt number could be interpreted physically as the ratio of the temperature gradient in the fluid immediately in contact with the surface to a reference temperature gradient $(T_s - T_\infty)/L$.   In practice the Nusselt number is a convenient measure of the convective-heat-transfer coefficient because, once its value is known, the convective-heat-transfer coefficient can be calculated from the relation

$$\bar{h}_c = \text{Nu} \frac{k_f}{L} \qquad (6\text{--}4)$$

We observe that, for a given value of the Nusselt number, the convective-heat-transfer coefficient is directly proportional to the thermal conductivity of the fluid but inversely proportional to the significant length dimension describing the system.

The temperature distribution for a fluid flowing past a hot wall, as sketched by the solid line in Fig. 6–4, shows that the temperature gradient in the fluid is confined to a relatively thin layer, δ_t, in the vicinity of the surface. We shall now simplify the true picture by replacing the actual temperature distribution by the dashed straight line shown in Fig. 6–4. The dashed line is tangent to the actual temperature curve at the wall and physically represents the temperature distribution in a hypothetical layer of fluid of thickness δ_t' which, if completely stagnant, offers the same thermal resistance to the flow of heat as the actual boundary layer. In this stagnant layer, heat can flow only by conduction and the rate of heat transfer per unit area is

$$\frac{q}{A} = k_f \frac{T_s - T_\infty}{\delta_t'} = \bar{h}_c (T_s - T_\infty) \qquad (6\text{–}5)$$

An inspection of Eq. 6–5 shows that $\bar{h}_c$ may be expressed as

$$\bar{h}_c = \frac{k_f}{\delta_t'} \qquad (6\text{–}6)$$

and the Nusselt number as

$$\mathrm{Nu} = \bar{h}_c \frac{L}{k_f} = \frac{L}{\delta_t'} \qquad (6\text{–}7)$$

While this picture is considerably oversimplified, it does illustrate the fact that the thinner the hypothetical boundary layer δ_t', the larger will be the convective conductance. To transfer large quantities of heat rapidly, one attempts to reduce the boundary-layer thickness as much as possible. This can be accomplished by increasing the velocity and/or the turbulence of the fluid. If insulation of the surface is the desired aim, a thick stagnant layer is beneficial. In fact, most commercial insulating materials simply trap air in small spaces to eliminate its mixing motion while at the same time taking advantage of its low thermal conductivity to reduce the transfer of heat.

6–5. EVALUATION OF CONVECTIVE-HEAT-TRANSFER COEFFICIENTS

There are four[2] general methods available for the evaluation of convective-heat-transfer coefficients:

1. Dimensional analysis combined with experiments.
2. Exact mathematical solutions of the boundary-layer equations.
3. Approximate analyses of the boundary layer by integral methods.
4. The analogy between heat, mass, and momentum transfer.

[2] An additional method has recently been suggested by Y. P. Chang ("A Theoretical Analysis of Heat Transfer in Natural Convection and in Boiling," *Trans. ASME*, Vol. 79, Oct. 1957, pp. 1501–1613). Its usefulness has not yet been established because it lacks reliable experimental verification.

All four of these techniques have contributed to our understanding of convective heat transfer. Yet, no single method can solve all the problems because each one has limitations which restrict its scope of application.

Dimensional analysis is mathematically simple and has found the widest range of application. The chief limitation of this method is that results obtained by it are incomplete and quite useless without experimental data. It contributes little to our understanding of the transfer process, but facilitates the interpretation and extends the range of application of experimental data by correlating them in terms of dimensionless groups.

There are two different methods for determining dimensionless groups suitable to correlate experimental data. The first of these methods, discussed in the following section, requires only the listing of the variables pertinent to a phenomenon. This technique is simple to use, but if a pertinent variable is omitted, erroneous results ensue. In the second method the dimensionless groups and similarity conditions are deduced from the differential equations describing the phenomenon. This method is preferable when the phenomena can be described mathematically, but the solution of the resulting equations is too involved to be practical. An illustration of this technique is presented in Sec. 7-1.

Exact mathematical analyses require the simultaneous solution of the equations describing the fluid motion and the transfer of energy in the moving fluid. The method presupposes that the physical mechanisms are sufficiently well understood to be described in mathematical language. This preliminary requirement limits the scope of exact solutions because complete mathematical equations describing the fluid flow and the heat-transfer mechanisms can be written only for laminar flow. Even for laminar flow the equations are quite complicated, but solutions have been obtained for a number of simple systems such as flow over a flat plate or a circular cylinder.

Exact solutions are important because the assumptions made in the course of the analysis can be specified accurately and their validity can be checked by experiment. They also serve as a basis of comparison and as a check on simpler, but approximate methods. Furthermore, the development of electronic computers has increased the range of problems amenable to mathematical solution, and results of computations for different systems are continually being published in the literature.

The details of the mathematical solution are quite complicated. They are, however, not essential to a correct application of the results. We shall here only derive the boundary-layer equations to introduce the fundamental concepts, indicate how they can be solved, and finally illustrate the application of the results for the simple case of flow over a flat plate.

For details regarding the methods of solution of the boundary-layer equations in geometrically more complex systems, the reader is referred to the translation of Schlichting's treatise on boundary-layer theory (1).

The approximate analysis of the boundary layer avoids the detailed mathematical description of the flow in the boundary layer. Instead, a plausible but simple equation is used to describe the velocity and temperature distributions in the boundary layer. The problem is then analyzed on a macroscopic basis by applying the equation of motion and the energy equation to the aggregate of the fluid particles contained within the boundary layer. This method is relatively simple; moreover, it yields solutions to problems which can not be treated by an exact mathematical analysis. In those instances where other solutions are available, they agree within engineering accuracy with the solutions obtained by this approximate method. The technique is not limited to laminar flow, but can also be applied to turbulent flow.

The analogy between heat, mass, and momentum transfer is a useful tool for analyzing turbulent transfer processes. Our knowledge of turbulent-exchange mechanisms is insufficient to write mathematical equations describing the temperature distribution directly, but the transfer mechanism can be described in terms of a simplified model. According to one such model which has been widely accepted, a mixing motion in a direction perpendicular to the mean flow accounts for the transfer of momentum as well as energy. The mixing motion can be described on a statistical basis by a method similar to that used to picture the motion of gas molecules in the kinetic theory. There is by no means general agreement that this model corresponds to conditions actually existing in nature, but for practical purposes its use can be justified by the fact that experimental results are substantially in agreement with analytical predictions based on the hypothetical model.

6-6. DIMENSIONAL ANALYSIS

The scope as well as the limitations of dimensional analysis have been summarized by Langhaar (2) who states:

"Dimensional analysis is a method by which we deduce information about a phenomenon from the single premise that the phenomenon can be described by a dimensionally correct equation among certain variables. The generality of the method is both its strength and its weakness. With little effort, a *partial* solution to nearly any problem is obtained. On the other hand, a complete solution is not obtained nor is the inner mechanism of a phenomenon revealed by dimensional reasoning alone."

Dimensional analysis differs from other methods of approach in that it does not yield equations which can be solved. It does however combine the variables into dimensionless groups, such as the Nusselt number, which facilitate the interpretation and extend the range of application of experimental data. In practice, convective-heat-transfer coefficients are generally calculated from empirical equations obtained by correlating experimental data with the aid of dimensional analysis.

The most serious limitation of dimensional analysis is that it gives no information about the nature of a phenomenon. In fact, to apply dimensional analysis it is necessary to know beforehand what variables influence the phenomenon, and the success or failure of the method depends on the proper selection of these variables. It is therefore necessary to have at least a preliminary theory or a thorough physical understanding of a phenomenon before a dimensional analysis can be performed. However, once the pertinent variables are known, dimensional analysis can be applied to most problems by a routine procedure which is outlined below.[3]

Primary dimensions and dimensional formulas. The first step is to select a system of primary dimensions. The choice of the primary dimensions is arbitrary, but the dimensional formulas of all pertinent variables must be expressible in terms of them. We shall use the primary dimensions of length L, time θ, temperature T, and mass M.

The dimensional formula of a physical quantity follows from definitions or physical laws. For instance, the dimensional formula for the length of a bar is $[L]$ by definition.[4] The average velocity of a fluid particle is equal to a distance divided by the time interval taken to traverse it. The dimensional formula of velocity is therefore $[L/\theta]$, or $[L\,\theta^{-1}]$, i.e., a distance or length divided by a time. The units of velocity could be expressed in feet per second, miles per hour, or knots, since they all are a length divided by a time.

The dimensional formulas and the symbols of physical quantities occurring frequently in heat-transfer problems are given in Table 6–1. The primary dimensions in the $ML\theta T$ column of Table 6–1 avoid the use of dimensional constants such as g_c or J. This standardizes the method, but conversion factors may have to be inserted in the final results (i.e., the dimensionless quantities) to comply with the system of units used (see Appendix II for conversion factors). For convenience the dimensional formulas are also listed in the $ML\theta TFQ$ system. In this system, sometimes called the engineering system, there are six primary dimensions.[5]

---

[3] The algebraic theory of dimensional analysis will not be developed here. For a rigorous and comprehensive treatment of the mathematical background, Chapters 3 and 4 of Ref. 2 are recommended.

[4] A square bracket [ ] denotes that the quantity has the dimensional formula stated within the bracket.

[5] Since the number of primary quantities is increased by two, the conversion constants g_c and J, whose dimensional formulas can be derived from the primary dimensions, must be included among the physical quantities.

TABLE 6–1

SOME PHYSICAL QUANTITIES WITH ASSOCIATED SYMBOLS, DIMENSIONS, AND UNITS

| QUANTITY | SYMBOL | DIMENSIONS | | UNITS IN THE ENGINEERING SYSTEM |
		$ML\theta T$ System	$ML\theta TFQ$ System	
Length	L, x	L	L	ft
Time	θ	θ	θ	sec or hr
Mass	M	M	M	lb_m
Force	F	ML/θ^2	F	lb_f
Temperature	T	T	T	F
Heat	Q	ML^2/θ^2	Q	Btu
Velocity	V	L/θ	L/θ	ft/sec
Acceleration	a, g	L/θ^2	L/θ^2	ft/sec²
Dimensional conversion factor	g_c	None	ML/θ^2F	32.2 lb_m ft/sec² lb_f
Energy conversion factor	J	None	FL/Q	778 ft-lb_f/Btu
Work	W	ML^2/θ^2	FL	ft-lb_f
Pressure	p	M/θ^2L	F/L^2	lb_f/sq ft
Density	ρ	M/L^3	M/L^3	lb_m/cu ft
Internal energy	u	L^2/θ^2	Q/M	Btu/lb_m
Enthalpy	h	L^2/θ^2	Q/M	Btu/lb_m
Specific heat	c	L^2/θ^2T	Q/MT	Btu/lb_m F
Dynamic viscosity	μ_f	$M/L\theta$	$F\theta/L^2$	lb_f-sec/sq ft
Absolute viscosity	μ	$M/L\theta$	$M/L\theta$	lb_m/ft-sec
Kinematic viscosity	$\nu = \mu/\rho$	L^2/θ	L^2/θ	sq ft/sec
Thermal conductivity	k	ML/θ^3T	$Q/LT\theta$	Btu/hr ft F
Thermal diffusivity	a	L^2/θ	L^2/θ	sq ft/hr
Thermal resistance	R	$T\theta^3/ML^2$	$T\theta/Q$	F hr/Btu
Coefficient of expansion	β	$1/T$	$1/T$	$1/F$
Surface tension	σ	M/θ^2	F/L	lb_f/ft
Shear per unit area	τ	$M/L\theta^2$	F/L^2	lb_f/sq ft
Unit surface conductance	h	M/θ^3T	$Q/\theta L^2T$	Btu/hr sq ft F
Mass flow rate	m	M/θ	M/θ	lb_m/sec

Buckingham π-theorem. To determine the number of independent dimensionless groups required to express the relation describing a phenomenon, the Buckingham π (pi) theorem may be used as a rule of thumb.[6] According to this rule, the required number of independent dimensionless groups which can be formed by combining the physical variables of a problem is equal to the total number of these physical quantities n (for example, density, viscosity, heat-transfer coefficient, etc.) minus the number of primary dimensions m required to express the dimensional formulas of the n physical quantities. If we call these groups π_1, π_2, etc., the equation expressing the relationship among the variables has a solution of the form

$$F(\pi_1, \pi_2, \pi_3, \ldots) = 0 \tag{6–8}$$

[6] A more rigorous rule has been proposed by van Driest (3) and is illustrated in Example 6–1.

In a problem involving five physical quantities and three primary dimensions, $n - m$ is equal to two and the solution either has the form

$$F\ (\pi_1,\pi_2)\ =\ 0 \qquad (6\text{--}9)$$

or the form $\qquad\qquad \pi_1\ =\ f\ (\pi_2)$

Experimental data for such a case can be presented conveniently by plotting π_1 against π_2. The resulting empirical curve reveals the functional relationship between π_1 and π_2 which can not be deduced from dimensional analysis.

For a phenomenon which can be described in terms of three dimensionless groups (i.e., if $n - m = 3$), Eq. 6–8 has the form

$$F\ (\pi_1,\pi_2,\pi_3)\ =\ 0 \qquad (6\text{--}10)$$

but can also be written as

$$\pi_1\ =\ f\ (\pi_2,\pi_3)$$

For such a case, experimental data can be correlated by plotting π_1 against π_2 for various values of π_3. Sometimes it is possible to combine two of the π's in some manner and to plot this parameter against the remaining π on a single curve.

Determination of dimensionless groups. A simple method for determining dimensionless groups will now be illustrated by applying it to the problem of correlating experimental convective-heat-transfer data for a fluid flowing across a heated tube. Exactly the same approach would be used for flow through a heated tube.

From the description of the convective-heat-transfer process, it is reasonable to expect that the physical quantities listed in Table 6–2 below are pertinent to the problem.

TABLE 6–2

Variable	Symbol	Dimensional Equation
Tube diameter	D	$[L]$
Thermal conductivity of the fluid	k	$[ML/\theta^3\ T]$
Velocity of the fluid	V	$[L/\theta]$
Density of the fluid	ρ	$[M/L^3]$
Viscosity of the fluid	μ	$[M/L\theta]$
Specific heat at constant pressure	c_p	$[L^2/\theta^2\ T]$
Heat-transfer coefficient	$\bar{h}_c$	$[M/\theta^3\ T]$

There are seven physical quantities and four primary dimensions. We therefore expect that three dimensionless groups will be required to correlate the data. To find these dimensionless groups, we write π as a product of the variables, each raised to an unknown power

$$\pi\ =\ D^a k^b V^c \rho^d \mu^e c_p{}^f \bar{h}_c{}^g \qquad (6\text{--}11)$$

and substitute the dimensional formulas

$$\pi = [L]^a[ML/\theta^3 T]^b[L/\theta]^c[M/L^3]^d[M/L\theta]^e[L^2/\theta^3 T]^f[M/\theta^3 T]^g \quad \textbf{(6–12)}$$

For π to be dimensionless, the exponents of each primary dimension must separately add up to zero. Equating the sum of the exponents of each primary dimension to zero, we obtain the set of equations

$$b + d + e + g = 0 \qquad \text{for } M$$

$$a + b + c + 3d - e + 2f = 0 \qquad \text{for } L$$

$$- 3b - c - e - 3f - 3g = 0 \qquad \text{for } \theta$$

$$- b - f - g = 0 \qquad \text{for } T$$

Evidently any set of values of a, b, c, d, and e that simultaneously satisfies this set of equations will make π dimensionless. There are seven unknowns, but only four equations. We can therefore choose values for three of the exponents in each of the dimensionless groups. The only restriction on the choice of the exponents is that each of the selected exponents be independent of the others. An exponent is independent if the determinant formed with the coefficients of the remaining terms does not vanish (i.e., is not equal to zero).

Since $\bar{h}_c$, the convective-heat-transfer coefficient, is the variable we eventually want to evaluate, it is convenient to select its exponent g and set it equal to unity. At the same time we let $c = d = 0$ to simplify the algebraic manipulations. Solving the equations simultaneously, we obtain $a = 1$, $b = -1$, $e = f = 0$, and the first dimensionless group is

$$\pi_1 = \frac{\bar{h}_c D}{k} \qquad \textit{Nusselt's \#}$$

which we recognize as the *Nusselt number*, $\overline{\text{Nu}}$.

For π_2 we select g equal to zero, so that $\bar{h}_c$ will not appear again, and let $a = 1$ and $f = 0$. Simultaneous solution of the equations with these choices yields $b = 0$, $c = d = 1$, $e = 1$, and

$$\pi_2 = \frac{VD\rho}{\mu} \qquad \textit{Reynolds \#}$$

This dimensionless group is a *Reynolds number*, Re_D, with the tube diameter as the length parameter.

If we let $e = 1$ and $c = g = 0$, we obtain the third dimensionless group

$$\pi_3 = \frac{c_p \mu}{k} \qquad \textit{Prandtl's \#}$$

which is known as the *Prandtl number*, Pr.

We observe that, although the heat-transfer coefficient is a function of six variables, with the aid of dimensional analysis, the seven original variables have been combined into three dimensionless groups. According to Eq. 6–10, the functional relationship can be written

$$\overline{\mathrm{Nu}} = f\,(\mathrm{Re}_D, \mathrm{Pr})$$

and experimental data can now be correlated in terms of three variables instead of the original seven. The importance of this reduction in the variables becomes apparent when we attempt to correlate experimental data.

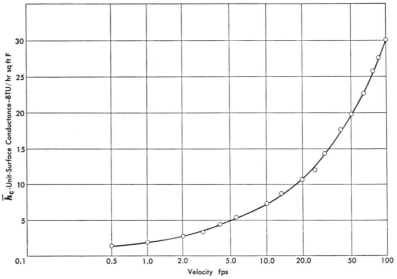

FIG. 6–5. Variation of heat-transfer coefficient with velocity for flow of air over a 1-in.-OD pipe.

Correlation of experimental data. Suppose that, in a series of tests with air flowing over a 1-in.-OD pipe, the heat-transfer coefficient has been measured experimentally at velocities ranging from 0.1 to 100 fps. This range of velocities corresponds to Reynolds numbers based on the diameter, $VD\rho/\mu$, ranging from 50 to 50,000. Since the velocity was the only variable in these tests, the results are correlated in Fig. 6–5 by plotting the heat-transfer coefficient $\bar{h}_c$ against the velocity V. The resulting curve permits a direct determination of $\bar{h}_c$ at any velocity for the system used in the tests, but it cannot be used to determine the heat-transfer coefficients for cylinders which are larger or smaller than the one used in the tests. Neither could the heat-transfer coefficient be evaluated if the air were under pressure and its density were different from that used in the tests.

Unless experimental data could be correlated more effectively, it would be necessary to perform separate experiments for every cylinder diameter, every density, etc. The amount of labor would obviously be enormous.

With the aid of dimensional analysis, however, the results of one series of tests can be applied to a variety of other problems. This is illustrated by Fig. 6–6, where the data of Fig. 6–5 are replotted in terms of pertinent dimensionless groups. The abscissa in Fig. 6–6 is the Reynolds number $VD\rho/\mu$, and the ordinate is the Nusselt number $\bar{h}_c D/k$. This correlation of the data permits the evaluation of the heat-transfer coefficient for air flowing over any size of pipe or wire as long as the Reynolds number of the system falls within the range covered in the experiment.

Experimental data obtained with air alone do not reveal the dependence of the Nusselt number on the Prandtl number since the Prandtl number

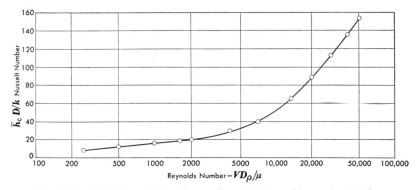

FIG. 6–6.   Variation of Nusselt number with Reynolds number for flow of air over a 1-in.-OD pipe.

is a combination of physical properties whose value does not vary appreciably for gases. To determine the influence of the Prandtl number it is necessary to use different fluids. According to the preceding analysis, experimental data with several fluids whose physical properties yield a wide range of Prandtl numbers are necessary to complete the correlation.

In Fig. 6–7 the experimental results of several independent investigations for heat transfer between air, water, and oils in cross flow over a tube or a wire are plotted for a wide range of temperatures, cylinder sizes, and velocities. The ordinate in Fig. 6–7 is the dimensionless quantity[7] $\overline{Nu}/Pr^{0.3}$ and the abscissa is Re_D. An inspection of the results shows

[7] Combining the Nusselt number with the Prandtl number for plotting the data is simply a matter of convenience. As mentioned previously, any combination of dimensionless parameters is satisfactory. The selection of the most convenient parameter is usually made on the basis of experience by trial and error with the aid of experimental results. Sometimes the characteristic groups are suggested by the results of analytical analyses.

that all of the data follow a single line reasonably well, so that they can be correlated empirically. For example, in the range of Reynolds numbers between 3 and 100 a straight line on the log-log plot is a satisfactory approximation to the best correlation, shown by a heavy dotted line in Fig. 6–7. The slope of this straight line is approximately 0.4 and its ordinate value at Re_D of unity is 0.82. The empirical correlation equation within the range of Reynolds numbers between 3 and 100 is therefore

$$\overline{Nu}/Pr^{0.3} = 0.82\ Re_D{}^{0.4}$$

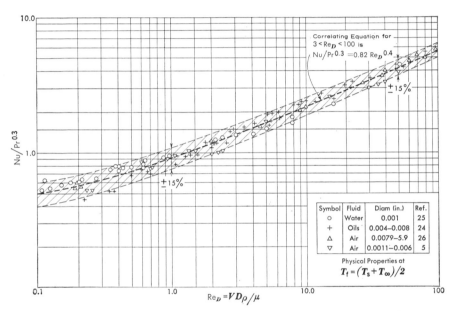

FIG. 6–7. Correlation of experimental heat-transfer data for various fluids in cross flow over cylinders of various diameters.

Principle of similarity. The remarkable result of Fig. 6–7 can be explained by the principle of similarity. According to this principle, often called the model law, the behavior of two systems will be similar if the ratios of their linear dimensions, forces, velocities, etc., are the same. Under conditions of forced convection in geometrically similar systems, the velocity fields will be similar provided the ratio of inertia forces to viscous forces is the same in both fluids. The Reynolds number is the ratio of these forces, and consequently we expect similar flow conditions in forced convection for a given value of the Reynolds number. The Prandtl number is the ratio of two molecular-transport properties, the kinematic viscosity $\nu = \mu/\rho$, which affects the velocity distribution, and the thermal diffusivity $k/\rho c_p$, which affects the temperature profile. In other words, it is a dimensionless group which relates the temperature distribution to the velocity distribution. Hence, in geometrically similar systems having the same Prandtl and Reynolds numbers, the temperature distribution will be similar. According to its definition (see Eq. 5–3), the Nusselt number is numerically equal to the ratio of the temperature gradient at a fluid-to-surface interface to a reference-temperature gradient. We expect therefore that, in systems having similar geometries and similar temperature fields, the numerical values of the Nusselt numbers will be equal. This fact is borne out by the experimental results in Fig. 6–7.

Limitation of the Buckingham π-theorem. The π-theorem holds as long as the set of simultaneous equations formed by equating the exponents of each primary dimension to zero is linearly independent. However, if one equation in the set is a linear combination of one or more of the other equations, i.e., if the equations are linearly dependent, then the number of dimensionless groups is equal to the total number of variables n minus the number of independent equations. Example 6–1 illustrates this point.

Example 6–1. The temperature-time history for a billet cooling in a constant-temperature bath was derived analytically in Sec. 4–2 under the assumption that the temperature of the billet is uniform at any instant (i.e., for an infinite thermal conductivity). Compare the analytical result with pertinent dimensionless groups relating the temperature difference between the billet and the bath with the cooling time.

Solution: The physical quantities affecting the cooling of the billet as variables are shown with their dimensional formulas in Table 6–3.

TABLE 6 3

Variable	Symbol	Dimension
Temperature of billet above bath temperature at time θ	$T - T_\infty$	$[T]$
Temperature of billet above bath temperature at time of immersion $(\theta = 0)$...............	$T_o - T_\infty$	$[T]$
Time after immersion.........................	θ	$[\theta]$
Surface conductance between billet and bath....	$K = \bar{h}A_s$	$\left[\dfrac{ML^2}{\theta^3 T}\right]$
Heat capacitance of billet....................	$c\rho V$	$\left[\dfrac{ML^2}{\theta^2 T}\right]$

In this problem there are five variables and four primary dimensions. Hence the Buckingham π-theorem predicts that only one dimensionless group is required to correlate the results. We perform the initial steps in the usual manner by writing π as

$$\pi = (T - T_\infty)^a \, (T - T_o)^b \, (\theta)^c \, (K)^d \, (c\rho V)^e$$

Substituting the dimensional formulas, we get

$$\pi = [T]^a \, [T]^b \, [\theta]^c \, [ML^2/\theta^3 T]^d \, [ML^2/\theta^2 T]^e$$

For π to be dimensionless the following set of equations must be satisfied.

$$
\begin{aligned}
a + b &= 0 \qquad \text{for } T \\
c - 3d - 2e &= 0 \qquad \text{for } \theta \\
d + e &= 0 \qquad \text{for } M \\
2d + 2e &= 0 \qquad \text{for } L
\end{aligned}
$$

At this point we note that the fourth equation is simply equal to two times the third equation and therefore is not independent. There are only three independent equations in the set, and thus the number of dimensionless groups required to correlate the results is two instead of just one as predicted by the Buckingham π-theorem.

To obtain the pertinent dimensionless group involving the temperature we let $a = 1$ and $c = 0$. Solving the three independent equations of the exponents simultaneously yields $e = 0$, $d = 0$, and $b = -1$, whence

$$
\pi_1 = \frac{T - T_\infty}{T_o - T_\infty}
$$

In the other dimensionless group we eliminate the temperature by setting the exponent a equal to zero and setting c, the exponent of time, equal to unity. The second dimensionless group is then found to be

$$
\pi_2 = \frac{\bar{h} A_s \theta}{c \rho V}
$$

The dimensionless groups obtained by dimensional analysis are identical to those obtained in Sec. 4–2 by a mathematical analysis. The functional relationship from Eq. 4–3 is

$$
\pi_1 = e^{-\pi_2}
$$

Dimensional analysis could only predict that π_1 is a function of π_2, but not the nature of the function.

Conversion of units. After the dimensionless groups of the variables in a given problem have been determined, it is often necessary to change the units of measurement of individual variables in order to express all of the variables in one consistent set of units. The numerical value of any dimensionless group is independent of the units of measurement employed, provided a consistent set is used throughout. In practice, however, it is often necessary to consult references using different systems of units. In order to avoid errors in changing units, the following procedure is recommended:

1. After the magnitude of the physical quantity write the names of the units in which it is measured.
2. Replace each name by its equivalent in the engineering system of units (e.g., 12 in. = 1 ft, so in. $= \frac{1}{12}$ ft).
3. Combine all numbers in the new expression arithmetically and cancel names of units as though they were numbers.

Example 6–2 illustrates this technique.

Example 6–2. The physical properties of glycerin obtained from various sources are listed below. The dimensionless Prandtl number is to be evaluated.

$$c = 0.60 \text{ Btu/lb F}$$
$$k = 0.15 \text{ Btu/hr ft F}$$
$$\mu = 10 \text{ centipoises}$$

Solution: Replacing the word centipoise by its equivalent (i.e., 1 centipoise = 2.42 lb$_m$/hr ft, from Table of Conversion Factors in Appendix II), the dimensionless Prandtl number is

$$\text{Pr} = \frac{c\mu}{k} = \frac{0.6 \cancel{\text{Btu}}}{\text{lb}_m \cancel{\text{F}}} \times \frac{\cancel{\text{hr}} \cancel{\text{ft}} \cancel{\text{F}}}{0.15 \cancel{\text{Btu}}} \times \frac{10 \times 2.42 \cancel{\text{lb}_m}}{\cancel{\text{hr}} \cancel{\text{ft}}} = 96.6 \qquad \textit{Ans.}$$

The following example illustrates a case in which property values obtained from the literature are not expressed in a consistent set of units. The case differs from the preceding example because the same symbol is used to denote different quantities. This is an unfortunate situation often encountered in practice and results from the ambiguous use of the word "pound" to stand for both force and mass. It is, however, a simple matter in such a situation to avoid numerical errors if the suggested method of checking units is used to ensure that the final expression is dimensionless.

Example 6–3. Using the physical properties from the steam tables,[8] evaluate the Prandtl number for steam at 400 F and 14.7 psia.

Solution: The pertinent physical properties of steam and their units are as read from the tables. Viscosity (Table 6), $\mu = 3.49 \times 10^{-7}$ lb sec/sq ft; thermal conductivity (Table 5), $k = 19 \times 10^{-3}$ Btu/hr ft F. The specific heat at constant pressure is obtained from Table 3 by dividing the enthalpy difference between 380 F and 420 F by the temperature difference, i.e., 40 F. This yields

$$\bar{c}_p = \frac{1244.9 - 1225.2}{40} = 0.49 \text{ Btu/lb F}$$

The Prandtl number is evaluated by substituting the above numerical values into its definition. We obtain

$$\text{Pr} = \frac{\bar{c}_p \mu}{k} = \frac{(0.49 \text{ Btu/lb F})(3.49 \times 10^{-7} \text{lb sec/sq ft})}{19 \times 10^{-3} \text{ Btu/hr ft F}}$$

The Prandtl number will be dimensionless only if all of the physical properties are expressed in one consistent set of units. We shall check whether or not this is the case by canceling the names or symbols. Performing the algebraic manipulation and canceling similar symbols in the numerator and denominator yields

$$\text{Pr} = 9.0 \times 10^{-6} \frac{\text{Btu F lb ft sec hr}}{\text{Btu F lb ft}} = 9.0 \times 10^{-6} \frac{\text{lb sec hr}}{\text{lb ft}}$$

Since the symbols do not cancel, it is apparent that the units of measurement are not consistent. At first glance we might be tempted to cancel the symbols of pound, lb.

[8] J. H. Keenan and F. G. Keyes, *Thermodynamic Properties of Steam* (New York: John Wiley & Sons, Inc., 1937).

We recall, however, that sometimes no distinction is made in the literature between lb_f and lb_m. In this case the viscosity is evidently expressed in lb_f sec/sq ft, while the enthalpy is in Btu/lb_m. We must therefore multiply the units of pound force by the conversion factor g_c, 32.2 lb_m ft/lb_f sec², and replace the symbol of hr by 3600 sec in order to make the Prandtl number dimensionless. This yields

$$\text{Pr} = 9.0 \times 10^{-6} \frac{lb_f}{lb_m} \frac{\text{sec}}{\text{ft}} \frac{3600 \text{ sec}}{\text{ft}} \times 32.2 \frac{lb_m}{lb_f} \frac{\text{ft}}{\text{sec}^2}$$

$$= 1.03 \text{ (dimensionless)}$$

Ans.

6–7. LAMINAR BOUNDARY LAYER ON A FLAT PLATE[9]

In the preceding section we determined dimensionless groups for correlating experimental data of heat transfer by forced convection. We found that the Nusselt number depends on the Reynolds number and the Prandtl number, i.e.,

$$\text{Nu} = \phi \text{ (Re) } \psi \text{ (Pr)} \tag{6–13}$$

To determine the functional relationship in this equation it is necessary to resort either to experiments or to analytical methods.

In this and the following sections of the chapter we shall consider analytical methods of approach and apply them to the problem of heat transfer between a flat plate and an incompressible fluid flowing parallel to its surface. This system has been selected primarily because it is the simplest to analyze. However, the results obtained from this analysis have many practical applications. They are good approximations to forced convection in flow over the surfaces of streamlined bodies or in the inlet regions of pipes and ducts. In some cases appropriate transformations can reduce the equations for the flow of a compressible fluid, or the equations for the flow over wedges and cones, to the same form as those of the boundary-layer equations for the flat plate. The results for this case are therefore of considerable value; for their application to other boundary-layer problems, the reader should consult Ref. 1.

In view of the difference in the flow characteristics, the frictional forces as well as the heat transfer are governed by different relations for laminar and turbulent types of boundary layers. We will first consider the laminar boundary layer, which is amenable to both an exact mathematical treatment and an approximate boundary-layer analysis. The turbulent boundary layer is taken up in Sec. 6–9.

Continuity. To derive the equations governing the flow in the boundary layer, consider an elementary control volume which is fixed in the flow field and has the shape of a parallelepiped with dimensions $dx, dy, 1$. The edges of the parallelepiped are orientated in such a manner that the side

---

[9] In the remainder of this chapter the mathematical details may be omitted in an introductory course without breaking the continuity of the presentation.

dx is parallel to the x axis, and the side dy is parallel to the y axis.   The third face has the dimension of unity and is parallel to the z axis (Fig. 6–8). In order to simplify the analysis we will assume that:

1. The flow is two-dimensional, i.e., the velocity distribution is the same in any plane perpendicular to the z axis (i.e., parallel to the surface of the paper).

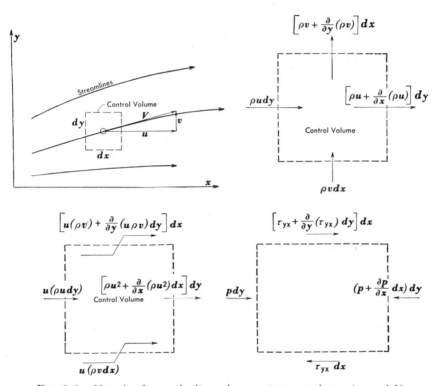

Fig. 6–8.   Notation for continuity and momentum equations.   (*upper left*) Control volume in boundary layer.   (*upper right*) Mass flow through surface of control volume.   (*lower left*) Momentum fluxes in x direction through surface of control volume.   (*lower right*) Forces acting on surface of control volume.

2. The fluid is incompressible.
3. The pressure is constant throughout the flow field.
4. The flow is steady with respect to time.
5. The physical properties of the fluid are constant.
6. The fluid flow is not affected by heat flow.

According to the principle of conservation of mass, the mass of fluid entering the volume $dx\,dy\,1$ during a time interval $d\theta$ must be equal to the mass of fluid leaving in the steady state. The mass of fluid entering through the left face of the control volume during $d\theta$ is

$$(\rho u) \, (dy) \, d\theta$$

The mass of fluid leaving through the right face during $d\theta$ is

$$\left(\rho u + \frac{\partial(\rho u)}{\partial x} \, dx\right) (dy) d\theta$$

The mass of fluid entering through the lower face during $d\theta$ is

$$(\rho v) \, (dx) \, d\theta$$

and the mass of fluid leaving through the upper face during $d\theta$ is

$$\left(\rho v + \frac{\partial(\rho v)}{\partial y} \, dy\right) (dx) d\theta$$

Equating the mass leaving to the mass entering per unit time we obtain

$$\rho u \, dy + \rho v \, dx = \rho u + \frac{\partial(\rho u)}{\partial x} \, dx \, dy + \rho v + \frac{\partial(\rho v)}{\partial y} \, dy \, dx$$

Simplifying the preceding equation by canceling like terms and dividing by the constant ρ yields

$$\frac{\partial u}{\partial x} + \frac{\partial v}{\partial y} = 0 \qquad\qquad (6\text{--}14)$$

The above expression is generally known as the *continuity equation for* incompressible, steady, two-dimensional flow. It must be satisfied by the flow in the boundary layer. In addition to the conservation of mass, the flow of fluid, like any dynamic process, is governed by Newton's second law of motion. In a form suitable for our purposes the law can be stated in symbolic form as

$$\Sigma F = \frac{1}{g_c} \frac{d(mV)}{d\theta}$$

or in words as, *The summation of forces acting on a body is equal to the time rate of change of its momentum* (i.e., mass × velocity).

While this principle is relatively easy to visualize when it is applied to a single solid body, its application to a fluid often causes some difficulty.[10] There is, however, no difference conceptually if we simply picture any body as made up of a number of particles, with or without ties between them, and consider the change of momentum taking place at the center of mass

[10] An excellent discussion of the application of the momentum principle to fluids, and a detailed discussion of the use of the control volume are presented in Ref. 29.

of the solid body or the aggregate of particles. Only external forces need to be considered because the internal forces of action and reaction exerted between the particles within the system cancel each other.

The time rate of change of momentum of the fluid particles flowing through the control volume $dxdy$ may be obtained by subtracting the momentum of the particles entering from the momentum of the particles leaving the volume per unit time. Since both force and velocity are vector quantities, the momentum principle must be applied with due regard to direction. In the boundary layer the velocity is nearly parallel to the wall and the velocity component normal to the wall v is very small. Hence we can ignore the viscous shear in the y direction and consider only the forces and the momentum change in the x direction. A more rigorous argument to justify this assumption may be found in Ref. 1.

Referring to Fig. 6–8, the mass of the fluid particles entering through the left face per unit time is $\rho u dy$. The velocity of these particles is u and therefore the x momentum per unit time entering from the left is

$$(\rho u dy)\, u \,=\, \rho u^2 \, dy$$

Fluid particles flow into the control volume through the lower face at the rate $\rho v dx$. Also these particles have a velocity component in the x direction, and their contribution to the x momentum entering per unit time is

$$(\rho v dx)\, u \,=\, \rho v u dx$$

The momentum per unit time leaving through the right face is

$$\left(\rho u + \frac{\partial(\rho u)}{\partial x}\, dx\right)\left(u + \frac{\partial u}{\partial x}\, dx\right) dy$$

Carrying out the multiplication and discarding the higher order term $[\partial(\rho u)/\partial x](\partial u/\partial x)\, dx^2 dy$ yields

$$\left[\rho u^2 + \rho u \frac{\partial u}{\partial x}\, dx + u \frac{\partial(\rho u)}{\partial x}\, dx\right] dy$$

Similarly, the momentum per unit time leaving through the upper face is

$$\left[\rho v u + \rho v \frac{\partial u}{\partial y}\, dy + u \frac{\partial(\rho v)}{\partial y}\, dy\right] dx$$

Subtracting the momentum per unit time entering from that leaving, the net increase of momentum per unit time of the fluid in the control volume becomes

$$\left\{\rho u \frac{\partial u}{\partial x} + \rho v \frac{\partial u}{\partial y} + u \left[\frac{\partial(\rho u)}{\partial x} + \frac{\partial(\rho v)}{\partial y}\right]\right\} dx dy$$

Since ρ is constant, the term $u[\partial(\rho u)/\partial x + \partial(\rho v)/\partial y]$ can be written as $\rho u(\partial u/\partial x + \partial v/\partial y)$. The bracket is identically zero from Eq. 6–14, and thus the term drops out. The net outgoing momentum flux can therefore be expressed as

$$\left(\rho u \frac{\partial u}{\partial x} + \rho v \frac{\partial u}{\partial y}\right) dx dy$$

The increase in momentum is produced by the forces acting on the surface of the control volume. In general there are three types of forces to be considered:

1. Inertia or body forces such as gravity.
2. Dynamical forces such as pressure.
3. Frictional forces such as viscous shear and wall friction.

In forced convection the forces due to gravity are usually negligible. Furthermore, for flow over a flat plate the static pressure in the flow field is nearly uniform and we need only consider the viscous shear.

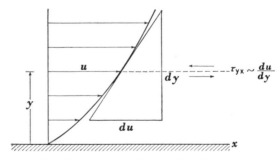

Fig. 6–9. Shearing stress in a laminar boundary layer.

Viscous shear is the result of a molecular interaction between faster- and slower-moving layers of fluid. It gives rise to a frictional force τ, which is proportional to the velocity gradient normal to the direction of flow. The factor of proportionality is a property of the fluid and is called the *dynamic viscosity* μ_f. For flow over a flat plate (Fig. 6–9) when the change of velocity occurs only in the y direction perpendicular to the surface, the shearing stress in a plane parallel to the plate is

$$\tau_{yx} = \mu_f \frac{du}{dy} = \frac{\mu}{g_c} \frac{du}{dy} \qquad (6\text{–}15)$$

where τ_{yx} = shearing stress per unit area in lb_f/sq ft;
    u = velocity, in ft/sec;
    y = distance, in ft;

μ_t = dynamic viscosity, in lb_f sec/sq ft;

μ = absolute viscosity, in lb_m/sec ft.

It should be emphatically noted that the dynamic viscosity is physically the same property of the fluid as the absolute viscosity—the difference between them is merely the system of units used in their evaluation. The only reason for distinguishing between μ_t and μ is to avoid errors in numerical computations by calling attention to the fact that some references list numerical values of viscosity in lb_f sec/sq ft, whereas this book uses the units lb_m/sec ft throughout. The subscript notation for the shearing stress τ indicates the axis to which the shear-affected area is perpendicular by the first letter and the direction of the stress by the second letter, e.g., τ_{yx} is the shear in the x direction on a plane perpendicular to the y axis.

At the lower face the shear acting on the fluid within the control volume is

$$(\tau_{yx})dx = \left(\frac{\mu}{g_c} \frac{\partial u}{\partial y}\right) dx$$

and at the upper face the shear is

$$\left[\tau_{yx} + \frac{\partial}{\partial y}(\tau_{yx})dy\right] dx = \left[\frac{\mu}{g_c} \frac{\partial u}{\partial y} + \frac{\partial}{\partial y}\left(\frac{\mu}{g_c} \frac{\partial u}{\partial y}\right) dy\right] dx$$

Since the wall is stationary, the shear on the fluid at the lower face of the control volume (Fig. 6–8) acts in a direction opposite to that of the flow (i.e., in the negative direction), while the shear on the upper face is caused by fluid tending to pull in the direction of motion. The net positive shear is thus

$$\left[\left(\tau_{yx} + \frac{\partial \tau_{yx}}{\partial y} dy\right) - \tau_{yx}\right] dx = \frac{\partial}{\partial y}\left(\frac{\mu}{g_c} \frac{\partial u}{\partial y}\right) dxdy$$

Equating the net force to the increase in the momentum per unit time produced by it yields the *momentum equation* for the boundary layer. After dividing by $\rho dxdy$, we obtain

$$u \frac{\partial u}{\partial x} + v \frac{\partial u}{\partial y} = \nu \frac{\partial^2 u}{\partial y^2} \qquad (6\text{–}16)$$

if we assume that both ρ and μ are constant.[11]

Boundary-layer thickness and skin friction. Equation 6–16 must be

[11] If the surface is slightly curved or if the pressure in the flow field is not constant, Eq. 6–16 is modified by a pressure force term and becomes

$$u \frac{\partial u}{\partial x} + v \frac{\partial u}{\partial y} = -\frac{g_c}{\rho} \frac{\partial p}{\partial x} + \nu \frac{\partial^2 u}{\partial y^2} \qquad (6\text{–}16a)$$

solved simultaneously with the continuity equation (Eq. 6–14) in order to determine the velocity distribution, the boundary-layer thickness, and the friction force at the wall. These equations are solved by first defining a stream function, $\psi(x,y)$, which automatically satisfies the continuity equation, or

$$u = \frac{\partial \psi}{\partial y} \quad \text{and} \quad v = -\frac{\partial \psi}{\partial x}$$

Introducing the new variable

$$\eta = y\sqrt{u_\infty/\nu x}$$

we can let

$$\psi = \sqrt{\nu x\, u_\infty}\, f(\eta)$$

where $f(\eta)$ denotes a dimensionless stream function. In terms of $f(\eta)$, the velocity components are

$$u = \frac{\partial \psi}{\partial y} = \frac{\partial \psi}{\partial \eta} \frac{\partial \eta}{\partial y} = u_\infty \frac{d[f(\eta)]}{d\eta}$$

and

$$v = -\frac{\partial \psi}{\partial x} = \tfrac{1}{2} \sqrt{\frac{\nu u_\infty}{x}} \left\{ \frac{d[f(\eta)]}{d\eta} - f(\eta) \right\}$$

Expressing $\partial u/\partial x$, $\partial u/\partial y$, and $\partial^2 u/\partial y^2$ in terms of η and inserting the resulting expressions in the momentum equation yields the ordinary, nonlinear, third-order differential equation

$$f(\eta) \frac{d^2[f(\eta)]}{d\eta^2} + 2\, \frac{d^3[f(\eta)]}{d\eta^3} = 0$$

which can be solved subject to the three boundary conditions that

$$\text{at } \eta = 0,\, f(\eta) = 0,\, \frac{d[f(\eta)]}{d\eta} = 0$$

and

$$\text{at } \eta = \infty,\, \frac{d[f(\eta)]}{d\eta} = 1$$

The solution to this partial-differential equation was obtained numerically by Blasius, in 1908 (6). The significant results are shown in Figs. 6–10 and 6–11.

In Fig. 6–10 the Blasius velocity profiles in the laminar boundary on a flat plate are plotted in dimensionless form together with experimental data obtained by Hansen (13). The ordinate in Fig. 6–10 is the local velocity in the x direction u divided by the free stream velocity u_∞, and the abscissa is a dimensionless distance parameter, $(y/x)\sqrt{(\rho u_\infty x)/\mu}$. We note that a single curve is sufficient to correlate the velocity distributions at all stations along the plate. The velocity u reaches 99 per cent of the free-stream value u_∞ at $(y/x)\sqrt{(\rho u_\infty x)/\mu} = 5.0$. If we define the hydrodynamic boundary-layer thickness as that distance from the surface at which

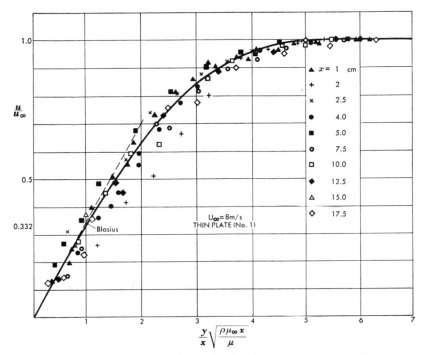

FIG. 6-10. Velocity profile in the laminar boundary layer according to Blasius with experimental data of Hansen (13). (Courtesy of National Advisory Committee for Aeronautics, *NACA TM* 585)

local velocity u reaches 99 per cent of the free-stream value u_∞, the boundary-layer thickness δ becomes

$$\delta = \frac{5x}{\sqrt{Re_x}} \qquad (6\text{-}17)$$

where $Re_x = (\rho u_\infty x)/\mu$, the local Reynolds number. Equation 6-17 satisfies the qualitative description of the boundary-layer growth, δ being zero at the leading edge ($x = 0$) and increasing with x along the plate. At any station, i.e., a given value of x, the thickness of the boundary layer is inversely proportional to the square root of the local Reynolds number. Hence, an increase in velocity will result in a decrease of the boundary-layer thickness.

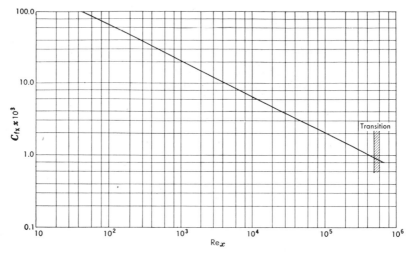

FIG. 6–11. Variation of local friction coefficient with dimensionless distance from leading edge for laminar flow over a flat plate.

The shear force at the wall can be obtained by substituting the velocity gradient at $y = 0$ into Eq. 6–15. From Fig. 6–10 we see that

$$\frac{\partial(u/u_\infty)}{\partial(y/x)\sqrt{\mathrm{Re}_x}}\bigg|_{y=0} = 0.332$$

and thus at any specified value of x the velocity gradient at the surface is

$$\frac{\partial u}{\partial y}\bigg|_{u=0} = 0.332\,\frac{u_\infty}{x}\sqrt{\mathrm{Re}_x}$$

Substituting this velocity gradient in Eq. 6–15, the wall shear per unit area τ_s becomes

$$\tau_s = \frac{\mu}{g_c}\frac{\partial u}{\partial y}\bigg|_{y=0} = 0.332\,\frac{\mu}{g_c}\frac{u_\infty}{x}\sqrt{\mathrm{Re}_x} \tag{6–18}$$

We note that the wall shear near the leading edge is very large and decreases with increasing distance from the leading edge.

For a graphical presentation it is more convenient to use dimensionless coordinates. Dividing both sides of Eq. 6–18 by the velocity pressure of the free stream $\rho u_\infty^2/2g_c$, we obtain

$$C_{fx} = \frac{\tau_s}{\rho u_s^2/2g_c} = 0.664/\sqrt{\mathrm{Re}_x} \tag{6–19}$$

where C_{fx} is a dimensionless number called the *local drag or friction coefficient.*

Figure 6–11 is a plot of C_{fx} against Re_x and shows the variation of the local friction coefficient graphically.

In many practical cases the average friction coefficient for a plate of finite length L is more important than the local friction coefficient. The average shear force is obtained by integrating Eq. 6–19 between the leading edge, $x = 0$, and $x = L$. For laminar flow over the flat plate we get

$$\bar{C}_f = \frac{1}{L} \int_0^L C_{fx}\, dx = 1.33 \Big/ \sqrt{\frac{u_\infty \rho L}{\mu}} \tag{6-20}$$

Thus, the average friction coefficient $\bar{C}_f$ is equal to twice the value of the local friction coefficient at $x = L$.

Energy equation. To evaluate the rate of heat transfer by convection we must determine the temperature gradient at the surface. The equation governing the temperature distribution in the boundary layer is obtained with the aid of the first law of thermodynamics, the principle of conservation of energy. Since we are dealing with a moving fluid, energy stored in fluid particles is transported by their motion. The rate of transport depends on the velocity of the fluid particles, and it is therefore always necessary to solve the hydrodynamic problem before the temperature distribution can be obtained.

To derive the equation governing the temperature distribution, consider the elementary control volume in the boundary layer shown in Fig. 6–12. Let the surfaces ab, bc, cd, and da define the boundaries of the system,

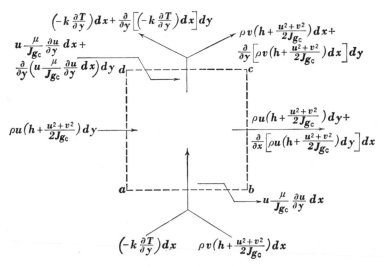

FIG. 6–12.   Control volume in the boundary layer illustrating energy balance.

and make an energy balance under the same assumptions used previously for the hydrodynamic equations. The energy equation for the system can be expressed semantically as

| Influx of enthalpy and kinetic energy | + | rate of heat in- flow by conduc- tion | + | rate at which work is done by frictional shear *on* the fluid in control volume | = | efflux of enthalpy and kinetic energy | + | rate of heat out- flow by conduc- tion | + | rate at which work is done as a result of frictional shear *by* the fluid in control volume |

or in symbolic form as

$$\rho u \left(h + \frac{u^2 + v^2}{2g_cJ} \right) dy + \rho v \left(h + \frac{u^2 + v^2}{2g_cJ} \right) dx$$

$$- k \left(\frac{\partial T}{\partial y} \right) dx + \frac{1}{J} \left[u \frac{\mu}{g_c} \frac{\partial u}{\partial y} dx + \frac{\partial}{\partial y} \left(u \frac{\mu}{g_c} \frac{\partial u}{\partial y} dx \right) \right] dy$$

$$= \rho u \left(h + \frac{u^2 + v^2}{2g_cJ} \right) dy + \frac{\partial}{\partial x} \left[\rho u \left(h + \frac{u^2 + v^2}{2g_cJ} \right) dy \right] dx$$

$$+ \rho v \left(h + \frac{u^2 + v^2}{2g_cJ} \right) dx + \frac{\partial}{\partial y} \left[\rho v \left(h + \frac{u^2 + v^2}{2g_cJ} \right) dx \right] dy$$

$$- k \left(\frac{\partial T}{\partial y} \right) dx + \frac{\partial}{\partial y} \left[-k \left(\frac{\partial T}{\partial y} \right) dx \right] dy + \frac{1}{J} \left(u \frac{\mu}{g_c} \frac{\partial u}{\partial y} \right) dx \quad \textbf{(6-21)}$$

The frictional work terms represent the work done by shearing forces on the surface of the control volume as faster fluid particles slide over slower ones. At the lower surface, the fluid inside the control volume exerts a force on the fluid outside because the former moves faster. The force times distance per unit time (i.e., velocity) $u \, (\mu/g_c) \, (\partial u/\partial y)$ represents the rate at which work is done *by* the fluid in the control volume. Similarly, the last term in square brackets on the left-hand side of Eq. 6–21 represents the rate at which work is done *on* the fluid in the control volume.

Conduction along the x direction has been omitted because, in the boundary layer, the term $- k \, \partial T/\partial x$ is negligible compared to $- k \, \partial T/\partial y$ and the convection terms.

The term $h + (u^2 + v^2)/2g_cJ$ can be written $c_p T_o$ for fluids having a constant specific heat. T_o is the stagnation temperature, i.e., the temperature reached by the fluid when it is isentropically slowed down to zero velocity. For low-speed flow, $T \simeq T_o$ because the kinetic energy of the flow is negligible. For high-speed flow, on the other hand, especially at supersonic velocities, this simplification is not permissible.

Adding up the terms of Eq. 6–21 and dropping those of higher order (i.e., terms involving triple products of d quantities) we obtain after simplifying[12]

$$\rho c_p u \frac{\partial T_o}{\partial x} + \rho c_p v \frac{\partial T_o}{\partial y} = k \frac{\partial^2 T}{\partial y^2} + \frac{\partial}{\partial y} \left(u \frac{\mu}{g_c} \frac{\partial u}{\partial y} \right) \qquad (6\text{--}22)$$

The last term of Eq. 6–22 represents the net rate at which shearing forces perform work on the fluid in the control volume. The mechanical energy or frictional power increases the internal energy of the fluid in the control volume appreciably only at high velocities, but for low subsonic flow in the main stream the frictional power term is small compared to the other terms and can be neglected. With these simplifications, Eq. 6–22 becomes

$$u \frac{\partial T}{\partial x} + v \frac{\partial T}{\partial y} = a \frac{\partial^2 T}{\partial y^2} \qquad (6\text{--}23)$$

where $a = k_f/\rho c_p$.

The velocities in the energy equation, u and v, have the same values at any point (x,y) as in the dynamic equation. For the case of the flat plate, Pohlhausen (7) used the velocities calculated previously by Blasius to obtain the solution of the heat-transfer problem. Without considering the details of this mathematical solution, we can obtain significant results by comparing Eq. 6–23, the heat-transfer equation for the boundary layer, with Eq. 6–16, the momentum equation for the boundary layer. The two equations are similar; in fact, a solution for the velocity distribution $u\ (x,y)$ is also a solution for the temperature distribution $T\ (x,y)$ if $v = a$ and if the temperature of the plate T_s is constant. We can easily verify this by replacing the symbol T in Eq. 6–23 by the symbol u and noting that the boundary conditions for both T and u are identical. If we use the surface temperature as our datum and let the variable in Eq. 6–23 be $(T - T_s)/(T_\infty - T_s)$, then the boundary conditions are:

$$\text{at } y = 0 \qquad \frac{T - T_s}{T_\infty - T_s} = 0 \qquad \text{and} \qquad \frac{u}{u_\infty} = 0$$

$$\text{at } y \to \infty \qquad \frac{T - T_s}{T_\infty - T_s} = 1 \qquad \text{and} \qquad \frac{u}{u_\infty} = 1$$

where T_∞ is the free-stream temperature.

[12] In this and in subsequent equations the energy conversion contant J has been omitted.

The condition that $\nu = a$ corresponds to a Prandtl number of unity since

$$\text{Pr} = \frac{c_p \mu}{k} = \frac{\nu}{a}$$

For $\text{Pr} = 1$ the velocity distribution is therefore identical to the temperature distribution. An interpretation in terms of physical processes is that the transfer of momentum is analogous to the transfer of heat when $\text{Pr} = 1$. The physical properties of most gases are such that they have Prandtl numbers ranging from 0.65 to 1.0, and the analogy is therefore satisfactory. Liquids, on the other hand, have Prandtl numbers considerably different from unity, and the preceding analysis cannot be applied directly.

Using the analytical results of Pohlhausen's work, the temperature distribution in the laminar boundary layer for $\text{Pr} = 1$ can be modified

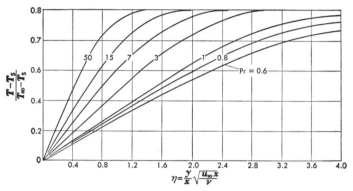

FIG. 6–13. Temperature distribution in a fluid flowing over a heated plate for various Prandtl numbers.

empirically to include fluids having Prandtl numbers different from unity. In Fig. 6–13 theoretically calculated temperature profiles in the boundary layer are shown for values of Pr of 0.6, 0.8, 1.0, 3.0, 7.0, 15, and 50. We now define a thermal-boundary-layer thickness δ_{th} as the distance from the surface at which the temperature difference between the wall and the fluid reaches 99 per cent of the free-stream value. Inspection of the temperature profiles shows that the thermal boundary layer is larger than the hydrodynamic boundary layer for fluids having Pr less than unity, but smaller when Pr is larger than one. According to Pohlhausen's calculations, the relationship between the thermal and hydrodynamic boundary layer is approximately

$$\delta_{th} = \delta / \text{Pr}^{\frac{1}{3}} \tag{6–24}$$

Using the same correction factor, i.e., $\text{Pr}^{\frac{1}{3}}$, at any distance from the surface, the curves of Fig. 6–13 are replotted in Fig. 6–14. The new abscissa is $\Pr^{\frac{1}{3}}(y/x)\sqrt{\mathrm{Re}_x}$ and the ordinate is the dimensionless temperature $(T - T_s)/(T_\infty - T_s)$, where T is the local fluid temperature of the fluid, T_s the surface temperature of the plate, and T_∞ the free-stream temperature. This modification of the ordinate brings the temperature profiles for a wide range of Prandtl numbers together on the curve for $\Pr = 1$.

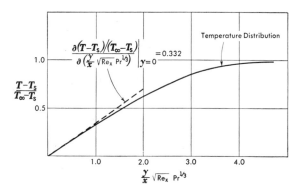

FIG. 6–14. Dimensionless correlation of temperature profiles for flow over a flat plate at constant temperature.

Evaluation of convective-heat-transfer coefficient. The rate of heat transfer by convection and the convective-heat-transfer coefficient can now be determined. The dimensionless temperature gradient at the surface (i.e., at $y = 0$) is

$$\frac{\partial \left(\dfrac{T - T_s}{T_\infty - T_s} \right)}{\partial \left(\dfrac{y}{x} \sqrt{\mathrm{Re}_x}\,\Pr^{\frac{1}{3}} \right)}\Bigg|_{y\,=\,0} = 0.332$$

Therefore, at any specified value of x

$$\frac{\partial T}{\partial y}\Bigg|_{y\,=\,0} = 0.332\frac{\mathrm{Re}_x^{\frac{1}{2}}\Pr^{\frac{1}{3}}}{x}\,(T_\infty - T_s) \qquad \textbf{(6–25)}$$

and the local rate of heat transfer by convection per unit area becomes on substituting $\partial T/\partial y$ from Eq. 6–25 in Eq. 6–1

$$\frac{q}{A} = -k\frac{\partial T}{\partial y}\Bigg|_{y\,=\,0} = 0.332k\,\frac{\mathrm{Re}_x^{\frac{1}{2}}\Pr^{\frac{1}{3}}}{x}\,(T_\infty - T_s) \qquad \textbf{(6–26)}$$

The total rate of heat transfer from a plate of width b and length L, obtained by integrating q from Eq. 6–26 between $x = 0$ and $x = L$, is

$$q = 0.664 k \mathrm{Re}_L^{\frac{1}{2}} \mathrm{Pr}^{\frac{1}{3}} bL(T_s - T_\infty) \qquad (6\text{–}27)$$

where $\mathrm{Re}_L = u_\infty L / \nu$.

The local convective-heat-transfer coefficient is

$$h_{cx} = \frac{q}{A(T_s - T_\infty)} = 0.332 \frac{k}{x} \mathrm{Re}_x^{\frac{1}{2}} \mathrm{Pr}^{\frac{1}{3}} \qquad (6\text{–}28)$$

and the corresponding local Nusselt number is

$$\mathrm{Nu}_x = \frac{h_{cx} x}{k} = 0.332 \mathrm{Re}_x^{\frac{1}{2}} \mathrm{Pr}^{\frac{1}{3}} \qquad (6\text{–}29)$$

The average Nusselt number, $\bar{h}_c L / k$, obtained by integrating the right-hand side of Eq. 6–28 between $x = 0$ and $x = L$ and dividing by k, is

$$\overline{\mathrm{Nu}}_L = 0.664 \mathrm{Re}_L^{\frac{1}{2}} \mathrm{Pr}^{\frac{1}{3}} \qquad (6\text{–}30)$$

The average value of the Nusselt number over a length L of the plate is therefore twice the local value of Nu_x at $x = L$. It can easily be verified that the same relation between the average and local value holds also for the heat-transfer coefficient, that is,

$$\bar{h}_c = 2 h_c{}_{(x=L)} \qquad (6\text{–}31)$$

In practice, the physical properties in Eqs. 6–24 to 6–30 vary with temperature, while for the purpose of analysis it was assumed that the physical properties are constant. Experimental data have been found to agree satisfactorily with the results predicted analytically if the properties are evaluated at a mean temperature halfway between that of the wall and the free-stream temperature.

Example 6–4. Air at 60 F and at a pressure of 1 atm is flowing over a plate at a velocity of 10 fps. If the plate is 1 ft wide and at 140 F, calculate the following quantities at $x = 1$ ft and $x = x_c$.

a) Boundary-layer thickness.
b) Local friction coefficient.
c) Average friction coefficient.
d) Local drag or shearing stress due to friction.
e) Thickness of thermal boundary layer.
f) Local convective-heat-transfer coefficient.
g) Average convective-heat-transfer coefficient.
h) Rate of heat transfer by convection.

Solution: Properties of air at 100 F from Table A–3 are:

$$\rho = 0.071 \text{ lb}_m/\text{cu ft}$$
$$c_p = 0.240 \text{ Btu/lb}_m \text{ F}$$
$$\mu = 1.285 \times 10^{-5} \text{ lb}_m/\text{ft sec}$$
$$k = 0.0154 \text{ Btu/hr ft F}$$
$$\text{Pr} = 0.72$$

The local Reynolds number at $x = 1$ ft is

$$\text{Re}_{x=1} = \frac{u_\infty \rho x}{\mu} = \frac{(10 \text{ ft/sec})(0.071 \text{ lb}_m/\text{cu ft})(1 \text{ ft})}{1.285 \times 10^{-5} \text{ lb}_m/\text{ft sec}} = 55{,}200$$

Assuming that the critical Reynolds number is 5×10^5, the critical distance is

$$x_c = \frac{5 \times 10^5 \mu}{u_\infty \rho} = \frac{(5 \times 10^5)(1.285 \times 10^{-5} \text{lb}_m/\text{ft sec})}{(10 \text{ ft/sec})(0.071 \text{lb}_m/\text{cu ft})} = 9 \text{ ft}$$

The desired quantities are determined by substituting appropriate values of the variable into the pertinent equations. The results of the calculations are shown in Table 6–4, and it is suggested that the reader verify them.

TABLE 6–4

Part	Symbol	Unit	Eq. Used	Result ($x = 1$ ft)	Result ($x = 9$ ft)
a	δ	ft	6–17	0.0212	0.064
b	C_{fx}	.....	6–19	0.00282	0.00094
c	$\bar{C}_f$	.....	6–20	0.00564	0.00188
d	τ_s	lb$_f$/sq ft	6–18	3.12×10^{-4}	1.04×10^{-4}
e	δ_{th}	ft	6–24	0.0236	0.0715
f	h_{cx}	Btu/hr sq ft F	6–28	1.03	0.36
g	$\bar{h}_c$	Btu/hr sq ft F	6–31	2.06	0.72
h	q_c	Btu/hr	6–27	206	648

A useful relation between the local Nusselt number Nu_x and the corresponding friction coefficient C_{fx} is obtained by dividing Eq. 6–29 by $\text{Re}_x \text{Pr}^{\frac{1}{3}}$, or

$$\left(\frac{\text{Nu}_x}{\text{Re}_x \text{Pr}} \right) \text{Pr}^{\frac{2}{3}} = \frac{0.322}{\text{Re}_x^{\frac{1}{2}}} = \frac{C_{fx}}{2} \tag{6–32}$$

The dimensionless ration $\text{Nu}_x/\text{Re}_x\text{Pr}$ is known as the *Stanton number*, St_x. According to Eq. 6–32 the Stanton number times the Prandtl raised to the two-thirds power is equal to one-half the value of the friction coefficient. This relation between heat transfer and fluid friction was proposed by Colburn (4) and illustrates the interrelationship of the two processes.

6–8. APPROXIMATE BOUNDARY-LAYER ANALYSIS

In the preceding section we analyzed the flow of mass, momentum, and heat in a laminar boundary layer mathematically. That is to say we derived equations describing the processes at any point in the boundary layer and then indicated how these equations can be solved subject to the physical boundary conditions. We saw that the momentum equation is a partial-differential equation with variable coefficients and that a solution is difficult to obtain even for as simple a geometry as a flat plate. The mathematical difficulties of an exact solution can be circumvented by an approximate analysis which simplifies the mathematical manipulations. In cases where exact solutions are available, they agree with satisfactory accuracy with the solutions obtained by the approximate method.

Instead of writing the equations of motion and heat transfer for a differential control volume, von Karman (8) suggested writing these equations

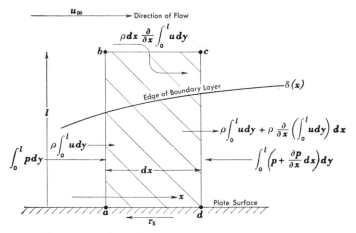

FIG. 6-15. Control volume for approximate momentum analysis of a boundary layer.

for the aggregate of particles in the boundary layer. For this purpose we choose a control volume (Fig. 6–15) bounded by the two planes ab and cd which are perpendicular to the wall and a distance dx apart, the surface of the plate, and a parallel plane in the free stream at a distance l from the surface. For a unit width in the z direction we can write the continuity equation, the momentum equation, and the heat-transfer equation, following the general procedure outlined in Sec. 6–7. Under steady-state conditions for a fluid of constant mass density ρ, the mass flow per unit time entering through the face ab is $\rho \int_0^l u\,dy$ and the mass flow per unit time leaving through the face cd is

$$\rho \int_0^l u\,dy + \rho \frac{\partial}{\partial x} \left(\int_0^l u\,dy \right) dx$$

Therefore, since the plate is impervious to the flow of mass,

$$\rho dx \frac{\partial}{\partial x} \int_0^l u \, dy$$

must flow into the control volume per unit time through upper boundary surface bc. The velocity at $y = l$ is for all practical purposes equal to the free-stream velocity u_∞ and the x momentum per unit time entering through face bc is therefore

$$u_\infty \rho dx \frac{\partial}{\partial x} \int_0^l u \, dy$$

The rate of momentum inflow through face ab is

$$\rho \int_0^l u^2 \, dy$$

and the rate of momentum outflow through face cd is

$$\rho \int_0^l u^2 \, dy + \rho \frac{\partial}{\partial x} \left(\int_0^l u^2 \, dy \right) dx$$

The increase of x momentum per unit time of the fluid in the control volume, obtained by subtracting the rate of x-momentum inflow from the rate of x-momentum outflow, is

$$-\rho dx \frac{\partial}{\partial x} \int_0^l u^2 \, dy + u_\infty \rho dx \frac{\partial}{\partial x} \int_0^l u \, dy = \rho dx \frac{\partial}{\partial x} \int_0^l (u_\infty - u) u \, dy$$

For $y > \delta$ (i.e., outside of the boundary layer) the velocity u becomes equal to the free-stream velocity u_∞. Therefore $u_\infty - u$ is zero for $y > \delta$ and we only have to consider the integrand within the limits from $y = 0$ to $y = \delta$. The net outgoing momentum flux is therefore

$$-\rho dx \frac{\partial}{\partial x} \int_0^\delta (u_\infty - u) u \, dy$$

The increase in x-momentum flux is equal to the summation of the forces in the x direction acting on the surface of the control volume. These forces, considered positive in the direction of flow, are

1. The shearing stress at the surface, $- \tau_s dx$.

2. The pressure on face ab, $\displaystyle\int_0^l p \, dy$.

3. The pressure on face cd, $-\int_0^l p\,dy + \dfrac{\partial}{\partial x}\left(\int_0^l p\,dy\right)dx$.

Since the velocities on both sides of the face bc are equal, no shearing stress exists there.

Equating the forces to the rate of momentum increase yields finally

$$\frac{\rho}{g_c}\frac{\partial}{\partial x}\int_0^\delta (u_\infty - u)u\,dy = \tau_s + \int_0^\delta \frac{\partial p}{\partial x}\,dy \qquad (6\text{-}33)$$

This is the *von Karman momentum integral equation of the boundary layer for incompressible flow*. It applies also to flow over slightly curved boundaries if x is measured along the surface and y normal to it. The last term can be determined if the pressure along the wall or the velocity distribution outside the boundary layer is known. In that case the pressure can be found from Bernoulli's equation

$$p_\infty + \frac{\rho u_\infty^2}{2g_c} = \text{const}$$

or

$$\frac{\partial p_\infty}{\partial x} = -\frac{\rho u_\infty}{g_c}\frac{\partial u_\infty}{\partial x}$$

Since the boundary layer is very thin, it may be assumed (1) that the pressure at any x location is constant throughout the boundary layer, i.e., $p(x) = p_\infty(x)$, and

$$\int_0^\delta \frac{\partial p}{\partial x}\,dy = \frac{\partial p_\infty}{\partial x}\delta = -\frac{\rho u_\infty}{g_c}\delta\frac{\partial u_\infty}{\partial x} \qquad (6\text{-}34)$$

For flow over a flat plate the velocity u_∞ is constant and consequently the last term in Eq. 6–33 becomes zero.

If one assumes a physically reasonable velocity distribution in the boundary layer, the momentum integral equation (Eq. 6–33) can be used to determine the boundary-layer thickness and the wall friction for specified geometries and flow conditions. The results naturally become more accurate the more closely the assumed velocity distribution resembles actual conditions. It has been found, however, that even a very rough assumption for the velocity distribution will yield satisfactory results. For this reason the approximate method is a powerful tool in engineering analysis. Example 6–5 illustrates the method.

Example 6–5. Determine the hydrodynamic boundary-layer thickness for laminar flow over a flat plate by means of the von Karman momentum equation of the boundary layer. Assume a straight-line velocity distribution in the boundary layer.

Solution: The equation describing the velocity distribution for a linear increase in velocity from $u = 0$ at $y = 0$ to $u = u_\infty$ at $y = \delta$ is

$$u = \frac{u_\infty y}{\delta}$$

The shearing stress at the wall τ_s is then

$$g_c \tau_s = \mu \left. \frac{\partial u}{\partial y} \right|_{y=0} = \frac{\mu u_\infty}{\delta}$$

Substituting for u and τ_s in Eq. 6–33 yields

$$\rho u_\infty^2 \frac{\partial}{\partial x} \int_0^\delta \left(1 - \frac{y}{\delta}\right) \frac{y}{\delta}\, dy = \frac{\mu u_\infty}{\delta}$$

Evaluating the integral above yields

$$\int_0^\delta \frac{y}{\delta}\, dy - \int_0^\delta \frac{y^2}{\delta^2}\, dy = \frac{1}{\delta} \frac{y^2}{2} \bigg|_0^\delta - \frac{1}{\delta^2} \frac{y^3}{3} \bigg|_0^\delta = \frac{\delta}{6}$$

Then, we get

$$\frac{\rho u_\infty^2}{6} \frac{d\delta}{dx} = \frac{\mu u_\infty}{\delta}$$

which yields

$$\delta d\delta = d\left(\frac{\delta^2}{2}\right) = \frac{6\mu}{\rho u_\infty}\, dx$$

Integrating the above equation gives the boundary-layer thickness δ as

$$\delta = \sqrt{(12\mu x)/(\rho u_\infty)} = 3.46\, x/\sqrt{\mathrm{Re}_x} \qquad \textit{Ans.}$$

The boundary-layer thickness calculated by means of a linear approximation to the velocity distribution is about 30 per cent less than the value obtained by Blasius (see Eq. 6–17). However, the approximate method can be considerably improved by taking a velocity distribution which resembles the true conditions more closely. Eckert (9) used a cubic parabola of the form

$$\frac{u}{u_\infty} = C_1 \frac{y}{\delta} - C_2 \left(\frac{y}{\delta}\right)^3 \qquad \textbf{(6–35)}$$

and obtained, by substituting the above relation for u in Eq. 6–33,

$$\delta = 4.64\, x / \sqrt{\mathrm{Re}_x} \qquad \textbf{(6–36)}$$

a value only 8 per cent below that of the exact analysis. Since most of the experimental measurements are only accurate to within 10 per cent, the results of the approximate analysis are satisfactory in practice.

To determine the rate of convective heat transfer to or from a surface we make an energy balance for the aggregate of fluid particles within the control volume of Fig. 6–16. To simplify the problem we shall neglect

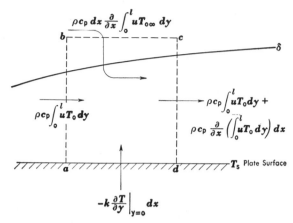

$$\rho c_p \, dx \, \frac{\partial}{\partial x} \int_0^l u T_{0\infty} \, dy$$

$$\rho c_p \int_0^l u T_0 \, dy$$

$$\rho c_p \int_0^l u T_0 \, dy + \\ \rho c_p \frac{\partial}{\partial x} \left(\int_0^l u T_0 \, dy \right) dx$$

$$-k \frac{\partial T}{\partial y} \bigg|_{y=0} \, dx$$

Fig. 6–16.　Control volume for approximate energy balance in a boundary layer.

the shear work due to the frictional forces along the wall and assume also that the physical properties are independent of the temperature.

Energy is convected into and out of the control volume as a result of the fluid motion, and there is also heat flow by conduction across the interface. The energy flow rates across the individual faces of the control volume are listed in Table 6–5. To satisfy the principle of conservation

TABLE 6–5

Face	Mass-Flow Rate	Heat-Flow Rate
ab	$\rho \int_0^l u \, dy$	$\rho c_p \int_0^l u T_o \, dy$
bc	$\rho \, dx \, \frac{\partial}{\partial x} \int_0^l u \, dy$	$\rho c_p \, dx \, \frac{\partial}{\partial x} \int_0^l u T_{o\infty} \, dy$
cd	$\rho \left[\int_0^l u \, dy + \frac{\partial}{\partial x} \left(\int_0^l u \, dy \right) dx \right]$	$\rho c_p \int_0^l u T_o \, dy + \rho c_p \frac{\partial}{\partial x} \left(\int_0^l u T_o \, dy \right) dx$
da	0	$-k \frac{\partial T}{\partial y} \bigg|_{y=0} \, dx$

of energy in the steady state, the rate of energy influx must equal the rate of energy efflux. Equating the net rate of convective energy outflow to the net rate of heat inflow by conduction we obtain

$$\frac{\partial}{\partial x} \int_0^l (T_{o\infty} - T_o) u \, dy = \frac{k}{\rho c_p} \frac{\partial T}{\partial y} \bigg|_{y=0}$$

Since the total temperature T_o equals the free-stream total temperature $T_{o\,\infty}$ outside the thermal boundary layer (i.e., $y > \delta_{th}$), the integrand becomes zero for values of y larger than δ_{th}. We therefore replace l, the upper limit of the integral, by δ_{th}, and the heat-transfer equation of the boundary layer becomes

$$\frac{\partial}{\partial x} \int_0^{\delta_{th}} (T_{o\,\infty} - T_o)u\,dy = \frac{k}{\rho c_p}\frac{\partial T}{\partial y}\bigg|_{y=0} \tag{6-37}$$

If we restrict our analysis to low-speed flow in which the kinetic energy is negligible compared with the enthalpy, the total temperatures in Eq. 6–37 are equal to the static temperatures for all practical purposes, i.e., $T_o \simeq T$ and $T_{o\,\infty} \simeq T_\infty$.

To determine the convective-heat-transfer coefficient we now select a suitable shape for the temperature distribution which meets the physical boundary conditions. Near the surface, where heat flows by conduction, the temperature gradient should be linear, and at $y = 0$, the fluid temperature should be equal to the plate temperature. At the edge of the thermal boundary layer (i.e., at $y = \delta_{th}$) the temperature should smoothly approach the free-stream temperature. Mathematically these boundary conditions are

$$\frac{\partial T}{\partial y} = C \qquad \text{and} \qquad (T - T_s) = 0 \qquad \text{at } y = 0$$

$$(T - T_s) = (T_\infty - T_s) \qquad \text{and} \qquad \frac{\partial(T - T_s)}{\partial y} = 0 \qquad \text{at } y = \delta_{th}$$

A cubic parabola of the form

$$T - T_s = C_1 y + C_2 y^3 \tag{6-38}$$

satisfies these boundary conditions if the constants C_1 and C_2 are selected appropriately. The conditions at $y = 0$ are automatically satisfied for any value of C_1 and C_2. At $y = \delta_{th}$ we have

$$T_\infty - T_s = C_1 \delta + C_2 \delta^3$$

and
$$\frac{\partial(T - T_s)}{\partial y}\bigg|_{y=\delta} = C_1 + 3C_2 \delta_{th}^2 = 0$$

Solving for C_1 and C_2, and substituting these expressions in Eq. 6–38 yields

$$\frac{T - T_s}{T_\infty - T_s} = \frac{3}{2}\left(\frac{y}{\delta_{th}}\right) - \frac{1}{2}\left(\frac{y}{\delta_{th}}\right)^3 \tag{6-39}$$

Using Eqs. 6–39 and 6–35 for $(T - T_s)$ and u respectively, the integral in Eq. 6–37 can be written as

$$\int_0^{\delta_{th}}(T_\infty - T)u\,dy = \int_0^{\delta_{th}}[(T_\infty - T_s) - (T - T_s)]u\,dy$$

$$= (T_\infty - T_s)u_\infty \int_0^{\delta_{th}}\left[1 - \frac{3}{2}\frac{y}{\delta_{th}} + \frac{1}{2}\left(\frac{y}{\delta_{th}}\right)^3\right]\left[\frac{3}{2}\left(\frac{y}{\delta}\right) - \frac{1}{2}\left(\frac{y}{\delta}\right)^3\right]dy$$

Performing the multiplication under the integral sign we obtain

$$(T_\infty - T_s)u_\infty \int_0^{\delta_{th}}\left[\left(\frac{3}{2\delta}\right)y - \left(\frac{9}{4\delta\delta_{th}}\right)y^2 + \left(\frac{3}{4\delta\delta_{th}^3}\right)y^4\right.$$

$$\left. -\left(\frac{1}{2\delta^3}\right)y^3 + \left(\frac{3}{4\delta_{th}\delta^3}\right)y^4 - \left(\frac{1}{4\delta_{th}^3\delta^3}\right)y^3\right]dy$$

which yields after integrating

$$(T_\infty - T_s)u_\infty\left[\frac{3}{4}\frac{\delta_{th}^2}{\delta} - \frac{3}{4}\frac{\delta_{th}^2}{\delta} + \frac{3}{20}\frac{\delta_{th}^2}{\delta} - \frac{1}{8}\frac{\delta_{th}^4}{\delta^3} + \frac{3}{20}\frac{\delta_{th}^4}{\delta^3} - \frac{1}{28}\frac{\delta_{th}^4}{\delta^3}\right]$$

If we let $\zeta = \delta_{th}/\delta$, the above expression can be written

$$(T_\infty - T_s)u_\infty\delta\left(\frac{3}{20}\zeta^2 - \frac{3}{280}\zeta^4\right)$$

For fluids having a Prandtl number equal to or larger than unity, ζ is equal to or less than unity and the second term in the bracket can be neglected compared to the first.[13] Substituting this approximate form for the integral in Eq. 6–37, we obtain

$$\frac{3}{20}u_\infty(T_s - T_\infty)\zeta^2\frac{\partial\delta}{\partial x} = a\left.\frac{\partial T}{\partial y}\right|_{y=0} = \frac{3}{2}a\frac{T_s - T_\infty}{\delta\zeta}$$

or

$$\frac{1}{10}u_\infty\zeta^3\delta\frac{\partial\delta}{\partial x} = a$$

From Eq. 6-36 we obtain

$$\delta\frac{\partial\delta}{\partial x} = 10.75\frac{\nu}{u_\infty}$$

and with this expression we get

$$\zeta^3 = \frac{10}{10.75}\frac{a}{\nu}$$

or

$$\delta_{th} = 0.9\delta\mathrm{Pr}^{-\frac{1}{3}} \tag{6-40}$$

---

[13] This assumption is not valid for liquid metals, which have Pr << 1.

Except for the numerical constant (0.9 compared with 1.0) the foregoing result is in agreement with the exact calculations of Pohlhausen (Eq. 6–24).

The rate of heat flow by convection from the plate per unit area is, from Eqs. 1–1 and 6–39,

$$\frac{q}{A} = -k \left.\frac{\partial T}{\partial y}\right|_{y=0} = -\frac{3}{2}\frac{k}{\delta_{th}}(T_\infty - T_s)$$

Substituting Eqs. 6–36 and 6–40 for δ_{th} yields

$$\frac{q}{A} = -\frac{3}{2}\frac{k}{x}\frac{\mathrm{Pr}^{\frac{1}{3}}\mathrm{Re}_x^{\frac{1}{2}}}{(0.9)(4.64)}(T_\infty - T_s) = 0.364\frac{k}{x}\mathrm{Re}_x^{\frac{1}{2}}\mathrm{Pr}^{\frac{1}{3}}(T_s - T_\infty) \quad \textbf{(6–41)}$$

and

$$\mathrm{Nu}_x = \frac{q}{A(T_s - T_\infty)}\frac{x}{k} = 0.364\mathrm{Re}_x^{\frac{1}{2}}\mathrm{Pr}^{\frac{1}{3}} \quad \text{(6–42)}$$

This result is in agreement with the exact analysis (Eq. 6–29) except for the numerical constant, which is about 9 per cent larger.

The foregoing example illustrates the usefulness of the approximate boundary-layer analysis. Guided by a little physical insight and intuition, this technique yields satisfactory results without the mathematical complications inherent in the exact boundary-layer equations. The approximate method has been applied to many other problems, and the results are available in the literature.

6–9. ANALOGY BETWEEN HEAT AND MOMENTUM TRANSFER IN TURBULENT FLOW

In a majority of practical applications the flow in the boundary layer is turbulent rather than laminar. It is therefore not surprising that many famous scientists, such as Osborn Reynolds, G. I. Taylor, Ludwig Prandtl, and T. von Karman, have studied problems dealing with turbulent-exchange mechanisms. Although these men as well as many others have contributed considerably to our understanding of turbulent flow, so far no one has succeeded in predicting friction and heat-transfer coefficients by a direct analysis. The reason for this lack of success is the extreme complexity of turbulent motion. In turbulent flow, irregular velocity fluctuations are always superimposed upon the motion of the main stream, and the fluctuating components can not be described by simple equations. Yet, it is precisely these fluctuations which are primarily responsible for the transfer of heat as well as momentum in turbulent flow.

Qualitatively the exchange mechanism in turbulent flow can be pictured as a magnification of the molecular exchange in laminar flow. In steady laminar flow, physical properties such as temperature and pressure remain constant at any point and fluid particles follow well-defined streamlines. Heat and momentum are transferred across streamlines only by molecular diffusion. The amount of cross flow is so small that, when a colored dye is injected at some point into the fluid, it follows a streamline without appreciable diffusion. In turbulent flow, on the other hand, the color will be distributed over a wide area a short distance downstream from the point of injection. The mixing mechanism consists of rapidly fluctuating eddies which transport blobs of fluid in an irregular manner. Groups of particles collide with each other at random, establish cross flow on a macroscopic scale, and effectively mix the fluid. Since the mixing in turbulent flow is on a macroscopic scale with groups of particles transported in a zigzag path through the fluid, the exchange mechanism is many times more effective than in laminar flow. As a result, the rates of heat and momentum transfer in turbulent flow and the associated friction and heat-transfer coefficients are many times larger than in laminar flow.

Instantaneous streamlines in turbulent flow are highly jagged, and it would be a hopelessly difficult task to trace the path of individual fluid elements. However, if the flow at a point is averaged over a period of time, long as compared with the period of a single fluctuation, the time-mean properties and the velocity of the fluid are constant if the average flow remains steady. It is therefore general practice to describe each fluid property and the velocity in turbulent flow in terms of a *mean value* which does not vary with time and a *fluctuating component* which is a function of time. To simplify the problem, consider a two-dimensional flow (Fig. 6–17) in which the mean value of velocity is parallel to the x direction. The instantaneous velocity components u and v can then be expressed in the form

$$u = \bar{u} + u'$$
$$v = v' \tag{6–43}$$

where the bar over a symbol denotes the temporal mean value, and the

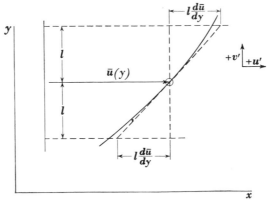

Fig. 6–17. Sketch illustrating mixing length for momentum transfer.

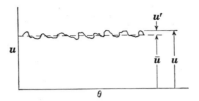

FIG. 6–18. Sketch illustrating time
variation of instantaneous velocity.

prime denotes the instantaneous deviation from the mean value. According to the model used to describe the flow,

$$\bar{u} = \frac{1}{\theta^*} \int_0^{\theta^*} u\,dt \qquad (6\text{–}44)$$

where θ^* is large compared with the period of the fluctuations. Figure 6–18
shows qualitatively the time variation of u and u'. From Eq. 6–44 or
from an inspection of the graph it is apparent that the time average of
u' is zero, i.e. $\overline{u'} = 0$. A similar argument shows that $\bar{v}'$ and $(\bar{\rho v})'$ are
also zero.

The fluctuating velocity components continuously transport mass, and
consequently momentum, across a plane normal to the y direction. The
instantaneous rate of transfer in the y direction of x-momentum per unit
area at any point is

$$- (\rho v)' (\bar{u} + u')$$

where the minus sign, as will be shown later, takes account of the statistical
correlation between u' and v'.

The time average of the x-momentum transfer gives rise to an *apparent
turbulent shear or Reynolds stress* τ_t defined by

$$g_c\tau_t = - \frac{1}{\theta^*} \int_0^{\theta^*} (\rho v)'(\bar{u} + u')d\theta \qquad (6\text{–}45)$$

Breaking this term up into two parts, the time average of the first is zero, or

$$\frac{1}{\theta^*} \int_0^{\theta^*} (\rho v)'\bar{u}d\theta = 0$$

since $\bar{u}$ is a constant and the time average of $(\rho v)'$ is zero. Integrating the
second term, Eq. 6–45 becomes

$$g_c\tau_t = - \frac{1}{\theta^*} \int_0^{\theta^*} (\rho v)'u'd\theta = - \overline{(\rho v)'u'} \qquad (6\text{–}45a)$$

or if ρ is constant

$$g_c \tau_t = -\rho \, \overline{(v'u')} \qquad\qquad (6\text{--}46)$$

It is not difficult to visualize that the time averages of the mixed products of velocity fluctuations, such as for example $\overline{v'u'}$, differ from zero. From Fig. 6–17 we can see that the particles which travel upward $(v' > 0)$ arrive at a layer in the fluid in which the mean velocity $\bar{u}$ is larger than in the layer from which they come. Assuming that the fluid particles preserve on the average their original velocity $\bar{u}$ during their migration, they will tend to slow down other fluid particles after they have reached their destination and thereby give rise to a negative component u'. Conversely, if v' is negative, the observed value of u' at the new destination will be positive. On the average, therefore, a positive v' is associated with a negative u', and vice versa. The time average of $u'v'$ is therefore on the average not zero but a negative quantity. The turbulent shearing stress defined by Eq. 6–46 is thus positive and has the same sign as the corresponding laminar shearing stress,

$$\tau_{yx} = \mu_f \frac{d\bar{u}}{dy} = \frac{\rho}{g_c} \nu \frac{d\bar{u}}{dy} \qquad\qquad [\,6\text{--}15\,]$$

It should be noted, however, that the laminar shearing stress is a true stress, whereas the apparent turbulent shearing stress is simply a concept introduced to account for the effects of the momentum transfer by turbulent fluctuations. This concept allows us to express the total shear stress in turbulent flow as

$$\tau = \frac{\text{viscous force}}{\text{unit area}} + \frac{1}{g_c}\,(\text{turbulent momentum flux}) \qquad (6\text{--}47)$$

To relate the turbulent momentum flux to the time-average velocity gradient, $d\bar{u}/dy$, Prandtl (10) postulated that fluctuations of macroscopic blobs of fluid in turbulent flow are, on the average, similar to the motion of molecules in a gas, i.e., they travel on the average a distance l perpendicular to $\bar{u}$ (Fig. 6–17) before coming to rest in another y plane. This distance l is known as Prandtl's mixing length and corresponds qualitatively to the mean free path of a gas molecule. Prandtl further argued that the fluid particles retain their identity and physical properties during the cross motion and that the turbulent fluctuation arises chiefly from the difference in the time-mean properties between y planes spaced a distance l apart. According to this argument, if a fluid particle travels from the layer y to the layer $y + l$,

$$u' \simeq l \frac{d\bar{u}}{dy} \qquad\qquad (6\text{--}48)$$

With this model we can write the turbulent shearing stress in a form analogous to the laminar shearing stress as

$$g_c \tau_t = -\rho \overline{v'u'} = \rho \epsilon_M \frac{d\bar{u}}{dy} \qquad (6\text{–}49)$$

where the symbol ϵ_M is called the eddy viscosity or the turbulent exchange coefficient for momentum. The eddy viscosity ϵ_M is formally analogous to the kinematic viscosity ν, but whereas ν is a physical property, ϵ_M depends on the dynamics of the flow. Combining Eqs. 6–48 and 6–49 shows that $\epsilon_M = -\overline{v'l}$. Substituting Eqs. 6–15 and 6–49 in Eq. 6–47 gives the total shearing stress in the form

$$\tau = \frac{\rho}{g_c} (\nu + \epsilon_M) \frac{d\bar{u}}{dy} \qquad (6\text{–}50)$$

In turbulent flow ϵ_M is much larger than ν and the viscous term may therefore be neglected.

The transfer of energy as heat in a turbulent flow can be pictured in an analogous fashion. Consider a two-dimensional time-mean temperature distribution as shown in Fig. 6–19. The fluctuating velocity components continuously transport fluid particles and the energy stored in them across a plane normal to the y direction. The instantaneous rate of energy transfer per unit area at any point in the y direction is

$$(\rho v') (c_p T) \qquad (6\text{–}51)$$

where $T = \bar{T} + T'$. Following the same line of reasoning which led to Eq. 6–46, the time average of energy transfer due to the fluctuations, called the turbulent rate of heat transfer q_t, is

$$q_t = A\rho c_p \overline{v'T'} \qquad (6\text{–}52)$$

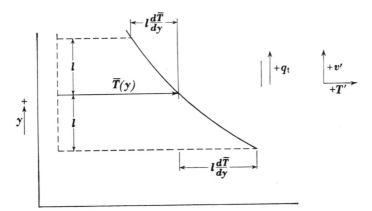

Fig. 6–19. Sketch illustrating mixing length for energy transfer.

Using Prandtl's concept of mixing length, we can relate the temperature fluctuation to the time-mean temperature gradient by the equation

$$T' \simeq l \frac{d\overline{T}}{dy} \tag{6-53}$$

This means physically that, when a fluid particle migrates from the layer y to another layer a distance l above or below, the resulting temperature fluctuation is caused chiefly by the difference between the time-mean temperatures in the layers. Assuming that the transport mechanisms of temperature (or energy) and velocity are similar, the mixing lengths in Eqs. 6–48 and 6–53 are equal. The product $\overline{v'T'}$, however, is positive on the average because a positive v' is accompanied by a positive T', and vice versa.

Combining Eqs. 6–52 and 6–53, the turbulent rate of heat transfer per unit area becomes

$$\frac{q_t}{A} = c_p\rho \, \overline{v'T'} = -c_p\rho \, \overline{v'l} \, \frac{d\overline{T}}{dy} \tag{6-54}$$

where the minus sign is a consequence of the second law of thermodynamics (see Sec. 1–2). To express the turbulent heat flux in a form analogous to the Fourier conduction equation we define ϵ_H, a quantity called the turbulent exchange coefficient for temperature, eddy diffusivity of heat, or eddy heat conductivity, by the equation $\epsilon_H = \overline{v'l}$. Substituting ϵ_H for $\overline{v'l}$ in Eq. 6–54, gives

$$\frac{q_t}{A} = -c_p\rho\epsilon_H \, \frac{d\overline{T}}{dy} \tag{6-55}$$

The total rate of heat transfer per unit area normal to the mean stream velocity can then be written as

$$\frac{q}{A} = \frac{\text{molecular conduction}}{\text{unit area}} + \frac{\text{turbulent transfer}}{\text{unit area}}$$

or in symbolic form as

$$\frac{q}{A} = -c_p\rho(a + \epsilon_H) \frac{d\overline{T}}{dy} \tag{6-56}$$

where $a = k/c_p\rho$, the molecular diffusivity of heat. The contribution to the heat transfer by molecular conduction is proportional to a, and the turbulent contribution is proportional to ϵ_H. For all fluids except liquid metals, ϵ_H is much larger than a in turbulent flow. The ratio of the molecular kinematic viscosity to the molecular diffusivity of heat ν/a has previously been named the Prandtl number. Similarly, the ratio of the turbulent eddy viscosity to the eddy diffusivity ϵ_M/ϵ_H could be considered a turbulent Prandtl number Pr_t. According to the Prandtl mixing-length theory, the turbulent Prandtl number is unity, since $\epsilon_M = \epsilon_H = \overline{v'l}$.

Although the model postulated by Prandtl in his treatment of turbulent flow is certainly grossly oversimplified, experimental results indicate it is at least qualitatively correct. Isakoff and Drew (11) found that Pr_t for the heating of mercury in turbulent flow inside a tube may vary from 1.0 to 1.6, and Forstall and Shapiro (12) found that Pr_t is about 0.7 for gases. The latter investigators also showed that Pr_t is substantially independent of the value of the laminar Prandtl number as well as of the type of experiment. For practical calculations it is usually satisfactory to assume that Pr_t is unity. With this simplification we can relate the turbulent heat flux to the turbulent shear stress by combining Eqs. 6–49 and 6–55 and obtain

$$\frac{q_t}{A} = -g_c \tau_t c_p \frac{d\overline{T}}{d\bar{u}} \tag{6-57}$$

This relation was originally derived in 1874 by the British scientist Osborn Reynolds and is called the Reynolds analogy in his honor. It is a good approximation whenever the flow is turbulent, and can be applied to turbulent boundary layers as well as to turbulent flow in pipes or ducts. However, the Reynolds analogy does not hold in the laminar sublayer. Since this layer offers a large thermal resistance to the flow of heat, Eq. 6–57 does in general not suffice for a quantitative solution. Only for fluids having a Prandtl number of unity can it be used directly to calculate the rate of heat transfer. This special case will now be considered.

6–10. REYNOLDS ANALOGY FOR TURBULENT FLOW OVER A FLAT PLATE

In this section we shall derive for flow over a plane surface a relation between the heat transfer and the skin friction for a Prandtl number of unity. In the following section we shall show how to calculate the skin friction and consider some improvements over the simple analogy.

In two-dimensional flow the shearing stress in the laminar sublayer τ_{yx} is

$$g_c \tau_{yx} = \mu \frac{du}{dy} \tag{6-15}$$

and the rate of heat flow per unit area across any plane perpendicular to the y direction is

$$\frac{q}{A} = -k \frac{dT}{dy} \tag{1-1}$$

Combining Eqs. 1–1 and 6–15 yields

$$\frac{q}{A} = -g_c \tau_{yx} \frac{k}{\mu} \frac{dT}{du} \tag{6–58}$$

An inspection of Eqs. 6–57 and 6–58 shows that if $c_p = k/u$ (i.e., for Pr = 1), the same equation of heat flow applies in the laminar and turbulent layers.

To determine the rate of heat transfer from a flat plate to a fluid with Pr = 1 flowing over it in turbulent flow, we replace k/u by c_p and separate the variables in Eq. 6–58. Assuming that q and r are constant, we get the equation

$$\frac{q_s}{A\tau_s c_p g_c} du = -dT \tag{6–59}$$

where the subscript s is used to indicate that both q and τ are taken at the surface of the plate. Integrating Eq. 6–59 between the limits $u = 0$ when $T = T_s$, and $u = u_\infty$ when $T = T_\infty$, yields

$$\frac{q_s}{A\tau_s c_p g_c} u_\infty = (T_s - T_\infty) \tag{6–60}$$

But since by definition

$$h_{cx} = \frac{q_s}{A(T_s - T_\infty)} \qquad \text{and} \qquad \tau_{sx} = C_{fx} \frac{\rho u_\infty^2}{2g_c}$$

Equation 6–60 can be written as

$$\frac{h_{cx}}{c_p \rho u_\infty} = \frac{\text{Nu}}{\text{Re}_x \text{Pr}} = \frac{C_{fx}}{2} \tag{6–61}$$

Equation 6–61 is satisfactory for gases in which Pr is approximately unity. Colburn (4) has shown that Eq. 6–61 can also be used for fluids having Prandtl numbers ranging from 0.6 to about 50 if it is modified in accordance with experimental results to read

$$\frac{\text{Nu}_x}{\text{Re}_x \text{Pr}} \text{Pr}^{\frac{2}{3}} = \text{St}_x \, \text{Pr}^{\frac{2}{3}} = \frac{C_{fx}}{2} \tag{6–62}$$

where the subscript x denotes the distance from the leading edge of the plate.

6–11. TURBULENT FLOW OVER PLANE SURFACES

To apply the analogy between heat transfer and momentum transfer in practice it is necessary to know the skin-friction coefficient C_{fx}. For turbulent flow over a plane surface the empirical equation for the local friction coefficient

$$C_{fx} = 0.0576 \left(\frac{u_\infty x}{\nu} \right)^{-\frac{1}{5}} \qquad (6\text{-}63)$$

is in good agreement with experimental results (1) in the Reynolds number range between 5×10^5 and 10^7 as long as no separation occurs. Assuming that the turbulent boundary layer starts at the leading edge, the average friction coefficient over a plane surface of length L can be obtained by integrating Eq. 6-63, or

$$\overline{C}_f = \frac{1}{L} \int_0^L C_{fx} dx = 0.072 \left(\frac{u_\infty L}{\nu} \right)^{-\frac{1}{5}} \qquad (6\text{-}64)$$

In reality, however, a laminar boundary layer precedes the turbulent boundary layer between $x = 0$ and $x = x_c$. Since the local frictional drag of a laminar boundary layer is less than the local frictional drag of a turbulent boundary layer at the same Reynolds number, the average drag calculated from Eq. 6-64 without correcting for the laminar portion of the boundary layer is too large. The actual drag can be closely estimated, however, by assuming that, behind the point of transition, the turbulent boundary layer behaves as though it had started at the leading edge.

Adding the laminar friction drag between $x = 0$ and $x = x_c$ to the turbulent drag between $x = x_c$ and $x = L$ gives

$$\overline{C}_f = 0.072 \, \text{Re}_L^{-\frac{1}{5}} - 0.072 \, \text{Re}_{xL}^{-\frac{1}{5}} + 1.33 \, \text{Re}_{xc}^{-\frac{1}{2}}$$

For a critical Reynolds number of 5×10^5 this yields

$$\overline{C}_f = 0.072 \, (\text{Re}_L^{-\frac{1}{5}} - 0.0464) \qquad (6\text{-}65)$$

Substituting Eq. 6-63 for C_{fx} in Eq. 6-62 yields the local Nusselt number at any value of x larger than x_c, or

$$\text{Nu}_x = \frac{h_{cx} x}{k} = 0.0288 \, \text{Pr}^{\frac{1}{3}} \left(\frac{u_\infty x}{\nu} \right)^{0.8} \qquad (6\text{-}66)$$

We observe that the local heat-transfer coefficient h_{cx} for heat transfer by convection through a turbulent boundary layer decreases with the distance x as $h_{cx} \propto 1/x^{0.2}$. Equation 6-66 shows that, in comparison with laminar flow where $h_{cx} \propto 1/x^{\frac{1}{2}}$, the heat-transfer coefficient in turbulent flow decreases less rapidly with x and that the turbulent-heat-transfer coefficient is much larger than the laminar-heat-transfer coefficient at a given value of the Reynolds number.

The average conductance in turbulent flow over a plane surface of length L can be calculated to a first approximation by integrating Eq. 6–66 between $x = 0$ and $x = L$, or

$$\bar{h}_c = \frac{1}{L} \int_0^L h_{cx} dx$$

In dimensionless form we get

$$\overline{\mathrm{Nu}_L} = \frac{\bar{h}_c L}{k} = 0.036 \ \mathrm{Pr}^{\frac{1}{3}} \ \mathrm{Re}_L{}^{0.8} \tag{6–67}$$

Equation 6–37 neglects the existence of the laminar boundary layer and is therefore valid only when $L \gg x_c$. The laminar boundary layer can be included in the analysis if Eq. 6–28 is used between $x = 0$ and $x = x_c$, and Eq. 6–66 between $x = x_c$ and $x = L$ for the integration of h_{cx}. This yields for $\mathrm{Re}_c = 5 \times 10^5$

$$\overline{\mathrm{Nu}_L} = 0.036 \ \mathrm{Pr}^{\frac{1}{3}} \ (\mathrm{Re}_L{}^{0.8} - 23{,}200) \tag{6–68}$$

Example 6–6. The crankcase of an automobile is approximately 30 in. long, 12 in. wide, and 4 in. deep. Assuming that the surface temperature of the crankcase is 160 F, estimate the rate of heat flow from the crankcase to atmospheric air at 40 F at a road speed of 60 mph. Assume that the vibration of the engine and the chassis induce the transition from laminar to turbulent flow so near to the leading edge that, for practical purposes, the boundary layer is turbulent over the entire surface. Neglect radiation and use for the front and rear surfaces the same average convective-heat-transfer coefficient as for the bottom and sides.

Solution: Using physical properties of air at 100 F from Table A–3 in Appendix III, the Reynolds number is

$$\mathrm{Re}_L = \frac{u_\infty \rho L}{\mu} = \frac{(60 \ \mathrm{mph})(88 \ \mathrm{ft/sec})/\mathrm{mph}(0.071 \ \mathrm{lb_m/cu \ ft})(30/12) \ \mathrm{ft}}{1.285 \times 20^{-5} \ \mathrm{lb_m/ft \ sec}}$$

$$= 1.21 \times 10^6$$

From Eq. 6–67 the average Nusselt number is

$$\overline{\mathrm{Nu}_L} = 0.036 \ \mathrm{Pr}^{\frac{1}{3}} \ \mathrm{Re}_L{}^{0.8}$$
$$= (0.036) \ (0.896) \ (73{,}480) = 2370$$

and the average convective-heat-transfer coefficient becomes

$$\bar{h}_c = \overline{\mathrm{Nu}_L} \ \frac{k}{L} = \frac{(2370)(0.0154 \ \mathrm{Btu/hr \ ft \ F})}{30/12 \ \mathrm{ft}}$$

$$= 14.55 \ \mathrm{Btu/hr \ sq \ ft \ F}$$

The over-all area is 4.84 sq ft and the rate of heat loss is therefore

$$q = \bar{h}_c \ A \ (T_s - T_\infty) = (14.55) \ (4.84) \ (160–40) = 8430 \ \mathrm{Btu/hr} \qquad Ans.$$

The thickness of a turbulent boundary layer in flow over a plane surface can be calculated by means of the Karman integral relations.   To improve the accuracy of the calculations, we shall use a velocity distribution determined by experiment.   Figure 6–20 shows several velocity profiles measured by Van der Hegge–Zynen (14).   Near the wall the velocity increases linearly with the distance from the surface.   This is the region called the laminar sublayer, although some recent measurements suggest that it is not completely devoid of turbulence.   In the fully turbulent portion of the boundary layer the velocity increases with the one-seventh power of distance and can be represented by the equation

$$\frac{u}{u_\infty} = \left(\frac{y}{\delta}\right)^{\frac{1}{7}} \tag{6–69}$$

Between the laminar sublayer and the turbulent portion of the boundary layer is a transition region where the turbulence level is variable.   Because

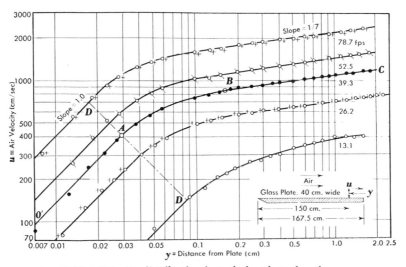

Fig. 6–20.   Velocity distribution in turbulent boundary layers over plane surfaces after Van der Hegge-Zynen (14).

the laminar sublayer as well as the transition layer are very thin we shall, as a first approximation, neglect both of them and use Eq. 6–69 to evaluate the momentum change in the integral equations.   This approximation cannot be used, however, to determine the shearing stress because, according to Eq. 6–69, the velocity gradient is

$$\frac{du}{dy} = \frac{1}{7}\frac{u_\infty}{\delta^{\frac{1}{7}}y^{\frac{6}{7}}}$$

which would lead to infinitely large shearing stress at the wall (i.e., at

$y = 0$). To overcome this difficulty we shall use an experimentally determined relation for the shearing stress.

In the Reynolds-number range between 10^5 and 10^7 the relation

$$g_c \tau_w = 0.0228 \, \rho u_\infty^2 \left(\frac{\nu}{u_\infty \delta} \right)^{\frac{1}{4}} \tag{6-70}$$

is in good agreement with experimental results obtained by Schultz–Grunow (15). Substituting Eq. 6–70 for the shearing stress and Eq. 6–69 for the velocity distribution in the integral of Eq. 6–22 gives

$$\frac{7}{72} \rho u_\infty^2 \frac{d\delta}{dx} = 0.0228 \, \rho u_\infty^2 \left(\frac{\nu}{u_\infty} \right)^{\frac{1}{4}}$$

Separation of the variables yields

$$\delta^{\frac{1}{4}} d\delta = 0.235 \left(\frac{\nu}{u_\infty} \right)^{\frac{1}{4}} dx$$

from which we obtain the boundary-layer thickness in the form

$$\delta = 0.376 \left(\frac{\nu}{u_\infty} \right)^{\frac{1}{5}} x^{\frac{4}{5}}$$

or

$$\frac{\delta}{x} = 0.376 \, \mathrm{Re}_x^{-\frac{1}{5}} \tag{6-71}$$

where $\mathrm{Re}_x = (u_\infty x / \nu)$. It can be seen from Eqs. 6–36 and 6–71 that, at any given value of x, a turbulent boundary layer increases at a faster rate than a laminar boundary layer. Despite its greater thickness, the turbulent boundary layer offers less resistance to heat flow than a laminar layer because the turbulent eddies produce continuous mixing between warmer and cooler fluids on a macroscopic scale. An inspection of the velocity profiles in Fig. 6–20 shows, however, that the eddies diminish in intensity in the buffer layer and hardly penetrate the laminar sublayer. Unless the Prandtl number equals unity, the relative magnitudes of the eddy conductivity and the molecular conductivity in the vicinity of the surface have a pronounced effect on the heat-transfer coefficient.

The effect of the diminution of the turbulent mixing near the surface on the heat-transfer coefficient for fluids having Prandtl numbers larger than unity was considered by Prandtl (16,17) von Karman (18), and most recently also by Deissler (19) in their respective improvements of the Reynolds analogy. Martinelli (20) also treated the problem of heat transfer to liquid metals, which have very small Prandtl numbers.

Prandtl divided the flow field into a laminar and a turbulent layer but neglected the buffer layer in his analysis.   The relation for flow over plane surfaces, derived in detail in Ref. 21, is

$$\frac{\mathrm{Nu}_x}{\mathrm{Re}_x\mathrm{Pr}} = \frac{C_{fx}/2}{1 + 2.1\,\mathrm{Re}_x^{-0.1}(\mathrm{Pr} - 1)} \tag{6-72}$$

We observe that, for $\mathrm{Pr} = 1$, Eq. 6–72 reduces to the simple Reynolds analogy.   The second term in the denominator is a measure of the thermal resistance in the laminar sublayer.   We see that this portion of the total thermal resistance increases as the Prandtl number becomes larger and accounts for most of the thermal resistance when the Prandtl number is very large.

Prandtl's analysis was later refined by von Karman (18), who divided the flow field into three zones: a laminar sublayer adjacent to the surface in which the eddy diffusivity is zero and heat flows only by conduction; next to it a buffer layer in which both conduction and convection contribute the heat-transfer mechanism (i.e., $k/c\rho$ and ϵ_H are of the same order of magnitude); and, finally, a turbulent region in which conduction is negligible compared to convection, and the Reynolds analogy applies.   He used experimental data for the velocity distribution and the shear stress to evaluate ϵ_M from Eq. 6–50 and assumed $\epsilon_M = \epsilon_H$ in his analysis.   He also postulated that the physical properties of the fluid are independent of the temperature.   With these simplifications he determined the thermal resistances in each of the three zones.   The results of von Karman's analysis are given below for flow over a flat plate:

Thermal resistance of laminar sublayer	$\dfrac{5\mathrm{Pr}}{c_p\sqrt{\rho g_c \tau_s}}$
Thermal resistance of buffer layer	$\dfrac{5\ln(5\,\mathrm{Pr} + 1)}{c_p\sqrt{\rho g_c \tau_s}}$
Thermal resistance of the turbulent region	$\dfrac{5(1 + \ln 6) + u_\infty/\sqrt{\tau_s g_c/\rho}}{c_p\sqrt{\rho g_c \tau_s}}$

Adding the thermal resistances and introducing the definitions for the Stanton number St and the local drag-friction coefficient C_{fx} yields, after some rearrangement, the expression

$$\mathrm{St}_x = \frac{\mathrm{Nu}_x}{\mathrm{Re}_x\mathrm{Pr}} = \frac{C_{fx}/2}{1 + 5\sqrt{C_{fx}/2}\left[(\mathrm{Pr} - 1) + \ln\dfrac{5\mathrm{Pr} + 1}{6}\right]} \tag{6-73}$$

for the local value of the Stanton number for flow over a plane surface at a given value of x. The average value of St or $\bar{h}_c$ over a surface of length L can be obtained by numerical or graphical integration.

To apply any of the equations relating the Stanton number and the friction coefficient in practice, the physical properties must be evaluated at some appropriate mean temperature. It is general practice to evaluate the physical properties at the *mean film temperature* T_f defined as $T_f = (T_s + T_\infty)/2$. This procedure is purely empirical, but has been found satisfactory for moderate-temperature ranges.

The three-distinct-layer concept is somewhat of an oversimplification of the real situation but is satisfactory for Prandtl numbers less than 25 or 30. For larger Prandtl numbers it is preferable to assume turbulent eddy generation near the outer edges of turbulent boundary layers and continuous damping of these eddies as they approach the wall. Some progress has been made recently with this approach (19,22), and the reader is referred to the original papers for details. An extensive review of the analogies is presented in Ref. 23.

6–12. CLOSURE

In this chapter we have studied the principles of heat transfer by forced convection. We have seen that the transfer of heat by convection is intimately related to the mechanics of the fluid flow, particularly to the flow in the vicinity of the heat-transfer surface. We have also observed that the nature of heat transfer as well as flow-phenomena depend greatly on whether the fluid far away from the surface is in laminar or in turbulent flow.

To become familiar with the basic principles of boundary layer theory and forced-convection heat transfer, we have considered the problem of convection in flow over a flat plate in some detail. This system is geometrically very simple, but it illustrates the most important features of forced convection. In subsequent chapters we shall treat heat transfer by convection in geometrically more complicated systems. In the next chapter we shall examine free-convection phenomena. In Chapter 8, heat transfer by convection to and from fluids flowing inside of pipes and ducts will be taken up. In Chapter 9, forced convection in flow over the exterior surfaces of bodies such as cylinders, spheres, tubes, and tube bundles will be considered. In Chapter 12 we shall study convection in high-speed flow, in particular the influence of frictional heating in the boundary on the convection process. The application of the principles of forced-convection heat transfer to the selection and design of heat-transfer equipment will be taken up in Chapter 11.

REFERENCES

1. H. Schlichting, *Boundary Layer Theory* (translated by J. Kestin). (New York: McGraw-Hill Book Company, Inc., 1955.)

2. H. L. Langhaar, *Dimensional Analysis and Theory of Models.* (New York: John Wiley & Sons, Inc., 1951.)

3. E. R. Van Driest, "On Dimensional Analysis and the Presentation of Data in Fluid Flow Problems," *J. Appl. Mech.*, Vol. 13 (1940), p. A-34.

4. A. P. Colburn, "A Method of Correlating Forced Convection Heat Transfer Data and a Comparison with Fluid Friction," *Trans. Am. Inst. Chem. Engrs.*, Vol. 29 (1933), pp. 174–210.

5. W. J. King, "The Basic Laws and Data of Heat Transmission," *Mech. Eng.*, Vol. 54 (1932), pp. 410–415.

6. M. Blasius, "Grenzschichten in Flüssigkeiten mit Kleiner Reibung," *Z. Math. u. Phys.*, Vol. 56, No. 1 (1908).

7. E. Pohlhausen, "Der Wärmeaustausch zwischen festen Körpern und Flüssigkeiten mit kleiner Reibung und kleiner Wärmeleitung," *ZAMM*, Vol. 1 (1921), p. 115.

8. T. von Karman, "Über laminare und turbulente Reibung," (translation) *NACA TM* 1092, 1946.

9. E. R. G. Eckert, *Introduction to the Transfer of Heat and Mass.* (New York: McGraw-Hill Book Company, Inc., 1950.)

10. L. Prandtl, "Über die ausgebildete Turbulenz," *ZAMM*, Vol. 5 (1925), p. 136; *Proc. 2nd Int. Cong. of Appl. Mech.*, Zurich (1926).

11. S. E. Isakoff and T. B. Drew, "Heat and Momentum Transfer in Turbulent Flow of Mercury," Inst. Mech. Eng. and ASME, *Proc. General Discussion on Heat Transfer* (1951), pp. 405–409.

12. W. Forstall, Jr. and A. H. Shapiro, "Momentum and Mass Transfer in Co-axial Gas Jets," *J. Appl. Mech.*, Vol. 17 (1950), p. 399.

13. M. Hansen, "Velocity Distribution in the Boundary Layer of a Submerged Plate," *NACA TM* 585, 1930.

14. Van der Hegge-Zynen, "Measurements of the Velocity Distribution in the Boundary Layer along a Plane Surface," *Thesis*, Delft, 1924. (Delft: I. Waltman, 1924.)

15. F. Schultz-Grunow, "A New Resistance Law for Smooth Plates," *Luftfahrt Forsch.*, Vol. 17 (1940), pp. 239–246: (translation) *NACA TM* 986, 1941.

16. L. Prandtl, "Bemerkungen über den Wärmeübergang im Rohr," *Phys. Zeit.*, Vol. 29 (1928), p. 487.

17. L. Prandtl, "Eine Beziehung zwischen Wärmeaustauch und Ströhmungswiederstand der Flüssigkeiten," *Phys. Zeit.*, Vol. 10 (1910), p. 1072.

18. T. von Karman, "The Analogy between Fluid Friction and Heat Transfer," *Trans. ASME*, Vol. 61 (1939), pp. 705–711.

19. R. G. Deissler, "Investigation of Turbulent Flow and Heat Transfer in Smooth Tubes Including the Effects of Variable Properties," *Trans. ASME*, Vol. 73 (1951), pp. 101–107.

20. R. C. Martinelli, "Heat Transfer to Molten Metals," *Trans. ASME*, Vol. 69 (1947), pp. 947–959.

21. J. M. Coulson and J. V. Richardson, *Chemical Engineering*, Vol. I, (New York: McGraw-Hill Book Company, Inc., 1954).

22. K. Goldmann, "Heat Transfer to Supercritical Water and Other Fluids with Temperature Dependent Properties," *Chem. Eng. Prog. Symp. Series Nuclear Eng.*, Part 1, Vol. 50, No. 11 (1954), pp. 105–110.

23.   J. G. Knudsen and D. L. Katz, "Fluid Dynamics and Heat Transfer," *Eng. Res. Bull.* 37, (Ann Arbor: Univ. of Michigan, 1953).

24.   A. H. Davis, "Convective Cooling of Wires in Streams of Viscous Liquids," *Phil. Mag.*, Vol. 47 (1924), pp. 1057–1091.

25.   E. L. Diret, W. James, and M. Stracy, "Heat Transmission from Fine Wires to Water," *Ind. Eng. Chem.*, Vol. 39 (1947), pp. 1098–1103.

26.   R. Hilpert, "Wärmeabgabe von geheizten Drähten und Rohren," *Forsch. Gebiete Ingenieurw.*, Vol. 4 (1933), pp. 215–224.

27.   D. Coles, "The Law of the Wake in the Turbulent Boundary Layer," *J. Fluid Mech.*, Vol. 1, Part 2 (1956), pp. 191–225.

28.   E. R. Van Direst, "Calculation of the Stability of the Laminar Boundary Layer in a Compressible Fluid on a Flat Plate with Heat Transfer," *J. Aero. Sci.*, Vol. 19 (1952), pp. 801–813.

29.   A. H. Shapiro, *The Dynamics and Thermodynamics of Compressible Fluid Flow.* Vol. 1, (New York: The Ronald Press Co., 1954).

PROBLEMS

6–1.   Evaluate the dimensionless groups $\bar{h}_c\,D/k$, $VD\rho\,/\mu$, $c_p\mu/k$, and $\bar{h}_c/c_p\,G$ for water, ethyl alcohol, mercury, hydrogen, air, and saturated steam over as wide a temperature range as possible and plot the results vs. temperature.   For the purpose of these calculations let $D = 1$ ft, $V = 1$ ft/sec, and $\bar{h}_c = 1$ Btu/hr sq ft F.

6–2.   The average Nusselt number for flow over a 2-ft-long plate is 100.   What is the value of the average surface conductance for the following fluids: (a) air at 60 F, (b) steam at 212 F and 15 psia, (c) water at 100 F, and (d) mercury at 200 F, and (e) ethyl alcohol at 212 F.

6–3.   Plot the velocity and temperature distributions in the laminar boundary layer for air at 60 F flowing over a flat plate at $\mathrm{Re}_x = 10^4$ if the free-stream velocity is 1.0 fps and the surface temperature is 160 F using (a) the Blasius solution, (b) an assumed straight line, and (c) a cubic parabola.

6–4.   Steam at 1 atm and 212 F is flowing across a 2-in.-OD pipe at a velocity of 20 fps.   Estimate the Nusselt number, the heat-transfer coefficient, and the rate of heat transfer per ft length of pipe if the pipe is at 400 F.

6–5.   Hydrogen at 60 F and at a pressure of 1 atm is flowing along a flat plate at a velocity of 10 fps.   If the plate is 1 ft wide and at 160 F, calculate the following quantities at $x = 1$ ft and at the distance corresponding to the transition point, i.e., $\mathrm{Re}_x = 5 \times 10^5$.   (Take properties at 110 F.)

a) Hydrodynamic boundary layer thickness, in inches.
b) Local friction coefficient, dimensionless.
c) Average friction coefficient, dimensionless.
d) Drag force, in lb$_f$.
e) Thickness of thermal boundary layer, in inches.
f) Local convective-heat-transfer coefficient, in Btu/hr sq ft F.
g) Average convective-heat-transfer coefficient, in Btu/hr sq ft F.
h) Rate of heat transfer, in Btu/hr.

6–6.   Repeat Prob. 6–5 for $x = 10$ ft and $u_\infty = 200$ fps, (a) taking the laminar boundary layer into account and (b) assuming that the turbulent boundary layer starts at the leading edge.

6–7.   Determine the rate of heat loss in Btu/hr from the wall of a building in a 10-mph wind blowing parallel to its surface.   The wall is 80 ft long, 20 ft high, its surface temperature is 80 F, and the temperature of the ambient air is 40 F.

6-8. Show that the energy equation (Eq. 6-21) can be expressed in the form

$$\rho u c_p \frac{\partial T}{\partial x} + \rho v c_p \frac{\partial T}{\partial y} = \frac{u}{g_c} \frac{\partial p}{\partial x} + k \frac{\partial^2 T}{\partial y^2} + \frac{\mu}{g_c} \left(\frac{\partial u}{\partial y} \right)^2$$

Hint: Multiply Eq. 6-16 by u and subtract the resulting expression from Eq. 6-21.

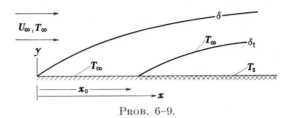

PROB. 6-9.

6-9. A fluid at temperature T_∞ is flowing at a velocity u_∞ over a flat plate which is at the same temperature as the fluid for a distance x_o from the leading edge, but at a temperature T_s beyond this point. Show by means of the integral boundary-layer equations that ζ, the ratio of the thermal boundary-layer thickness to the hydrodynamic boundary-layer thickness, over the heated portion of the plate is approximately

$$\zeta \simeq \mathrm{Pr}^{-\frac{1}{3}} \left[1 - \left(\frac{x_o}{x} \right)^{\frac{3}{4}} \right]^{\frac{1}{3}}$$

if the flow is laminar.

Hint: Assume that the temperature distribution is a cubic parabola and use T_s as your datum to simplify the boundary conditions, i.e., let

$$(T - T_s) = a y + c y^3$$

Also, inspect each equation and drop those terms which are small in comparison with others. Show also that, for the partially heated plate, the Nusselt number at x, if $x > x_o$, is approximately

$$\mathrm{Nu}_x \simeq 0.33 \left(\frac{\mathrm{Pr}}{1 - (x_o/x)^{\frac{3}{4}}} \right)^{\frac{1}{3}} \mathrm{Re}_x^{\frac{1}{2}}$$

6-10. Plot the local heat-transfer coefficient as a function of length for air at 1000 F flowing over a 5-ft-long flat plate at 3000 F with a velocity of 100 fps.

6-11. When a sphere falls freely through a homogeneous fluid, it reaches a terminal velocity at which the weight of the sphere is balanced by the buoyant force and the frictional resistance of the fluid. Make a dimensional analysis of this problem and indicate how experimental data for this problem could be correlated. Neglect compressibility effects and the influence of surface roughness.

6-12. Experiments have been performed on the temperature distribution in a homogeneous long cylinder (0.40 ft diameter, thermal conductivity of 0.12 Btu/hr ft F) with uniform internal heat generation. By dimensional analysis determine the relation between the steady-state temperature at the center of the cylinder T_c, the diameter, the thermal conductivity, and the rate of heat generation. Take the temperature at the surface as your datum. What is the equation for the center temperature if the difference between center and surface temperature is 80 F when the heat generation rate is 960 Btu/hr cu ft?

6-13. Air at 100 fps flows between two parallel flat plates spaced 2 in. apart. Estimate the distance from the entrance where the boundary layers meet.

6-14. For Prob. 6-13 estimate the frictional pressure drop in the entrance section, taking into account the pressure drop due to the frictional drag as well as the pressure drop due to the momentum change. Assume that the velocity at the inlet is uniform and that the velocity profiles of both boundary layers can be approximated by cubic parabolas.

6-15. Experimental pressure-drop data obtained in a series of tests in which water was heated while flowing through an electrically heated tube of 0.527 in. ID, 38.6 in. long, are tabulated below.

Mass Flow Rate m (lb/sec)	Fluid Bulk Temperature T_b (F)	Surface Temperature T_s (F)	Pressure Drop with Heat Transfer Δp_{ht} (psi)
3.04	90	126	9.56
2.16	114	202	4.74
1.82	97	219	3.22
3.06	99	248	8.34
2.15	107	283	4.45

Isothermal pressure-drop data for the same tube are given in terms of the dimensionless friction coefficient $f = (\Delta p/\rho \ V^2) \ (D/2L \ g_c)$ and the Reynolds number based on the pipe diameter, $\mathrm{Re}_D = VD/\nu$ below.

Re_D	1.71 x 10⁵	1.05 x 10⁵	1.9 x 10⁵	2.41 x 10⁵
f	0.00472	0.00513	0.00463	0.00445

By comparing the isothermal with the nonisothermal friction coefficients at similar bulk Reynolds numbers, derive a dimensionless equation for the nonisothermal friction cofficients of the form

$$f = \text{constant} \times \mathrm{Re}_D{}^n \ (\mu_s/\mu_b)^m$$

where μ_s = viscosity at surface temperature;
    μ_b = viscosity at bulk temperature;
n and m = empirical constants.

6-16. Tabulated below are some experimental data obtained by heating n-butyl alcohol at a bulk temperature of 60 F while flowing over a heated flat plate (1 ft long, 3 ft wide, surface temperature of 140 F). Correlate the experimental data by appropriate dimensionless numbers and compare the line which best fits the data with Eq. 6-30.

Velocity (fps)	0.26	1.0	1.6	3.74
Unit-Surface Conductance (Btu/hr sq ft F)	11.4	23	34.6	69

6-17. Tabulated below are reduced test data from measurements made to determine the heat-transfer coefficient inside tubes at Reynolds numbers only slightly above transition and at relatively high Prandtl numbers (as associated with oils). Tests were made in a double-tube exchanger with a counterflow of water to provide the cooling. The pipe used to carry the oils was $\frac{5}{8}$-in. OD, 18 BWG, 121 in. long. Correlate the data in terms of appropriate dimensionless parameters.

Test No.	Fluid	$\bar{h}_c$	ρV	c_p	k	μ_b	μ_f
11	10C oil	87.0	1,072,000	0.471	0.0779	13.7	19.5
19	10C oil	128.2	1,504,000	0.472	0.0779	13.3	19.1
21	10C oil	264.8	2,460,000	0.486	0.0776	9.60	14.0
23	10C oil	143.8	1,071,000	0.495	0.0773	7.42	9.95
24	10C oil	166.5	2,950,000	0.453	0.0784	23.9	27.3
25	10C oil	136.3	1,037,000	0.496	0.0773	7.27	11.7
36	1488 pyranol	140.7	1,795,000	0.260	0.0736	12.1	16.9
39	1488 pyranol	133.8	2,840,000	0.260	0.0740	23.0	29.2
45	1488 pyranol	181.4	1,985,000	0.260	0.0735	10.3	12.9
48	1488 pyranol	126.4	3,835,000	0.260	0.0743	40.2	53.5
49	1488 pyranol	105.8	3,235,000	0.260	0.0743	39.7	45.7

where $\bar{h}_c$ = mean surface heat-transfer coefficient, based on the mean temperature difference, Btu/hr sq ft F;

ρV = mass velocity, lb/hr sq ft;

c_p = specific heat, Btu/lb F;

k = thermal conductivity, Btu/hr ft F (based on average bulk temperature);

μ_b = viscosity, based on average bulk (mixed mean) temperature, lb_m/hr ft;

μ_f = viscosity, based on average film temperature, lb_m/hr ft.

Hint: Start by correlating $\overline{Nu}$ and Re_D irrespective of the Prandtl numbers, since the influence of the Prandtl number on the Nusselt number is expected to be relatively small. By plotting $\overline{Nu}$ vs. Re on log-log paper, one can guess the nature of the correlation equation, $\overline{Nu} = f_1$ (Re). A plot of $\overline{Nu}/f_1$(Re) vs. Pr will then reveal the dependence upon Pr. For the final equation, the influence of the viscosity variation should also be considered.

One possible answer: $\overline{Nu}_D = 0.0067 \dfrac{\rho V D}{\mu_b} \left(\dfrac{c\mu_b}{k_b}\right)^{0.2} \left(\dfrac{\mu_b}{\mu_f}\right)^{0.3}$

6–18. A thin flat plate 6 in. square is suspended from a balance into a uniformly flowing stream of glycerin in such a way that the glycerin flows parallel to and along the top and bottom surfaces of the plate. The total drag on the plate is measured and found to be 9 lb_f. If the glycerin flows at the rate of 50 fps and is at a temperature of 112 F what is the heat-transfer coefficient $\bar{h}_c$ in Btu/hr sq ft F?

6–19. Mercury at 60 F flows over and parallel to a flat surface at a velocity of 10 fps. Calculate the thickness of the hydrodynamic boundary layer at a distance 12 in. from the leading edge of the surface.

6–20. A thin flat plate 6 in. square is tested for drag in a wind tunnel with air at 100 fps, 14.7 psia, and 60 F flowing across and parallel to the top and bottom surfaces. The observed total drag force is 0.150 lb. Calculate the rate of heat transfer from this plate when the surface temperature is maintained at 250 F. Neglect radiation.

Ans. 9600 Btu/hr

6–21. The convection equations relating the Nusselt, Reynolds, and Prandtl numbers can be rearranged to show the heat-transfer coefficient $\bar{h}_x$ explicitly as a function of the absolute temperature T and the group $\sqrt{u_\infty/x}$. This formulation is of the form $\bar{h}_x = CT^n \sqrt{u_\infty/x}$, where n and C are constants. Indicate clearly how such a relationship could be obtained for the laminar flow case from $Nu_x = 0.332 \, Re_x^{0.5} Pr^{0.333}$ for the condition $0.5 < Pr < 5.0$. State restrictions on method if any such restrictions are necessary.

6-22. Experimental data for the transient cooling of a thick slab are to be correlated by dimensional analysis. The temperature of the slab is originally uniform at T_o. At time $\theta = 0$, the temperature at face $x = 0$ is suddenly lowered to T_s. Thermocouples are imbedded at various depths. Determine dimensionless groups relating T_x, the temperature at x, to the cooling time θ.

6-23. The boundary-layer-displacement thickness δ^* is defined as the distance by which a plane surface, past which a fluid is flowing, would have to be shifted into the stream to obtain the same flow rate with an inviscid fluid as with the real fluid. Mathematically δ^* is defined by the equation

$$\delta^* = \int_0^\infty \left(1 - \frac{u}{u_\infty}\right) dy$$

Show that $\delta^* \simeq \delta/3$ for laminar flow past a flat plate.

6-24. A 1-in.-diam, 6-in.-long transite rod ($k = 0.56$ Btu/hr ft F, $\rho = 100$ lb/cu ft, $c = 0.20$ Btu/lb F) on the end of a 1-in.-diam wood rod at a uniform temperature of 212 F is suddenly placed into a 60 F, 100 ft/sec air stream flowing parallel to the axis of the rod. Estimate the center line temperature of the transite rod 8 min after cooling starts. Assume radial heat conduction, but include radiation losses, based on an emissivity of 0.90, to black surroundings at air temperature.

6-25. The thickness of the laminar sublayer has been estimated (18) to be given by $y\sqrt{\tau_s/\rho}/\nu = 5.0$. Compare this estimate with the experimental data (14) shown in Fig. 6-20.

6-26. Replot the data points of Fig. 6-6 on log-log paper and find an equation approximating the best correlation line. Compare your results with Fig. 6-7.

7 Free Convection

7-1. INTRODUCTION

Free-convection heat transfer occurs whenever a body is placed in a fluid at a higher or a lower temperature than that of the body. As a result of the temperature difference, heat flows between the fluid and the body and causes a change in the density of the fluid layers in the vicinity of the surface. The difference in density leads to downward flow of the heavier fluid and upward flow of the lighter. If the motion of the fluid is caused solely by differences in density resulting from temperature gradients, without the aid of a pump or a fan, the associated heat-transfer mechanism is called *natural* or *free convection*. Free-convection currents transfer internal energy stored in the fluid in essentially the same manner as forced-convection current. However, the intensity of the mixing motion is generally less in free convection, and consequently the heat-transfer coefficients are lower than in forced convection.

Although free-convection heat-transfer coefficients are relatively low, many devices depend largely on this mode of heat transfer for cooling. In the electrical-engineering field, transmission lines, transformers, rectifiers, and electrically heated wires such as the filament of an incandescent lamp or the heating elements of an electric furnace are cooled by free convection. As a result of the heat generated internally, the temperature of these bodies rises above that of the surroundings. As the temperature difference increases, the rate of heat flow also increases until a state of equilibrium is reached where the rate of heat generation is equal to the rate of heat dissipation.

Free convection is the dominant heat-flow mechanism from steam radiators, walls of a building, or the stationary human body in a quiescent atmosphere. The determination of the heat load on air-conditioning or refrigeration equipment requires, therefore, a knowledge of free-convection heat-transfer coefficients. Free convection is also responsible for heat losses from pipes carrying steam or other heated fluids. Recently natural convection has been proposed in nuclear-power applications to cool the surfaces of bodies in which heat is generated by fission (1).

In all of the aforementioned examples the body force responsible for the convection currents is the gravitational attraction. Gravity, however, is not the only body force which can produce free convection. In certain aircraft applications there are components such as the blades of gas turbines and helicopter ramjets which rotate at high speeds. Associated with these rotative speeds are large centrifugal forces whose magnitudes, like the gravitational force, are also proportional to the fluid density and hence can generate strong free-convection currents. Cooling of rotating components by free convection is therefore feasible even at high heat fluxes.

The fluid velocities in free-convection currents, especially those generated by gravity, are generally low, but the characteristics of the flow

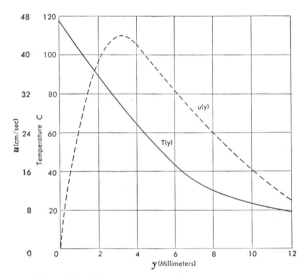

Fig. 7–1. Temperature and velocity distributions in the vicinity of a heated flat plate placed vertically in still air. (After E. Schmidt and W. Beckman, Ref. 3)

in the vicinity of the heat-transfer surface are similar to those in forced convection. A boundary layer forms near the surface and the fluid velocity at the interface is zero. Figure 7–1 shows the velocity and temperature distributions near a heated flat plate placed in a vertical position in air (3). At a given distance from the bottom of the plate, the local upward velocity increases with increasing distance from the surface to reach a maximum value at a distance between 0.1 and 0.2 in., then decreases and approaches zero again about 1 to 2 in. from the surface. Although the velocity profile is different from that observed in forced convection over a flat plate where the velocity approaches the free-stream velocity asymtotically, in the vicinity of the surface the characteristics of both types of boundary layer are similar. In free convection, as in forced convection, the flow may be laminar or turbulent, depending on the distance from the leading edge, the fluid properties, the body force, and the temperature difference between the surface and the fluid.

The temperature field in free convection (Fig. 7–1) is similar to that observed in forced convection. Hence, the physical interpretation of the Nusselt number presented in Sec. 6–4 applies. For practical application however, Newton's equation

$$dq = h_c \, dA \, (T_s - T_\infty) \hspace{3cm} [1\text{–}13]$$

is generally used. The reason for writing the equation for a differential area dA is that, in free convection, the heat-transfer coefficient h_c is not uniform over a surface. As in forced convection over a flat plate, we shall therefore distinguish between a local value of h_c and an average value $\bar{h}_c$ obtained by averaging h_c over the entire surface. The temperature T_∞ refers to a point in the fluid sufficiently removed from the body that the temperature of the fluid is not affected by the presence of a heating (or cooling) source.

An exact evaluation of the heat-transfer coefficient for free convection from the boundary layer is very difficult. The problem has only been solved for simple geometries, such as a vertical flat plate and a horizontal cylinder (3,4,19). We shall not discuss these specialized solutions here. Instead, we shall set up the differential equations for free convection from a vertical flat plate using only fundamental physical principles. From these equations, without actually solving them, we shall determine the similarity conditions and associated dimensionless moduli which correlate experimental data. In Sec. 7–3 pertinent experimental data for various shapes of practical interest will be presented in terms of these dimensionless moduli, and their physical significance will be discussed.

7–2. SIMILARITY PARAMETERS FOR FREE CONVECTION

In the analysis of free convection we shall make use of a phenomenon observed by the Greeks over 2000 years ago and phrased by Archimedes somewhat as follows: A body immersed in a fluid experiences a buoyant or lifting force equal to the mass of the displaced fluid. Hence, a submerged body rises when its density is less than that of the surrounding fluid and sinks when its density is greater. The buoyant effect is the driving force in free convection.

For the purpose of analysis, consider a domestic heating panel which can be idealized by a vertical flat plate, very long and wide in the plane perpendicular to the floor so that the flow is two-dimensional (Fig. 7–2). When the heater is turned off, the panel is at the same temperature as the surrounding air. The gravitational or body force acting on each fluid element is in equilibrium with the hydrostatic pressure gradient, and the air is motionless.   When the heater is turned on, the fluid in the vicinity of the panel will be heated and its density will decrease.   Hence, the body force (defined as the force per unit mass) on a unit volume in the heated portion of the fluid is less than in the unheated fluid.   This unbalance causes the heated fluid to rise, a phenomenon which is well known from experience.   In addition to the buoyant force there are pressure forces and also frictional forces acting when the air is in motion.   Once steady-

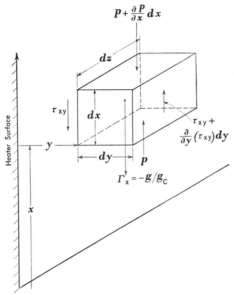

Fig. 7–2.   Sketch illustrating forces acting on a fluid element in free-convection flow.

state conditions have been established, the total force on a volume element, $dxdydz$ in the positive x direction perpendicular to the floor consists of

1. The force due to the pressure gradient

$$p\,dydz \; - \left(p + \frac{\partial p}{\partial x}\, d \; \right) dydz \; = \; - \frac{\partial p}{\partial x}\,(dxdydz)$$

2. The body force $\Gamma_x \rho \; (dxdydz)$, where $\Gamma_x \; = \; - \; g/g_c$, since gravity alone is active.

3. The frictional shearing forces due to the velocity gradient

$$(-\tau_{xy})dxdz \; + \left(\tau_{xy} + \frac{\partial \tau_{xy}}{\partial y}\, dy \right) dxdz$$

Since $\tau_{xy} = \mu(\partial u/\partial y)/g_c$ in laminar flow, the net frictional force is

$$\left(\frac{\mu}{g_c} \frac{\partial^2 u}{\partial y^2} \right) dxdydz$$

Forces due to the deformation of the fluid element will be neglected in view of the low velocity.[1]

The rate of change of momentum of the fluid element is $\rho dxdydz$ $[u(\partial u/\partial x) + v(\partial u/\partial y)]$ as shown in Sec. 6–6. Applying Newton's second law to the elemental volume yields

$$\rho \left(u \frac{\partial u}{\partial x} + v \frac{\partial u}{\partial y} \right) = - g_c \frac{\partial p}{\partial x} - \rho g + \mu \frac{\partial^2 u}{\partial y^2} \qquad (7\text{--}1)$$

after canceling $dxdydz$. The unheated fluid far removed from the plate is in hydrostatic equilibrium, or $g_c(\partial p_e/\partial x) = - \rho_e g$ where the subscript e denotes equilibrium conditions. At any elevation the pressure is uniform and therefore $\partial p/\partial x = \partial p_e/\partial x$. Substituting $\rho_e g$ for $-(\partial p/\partial x)$ in Eq. 7–1 gives

$$\rho \left(u \frac{\partial u}{\partial x} + v \frac{\partial u}{\partial y} \right) = (\rho_e - \rho)g + \mu \frac{\partial^2 u}{\partial y^2} \qquad (7\text{--}2)$$

A further simplification can be made by assuming that the density ρ depends only on the temperature, and not on the pressure. For an incompressible fluid this is self-evident, but for a gas it implies that the vertical dimension of the body is small enough that the hydrostatic density ρ_e is constant. With these assumptions the buoyant term can be written

$$g \, (\rho_e - \rho) = g \, (\rho_\infty - \rho) = - g\rho\beta(T_\infty - T) \qquad (7\text{--}3)$$

where β is the coefficient of thermal expansion, defined as

$$\beta = \frac{\rho_\infty - \rho}{\rho(T - T_\infty)} \qquad (7\text{--}4)$$

For an *ideal gas* (i.e., $\rho = p/\mathcal{R}T$) the coefficient of expansion is

$$\beta = \frac{\rho_\infty/\rho - 1}{T - T_\infty} = \frac{T/T_\infty - 1}{T - T_\infty} = \frac{1}{T_\infty} \qquad (7\text{--}5)$$

and $$g\rho\beta(T_\infty - T) = -g\rho \left(\frac{T}{T_\infty} - 1 \right)$$

The equation of motion for free convection is obtained finally by substi-

---

[1] The effects of the compression work and frictional heating are discussed in Ref. 1.

tuting the buoyant term as expressed by Eq. 7–3 into Eq. 7–2 and we get

$$\rho\left(u\frac{\partial u}{\partial x} + v\frac{\partial u}{\partial y}\right) = g\rho\beta(T - T_\infty) + \mu\frac{\partial^2 u}{\partial y^2} \qquad (7\text{–}6)$$

Equation 7–6 is identical to the boundary-layer equation for forced convection over a flat plate except for the term $g\rho\beta(T - T_\infty)$, which appears as a result of the body force which was ignored in forced convection.

The problem now is to determine the conditions for which the velocity field in one free-convection system is similar to the velocity field in another. The boundary conditions are the same for all free-convection systems, that is the velocity is zero both at the surface and a distance far removed from the surface. Hence, dynamic similarity for different systems exists if Eq. 7–6 applies.

Let us first write Eq. 7–6 for system A as

$$\rho_A\left(u_A\frac{\partial u_A}{\partial x_A} + v_A\frac{\partial u_A}{\partial y_A}\right) = \rho_A g_A \beta_A(T - T_\infty)_A + \mu_A\frac{\partial^2 u_A}{\partial y_A^2} \qquad (7\text{–}7)$$

Now consider another system, B, related to system A by the equations

$$\begin{aligned} u_B &= C_V u_A & \beta_B &= C_\beta \beta_A \\ v_B &= C_V v_A & (T - T_\infty)_B &= C_T(T - T_\infty)_A \\ x_B &= C_L x_A & \mu_B &= C_\mu \mu_A \\ y_B &= C_L y_A & \rho_B &= C_\rho \rho_A \\ g_B &= C_g g_A & & \end{aligned}$$

These equations state that a velocity in system B is equal to C_V, a velocity constant or reference quantity, times the velocity in system A; the viscosity in system B is equal to a constant C_μ times the viscosity in system A; etc. Equation 7–6 applies also to system B, or

$$\rho_B\left(u_B\frac{\partial u_B}{\partial x_B} + v_B\frac{\partial u_B}{\partial y_B}\right) = \rho_B g_B \beta_B(T - T_\infty)_B + \mu_B\frac{\partial^2 u_B}{\partial y_B^2} \qquad (7\text{–}7a)$$

We can express the equation of motion for system B in terms of the quantities pertaining to system A by inserting the relations previously listed. Then Eq. 7–7a becomes

$$\frac{C_\rho C_V^2}{C_L}\left[\rho_A\left(u_A\frac{\partial u_A}{\partial x_A} + v_A\frac{\partial u_A}{\partial y_A}\right)\right]$$

$$= C_\rho C_g C_\beta[\rho_A g_A \beta_A(T - T_\infty)_A] + \frac{C_\mu C_V}{C_L^2}\left[\mu_A\frac{\partial^2 u_A}{\partial y_A^2}\right] \qquad (7\text{–}8)$$

The next step is crucial in this type of analysis and should be noted carefully. Equation 7–8, the equation of motion for system B, is identical to the equation of motion of system A if the coefficients of each of the terms in square brackets are identical. Then, the solutions of the equations of motion for both systems (the boundary conditions being similar) will be the same and the systems are said to be dynamically similar. Therefore, the dynamic similarity requirements are that

$$\frac{C_\rho C_V{}^2}{C_L} = C_\rho C_g C_\beta = \frac{C_\mu C_V}{C_L{}^2} \tag{7-9}$$

To see the physical significance of Eq. 7–9, we substitute for the reference quantities (i.e., the C's), the equalities relating systems A and B in the tabulation (for instance $C_\beta = \beta_B/\beta_A$, $C_\mu = \mu_B/\mu_A$, etc.). To simplify the relationships we shall use the symbol V for the significant velocity and L for the significant length. Then we have

$$\frac{\rho_B V_B{}^2/L_B}{\rho_A V_A{}^2/L_A} = \frac{\rho_B g_B \beta_B (T - T_\infty)_B}{\rho_A g_A \beta_A (T - T_\infty)_A} = \frac{\mu_B V_B/L_B{}^2}{\mu_A V_A/L_A{}^2} \tag{7-10}$$

Any combination of terms in the above similarity equation is permissible, but only those combinations which have some physical significance are of practical use. However, it is not always obvious which of the many possibilities is most convenient and significant. Often a trial-and-error approach, with some experimental data as a guide, is required to find the right combination.

If we combine the first and the last term of Eq. 7–10 we get

$$\frac{\rho_B V_B L_B}{\mu_B} = \frac{\rho_A V_A L_A}{\mu_A} \tag{7-11}$$

which are equivalent expressions of the Reynolds number. The equality of the Reynolds numbers means that the ratios of inertia forces to frictional forces are identical at corresponding points.

Combining the second and the third term of Eq. 7–10 we obtain

$$\frac{\rho_B g_B \beta_B (T - T_\infty)_B L_B{}^2}{\mu_B V_B} = \frac{\rho_A g_A \beta_A (T - T_\infty)_A L_A{}^2}{\mu_A V_A} \tag{7-12}$$

that is, the ratios of buoyant to frictional forces are equal.

From the physical aspects of the problem we recall that the velocity of the fluid is not an independent quantity, but depends upon the buoyant driving force. Hence, we can eliminate V from Eq. 7–12 by substituting its value from Eq. 7–11. We then obtain

$$\frac{\rho_B{}^2 g_B \beta_B (T - T_\infty)_B L_B{}^3}{\mu_B{}^2} = \frac{\rho_A{}^2 g_A \beta_A (T - T_\infty)_A L_A{}^3}{\mu_A{}^2} \tag{7-13}$$

The dimensionless modulus $\rho^2 g \beta (T - T_\infty) L^3 / \mu^2$ is called the Grashof number, Gr, and represents the ratio of buoyant to viscous forces.[2] Consistent units are:

ρ	lb_m/cu ft		L	ft
μ	lb_m/sec ft	$(T - T_\infty)$		F
β	1/R		g	ft/sec^2

When the buoyancy is the only driving force, the fluid velocity is determined entirely by the quantities contained in the Grashof modulus. Therefore, the Reynolds number is superfluous for free convection, and *equality of the Grashof numbers establishes dynamic similarity.*

The equation describing the temperature field in free convection is

$$\rho c_p \left(u \frac{\partial T}{\partial x} + v \frac{\partial T}{\partial y} \right) = k \frac{\partial^2 T}{\partial y^2} \qquad [\,6\text{--}23\,]$$

This equation is identical to the heat-transfer equation for forced convection over a flat plate, and its derivation has been presented previously (Sec. 6–6). For similarity of temperature fields in forced convection, we found that the Prandtl numbers, $c_p \mu / k$, must be equal. This applies also to free convection. Therefore, when geometrically similar bodies are cooled or heated by free convection, both the velocity and temperature fields are similar provided Gr and Pr are equal at corresponding points. It follows also from the same arguments used in the case of forced convection that, when the Grashof and Prandtl numbers are equal, the Nusselt numbers for the bodies are the same. Hence, experimental results for free-convection heat transfer can be correlated by an equation of the type

$$\text{Nu} = \phi\,(\text{Gr})\,\psi\,(\text{Pr}) \qquad (7\text{--}14)$$

where ϕ and ψ denote functional relationships.

The Prandtl number of gases having the same number of atoms per molecule is nearly constant. For a group of gases having the same number of atoms, Eq. 7–14 can therefore be reduced to

$$\text{Nu} = \phi\,(\text{Gr}) \qquad (7\text{--}15)$$

As a first approximation, data for different fluids can also be correlated on a single curve. If the velocities are sufficiently small that inertia forces can be neglected in comparison with the forces of friction and buoyancy, the left-hand side of Eq. 7–9, which represents the inertia forces, can be discarded (see Prob. 7–15). Then, the similarity condition is

$$C_\rho C_g C_\beta C_T = \frac{C_\mu C_V}{C_L{}^2} \qquad (7\text{--}16)$$

---

[2] In Table A–3 the combination $\rho^2 g \beta / \mu^2$ is listed to facilitate numerical computations.

By substituting the equality relations for systems A and B it can easily be verified that the dimensional similarity parameter is (Gr Pr). Hence, the Nusselt number becomes a function of the single variable (Gr Pr) and we have

$$\text{Nu} = \phi \, (\text{Gr Pr}) \qquad\qquad (7\text{--}17)$$

when the inertia forces are negligible. Using an equation of this type, experimental data from various sources for free convection from horziontal

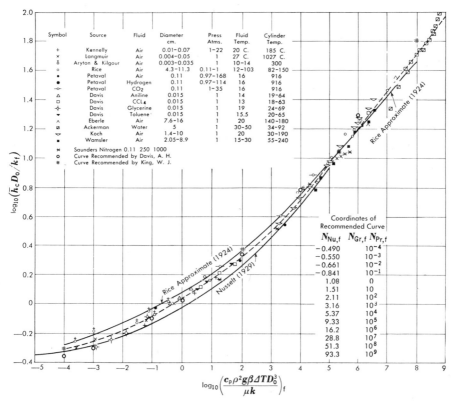

FIG. 7–3. Correlation of data for free-convection heat transfer from horizontal cylinders in gases and liquids. (By permission from W. H. McAdams, *Heat Transmission*, 3d ed., New York: McGraw-Hill Book Company Inc., 1954)

wires and tubes are correlated in Fig. 7–3 by plotting $\bar{h}_c D/k$, the average Nusselt number, against $c_p \rho^2 g \beta \Delta T D^3/\mu k$, the product of the Grashof and Prandtl numbers. The physical properties are evaluated at the arithmetic mean temperature. We observe that data for fluids as different as air, glycerin, and water are well correlated over a range of Grashof numbers from 10^{-5} to 10^7 for cylinders ranging from small wires to large pipes.

King (18) has shown that the correlation in Fig. 7–3 gives approximate results also for three-dimensional shapes such as short cylinders and blocks if the characteristic length dimension is determined by the equation

$$\frac{1}{L} = \frac{1}{L_{\text{hor}}} + \frac{1}{L_{\text{vert}}}$$

where L_{vert} is the height and L_{hor} the average horizontal dimension of the body. For spheres, the radius is the pertinent length dimension.

A similar correlation for free convection from vertical plates and vertical cylinders is shown in Fig. 7–4. The ordinate is $\bar{h}_c L/k$, the average Nusselt

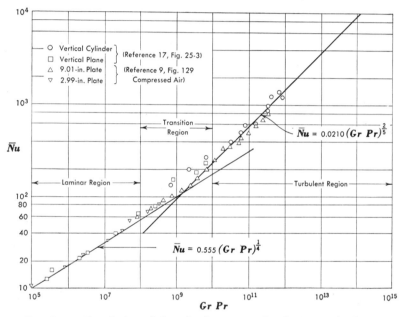

Fig. 7–4. Correlation of data for free-convection heat transfer from vertical plates and cylinders.

number based on the height of the body, and the abscissa is the product of Gr and Pr, i.e., $c_p \rho^2 \beta g \Delta T L^3 / \mu k$. We note the flow is laminar up to a Grashof number of about 10^8, passes through a transition regime between 10^8 and 10^{10}, and becomes fully turbulent at Grashof numbers above 10^{10}. This type of behavior is typical of free convection on vertical surfaces, and under normal conditions the critical value of Grashof number is usually taken at 10^9.

A complication arises when the physical properties of the fluid vary considerably with temperature and the temperature difference between the body surface T_s and the surrounding medium T_∞ is large. It has been suggested that, for such cases, an additional parameter $(T_s - T_\infty)/T_\infty$ be introduced. However, for practical purposes satisfactory results are obtained without this parameter by evaluating the physical properties in Eq. 7–14 at the mean temperature $(T_s + T_\infty)/2$. When the surface temperature is not known, a value must be assumed initially. It can be used to calculate the unit-surface conductance to a first approximation and is then recalculated. If there is a discrepancy between the assumed and the calculated value of T_s, the latter is used to recalculate the heat-transfer coefficient, and so on.

7–3. EVALUATION OF UNIT-SURFACE CONDUCTANCE

After experimental data have been correlated by dimensional analysis, it is general practice to write an equation for the line faired through the data and to compare the experimental results with those obtained by analytic means. In this section we shall discuss and interpret the results of some analytical and experimental studies on free convection for a number of geometric shapes of practical interest. Each shape is identified by a characteristic dimension, such as its length L, diameter D, etc. The characteristic dimension is attached as a suffix to the dimensionless parameters Nu and Gr. Average values of the Nusselt number for a given surface are identified by a bar, i.e., $\overline{\text{Nu}}$; local values are without a bar. Unless stated otherwise, all physical properties are to be evaluated at the arithmetic mean between the surface temperature T_s and the temperature of the undisturbed fluid T_∞. The temperature difference in the Grashof number ΔT represents the absolute value of the difference between the temperatures T_s and T_∞. All of the equations to be discussed apply strictly to bodies immersed in an effectively infinite medium in which the flow pattern is influenced only by the body transferring the heat. The accuracy with which in practice the unit-surface conductance can be predicted from any of the equations is generally no better than 20 per cent, because most experimental data scatter by as much as ± 15 per cent or more and in a majority of engineering applications stray currents due to some interaction with surfaces other than the one transferring the heat are unavoidable.

Flat plates and vertical cylinders. In recent investigations, Eckert and Soehnghen (6,7) obtained photographs which illustrate important features of free convection. These investigators observed, in air, free convection from flat plates, cylinders, and composite shapes by means of a *Mach-Zehnder* (20) *optical interferometer*. This instrument produces interference fringes which are recorded by a camera. The fringes are the result of density gradients caused by temperature gradients in gases. The spacing of the fringes is a direct measure of the density distribution, which is related to the temperature distribution. Figure 7–5 shows the fringe pattern observed near a heated vertical flat plate in air, 3 ft high and 1.5 ft wide. We observe that the flow is laminar for about 20 in. from the bottom of the plate. Transition to turbulent flow begins at 21 in., corresponding to a critical Grashof number of about 4×10^8. Near the top of the plate, turbulent flow is approached.

Temperature profiles for laminar flow at various distances from the lower edge are shown in Fig. 7–6 for a temperature difference of 90 F between the plate and the surrounding air. We note that the temperature gradients are largest near the leading edge and become smaller with increasing distance from the bottom. These results are in good agreement with the equation

$$h_{cx} = 0.360 \frac{k}{x} (\mathrm{Gr}_x)^{\frac{1}{4}} \qquad (7\text{–}18)$$

which was derived analytically by Schmidt and Beckman (3) for air having a Prandtl number of 0.74. According to this relation h_{cx}, the local heat-transfer coefficient at a distance x from the leading edge, decreases with increasing x, or

$$h_{cx} \propto x^{-\frac{1}{4}}$$

The average heat-transfer coefficient for a plate of length L is obtained by integrating Eq. 7–18 between the limits of $x = 0$ and $x = L$ and dividing by L. In dimensionless form we get

$$\overline{\mathrm{Nu}}_L = \frac{\bar{h}_c L}{k} = 0.480 \; (\mathrm{Gr}_L)^{\frac{1}{4}} \qquad (7\text{–}19)$$

The numerical coefficient in this equation agrees within 10 per cent with the value obtained by fairing a line through the experimental data shown in Fig. 7–4. For fluids having Prandtl numbers different from 0.74, Eckert (8) derived, by means of the integral relations presented in Chapter 6, the equation

$$\mathrm{Nu}_x = 0.508 \left(\frac{\mathrm{Pr}}{0.952 + \mathrm{Pr}} \, \mathrm{Gr}_x \mathrm{Pr} \right)^{\frac{1}{4}} \qquad (7\text{–}20)$$

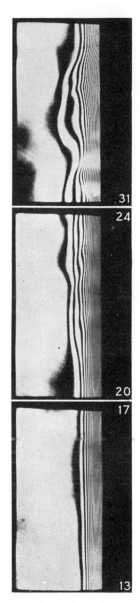

Fig. 7–5. Interference photograph illustrating laminar and turbulent free-convection flow of air along a vertical flat plate. (Courtesy of Professor E. R. G. Eckert)

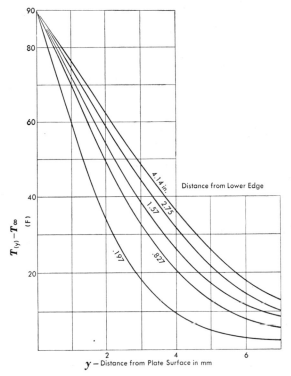

Fig. 7–6. Temperature profiles at various distances from the leading edge for vertical plate in free convection. (Courtesy of U. S. Air Force, from "Studies on Heat Transfer in Laminar Free Convection with the Zehnder-Mach Interferometer," by E. R. G. Eckert and E. E. Soehngen, Ref. 7)

for the local value of the laminar free-convection heat-transfer coefficient from a vertical flat plate. Equation 7–20 agrees satisfactorily with experimental results for gases and liquids. It also predicts the right order of magnitude for free-convection heat-transfer coefficients in liquid metals, which have very small Prandtl numbers (12). This relation can also be extended to a moderately inclined surface (Fig. 7–7) by modifying the value of the body force. If we orient the coordinate axis relative to the plate as shown, the component of the body force along the x axis is $g\beta(T - T_\infty) \cos \alpha$. For inclined surfaces, the local Nusselt number Nu_x becomes therefore

$$\mathrm{Nu}_x = 0.508 \left(\frac{\mathrm{Pr}^2}{0.952 + \mathrm{Pr}}\right)\left(\frac{g\beta\Delta T \cos \alpha\, x^3}{\nu^2}\right) \qquad \textbf{(7–21)}$$

where x is measured along the surface.

For turbulent free convection over a vertical plane Eckert (5) derived the equation

$$\overline{\mathrm{Nu}}_L = 0.024 \left(\frac{\mathrm{Pr}^{1.17}}{1 + 0.494 \mathrm{Pr}^{\frac{2}{3}}} \mathrm{Gr}_L \right)^{\frac{2}{5}} \qquad (7\text{--}22)$$

assuming a completely turbulent boundary layer. Since in reality the boundary layer is first laminar and becomes turbulent only at a certain distance from the lower edge of the plate, the preceding expression for the average heat-transfer coefficient can be expected to yield good results only at Grashof numbers so high that the extent of the laminar region is small compared to the turbulent region. This limit for the Grashof number seems to be near 10^{10}. An inspection of Fig. 7–4 shows that Eq. 7–22 agrees quite well with experimental data at $\mathrm{Gr} > 10^{10}$. It should be noted that, in the turbulent region, the value of h_{cx}, the local heat-transfer

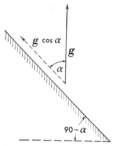

FIG. 7–7.   Sketch illustrating body force acting on a fluid on or near an inclined surface.

coefficient, is nearly constant over the surface. In fact, McAdams (9) recommends for $\mathrm{Gr} > 10^9$ the equation

$$\frac{\bar{h}_c L}{k} = 0.13 (\mathrm{Gr}_L \mathrm{Pr})^{\frac{1}{3}} \qquad (7\text{--}23)$$

where the length, L, actually cancels.

A theoretical analysis by Sparrow and Gregg (10), supported by experimental data by Dotson (11), indicates that the equations for laminar free convection from a vertical flat plate apply to a constant surface temperature as well as to a uniform heat flux over the surface. In the latter case the surface temperature T_s is to be taken at one-half of the total height of the plate.

Example 7–1.   The maximum allowable surface temperature at the center of an electrically heated vertical plate, 6 in. high and 4 in. wide, is 270 F. Estimate the maximum rate of heat dissipation from both sides of the plate in 70 F atmospheric air if the unit-surface conductance for radiation $\bar{h}_r$ is 1.5 Btu/hr sq ft F for the specified maximum surface temperature.

Solution: The arithmetic mean temperature is 140 F and the corresponding value of Gr_L is found to be $1.2 \times 10^6 L^3 (T_s - T_\infty)$, from the last column in Table A–3 by interpolation. For the specified conditions we get

$$Gr_L = (1.2 \times 10^6) (6/12)^3 (200) = 3 \times 10^7$$

Since the Grashof number is less than 10^9, the flow is laminar. For air at 170 F the Prandtl number is 0.71 and GrPr is therefore 2.1×10^7. From Fig. 7–4 the average Nusselt number is 38 at GrPr of 2.1×10^7 and therefore

$$\bar{h}_c = 38 \times k_f/L = 38 \frac{0.0172}{0.5} \frac{\text{Btu/hr ft F}}{\text{ft}} = 1.31 \text{ Btu/hr sq ft F}$$

The maximum total heat-dissipation rate is therefore

$$q = A (\bar{h}_c + \bar{h}_r)(T_s - T_\infty)$$

$$= \left[\frac{(2)(6)(4)}{144} \text{ sq ft} \right] [(1.31 + 1.5) \text{ Btu/hr sq ft F}] (200 \text{ F})$$

$$= 187 \text{ Btu/hr} \qquad\qquad\qquad Ans.$$

Note that more than half of the heat is transferred by radiation.

The equations for vertical plates can also be used to calculate free-convection heat-transfer coefficients from the vertical surfaces of cylinders with satisfactory accuracy.

The behavior of horizontal surfaces, however, is slightly different. For heated square plates facing upward or cooled plates facing downward, McAdams (9) recommends the equation

$$\frac{\bar{h}_c L}{k} = 0.14(Gr_L Pr)^{\frac{1}{3}} \qquad\qquad (7\text{–}24)$$

in the turbulent range, Gr from 2×10^7 to 3×10^{10}, and

$$\frac{\bar{h}_c L}{k} = 0.54(Gr_L Pr)^{\frac{1}{4}} \qquad\qquad (7\text{–}25)$$

in the laminar range, Gr from 10^5 to 2×10^7, where L is length of the side of the square. For heated plates facing downward and cooled plates facing upward, the equation

$$\frac{\bar{h}_c L}{k} = 0.27(Gr_L Pr)^{\frac{1}{4}} \qquad\qquad (7\text{–}26)$$

is recommended (9) in the laminar range, (i.e., Gr from 3×10^5 to 3×10^{10}). Data in the turbulent range are lacking. As a first approximation, the foregoing three equations can be applied to horizontal circular disks if L is replaced by $0.9 D$, where D is the diameter of the disk.

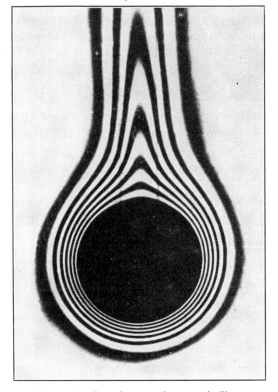

Fig. 7–8. Interference photograph illustrating temperature field around a horizontal cylinder in laminar flow. (Courtesy of Professor E. R. G. Eckert)

Horizontal cylinders and spheres. The temperature field around a horizontal cylinder heated in air is illustrated in Fig. 7–8, which shows interference fringes photographed by Eckert and Soehnghen (7). The flow is laminar over the entire surface. The closer spacing of the interference fringes over the lower portion of the cylinder indicates a steeper temperature gradient and consequently a larger local unit-surface conductance than over the top portion. The variation of the surface conductance with angular position α is shown in Fig. 7–9 for two Grashof numbers. The experimental results do not differ appreciably from the theoretical calculations of Herman (4) who derived the equation

$$\mathrm{Nu}_{D\alpha} = 0.604 \ \mathrm{Gr}_D^{\frac{1}{4}} \ \phi \ (\alpha) \qquad (7\text{–}27)$$

for air, i.e., $\mathrm{Pr} = 0.74$. The angle α is measured from the horizontal position and numerical values of the function $\phi \ (\alpha)$ are as follows:

α	90	60	30	0	30	60	75	90
$\phi(\alpha)$	0.76	0.75	0.72	0.66	0.58	0.46	0.36	0
	Bottom half				Top half			

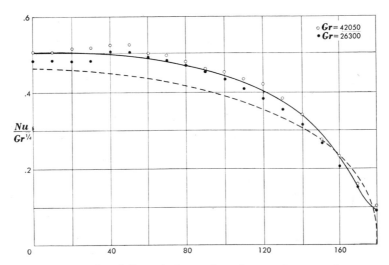

FIG. 7–9. Local dimensionless unit-surface conductance along the circumference of a horizontal cylinder in laminar free convection (dashed line according to Ref. 4). (Courtesy of U. S. Air Force, from "Studies on Heat Transfer in Laminar Free Convection with the Zehnder-Mach Interferometer," by E. R. G. Eckert and E. E. Soehngen, Ref. 7)

An equation for the average heat-transfer coefficient from single horizontal wires or pipes in free convection, recommended by McAdams (9) on the basis of the experimental data in Fig. 7–3, is

$$\overline{\mathrm{Nu}}_D = 0.53 \, (\mathrm{Gr}_D \, \mathrm{Pr})^{\frac{1}{4}} \qquad (7\text{–}28)$$

This equation is valid for Prandtl numbers larger than 0.5 and Grashof numbers ranging from 10^3 to 10^9. Whereas in the case of the vertical flat plate the lower limit of Gr for which Eq. 7–20 is valid does not imply a serious restriction in practical applications, it does in the case of Eq. 7–28 for a cylinder. There are many engineering problems where the heat transfer from small wires is important. Since the diameter appears to the third power in the Grashof number, very small values of this parameter are not uncommon. For very small diameters, Langmuir has shown that the rate of heat dissipation per unit length is nearly independent of the wire diameter, a phenomenon he applied in his invention of the coiled filaments in gas-filled incandescent lamps. The average unit-surface conductance for Gr less than 10^3 is most conveniently evaluated from the curve A–A drawn through the experimental points in Fig. 7–3 in the low Grashof-number range.

The onset of turbulence in free-convection flow over horizontal cylinders for fluids other than liquid metals occurs at a value of $Gr\,Pr/D^3$ of about 10^{11} (12). In turbulent flow it has been observed (12) that the heat flux can be increased substantially without a corresponding increase in the surface temperature. It appears that in free convection the turbulent-exchange mechanism increases in intensity as the rate of heat flow is increased and thereby reduces the thermal resistance.

Simplified equations for moderate surface temperatures are given in Ref. 9 for air at atmospheric pressure. They are

$$\bar{h}_c = 0.18\,\Delta T^{\frac{1}{3}} \tag{7--29}$$

for Gr from 10^9 to 10^{12}, and

$$\bar{h}_c = 0.27\left(\frac{\Delta T}{D}\right)^{\frac{1}{4}} \tag{7--30}$$

for Gr from 10^3 to 10^9, where $\bar{h}_c$ is in Btu/hr sq ft F and ΔT is in F.

For liquid metals in laminar flow the equation

$$\overline{\mathrm{Nu}}_D = 0.53\left(\frac{Pr^2}{0.952 + Pr}\,Gr_D\right)^{\frac{1}{4}} \tag{7--31}$$

correlates the available data (12) for cylinders larger than small wires. No data on small wires are available to date.

Equation 7–28 also applies to spheres at $Gr > 10^3$ when the sphere radius is used as the characteristic length in $\overline{Nu}$ and Gr. For very small spheres when the Grashof number approaches zero, the Nusselt number approaches a value of 2. This condition corresponds to pure conduction through a stagnant layer adjacent to the surface.

Example 7–2. A $1\frac{1}{2}$-in.-OD pipe carrying slightly wet steam at 15 psig is installed in a location where it is covered by water after a heavy rain but is exposed to air under normal conditions. Compare the rate of heat transfer to air with the rate of heat transfer to water, assuming that both fluids are at 50 F.

Solution: From steam tables we find that the temperature of the steam at 15 psig is 250 F. Assuming that the pipe temperature equals the steam temperature because the heat-transfer coefficient inside the pipe is large (Table 1–1), the mean film temperature is 150 F. From Table A–3, the product of the Grashof and Prandtl numbers is

$$Gr_D Pr = (1.2 \times 10^9)(200)\left(\frac{1.50}{12}\right)^3 = 4.7 \times 10^8 \qquad \text{for water}$$

$$Gr_D Pr = (0.85 \times 10^6)(200)\left(\frac{1.5}{12}\right)^3 = 3.3 \times 10^5 \qquad \text{for air}$$

From Fig. 7–3 the respective Nusselt numbers are therefore

$$\overline{\mathrm{Nu}}_D = 7.7 \qquad \text{for water}$$

$$\overline{\mathrm{Nu}}_D = 12.6 \qquad \text{for air}$$

The respective heat-transfer coefficients are therefore

$$\bar{h}_c = \mathrm{Nu}\,\frac{k}{D} = 7.7\,\frac{0.384\ \mathrm{Btu/hr\ ft\ F}}{1.5/12\ \mathrm{ft}} = 23.6\ \mathrm{Btu/hr\ sq\ ft\ F} \qquad \text{for water}$$

$$\bar{h}_c = 12.6\,\frac{0.0164}{1.5/12} = 1.66\ \mathrm{Btu/hr\ sq\ ft\ F} \qquad \text{for air}$$

The rate of heat loss by convection per foot length of pipe is therefore

$$q_c = \bar{h}_c A(T_s - T_\infty) = (236)(1.5/12)(200) = 18{,}500\ \mathrm{Btu/hr\ ft} \qquad \text{in water}$$

$$q_c = (1.66)(1.5/12)(200) = 130\ \mathrm{Btu/hr\ ft} \qquad \text{in air}$$

There is no appreciable radiation in water, but in air the heat transfer by radiation is from Eq. 1–7

$$q_r = (0.173)(0.9)(1.5/12)\,[(7.10)^4 - (5.10)^4] = 115\ \mathrm{Btu/hr\ ft}$$

if the emissivity of the pipe is 0.9. The total heat-transfer rate in air is therefore 245 Btu/hr ft, which is only a small fraction of the heat-transfer rate when the pipe is covered by water. *Ans.*

Parallel vertical plates. The cooling ribs of some industrial devices such as transformers, central-heating radiators, and certain electronic instruments can often be idealized by parallel flat plates. The addition of cooling ribs, as discussed in Sec. 3–5, serves to increase the rate of heat dissipation at a given surface temperature. Laminar free-convection heat

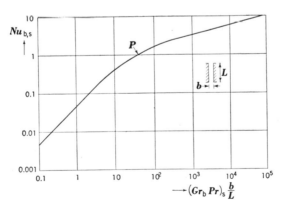

Fig. 7–10. Free-convection heat transfer from two parallel vertical plates spaced a distance b apart. At P the rate of heat transfer per unit area is the maximum. (Courtesy of W. Elenbaas, N. V. Philips' Gloeilampenfabrieken, Ref. 13)

transfer between two parallel vertical flat plates (see insert of Fig. 7–10) had been investigated experimentally by Elenbaas (13). His results are shown in Fig. 7–10. The ordinate is $\overline{\text{Nu}}$, the average Nusselt number $\bar{h}_c b/k$ and the abscissa is the product of the Grashof number Gr_b, the Prandtl number Pr, and the ratio of the distance between the plates b and their height L. In this correlation all of the physical properties except β are evaluated at the surface temperature T_s. The coefficient of thermal expansion β is evaluated at T_∞.

When the object of a design is to space the fins to dissipate the maximum amount of heat for a given base area of height L, Elenbaas recommends that the optimum spacing b_{opt} between plates be selected according to the relation

$$\frac{b_{opt}}{L} \, \text{Gr}_{b \text{ opt}} \, \text{Pr} \simeq 50 \qquad (7\text{–}32)$$

For diatomic gases the optimum spacing is

$$b_{opt} \simeq 2.9 \, \frac{L^{\frac{1}{4}} \mu_s^{\frac{1}{2}} T_\infty^{\frac{1}{4}}}{g^{\frac{1}{4}} \rho_s^{\frac{1}{2}} \Delta T^{\frac{1}{4}}} \qquad (7\text{–}33)$$

where the subscript s indicates that μ and ρ are to be taken at T_s.

Example 7–3. Estimate (a) the optimum spacing and (b) the average heat-transfer coefficient for vertical rectangular fins attached to the sides of an electronic device having the shape of a box. The height of the box is 6 in. and the maximum allowable surface temperature is 200 F. The cooling medium is still air at 100 F.

Solution: (a) The optimum spacing is calculated from Eq. 7–33. Using property values from Table A–3 we get

$$b_{opt} = \frac{(0.5 \text{ ft})^{\frac{1}{4}}(0.144 \times 10^{-4} \text{lb}_m/\text{ft sec})^{\frac{1}{2}}(560 \text{ R})^{\frac{1}{4}}}{(32.2 \text{ ft/sec}^2)^{\frac{1}{4}}(0.06 \text{lb}_m/\text{cu ft})^{\frac{1}{2}}(100 \text{ R})^{\frac{1}{4}}} \left(12 \, \frac{\text{in.}}{\text{ft}} \right)$$

$$= 0.295 \text{ in.}$$

Thus, the fins should be spaced about 0.3 in. apart. *Ans.*

b) Although the temperature is not constant along the cooling ribs, we shall neglect the temperature variation to simplify the calculations. From Table A–3 we find

$$\frac{\rho^2 \beta g c_p}{\mu k} = \frac{(\text{Gr}_b \text{Pr})_s}{b^3 \Delta T} = 0.594 \times 10^6 \text{ at } 200 \text{ F}$$

For $b = 0.3/12$ ft, $L = 0.5$ ft, and $\Delta T = 100$ F, we get $b/L \, (\text{Gr}_b \text{ Pr})_s = 0.464$. From Fig. 7–10 we find $\text{Nu}_{bs} \simeq 1.0$ and

$$\bar{h}_c = \frac{k_s}{b} \text{Nu}_b = \frac{0.0174}{0.025} \times 1.0 = 0.696 \text{ Btu/hr sq ft F} \qquad Ans.$$

Additional information on free convection between parallel plates is presented in Refs. 21 and 22.

Vertical ducts. The heat transfer by laminar free convection at the inside surfaces of ducts having various cross-sectional geometries has also been studied by Elenbaas (13). His results are summarized by various curves in Fig. 7–11 where the characteristic dimension for Nu and Gr is r which is defined as

$$r = 2 \frac{\text{cross-sectional area}}{\text{wetted perimeter}} \quad (7\text{–}34)$$

The ordinate in Fig. 7–11 is the Nusselt number $\overline{\text{Nu}}_r = \bar{h}_c \, r/k_s$ and the abscissa is $(r/L) \, \text{Gr}_r \, \text{Pr}$ where, as in the previous case, the physical proper-

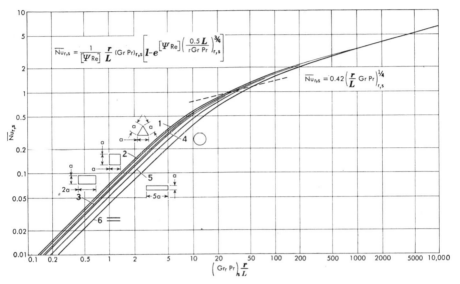

FIG. 7–11. Free-convection heat transfer from the interior surfaces of vertical ducts having various cross-sectional geometries. ($\text{Nu}_{r,s}$ as a function of $(\text{Gr Pr})_{r,s} r/L$ for the cooling of the inner surface of vertical tubes according to Ref. 13 for different values of (Ψ Re). For infinitely long parallel plates (case b) (Ψ Re) = 24 (curve 6). For rectangular cross-sections with the following proportions of the sides of the rectangles 1:1, 1:2, and 1:5, (Ψ Re) is 19.05, 15.55, and 14.22, respectively (curves 2, 3, and 5). For circular cross-sections (Ψ Re) is 16 (curve 4), and for cross-sections in the shape of an equilateral triangle (Ψ Re) = $13\frac{1}{3}$ (curve 1). The points of intersection with the dashed line indicate the points where the cooling unit area of the horizontal cross-section is a maximum. (Courtesy of W. Elenbaas, N. V. Philips' Gloeilampenfabrieken, Ref. 13)

ties with the exception of β are to be taken at T_s. The small symbols indicate the cross-sectional geometry. Thus, curve 1 is for a duct having an equilateral-triangular cross section, curve 2 is for a square duct, and so on. When the ducts or cooling ribs are inclined by an angle from the vertical, the body force should be taken as $g \cos \alpha$, as shown in Fig. 7–7.

Enclosed air spaces. Free convection in enclosed air spaces is of importance in the design and analysis of insulation. Since the thermal conductivity of air is very low, it is an excellent insulator as long as free-convection currents are small. An extensive study of the phenomena associated with heat transfer in enclosed-plane air layers was made by DeGraaf and von der Held (14) and Mull and Reiher (15), who measured the over-all heat-transfer coefficient U between two parallel plates enclosed

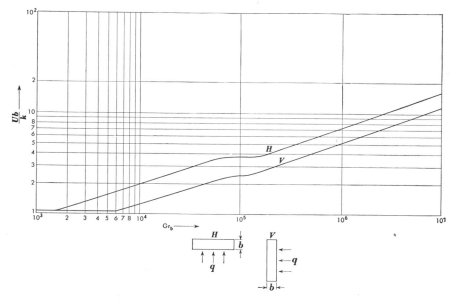

FIG. 7–12. Free-convection heat transfer through enclosed-plane air layer.

around their edges to form a box. For this system the over-all heat-transfer coefficient between the plates U is defined as

$$\frac{1}{U} = \frac{1}{\bar{h}_{c1}} + \frac{b}{k_f} + \frac{1}{\bar{h}_{c2}}$$

where $\bar{h}_{c1}$ and $\bar{h}_{c2}$ are the unit-surface conductances for free convection at the inner surfaces of plates 1 and 2 respectively and b/k_f represents the thermal resistance per unit area for pure conduction through the air between plates spaced a distance b apart. The results of these investigations for enclosed-plane air layers in horizontal and vertical positions respectively are shown in Fig. 7–12. The ordinate is the ratio of the over-all unit conductance U to the unit conductance for heat conduction alone k_f/b and the abscissa is the Grashof number Gr_b, with the thickness of the air layer b as the characteristic dimension. All physical properties are taken at the mean temperature. We note that $Ub/k_f = 1$ when Gr_b is less than 2000 for horizontal layers heated from below and when Gr_b is less than 8000 for vertical layers. This means that, below these values of Gr_b, heat flows only by conduction, or $U = k_f/b$. As the Grashof number is increased, convection currents are set in motion and the over-all unit conductance increases. The motion is laminar until the Grashof numbers reach about 6×10^4. In the horizontal position, the laminar motion is cellular and looks somewhat like a honeycomb (Fig. 7–13). In the transition stage between laminar and turbulent flow, Ub/k_f is nearly independent of Gr_b. For Gr_b larger than 2×10^5, the flow is fully turbulent and

$$\frac{Ub}{k_f} = 0.0426 \, Gr_b^{0.37} \qquad \text{for horizontal layers} \qquad \textbf{(7–35)}$$

$$\frac{Ub}{k_f} = 0.0317 \, Gr_b^{0.37} \qquad \text{for vertical layers} \qquad \textbf{(7–36)}$$

It appears from the available data that the heat transfer per unit area in enclosed air layers is independent of the size of the heat-transfer area as

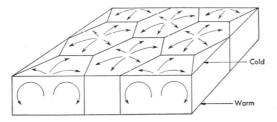

Fig. 7–13. Cellular motion in enclosed-plane air layer heated from the bottom.

long as the distance between the plates is small. One would therefore not expect that compartmental partitions would influence the heat transfer.

At high temperature, radiation between the plates transfers appreciable amounts of heat and the problem of insulation becomes one of reducing radiation rather than convection.

7–4. FREE CONVECTION CAUSED BY CENTRIFUGAL FORCES

In all of the problems considered so far in this chapter, the force actuating free convection was gravity. However, free-convection processes, similar to those discussed previously, occur also under the influence of centrifugal forces. For example, in rotating components of turbines, compressors, and jet-propulsion devices, the centrifugal-force field may be many times larger than the gravitational force, and substantial free-convection velocities and effective heat transfer can be achieved without external pumps or fans. One of the most important potential applications of free convection is in cooling the blades of gas turbines.   The efficiency of gas turbines can be substantially improved by increasing the temperature of the gases entering the turbine.   The maximum inlet temperature is at present limited by the stresses which the rotating blades can withstand.   Internal cooling of the blades reduces the metal temperature and thereby allows the metal to withstand high stresses even at elevated gas temperatures.

Free-convection cooling of gas-turbine blades was first proposed by E. Schmidt, and Fig. 7–14 shows the cooling arrangement suggested by him. Cooling passages are drilled into the blade from the root and are closed at the ends near the blade tip.   The openings near the root of the blade are

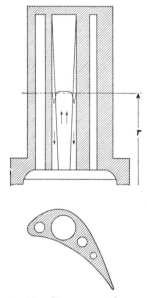

Fig. 7–14.   Free-convection-cooled gas-turbine blade. (Courtesy of National Advisory Committee for Aeronautics, *NACA RM* E50D25)

connected to a coolant supply, and the cooling fluid fills the entire passage. When the blades are heated by the combustion gases, the layer of cooling fluid near the surface of the holes is heated and its density becomes smaller than the density of the cooler liquid in the center of the passage.   In the rotating turbine, the fluid in the cooling passage is subjected to a centrifugal acceleration equal to $r\omega^2$, where ω is the angular velocity and r is the radius. Since the resultant centrifugal forces per unit volume $\rho r\omega^2$ are smaller in the heated layer where the density is less than in the center, the warmer fluid flows towards the axis of rotation.   This motion is similar to that of hot air rising near the surface of a vertical heated flat plate (Sec. 7–2).

In the turbine blade it produces continuous circulation because the hot fluid leaving the cooling passages is replaced by cool fluid flowing outward from the core. The velocity profile at a cross section of the cooling passage has a shape similar to that shown in Fig. 7–14 as long as the cross-sectional area of the cooling passage is large compared with the area occupied by the heated boundary layer (Fig. 7–1). Under these conditions the average heat-transfer coefficient can be computed from Eq. 7–22 or Eq. 7–23 if the Grashof number is built with the centrifugal acceleration $r\omega^2$ instead of the gravitational acceleration g, or

$$\text{Gr} = \frac{r\omega^2\beta\Delta T L^3}{\nu^2} \tag{7–37}$$

where L is the length of the cooling passage.[3] Under normal operating conditions, the Grashof number will be larger than 10^{12}, so that the flow is fully turbulent.

Example 7–4. A turbine blade is cooled by free convection with water as the coolant. The cooling passage is a hole 0.25 in. in diameter and 2.5 in. long. The circumferential velocity V_{cir} at the mean radius of 8 in. is 700 fps, and the cooling water is available at 110 F. Estimate the average heat-transfer coefficient.

Solution: The average centrifugal acceleration $r_m\,\omega^2$, evaluated at the mean radius r_m is equal to

$$r_m\omega^2 = \frac{V_{\text{cir}}^2}{r_m} = \frac{700^2 \text{ sq ft/sec}^2}{8/12 \text{ ft}} = 735{,}000 \text{ ft/sec}^2$$

Evaluating the physical properties at an average film temperature of 200 F, $\text{Pr} = 1.75$ and $\text{Gr} = 9.1 \times 10^{13}$. Equation 7–22 applies approximately and we get

$$\overline{\text{Nu}}_L = 0.0246 \left(\frac{\text{Pr}^{1.17}}{1 + 0.494 \text{ Pr}^{\frac{2}{3}}} \text{ Gr}\right)^{\frac{2}{5}}$$

$$= 0.0246 \ (7.2 \times \omega^{13})^{\frac{2}{5}} = 8600$$

and $\qquad \bar{h}_c = \frac{k}{L} 8600 = \frac{0.393 \text{ Btu/hr ft F}}{2.5/12 \text{ ft}} 8600 = 16{,}200 \text{ Btu/hr sq ft F}$ $\qquad Ans.$

As shown in the preceding example, heat-transfer coefficients inside a cooling passage become very large when the centrifugal forces give rise to high Grashof numbers. The heat-transfer coefficient at the outer surface of a turbine blade is of the order of 80 Btu/hr sq ft F (16). Consequently the temperature drop between the hot gas and the surface of the turbine blade is of the order of 100 times as large as the temperature difference between the surface of the cooling passage and the coolant. The blade can therefore be cooled effectively as long as the thermal resistance of the metal between the outer blade surface and the surface of the cooling passage does not cause too large a temperature drop. Difficulties are encountered

---

[3] Coriolis forces, although present, do not affect the heat transfer appreciably (16).

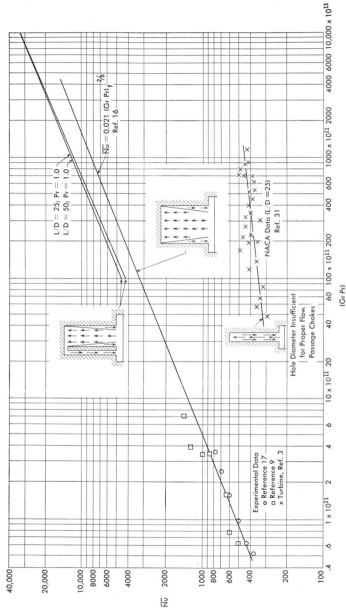

FIG. 7-15. Comparison of experimental and theoretical turbulent free convection in restricted and unrestricted flow.

when the diameter of the cooling passage is small compared with its length, so that the boundary layer fills most of the passages and the cooler core becomes too small to provide effective circulation. This effect is illustrated in Fig. 7–15 where experimental data for natural convection cooling of turbine blades with coolant passages of 0.06 to 0.125 in. diam are compared with Eq. 7–22. The solid line was calculated from Eq. 7–22 with Pr = 0.72, while the heavy dotted line represents an average of the experimental results obtained at NACA by Freche and Diaguila (31) with a 14-in.-diam water-cooled turbine. While experimental results of several investigators,

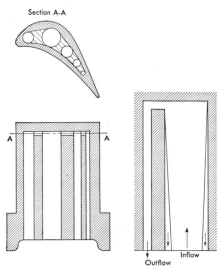

Section A-A

FIG. 7–16. Improved arrangement of cooling passages in free-convection-cooled gas-turbine blade to prevent choking. (Courtesy of National Advisory Committee for Aeronautics)

obtained with compressed air on a plate and a vertical cylinder in the range $Gr_f Pr_f$ from 5×10^{10} to 100×10^{10}, are in good agreement with Eq. 7–22, the experimental data obtained with free-convection cooling of the turbine blade fall below the calculated values, being essentially constant over the range of Grashof numbers investigated. This indicates that the passage size limited the flow and reduced heat transfer, compared with unrestricted flow. Eckert and Jackson (16) have estimated the thickness of free-convection boundary layers, and the reader is referred to their work for further information. When small holes must be used to reduce the thickness of solid material through which the heat must flow before reaching the coolant passage, the circulation can often be improved by connecting a small hole to a larger one, as shown in Fig. 7–16. The flow through the smaller hole is then only in one direction and is similar to flow through a pipe in forced convection.

7–5. CONVECTION FROM ROTATING DISKS AND CYLINDERS

Heat transfer by convection between a rotating body and a surrounding fluid is of importance in the thermal analysis of shafting, flywheels, turbine rotors, and other rotating components of various machines. Despite the wide range of application of rotating machinery, relatively little information on convection phenomena associated with rotating bodies is available. The only geometrical configurations on which experimental measurements have been made are the circular cylinder and the disk.

Convection heat transfer from a heated rotating horizontal cylinder to ambient air has been studied by Anderson and Saunders (23) and Etemad (24). The smoke photographs in Fig. 7–17 show the flow patterns in the vicinity of a horizontal cylinder rotating at various speeds. At low rotational speeds the flow clings to the surface and the heated air rises vertically in a narrow chimney by free convection. As the rotational speed increases, the point of departure of the heated air moves downward along the side in the direction of rotation. When the rotational surface speed reaches a certain critical value, the flow becomes turbulent in the vicinity of the cylinder. Particles are then thrown off randomly from the surface, owing to centrifugal force, and replaced by other particles drawn inward. In isothermal flow, turbulence begins to appear at a critical peripheral speed Reynolds number, $\text{Re}_w = \omega \pi D^2 / \nu$, of about 50. With heat transfer the critical speed is reached when the circumferential speed of the cylinder surface becomes approximately equal to upward free-convection velocity at the side of a heated stationary cylinder. The photograph at 480 rpm illustrates the flow pattern in the turbulent regime.

Below the critical velocity free convection, characterized by the conventional Grashof number $\beta g \ (T_s - T_\infty) \ D^3/\nu^2$, controls the rate of heat transfer. At speeds greater than critical ($\text{Re}_w > 8000$ in air) the peripheral speed Reynolds number $\pi D^2 \omega / \nu$ becomes the controlling parameter. The combined effects of the Reynolds, Prandtl, and Grashof numbers on the average Nusselt number for a horizontal cylinder rotating in air above the critical velocity can be expressed by the empirical equation

$$\overline{\text{Nu}_D} = \frac{\bar{h} D}{k} = 0.11 [\, (0.5 \ \text{Re}_w{}^2 + \text{Gr}) \ \text{Pr} \,]^{0.35} \qquad (7\text{--}38)$$

A semi-empirical theory for predicting the heat transfer from cylinders rotating above the critical velocity in a fluid having Prandtl numbers larger than unity, has been proposed by Kays (25), but it has not been verified experimentally. Gazley (26) studied convection heat transfer to air in the annular gap between a rotating inner cylinder and a stationary

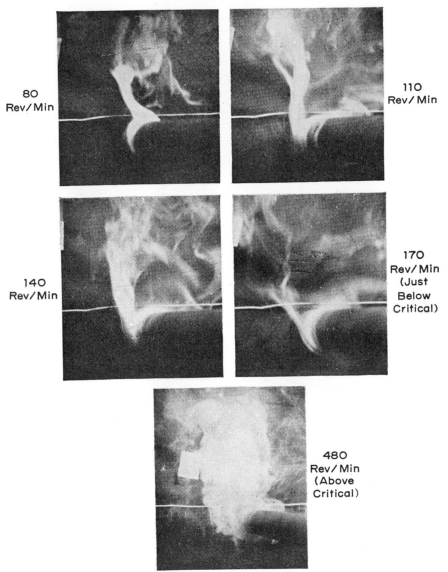

80
Rev/Min

110
Rev/Min

140
Rev/Min

170
Rev/Min
(Just
Below
Critical)

480
Rev/Min
(Above
Critical)

FIG. 7–17. Titanium tetrachloride smoke photographs. A 1 in. by 82 in. cylinder heated to 50 F above surrounding air, with counterclockwise rotation. (Courtesy of J. T. Anderson and O. A. Saunders, "Convection from an Isolated Heated Horizontal Cylinder Rotating About its Axis," *Proc. Roy. Soc., A.*, Vol. 217, 1953)

outer cylinder. He used both smooth and slotted surfaces to simulate conditions in electric motors or generators, and also investigated the effect of axial flow on the heat transfer.

Heat transfer from a rotating disk has been investigated experimentally by Cobb and Saunders (27) and theoretically, among others, by Millsaps and Pohlhausen (28) and Kreith and Taylor (29). The flow and the boundary-layer profiles in the vicinity of a horizontal disk rotating in an infinite environment are illustrated schematically in Fig. 7–18. Flow towards the plate is induced by the frictional drag and the accompanying centrifugal forces which tend to throw the rotating fluid particles radially outward. The boundary layer on the disk is laminar and of uniform thickness at rotational Reynolds numbers $\omega r^2/\nu$ below about 250,000. At higher Reynolds numbers the flow becomes turbulent and the boundary layer thickens with increasing radius.

Pure free-convection phenomena, similar to those for a stationary heated plate, become negligible at Reynolds numbers above 3×10^4. At larger Reynolds numbers the heat transferred from the disk to the fluid is

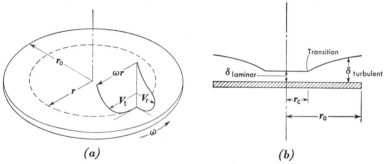

(a) $\qquad\qquad\qquad\qquad\qquad$ (b)

FIG. 7–18. Velocity and boundary layer profiles for a disk rotating in an infinite environment.

carried away at the rim by the radial velocity component as energy stored in the fluid. The total rate of heat transfer from the disk to the fluid can therefore be expressed as (see Fig. 7–18)

$$q_c \pi r_o^2 = 2\pi r_o \int_o^\infty \left[V_r(y) c_p \rho T(y) \right] dy \qquad (7\text{–}39)$$

where the upper limit in the integral may be replaced by δ, the boundary layer thickness. For a disk rotating in air below the critical velocity Wagner (30) evaluated the integral in Eq. 7–39 and found that

$$\overline{\mathrm{Nu}}_{r_o} = \frac{\bar{h}_c r_o}{k} = C\left(\frac{\omega r_o^2}{\nu}\right)^{\frac{1}{2}} \qquad (7\text{–}40)$$

where $C = 0.335$ for $\mathrm{Pr} = 0.74$.

Wagner's results are in good agreement with experimental data in Ref. 26. An exact solution (27) yields a coefficient of 0.35 in the place of

0.335 in Eq. 7–40. The corresponding coefficients at other values of Prandtl number are tabulated in Table 7–1.

TABLE 7–1

VALUES OF COEFFICIENT C IN EQ. 1-40 FOR VARIOUS VALUES OF PR

Pr	0.7	1.0	2.0	5.0	10.0
C	0.35	0.38	0.5	0.8	1.1

In the turbulent flow regime heat-transfer data have been published only for rotation in air (27). For this system the local value of the Nusselt number in the turbulent regime at a radius r is approximately given by

$$\mathrm{Nu}_r = \frac{h_c r}{k} = 0.0195 \, (\omega r^2/\nu)^{0.8} \tag{7-41}$$

and the average value of the Nusselt number for laminar flow between $r = 0$ and r_c, and turbulent flow in the outer ring between $r = r_c$ and r_o is approximately

$$\overline{\mathrm{Nu}}_{r_o} = \frac{\bar{h}_c r_o}{k} = 0.015 \left(\frac{\omega r_o^2}{\nu}\right)^{0.8} - 100 \left(\frac{r_c}{r_o}\right)^2 \tag{7-42}$$

To estimate the Nusselt number in the turbulent regime for heat transfer to a fluid having Prandtl numbers larger than unity it is recommended that the right-hand side of Eq. 7–41 be multiplied by $\mathrm{Pr}^{\frac{1}{3}}$. This recommendation is based on unpublished experimental data obtained by the author in a system corresponding to $\mathrm{Pr} = 2.5$.

REFERENCES

1. S. Ostrach, "New Aspects of Natural-Convection Heat Transfer," *Trans. ASME*, Vol. 75 (1953), pp. 1287–1290.

2. E. Griffith and A. H. Davis, "The Transmission of Heat by Radiation and Convection," *Special Report* 9, Ford Investigation Board, British Dept. of Sci. and Ind. Res., 1922.

3. E. Schmidt and W. Beckman, "Das Temperatur und Geschwindigkeitsfeld vor einer wärmeabgebenden senkrechten Platte bei natürlicher Konvection," *Tech. Mech. u. Thermodynamic*, Bd. 1, No. 10 (October, 1930), pp. 341–349; cont. Bd. 1, No. 11 (November, 1930), pp. 391–406.

4. R. Herman, "Wärmeübergang bei freier Ströhmung am wagrechten Zylinder in zwei-atomic Gasen," *VDI—Forschungsheft*, No. 379 (1936); translated in *NACA TM* 1366, November, 1954.

5. E. R. G. Eckert and T. W. Jackson, "Analysis of Turbulent Free Convection Boundary Layer on Flat Plate," *NACA Report* 1015, July, 1950.

6. E. R. G. Eckert and E. Soehnghen, "Interferometric Studies on the Stability and Transition to Turbulence of a Free-Convection Boundary Layer," *Proc. of the General Discussion on Heat Transfer* (London: ASME-IME, 1951), pp. 321–323.

7. E. R. G. Eckert and E. Soehnghen, "Studies on Heat Transfer in Laminar Free Convection with the Zehnder-Mach Interferometer," *USAF Tech. Report* 5747, December, 1948.

8. E. R. G. Eckert, *Introduction to the Transfer of Heat and Mass.* (New York: McGraw-Hill Book Company, Inc., 1951.)

9. W. H. McAdams, *Heat Transmission*, 3d ed. (New York: McGraw-Hill Book Company, Inc., 1954.)

10. E. M. Sparrow and J. L. Gregg, "Laminar Free Convection from a Vertical Flat Plate," *Trans. ASME*, Vol. 78 (1956), pp. 435–440.

11. J. P. Dotson, *Heat Transfer from a Vertical Flat Plate by Free Convection*, M.S. Thesis, Purdue University, May, 1954.

12. S. C. Hyman, C. F. Bonilla, and S. W. Ehrlich, "Heat Transfer to Liquid Metals and Non-metals at Horizontal Cylinders," *AIChE Symposium on Heat Transfer*, Atlantic City, 1953, pp. 21–33.

13. W. Elenbaas, "Dissipation of Heat by Free Convection," Parts I and II, *Philips Research Report* 3, N.V. Philips' Gloeilampenfabrieken, Eindhoben, Netherlands, 1948, pp. 338–360 and 450–465.

14. J. G. A. DeGraaf and E. F. M. von der Held, "The Relation between the Heat Transfer and the Convection Phenomena in Enclosed Plane Air Layers," *App. Sci. Res.*, Sec. A, Vol. 3 (1953), pp. 393–410.

15. W. Mull and H. Reiher, "Der Wärmeschutz von Luftschichten," Reihe 1, *Gesundh.-Ing. Beihefte*, Heft No. 28, Munich and Berlin, Germany, 1930.

16. E. R. G. Eckert and T. W. Jackson, "Analytic Investigation of Flow and Heat Transfer in Coolant Passages of Free Convection Liquid-Cooled Turbines," *NACA RM* E50D25, July, 1950.

17. M. Jacob, *Heat Transfer*, Vol. I (New York: John Wiley & Sons, Inc., 1949).

18. W. J. King, "The Basic Laws and Data of Heat Transmission," *Mech. Eng.*, Vol. 54 (1932), pp. 347–353.

19. E. M. Sparrow and J. L. Gregg, "Similar Solutions for Free Convection from a Nonisothermal Vertical Flat Plate," *ASME Paper* 57-SA-3 (presented at the Semi-Annual Meeting of ASME, San Francisco, Calif., 1957).

20. E. R. G. Eckert, R. M. Drake, and E. Soehnghen, "Manufacture of a Zehnder-Mach Interferometer," *Tech. Rep.* 5721, Air Material Command, Wright Patterson Air Force Base, Ohio, August, 1948.

21. A. F. Lietzke, "Theoretical and Experimental Investigation of Heat Transfer by Laminar Free Convection Between Parallel Plates," *NACA TN* 3328, December, 1954.

22. S. Ostrach, "Laminar Natural-Convection Flow and Heat Transfer of Fluids with and without Heat Sources in Channels with Constant Wall Temperatures," *NACA TN* 2863, 1952.

23. J. T. Anderson and O. A. Saunders, "Convection from an Isolated Heated Horizontal Cylinder Rotating About its Axis," *Proc. Roy. Soc.*, A., Vol. 217, 1953, pp. 555–562.

24. G. A. Etemad, "Free-Convection Heat Transfer from a Rotating Horizontal Cylinder to Ambient Air with Interferometer Study of Flow," *Trans. ASME*, Vol. 77, 1955, pp. 1283–1289.

25. W. M. Kays and I. S. Bjorklund, "Heat Transfer from a Rotating Cylinder with and without Cross Flow," *Trans. ASME*, Vol. 80, 1958, pp. 70–78.

26. Carl Gazley, Jr., "Heat Transfer Characteristics of the Rotational and Axial Flow Between Concentric Cylinders," *Trans. ASME*, Vol. 80, 1958, pp. 79–90.

27. E. C. Cobb and O. A. Saunders, "Heat Transfer from a Rotating Disk," *Proc. Roy. Soc.*, A., Vol. 220, 1956, pp. 343–351.

28. K. Millsap and K. Pohlhausen, "Heat Transfer by Laminar Flow from a Rotating Plate," *J. of the Aero. Sci.*, Vol. 19, 1952, pp. 120–126.

29. F. Kreith and J. H. Taylor, Jr., "Heat Transfer from a Rotating Disk in Turbulent Flow," *ASME Paper* No. 56-A-146, 1956.

30. C. Wagner, "Heat Transfer from a Rotating Disk to Ambient Air," *J. of Appl. Phys.*, Vol. 19, 1948, pp. 837–841.

31. J. C. Freche and A. J. Diagulia, "Heat Transfer and Operating Characteristics of Aluminum Forced-Convection and Stainless-Steel Natural-Convection Water-Cooled Single-Stage Turbines," *NACA RM* E50D03a, 1950.

PROBLEMS

7-1. An empirical equation proposed by Heilman (*Trans. ASME*, Vol. 51, 1929, p. 287) for the unit-surface conductance in free convection from long horizontal cylinders to air is

$$\bar{h}_c = \frac{1.016(T_s - T_\infty)^{0.266}}{D^{0.2}T_f^{0.181}}$$

The corresponding equation in dimensionless form is

$$\frac{h_c D}{k_f} = C \operatorname{Gr}_f{}^m \operatorname{Pr}_f{}^n$$

By comparing the two equations, determine those values of the constants C, m, and n in the latter equation which will give the same results as the first equation.

7-2. Consider a design for a nuclear reactor using free-convection heating of liquid bismuth. The reactor core is to be constructed of parallel vertical plates, 6 ft tall and 4 ft wide, in which heat is generated uniformly. Estimate the maximum possible heat-dissipation rate from each plate if the surface temperature of the plate is not to exceed 1600 F and the lowest allowable bismuth temperature is 600 F.

7-3. A 10-gal tank full of water at 60 F is to be heated to 120 F by means of a $\frac{3}{8}$-in.-OD copper steam coil having 10 turns of 12 in. diameter. The steam is at atmospheric pressure, and its thermal resistance is negligibly small. Neglecting heat losses from the tank, estimate the heating time required.

7-4. An 8-in.-diam sphere containing liquid air (− 220 F) is covered with 2-in.-thick glass wool. Estimate the rate of heat transfer to the liquid air from the surrounding air at 70 F by convection and radiation. How would you reduce the heat transfer?

7-5. A horizontal $2\frac{3}{8}$-in.-OD, $2\frac{1}{6}$-in.-ID steam pipe carrying saturated steam at 50 psia is covered by 1-in.-thick molded-asbestos insulation. Estimate the rate of heat loss to surrounding air at 70 F for a 100-ft length. What would be the quality of the steam at the outlet if it is saturated at the inlet? The unit-surface conductance at the steam side is 2000 Btu/hr sq ft F and the average velocity is 10 fps.

7-6. A small transformer is to be cooled by free convection. The shell is 1 ft tall and 1 ft by $1\frac{1}{2}$-in. in cross section. Estimate the optimum spacing of vertical 4-in.-wide flat-plate fins in air and in a light heat-transfer oil for an average surface temperature of 200 F and a coolant temperature of 100 F. What is the rate of heat dissipation in both cases?

7-7. Estimate the rate of heat transfer by free convection and radiation across a $\frac{1}{2}$-in. air space formed between two horizontal 24-ST aluminum sheets, the upper one of which is maintained at 300 F while the lower one remains at 70 F.

7-8. Repeat Prob. 7-7 for the case in which the air space is divided in half by a very thin sheet of bright aluminum foil, placed parallel to the surface.

7-9. Estimate the heat-transfer coefficient in a free-convection-cooled turbine blade with air as the coolant. The cooling passage is a slot of $\frac{1}{2}$-in. by 0.2-in. area, 2-in. length. The circumferential velocity at the mean radius of 14 in. is 700 fps. The inlet air is available at 100 F, the hot gases on the outside of the blade are at 1400 F, and the unit-surface conductance on the outer-blade surface is 100 Btu/hr sq ft F.

7–10. Repeat Prob. 7–9 with water as the coolant. What is the approximate blade temperature?

7–11. Starting with the equation

$$\mathrm{Nu}_D = 0.53 \left(\frac{\mathrm{Pr}^2}{0.452 + \mathrm{Pr}}\,\mathrm{Gr}\right)^{\frac{1}{4}}$$

show that, if Pr is much larger than unity,

$$\mathrm{Nu} \simeq (\mathrm{Gr\ Pr})^{\frac{1}{4}}$$

and when Pr is much less than unity (e.g., liquid metals)

$$\mathrm{Nu} \simeq (\mathrm{Gr\ Pr}^2)^{\frac{1}{4}}$$

7–12. Consider a thin vertical flat plate L feet high and 1 ft wide at a temperature difference between surrounding medium ($\mathrm{Pr} = 1$) and plate surface of ΔT. If heat exchange is taking place by free convection in laminar flow, derive an expression for the lifting force acting on the plate as a result of the temperature difference ΔT.

7–13. A light oil is maintained at 150 F in a 2-ft-square sump tank by ten 2-ft-long, $\frac{1}{2}$-in.-OD tubes which are widely spaced and arranged horizontally in the lower third of the 6-ft tank depth. The tube surface temperature is maintained at 50 F by cooling water circulated at a high rate through the tubes. Estimate the oil cooling rate in Btu/hr if the heat-transfer area is 2.62 sq ft. *Ans.* ~ 6500 Btu/hr

7–14. A thermocouple ($\frac{1}{32}$-in.-OD) is located horizontally in a large enclosure whose walls are at 100 F. The enclosure is filled with a transparent quiescent gas which has the same properties as air. The electromotive force (emf) of the thermocouple indicates a temperature of 450 F. Estimate the true gas temperature if the emissivity of the thermocouple is 0.8.

7–15. Starting with Eqs. 7–2 and 7–6 verify the validity of Eq. 7–16 under the assumption that inertia forces are negligible.

7–16. Show from Eq. 7–39 that if $V_r = 0.162\omega r(y/\delta)^{\frac{1}{7}}\,[1 - (y/\delta)]$ and $\delta = 0.526r$ $(r^2\omega/\nu)^{-\frac{1}{5}}$ (see *ZAMM*, Vol. 1, 1921, p. 231) and $(T - T_\infty) = (T_s - T_\infty)\,[1 - (y/\delta)^{\frac{1}{7}}]$ the average Stanton number for turbulent flow of a fluid with $\mathrm{Pr} = 1$ on a rotating disk of radius r_o is given by

$$\overline{\mathrm{St}} = \frac{\bar{h}_c}{c_p \rho \omega r_o} = 0.0116(\nu/r^2\omega)^{\frac{1}{5}}$$

7–17. A mild steel, 1-in.-OD shaft, rotating in 70 F air at 20,000 rpm, is attached to two bearings, 2 ft apart. If the temperature at the bearings is 200 F, determine the temperature distribution along the shaft. HINT: Show that for high rotational speeds Eq. 7–38 approaches $\overline{\mathrm{Nu}}_D = 0.076\,(\pi D^2\omega/\nu)^{0.7}$.

7–18. Estimate the rate of heat transfer from one side of a 6-ft-diam disk rotating at 600 rpm in 70 F air, if its surface temperature is 120 F.

7–19. A 4 ft by 4 ft flat, chromeplated plate, supported horizontally on 6-ft legs, is exposed to the sun at 12 o'clock noon on May 1. If the air temperature is 80 F, (a) determine the equilibrium temperature on an average clear day; (b) determine the equilibrium temperature for an irradiation of 350 Btu/sq ft hr.

7–20. Estimate the equilibrium temperature of a polished aluminum plate mounted on an insulating pad when exposed on a clear day to the noon sun. The irradiation is 255 Btu/sq ft hr and the ambient temperature is 80 F. Assume that the effective sky temperature is also 80 F.

8 Forced Convection Inside Tubes and Ducts

8–1. INTRODUCTION

The heating and cooling of fluids flowing inside conduits are among the most important heat-transfer processes in engineering. The design and analysis of all types of heat exchangers requires a knowledge of the heat-transfer coefficient between the wall of the conduit and the fluid flowing inside it. The sizes of boilers, economizers, superheaters, and preheaters depend largely on the unit-convective conductance between the inner surface of the tubes and the fluid. Also, in the design of air-conditioning and refrigeration equipment, it is necessary to evaluate heat-transfer coefficients for fluids flowing inside ducts. Once the heat-transfer coefficient for a given geometry and specified flow conditions is known, the rate of heat transfer at the prevailing temperature difference can be calculated from the equation

$$q_c = \bar{h}_c \, A \, (T_{\text{surf}} - T_{\text{fl}}) \qquad [\,1\text{–}13\,]$$

The same relation can also be used to determine the area required to transfer heat at a specified rate for a given temperature potential.

The heat-transfer coefficient $\bar{h}_c$ can be calculated from the Nusselt number $\bar{h}_c \, D_H/k$, as shown in Sec. 6–4. For flow in long tubes or conduits (Fig. 8–1a) the significant length in the Nusselt number is the hydraulic diameter D_H, defined as

$$D_H = 4 \, \frac{\text{flow cross-sectional area}}{\text{wetted perimeter}} \qquad (8\text{–}1)$$

For a tube or a pipe the flow cross-sectional area is $\pi D^2/4$, the wetted perimeter is πD, and therefore the inside diameter of the tube equals the hydraulic diameter. For an annulus formed between two concentric tubes (Fig. 8–1b) we have

$$D_H = 4 \, \frac{(\pi/4)(D_1{}^2 - D_2{}^2)}{\pi(D_1 - D_2)} = D_1 - D_2 \qquad (8\text{–}1a)$$

In engineering practice the Nusselt number for flow in conduits is usually evaluated from empirical equations based on experimental results, although in recent years semi-analytic methods of approach have made considerable strides toward an understanding of the basic principles of forced convection in tubes and annuli. From a dimensional analysis, as shown in Sec. 6–6, the experimental results obtained in forced-convection heat-transfer experiments can be correlated by an equation of the form

$$\text{Nu} = \phi\ (\text{Re})\ \psi\ (\text{Pr}) \tag{8–2}$$

where the symbols ϕ and ψ denote functions of the Reynolds number and Prandtl number respectively.

Selection of reference fluid temperature. The convective-heat-transfer coefficient used to build the Nusselt number for heat transfer to a fluid flowing in a conduit is defined by Eq. 1–13. The numerical value of $\bar{h}_c$, as

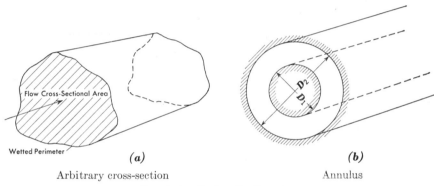

(a)   (b)

Arbitrary cross-section   Annulus

Fig. 8–1.   Hydraulic diameter.

mentioned previously, depends on the choice of the reference temperature in the fluid. For flow over a plane surface the temperature of the fluid far away from the heat source is generally constant, and its value is a natural choice for the fluid temperature in Eq. 1–13. In heat transfer to or from a fluid flowing in a conduit, the temperature of the fluid does not level out but varies both along the direction of mass flow and in the direction of heat flow. At a given cross section of the conduit, the temperature of the fluid at the center could be selected as the reference temperature in Eq. 1–13. However, the center temperature is difficult to measure in practice; furthermore, it is not a measure of the change in internal energy of all the fluid flowing in the conduit. It is therefore a common practice, and one we shall follow here, to use the average bulk temperature T_b as the reference fluid temperature in Eq. 1–13. The average bulk temperature at a station of the conduit is often called the cup mixing temperature because it is the temperature which the fluid passing a cross-sectional area of the conduit during a given time interval would assume if the fluid were collected and mixed in a cup.

The use of the fluid bulk temperature as the reference temperature in Eq. 1–13 allows us to make heat balances readily because, in the steady state, the difference in the average bulk temperature between two sections of a conduit is a direct measure of the rate of heat transfer, or

$$q = mc_p\Delta T_b$$

where q = rate of heat transfer to fluid, in Btu/hr;
  m = flow rate, in lb_m/hr;
  c_p = specific heat, in But/lb_m F;
  ΔT_b = difference in bulk temperature between cross sections in question.

The problems associated with variations of the bulk temperature in the direction of flow will be considered in detail in Chapter 11, where the analysis of heat exchangers is taken up. For preliminary calculations, it is common practice to use the bulk temperature halfway between the inlet and the outlet section of a duct as the reference temperature in Eq. 1–13. This procedure is satisfactory when the wall temperature of the duct is constant but requires some modification when the heat is transferred between two fluids separated by a wall as, for example, in a heat exchanger where one fluid flows inside a pipe while another passes over the outside of the pipe. Although this type of problem is of considerable practical importance, it will not concern us in this chapter, where the emphasis is placed on the evaluation of convective-heat-transfer coefficients, which can be determined in a given flow system when the pertinent bulk and wall temperatures are specified.

Effect of Reynolds number on heat transfer and pressure drop in fully established flow. For a given fluid the Nusselt number depends primarily on the flow conditions, which can be characterized by the Reynolds number Re. For flow in long conduits the characteristic length in the Reynolds number, as in the Nusselt number, is the hydraulic diameter, or

$$\mathrm{Re}_D = \frac{VD_H\rho}{\mu} = VD_H/\nu$$

In long ducts, where the entrance effects are not important, the flow is laminar when the Reynolds number is below 2100. In the range of Reynolds numbers between 2100 and 10,000, the transition from laminar to turbulent flow takes place. The flow in this regime is called transitional. At a Reynolds number of about 10,000, the flow becomes fully turbulent.

In laminar flow through a duct, just as for laminar flow over a plate, there is no mixing of warmer and colder fluid particles by eddy motion and the heat transfer takes place solely by conduction. Since all fluids with the exception of liquid metals have small thermal conductivities, the heat-transfer coefficients in laminar flow are relatively small. In transitional flow a certain amount of mixing occurs by means of eddies which carry warmer fluid into cooler regions, and vice versa. Since the mixing motion, even if it is only on a small scale, accelerates the transfer of heat considerably, a marked increase in the heat-transfer coefficient occurs above Re = 2100. This is illustrated in Fig. 8–2 where experimentally measured values of the average Nusselt number for atmospheric air flowing

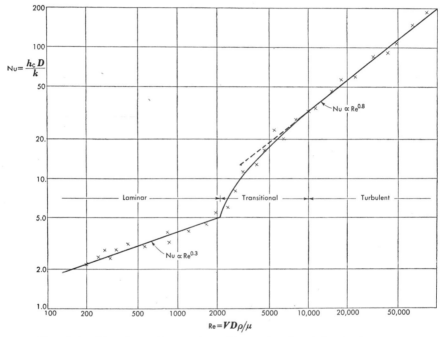

FIG. 8–2.   Nusselt number vs. Reynolds number for air flowing in a pipe.

through a 60-in.-long, 1-in.-ID heated tube are plotted as a function of the Reynolds number. Since the Prandtl number for air does not vary appreciably, Eq. 8–2 reduces to Nu = ϕ(Re), and the curve drawn through the experimental points shows the dependence of Nu on the flow conditions. We note that, in the laminar regime, the Nusselt number remains small, increasing from about 2.2 at Re = 200 to 5.0 at Re = 2100. Above a Reynolds number of 2100, the Nusselt number begins to increase rapidly until the Reynolds number reaches about 8000. As the Reynolds number is further increased, the Nusselt number continues to increase, but at a slower rate. A qualitative explanation for this behavior can be given by observing the fluid-flow field shown schematically in Fig. 8–3. At Reynolds numbers above 8000, the flow inside the conduit is fully turbulent except for a very thin layer of fluid adjacent to the wall. In this layer turbulent eddies are damped out as a result of the viscous forces which predominate near the surface, and therefore heat flows through it mainly by conduction. The edge of this so-called laminar sublayer is indicated by a dotted line in Fig. 8–3. The flow beyond it is turbulent and the circular arrows in the turbulent-flow regime represent the eddies which sweep the edge of the laminar layer, probably penetrate it, and carry along with them fluid at the temperature prevailing there. The eddies mix the warmer and cooler fluids so effectively that heat is transferred very rapidly between the edge of the laminar boundary layer and the turbulent bulk of the fluid. It is thus apparent that, except for fluids of high thermal conductivity (e.g., liquid metals), the thermal resistance of the laminar layer controls the rate of heat transfer, and that most of the temperature drop between the bulk of the fluid and

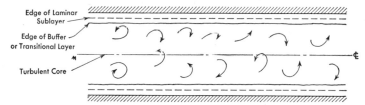

Edge of Laminar Sublayer

Edge of Buffer or Transitional Layer

Turbulent Core

FIG. 8–3. Flow pattern for a fluid flowing turbulently through a pipe.

the surface of the conduit occurs in this layer. The turbulent portion of the flow field, on the other hand, offers little resistance to the flow of heat. The only effective method of increasing the heat-transfer coefficient is therefore to decrease the thermal resistance of the laminar boundary layer. This can be accomplished by increasing the turbulence in the main stream so that the turbulent eddies can penetrate deeper into the laminar layer. An increase in turbulence, however, is accompanied by large energy losses which increase the frictional pressure drop in the conduit. In the design and selection of industrial heat exchangers, where not only the initial cost but also the operating expenses must be considered, the pressure drop is an important factor. An increase of the flow velocity yields higher heat-transfer coefficients which, in accordance with Eq. 1–13, decrease the size and consequently also the initial cost of the equipment for a specified heat-transfer rate. At the same time, however, the pumping cost increases. The optimum design therefore requires a compromise between the initial and operating costs. In practice it has been found that increases in pumping costs and operating expenses often outweigh the saving in the initial cost of heat-transfer equipment under continuous operating conditions. As a result, the velocities used in a majority of commercial heat-exchange equipment are relatively low, corresponding to Reynolds numbers of no more than 50,000. Whenever possible, laminar flow is avoided in heat-exchange equipment because of the low heat-transfer coefficients obtained. However, in the chemical industry, where frequently very viscous liquids must be handled, laminar flow sometimes can not be avoided without producing undesirably large pressure losses.

It was shown in Sec. 6–10 that for turbulent flow of liquids and gases over a flat plate, the Nusselt number is proportional to the Reynolds number raised to the 0.8 power. Since in turbulent forced convection the laminar sublayer generally controls the rate of heat flow irrespective of the geometry of the system, it is not surprising that also for turbulent forced convection in conduits the Nusselt number is related to the Reynolds number by the same type of power law. For the case of air flowing in a pipe, this relation is illustrated in the graph of Fig. 8–2.

Effect of Prandtl number. The Prandtl number Pr is a function of the fluid properties alone. It has been defined previously as the ratio of the kinematic viscosity of the fluid to the thermal diffusivity of the fluid, that is,

$$\text{Pr} = \frac{\nu}{a} = \frac{c_p \mu}{k_f}$$

The kinematic viscosity ν, or μ/ρ, is often referred to as the molecular diffusivity of momentum because it is a measure of the rate of momentum transfer between the molecules. The thermal diffusivity of a fluid $k_f/c_p\rho$ is often called the molecular diffusivity of heat. It is a measure of the ratio of the heat transmission and energy storage capacities of the molecules.

The Prandtl number relates the temperature distribution to the velocity distribution, as shown in Secs. 6–7 and 6–10 for flow over a flat plate. For flow in a pipe, just as over a flat plate, the velocity and temperature profiles are similar for fluids having a Prandtl number of unity. When the Prandtl number is smaller, the temperature gradient near a surface is less steep than the velocity gradient, and for fluids whose Prandtl number is larger than one, the temperature gradient is steeper than the velocity gradient. The effect of the Prandtl number on the temperature gradient in turbulent flow at a given Reynolds number in tubes is illustrated schematically in Fig. 8–4, where temperature profiles at different Prandtl numbers are shown at $\text{Re}_D = 10,000$. These curves reveal that, at a specified Reynolds number, the temperature gradient at the wall is steeper in a fluid having a large Prandtl number than in a fluid having a small Prandtl number. Consequently, at a given Reynolds number fluids with larger Prandtl numbers have larger Nusselt numbers.

Liquid metals generally have a high thermal conductivity and a small

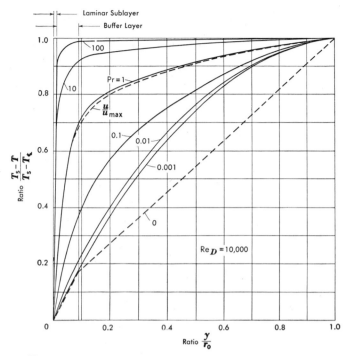

Fig. 8–4.   Effect of Prandtl number on the temperature
profile for turbulent flow in a long pipe. (Extracted from
"Heat Transfer to Molten Metals," by R. C. Martinelli,
Trans. ASME, Vol. 69, 1947, with permission of the publishers, The American Society of Mechanical Engineers)

specific heat; their Prandtl numbers are therefore small, ranging from
0.005 to 0.01.   The Prandtl numbers of gases range from 0.6 to 0.9.   Most
oils, on the other hand, have large Prandtl numbers because their viscosity
is large and their thermal conductivity is small.

Entrance effects.   In addition to the Reynolds number and the Prandtl
number, several other factors can influence the conditions of heat transfer by
forced convection.   For example, when the conduit is short ($L/D_H < 50$),
entrance effects are important.   As a fluid enters a duct with a uniform
velocity, the fluid immediately adjacent to the tube wall is brought to
rest.   For a short distance from the entrance a laminar boundary layer is
formed along the tube wall.   If the turbulence in the entering fluid stream
is high, the boundary layer will quickly become turbulent.   Irrespective
of whether the boundary layer remains laminar or becomes turbulent, it
will increase in thickness until it fills the entire duct.   From this point on,
the velocity profile across the duct remains essentially unchanged.

The development of the thermal boundary layer in a fluid which is
heated or cooled in a duct is qualitatively similar to that of the hydro-

dynamic boundary layer. At the entrance, the temperature is generally uniform transversely, but as the fluid flows along the duct, the heated or cooled layer increases in thickness until heat is transferred to or from the fluid in the center of the duct. Beyond this point the temperature profile remains essentially constant if the velocity profile is fully established.

The final shapes of the velocity and temperature profiles depend on whether the fully developed flow is laminar or turbulent. Figures 8–5

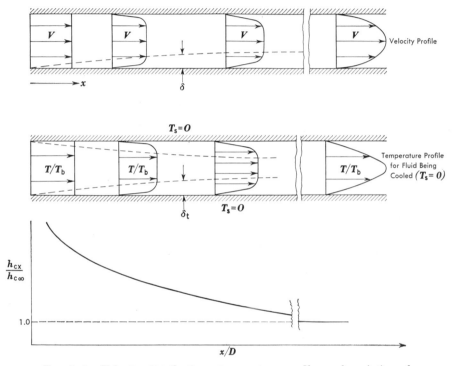

FIG. 8–5. Velocity distributions, temperature profiles and variation of the unit-convective conductance near the inlet of a tube for air being cooled in laminar flow.

and 8–6 illustrate qualitatively the growths of the boundary layers as well as the variations in the local unit-convective conductance near the entrance of a tube for laminar and turbulent conditions respectively. An inspection of these figures shows that the unit-thermal conductance varies considerably near the entrance. If the entrance is square-edged, as in most heat exchangers, the initial development of the hydrodynamic and thermal boundary layers along the walls of the tube is quite similar to that along a flat plate. Consequently, the conductance is largest near the entrance and decreases along the duct until both the velocity and the temperature profiles for the fully developed flow have been established. If the pipe Reynolds number for the fully developed flow $VD\rho/\mu$ is below 2100, the entrance effects may be appreciable for a length as much as 50 diameters from the entrance. For velocities corresponding to turbulent-pipe Reynolds numbers, the entrance effects disappear about 10 diameters from the entrance.

Variation of physical properties. Another factor which can influence the heat transfer and friction considerably is the variation of physical

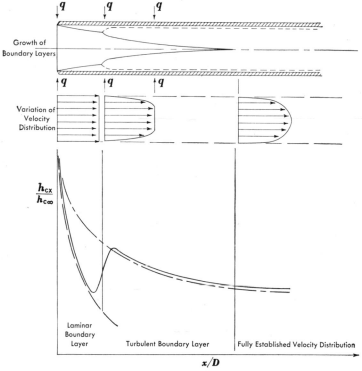

FIG. 8–6. Velocity distribution and variation of unit-convective conductance near the entrance of a tube for a fluid in turbulent flow.

properties with temperature. When a fluid flowing in a duct is heated or cooled, its temperature, and consequently also its physical properties, vary along the duct as well as over any given cross section. For liquids, only the temperature dependence of the viscosity is of major importance. For gases, on the other hand, the temperature effect on the physical properties is more complicated than for liquids because the thermal conductivity and the density, in addition to the viscosity, vary significantly with temperature. In either case, the numerical value of the Reynolds number depends on the location at which the viscosity is evaluated. It is believed that the Reynolds number based on the bulk temperature is the significant parameter to describe the flow conditions. However, considerable success in the empirical correlation of experimental heat-transfer data has been achieved by evaluating the viscosity at an *average film* temperature, defined as a temperature approximately halfway between the wall and the bulk mean temperatures. Another method of taking account of the variation of physical properties with temperature is to evaluate all properties at the bulk mean temperature and to correct for the thermal effects by multiplying the right-hand side of Eq. 8–2 by a function proportional to the ratio of bulk to wall temperatures or viscosities. The latter is preferred because it is simpler to apply in practice and can also be justified on the basis of more advanced boundary-layer theory.

Thermal boundary conditions and compressibility effects. For fluids having a Prandtl number of unity or less, the heat-transfer coefficient also depends on the thermal-boundary condition. For example, in geometrically similar systems a uniform wall temperature yields smaller convective conductances than a uniform heat input at the same Reynolds and Prandtl numbers.[1]

When heat is transferred to or from gases flowing at very high velocities, compressibility effects influence the flow and the heat transfer. Some problems associated with heat transfer to or from fluids at high Mach numbers will be considered in Chapter 12.

Limits of accuracy in predicted values of convective heat-transfer coefficients. In the application of any empirical equation for forced convection to practical problems it is important to bear in mind that the predicted values of the heat-transfer coefficient are not exact. The results obtained by various experimenters, even under carefully controlled conditions, differ appreciably. In turbulent and in laminar flow the accuracy of a heat-transfer coefficient predicted from any available equation or graph may be no better than 30 per cent. In the transition region, where experimental data are scant, the accuracy of the Nusselt number predicted from available information may be even lower.

8–2. ANALOGY BETWEEN HEAT AND MOMENTUM TRANSFER

To illustrate the most important physical variables affecting heat transfer by turbulent forced convection to or from fluids flowing in a long tube or duct, we shall apply the analogy between heat and momentum

---

[1] Sellars, Tribus, and Klein (*Trans. ASME*, Vol. 78, 1956, p. 441) have recently presented a generalized procedure for the evaluation of the Nusselt number in laminar flow through ducts or tubes, subject to arbitrary variations of wall temperature or heat flux distribution along the duct. Schleicher and Tribus (*Trans. ASME*, Vol. 79, 1957, pp. 789–797) have treated the problem of heat transfer in a pipe with turbulent flow and arbitrary wall-temperature distribution.

transfer. The basic concepts of this analogy, introduced by Osborn Reynolds in 1874 (1), have been discussed in Sec. 6–9. The basic analogy was later improved by Prandtl (2), and additional refinements, particularly applicable to forced convection in circular ducts, were made over the years by von Karman (3), Boelter et al. (4), Martinelli (5), and most recently by Deissler (6,7). In this section we shall develop the analogy for pipe flow only in its simplest form and then present some of the important practical results of the more advanced refinements.

The assumptions necessary for the simple analogy are valid only for fluids having a Prandtl number of unity, but the fundamental relation between heat transfer and fluid friction for flow in ducts can be illustrated for this case without introducing mathematical difficulties. The results of the simple analysis can also be extended to other fluids by means of empirical correction factors, as will be shown in Sec. 8–3.

The rate of heat flow per unit area in a fluid can be related to the temperature gradient by the equation

$$\frac{q}{A\rho c_p} = -\left(\frac{k}{\rho c_p} + \epsilon_H\right)\frac{dT}{dy} \qquad [6\text{-}56]$$

This relation, as shown in Sec. 6–9, takes into account the heat flow by conduction as well as by eddy convection. In purely laminar flow $\epsilon_H = 0$, and, except for liquid metals, the term $k/\rho c_p$ is negligible in highly turbulent motion. Similarly, the shearing stress caused by the combined action of the viscous forces and the turbulent momentum transfer is given by

$$\frac{\tau g_c}{\rho} = \left(\frac{\mu}{\rho} + \epsilon_M\right)\frac{du}{dy} \qquad [6\text{-}50]$$

According to the Reynolds analogy, heat and momentum are transferred by analogous processes in turbulent flow. Consequently, both q and τ vary with y, the distance from the surface, in the same manner. For fully developed turbulent flow in a pipe, the local shearing stress decreases linearly with the radial distance r. Hence we can write

$$\frac{\tau}{\tau_s} = \frac{r}{r_s} = 1 - \frac{y}{r_s} \qquad (8\text{-}3)$$

and

$$\frac{q/A}{(q/A)_s} = \frac{r}{r_s} = 1 - \frac{y}{r_s} \qquad (8\text{-}4)$$

where the subscript s denotes conditions at the inner surface of the pipe. Introducing Eqs. 8–3 and 8–4 into Eqs. 6–50 and 6–56 respectively yields

$$\frac{\tau_s g_c}{\rho}\left(1 - \frac{y}{r_s}\right) = -\left(\frac{\mu}{\rho} + \epsilon_M\right)\frac{du}{dy} \qquad (8\text{-}5)$$

and

$$\frac{q_s}{A_s \rho c_p}\left(1 - \frac{y}{r_s}\right) = -\left(\frac{k}{\rho c_p} + \epsilon_H\right)\frac{dT}{dy} \tag{8-6}$$

If $\epsilon_H = \epsilon_M$, the brackets on the right-hand side of Eqs. 8–5 and 8–6 are equal provided the molecular diffusivity of momentum μ/ρ equals the molecular diffusivity of heat $k/\rho c_p$, that is, when the Prandtl number is unity. Dividing Eq. 8–6 by Eq. 8–5 yields under these restrictions

$$\frac{q_s}{A_s c_p g_c T_s}\, du = -dT \tag{8-7}$$

Equation 8–7 can be integrated between the wall where $u = 0$ and $T = T_s$, and the bulk of the fluid where $u = V$ and $T = T_b$. The integration then yields

$$\frac{q_s V}{A_s c_p g_c T_s} = T_s - T_b \tag{8-8}$$

which can also be written in the form

$$\frac{\tau_s g_c}{\rho V^2} = \frac{q_s}{A_s(T_s - T_b)}\frac{1}{c_p \rho V} = \frac{\bar{h}_c}{c_p \rho V} \tag{8-9}$$

since $\bar{h}_c$ is by definition equal to $q_s/A_s(T_s - T_b)$. Multiplying the numerator and the denominator of the right-hand side of Eq. 8–9 by $D_H \mu k$ and regrouping yields

$$\frac{\bar{h}_c}{c_p \rho V}\frac{D_H \mu k}{D_H \mu k} = \frac{\bar{h}_c D_H}{k}\frac{k}{c_p \mu}\frac{\mu}{V D_H \rho} = \frac{\mathrm{Nu}}{\mathrm{Re\ Pr}}$$

which we recognize as the Stanton number, St. To bring the left-hand side of Eq. 8–9 into a more convenient form, we make a force balance on a cylindrical mass of fluid as shown in Fig. 8–7. The pressure difference $p_1 - p_2$ exerts the force $(p_1 - p_2)\,\pi D^2/4$, which is balanced in steady flow by the shear at the wall, or

$$(p_1 - p_2)\frac{\pi D^2}{4} = \tau_s \pi D L \tag{8-10}$$

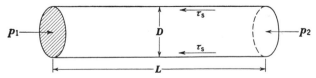

FIG. 8–7. Sketch illustrating nomenclature for force balance on a fluid element in a tube.

Solving for the wall shear per unit area yields

$$\tau_s = \frac{(p_1 - p_2)D}{4L} \tag{8-11}$$

In fluid mechanics the pressure drop is usually expressed in terms of a drag-friction coefficient f as[2]

$$p_1 - p_2 = 4f \frac{L}{D} \frac{\rho V^2}{2g_c} \tag{8-12}$$

Substituting Eq. 8–12 for $p_1 - p_2$ in Eq. 8–11 gives

$$\tau_s = f \frac{\rho V^2}{2g_c} \tag{8-13}$$

Substituting Eq. 8–13 for τ_s in Eq. 8–9 finally yields the equation

$$St = \frac{Nu}{Re\ Pr} = \frac{f}{2} \tag{8-14}$$

which is known as the *Reynolds analogy*.[3] It agrees fairly well with experimental data for heat transfer in gases whose Prandtl number is nearly unity.

According to experimental data for fluids flowing in smooth tubes in the range of Reynolds numbers from 10,000 to 120,000, the friction coefficient f is given by the empirical relation

$$f = 0.046\ Re_D^{-0.2} \tag{8-15}$$

Using this relation, Eq. 8–14 can be written as

$$St = \frac{Nu}{Re\ Pr} = 0.023\ Re_D^{-0.2} \tag{8-16}$$

or, since Pr was assumed unity, as

$$Nu = 0.023\ Re_D^{0.8} \tag{8-17}$$

or

$$\bar{h}_c = 0.023 V^{0.8} D^{-0.2} k \left(\frac{\mu}{\rho}\right)^{-0.8}$$

---

[2] It should be noted that some authors write Eq. 8–12 in the form

$$p_1 - p_2 = f_{D-W} \frac{L}{D} \frac{\rho V^2}{2g_c}$$

This expression is called the Darcy-Weisbach form. The Darcy-Weisbach friction factor f_{D-W} is four times larger than the drag-friction coefficient *by definition*.

[3] The Reynolds analogy can be extended to mass transfer. The analogies among mass-, heat-, and momentum-transfer will be discussed in Chapter 13.

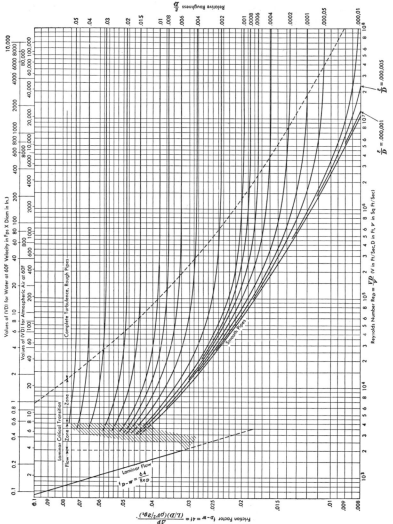

FIG. 8–8. Friction vs. Reynolds number for laminar and turbulent flow in tubes of various surface roughnesses. (Extracted from "Friction Factor for Pipe Flow," by L. F. Moody, published in *Trans. ASME*, Vol. 66, 1944, with permission of the publishers, The American Society of Mechanical Engineers)

We observe that, in fully established turbulent flow, the convective-unit conductance is directly proportional to the velocity raised to the 0.8 power and inversely proportional to the tube diameter raised to the 0.2 power. For a given flow rate, an increase in the tube diameter reduces the velocity and thereby causes a decrease in $\bar{h}_c$ proportional to $1/D^{1.8}$. The use of small tubes and high velocities is therefore conducive to large heat-transfer coefficients, but at the same time the power required to overcome the frictional resistance is increased. In the design of heat-exchange equipment it is therefore necessary to strike a balance between the gain in heat-transfer rates achieved by the use of ducts having small cross-sectional areas, and the accompanying increase in pumping requirements.

Figure 8–8 shows the effect of surface roughness on the friction coefficient. We observe that the friction coefficient increases appreciably with the relative roughness, defined as ratio of the average asperity height ϵ to the diameter D. According to Eq. 8–14 one would expect that roughening the surface, which increases the friction coefficient, also increases the convective conductance. Experiments performed by Cope (8) are qualitatively in agreement with this prediction, but even a considerable increase in surface roughness improves the rate of heat transfer only very little.[4] Since an increase in the surface roughness causes a substantial increase in the frictional resistance, Cope found that, for the same pressure drop, the rate of heat transfer obtained from a smooth tube is larger than from a rough one.

The equations relating the Nusselt number to the flow conditions have been developed above for fluids having a Prandtl number of unity. The analogy between heat and momentum transfer has also been applied to fluids having Prandtl numbers other than unity (2,3,4,5,6,7). However, when the Prandtl number is not equal to unity, it is necessary to obtain a relationship between the velocity u and the coordinate y, as well as between the molecular diffusivities of heat and momentum, to integrate Eq. 8–6. Martinelli (5), in a refinement of the simple analogy, assumed that $\epsilon_M = \epsilon_H$ and used experimental data obtained by Nikuradse (9) to perform the integration. For the purpose of his analysis he divided the flow field into three separate regions:

1. A laminar sublayer adjacent to the surface where the heat-flow mechanism is conduction alone and $\epsilon_M = \epsilon_H = 0$.
2. A buffer layer in which heat is transferred by conduction as well as convection. In this buffer layer between the edge of the laminar

sublayer and the turbulent core, the eddies build up in intensity and the transition between laminar and turbulent flow takes place.

3. A turbulent core in the center of the duct.

Although, as Deissler (7) has pointed out, the subdivision of the flow field is somewhat artificial and ceases to be valid for large Prandtl numbers, it is helpful in visualizing the fluid flow and heat-flow mechanisms. Figure 8–4 shows the cross-sectional temperature distribution in dimensionless coordinates for flow through a tube at a Reynolds number of 10,000. We observed that, for a viscous oil (Pr = 100), about 95 per cent of the total temperature drop occurs in the laminar sublayer, whereas for a liquid metal (Pr = 0.01), it is less than 5 per cent. For air, the temperature and velocity fields are nearly identical, as would be expected from the Reynolds analogy. As mentioned earlier, the reason why the thermal resistance of the laminar sublayer is only a small fraction of the total resistance in the case of a liquid metal is that the molecular diffusivity term $k/\rho c_p$ in Eq. 8–6 is much larger than ϵ_H when the thermal conductivity of the liquid is large. Hence, the main contribution to the total heat transfer comes from the conduction mechanism when the Prandtl number is small, whereas for fluids having a large Prandtl number the conduction is negligible compared to mixing in the bulk of the fluid.

8–3. HEAT-TRANSFER COEFFICIENTS FOR TURBULENT FLOW

The final expressions obtained from more advanced analogies are very complicated and the evaluation of the Nusselt number under given flow and thermal-boundary conditions requires usually a numerical integration. For this reason it is more convenient for engineering purposes to use semi-empirical equations, or graphs based on the advanced analogies. In this section we shall present some of the engineering equations and graphs relating the Nusselt number to the Reynolds number, Prandtl number, the geometrical configuration of the system, the temperature gradient, and the thermal boundary condition.

For fluids having Prandtl numbers in the range from 0.5 to 100, Colburn (10) recommends, on the basis of experimental data, that the Stanton number in Eq. 8–16 be multiplied by $Pr^{\frac{2}{3}}$, or

$$\text{St}Pr^{\frac{2}{3}} = j = 0.023\,\text{Re}^{-0.2} = \frac{f}{2} \qquad (8\text{–}18)$$

The term $\text{St}Pr^{\frac{2}{3}}$ is usually called the Colburn j-factor in the heat-transfer literature.

To account for the variation in physical properties due to the temperature gradient, McAdams (11) recommends that all of the physical properties in Eq. 8–18 except c_p be evaluated at the average film temperature of the fluid T_f defined as

$$T_f = 0.5 \, (T_s + T_b) \tag{8–19}$$

where T_s is the temperature of the heat-transfer surface, or the wall temperature.

Denoting properties evaluated at T_f by the subscript f, Eq. 8–18 can be written as

$$\frac{\bar{h}_c}{c_p G} = 0.023 \left(\frac{\mu_f}{D_H G} \right)^{0.2} \mathrm{Pr}_f^{-\frac{2}{3}} \tag{8–20}$$

where $G = \rho V$, i.e., the mass velocity per square foot of cross section in $\mathrm{lb_m/hr}$ sq ft. Equation 8–20 has been found to correlate the results of numerous experimenters for moderate temperature differences, $T_s - T_b$, within 30 per cent. In many practical problems the wall temperature and the bulk temperature are unfortunately not directly available, and then a trial-and-error solution becomes necessary. For this type of problem the Stanton number can often be evaluated more conveniently by a method which was originally suggested by Sieder and Tate (12) and later improved by Kays and London (13). This method uses, for gases flowing in long ducts, an equation of the type

$$\mathrm{StPr}^{\frac{2}{3}} = C \, \mathrm{Re}^{-0.2} \left(\frac{T_b}{T_s} \right)^n \tag{8–21}$$

and, for liquids, an equation of the type

$$\mathrm{St} = \phi(\mathrm{Re})\psi(\mathrm{Pr}) \left(\frac{\mu_b}{\mu_s} \right)^n \tag{8–22}$$

In both of these equations all of the physical properties are evaluated at the *average fluid bulk temperature* T_b, and the variations in physical properties caused by the temperature gradient are accounted for either by the temperature or by the viscosity correction factor. The constant C in Eq. 8–21 which gives the best correlation with the available data for gases is

$C = 0.020$ for a constant duct-wall temperature

and

$C = 0.021$ for constant heat input per unit tube length or constant temperature difference in the flow direction

The exponent of the temperature-correction factor n in Eq. 8–21 is

$$\begin{aligned} n &= 0.575 \qquad \text{for gas heating} \\ n &= 0.15 \qquad \text{for gas cooling} \end{aligned}$$

For liquids having Prandtl numbers larger than 1.0 the exponent n of the viscosity ratio (μ_s/μ_b) in Eq. 8–22 is

$$n = 0.36 \qquad \text{for liquid heating}$$
$$n = 0.20 \qquad \text{for liquid cooling}$$

The variation of the Stanton number with the Prandtl number in Eq. 8–22 is shown graphically in Fig. 8–9 for various values of the bulk Reynolds number GD_H/μ. This graph is based on an analysis by Deissler (7) for long circular tubes which is in excellent agreement with available experimental results. Its use is recommended to evaluate the Nusselt number for heating and cooling of liquids when large wall-to-fluid temperature differences exist. For liquids having Prandtl numbers larger than unity, Eq. 8–22 applies to any type of wall-temperature variation, so that no distinction between uniform heat input and uniform wall temperature is necessary.

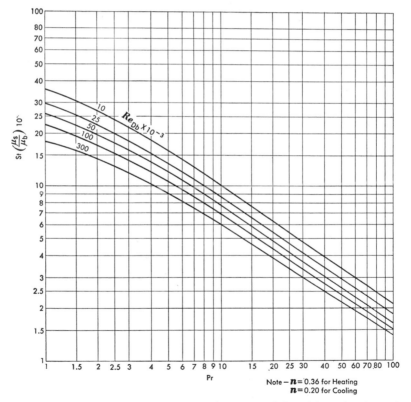

Fig. 8–9. Variation of the Stanton number with Prandtl number for various values of the bulk Reynolds number. (By permission from W. M. Kays and A. L. London, *Compact Heat Exchangers*, National Press, Palo Alto, 1955)

For gases and liquids flowing in *short* circular tubes ($2 < L/D < 60$) with abrupt contraction entrances, the entrance configuration of greatest interest in heat-exchanger design, the entrance effect for Reynolds numbers corresponding to turbulent flow (11) can be represented approximately by the equation

$$\frac{\bar{h}_{cL}}{\bar{h}_c} = 1 + (D/L)^{0.7} \qquad (8\text{--}23)$$

when L/D is less than 20 but larger than 2, and by the equation

$$\frac{\bar{h}_{cL}}{\bar{h}_c} = (1 + 6\,D/L) \qquad (8\text{--}23a)$$

when L/D is larger than 20. In both of the above equations, $\bar{h}_{cL}$ is the average unit conductance for the tube of finite length L and $\bar{h}_c$ is the conductance for an infinitely long tube evaluated either from Eq. 8–21 or Eq. 8–22.

An extensive theoretical analysis of the heat transfer and the friction drop in the entrance regions of smooth passages is given in Ref. 14, and a complete survey of experimental results for various types of inlet condition in Refs. 21 and 22.

In many applications the fluid temperature, and thus also the physical properties, vary considerably along the direction of flow. For practical purposes it has been found sufficiently accurate to evaluate the physical properties of the bulk of the fluid at a mean temperature with respect to the flow-tube length, i.e., halfway between the inlet and the outlet temperature. This mean temperature is then also used to correct for property variations at a flow section, as discussed previously.

Liquid metals. Liquid metals have in recent years been employed as heat-transfer media because they possess certain advantages over other common liquids used for heat-transfer purposes. Liquid metals, such as sodium, mercury, lead, and lead-bismuth alloys, have relatively low melting points and combine high densities with low vapor pressures at high temperatures as well as with large thermal conductivities, ranging from 5 to 50 Btu/hr ft F. These metals can be used over wide ranges of temperatures, they possess a large heat capacity per unit volume, and also have large unit thermal convective conductances. They are especially suitable for use in nuclear power plants where large amounts of heat are liberated and must be removed in a small volume. Liquid metals pose some difficulties in handling and pumping, but the development of electromagnetic pumps has eliminated most of these problems.

A comprehensive summary of the available information on liquid-metal heat transfer is contained in Refs. 15 and 20. The material presented here has been taken mainly from these references.

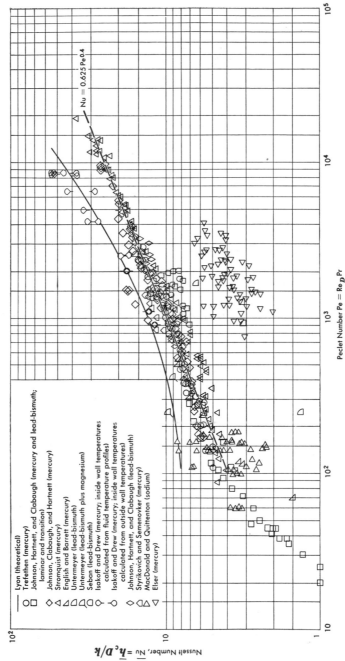

FIG. 8–10. Comparison of measured and predicted Nusselt number for liquid metals heated in long tubes with constant heat input. (Courtesy of National Advisory Committee for Aeronautics, *NACA TN* 3336)

In liquid metals the most important heat-transfer mechanism is conduction, and even in a highly turbulent stream the effect of eddying is of secondary importance.   As a result, the empirical equations for gases and liquids do not apply.   Several theoretical analyses for the evaluation of the Nusselt number are available, but there still exist some unexplained discrepancies between many of the experimental data and the analytic results.   This is illustrated in Fig. 8–10 where the experimentally measured Nusselt numbers for heating of mercury in long tubes by various observers are compared with the analysis of Martinelli (5).   The results of Martinelli's analysis were simplified by Lyon (15) who found that the equation

$$Nu = 7 + 0.25 \; (Re_D \; Pr)^{0.8} \tag{8–24}$$

approximates the more complex relation of Ref. 5 with satisfactory accuracy for a uniform heat input along the tube, whereas the equation

$$Nu = 5 + 0.25 \; (Re_D \; Pr)^{0.8} \tag{8–25}$$

applies when the tube-wall temperature is constant.   An inspection of the experimental data obtained by several independent investigations shows that they fall within 60 to 80 per cent of their predicted values.   Lubarsky and Kaufman (20) found that the empirical equation

$$Nu = 0.625 \; (Re_D \; Pr)^{0.4} \tag{8–26}$$

represents most of the fully developed turbulent heat-transfer data.   Those points that fall very far below the average are believed to have been obtained in systems where the liquid metal did not wet the surface.   However, no final conclusions regarding the effect of wetting have been reached to date.   No reliable data showing the effect of the cross-sectional variation of the properties of liquid metals during heating or cooling are available to date, and the use of a mean film temperature is recommended.

The entrance corrections obtained from Eqs. 8–23 and 8–23a do not apply to liquid metals.   The conditions in the entrance regions for fluids with small Prandtl numbers have been investigated analytically by Deissler (14) and experimental data supporting the analysis are summarized in Ref. 21.

Calculation of the heat-transfer coefficient.   The application of the formulas for convective heat transfer requires a knowledge of the physical properties of the medium.   As every practicing engineer knows from experience, the physical properties of fluids have only been measured accurately for some of the more common fluids.   In many instances it is necessary to estimate the value of properties, especially at elevated temperatures.   Since physical properties have been published by investigators of many countries, it is always important to note carefully the units used.   The use of dimensionless numbers in the presentation of experimental data has eliminated many of the difficulties involved in the practical application. However, it cannot be overemphasized that a careful checking of the units of the quantities used in building the dimensionless numbers is a prerequisite to obtaining correct results. It is also suggested that a common-sense order-of-magnitude check be applied to the final result. The order of magnitudes for heat-transfer coefficients under typical conditions in Table 1–2, will aid in this task.

The use of the equations for evaluating the heat-transfer coefficient in turbulent forced convection is illustrated in the following examples. It is suggested that the reader work each of these examples independently in order to gain facility in the application of the various equations presented in this section.

Example 8–1. An aniline-alcohol solution is flowing at a velocity of 10 fps through a long 1-in.-ID thin-wall tube. On the outer surface of the tube, steam is condensing at atmospheric pressure, and the tube-wall temperature is 212 F. The tube is clean, and there is no thermal resistance due to a scale deposit on the inner surface. Using the physical properties tabulated below, estimate the unit-surface conductance between the fluid and the pipe by means of Eq. 8–20, as well as Eq. 8–22 and Fig. 8–9, and compare the results. Assume that the bulk temperature of the aniline solution is 68 F and neglect entrance effects.

Physical properties of the aniline solution:

Temp (F)	Viscosity (centipoises)	Thermal Conductivity (Btu/hr ft F)	Specific Gravity	Specific Heat (Btu/lb F)
68	5.1	0.100	1.03	0.50
140	1.4	0.098	0.98	0.53
212	0.6	0.095	. . . .	0.56

Solution: First we determine the Reynolds number to determine whether the flow is laminar or turbulent. Evaluating the viscosity at the bulk temperature we get

$$\mathrm{Re}_{Db} = \frac{VD\rho}{\mu} = \frac{(10 \text{ ft/sec})(1/12 \text{ ft})(1.03)(62.4 \text{ lb}_m/\text{ft}^3)}{(5.1 \text{ centipoises})(0.000672 \text{ lb}_m/\text{sec ft/centipoise})} = 15{,}600$$

and thus establish that the flow is turbulent. The average film temperature according to Eq. 8–19 is

$$T_f = 0.5 \ (T_s + T_b = 0.5 \ (68 + 212) = 140 \text{ F}$$

and the Reynolds number Re_{Df} is 56,800 when the viscosity is taken at T_f. The Prandtl number, based on the property values at the bulk temperature, is

$$\mathrm{Pr} = \frac{c\mu}{k} = \frac{(0.5 \text{ Btu/lb}_m \text{ F})(5.1)(0.000672 \text{ lb}_m/\text{sec ft})(3600 \text{ sec/hr})}{0.100 \text{ Btu/hr ft F}} = 61.5$$

[The conversion factor (0.000672 lb$_m$/sec ft/centipoise) is taken from Appendix II.] When the properties are taken at T_f, the Prandtl number is 18.4. Using Eq. 8–20 to evaluate the unit-convective conductance we have, after some rearrangement,

$$\bar{h}_c = 0.023 \frac{k_f}{D} \ \mathrm{Re}_{Df}{}^{0.8}\mathrm{Pr}_f{}^{0.33} = 0.023\left(\frac{0.098}{1/12}\right)(10{,}100)(2.58) = 710 \text{ Btu/hr sq ft F}$$

From Fig. 8–9 at $Pr = 61.5$ and $Re_D = 15,600$ we find

$$St \left(\frac{\mu_s}{\mu_f}\right)^n = 2.7 \times 10^{-4}$$

For heating liquids $n = 0.36$ and the viscosity correction factor is

$$\left(\frac{\mu_b}{\mu_s}\right)^n = \left(\frac{5.1}{0.6}\right)^{0.36} = 2.16$$

Using Eq. 8–22 to evaluate $\bar{h}_c$ we get

$$\bar{h}_c = \frac{0.100 \text{ Btu/hr sq ft } (F/ft)}{1/12 \text{ ft}} \, (15,600)(61.5)(2.16)(2.7 \times 10^{-4})$$

$$= 670 \text{ Btu/hr sq ft F} \qquad\qquad Ans.$$

We note that, for the example which represents unusually large viscosity variations ($\mu_b/\mu_s = 8.5$), Deissler's analysis predicts a value of $\bar{h}_c$ which is 6 per cent smaller than the value predicted by McAdams' empirical equation. This sort of discrepancy between different methods is not unusual in convective heat transfer.

Example 8–2. Determine the unit thermal convective conductance for water flowing at a velocity of 10 fps in an annulus formed between a 1-in.-OD tube and a $1\frac{1}{2}$-in.-ID tube. The water is at 180 F and is being cooled. The temperature of the inner wall is 100 F, and the outer wall of the annulus is insulated. Neglect entrance effects and compare the results of Eqs. 8–20 and 8–22. The properties of water are given in the accompanying tabulation.

T (F)	μ (lb$_m$/hr ft)	k (Btu/hr ft F)	ρ (lb$_m$/cu ft)	c (Btu/lb$_m$ F)
100	1.67	0.36	62.0	1.0
140	1.14	0.38	61.3	1.0
180	0.75	0.39	60.8	1.0

Solution: The hydraulic diameter D_H for this geometry is 0.5 in. The Reynolds number based on the hydraulic diameter and the bulk temperature properties is

$$Re_{Db} = \frac{VD_H\rho}{\mu} = \frac{(10 \text{ ft/sec})(0.5/12 \text{ ft})(62 \text{ lb}_m/\text{cu ft})(3600 \text{ sec/ hr})}{0.75 \text{ lb}_m/\text{hr ft}}$$

$$= 125,000$$

Based on the mean film temperature T_f, the Reynolds number is $Re_{Df} = 82,000$. The Prandtl number at the bulk temperature is

$$Pr_b = \frac{c\mu}{k} = \frac{(1.0 \text{ Btu/lb}_m \text{ F})(0.75 \text{ lb}_m/\text{hr ft})}{0.39 \text{ Btu/hr ft F}} = 1.92$$

and at T_f, we find that $Pr_f = 3.0$. According to Eq. 8–20 we have

$$St = \frac{\bar{h}_c}{c\rho V} = 0.023 \, Re_{Df}^{-0.2} \, Pr_f^{-\frac{2}{3}}$$

$$= 0.023/(9.6 \times 2.08) = 0.00115$$

so that $\bar{h}_c$ = (1 Btu/lb$_m$ F) (62 lb$_m$/cu ft) (10 ft/sec) (3600 sec/hr) (0.00115)

$\qquad$ = 2570 Btu/hr sq ft F

Using Fig. 8–9, we get

$$\text{St}\ (\mu_s/\mu_b)^n = 16 \times 10^{-4}$$

with $n = 0.20$ for cooling. Therefore, the unit-convective conductance is

$$\bar{h}_c = (16 \times 10^{-4})\ \frac{k_b}{D_H}\ \text{Re}_{Db}\ \text{Pr}_b\ (\mu_b/\mu_s)^{0.2}$$

$$= (16 \times 10^{-4}) \left(\frac{0.39}{0.5/12}\right) (125{,}000)(1.92)(0.85)$$

$$= 3060\ \text{Btu/hr sq ft F} \qquad\qquad Ans.$$

We see that the results obtained by two different methods of calculating $\bar{h}_c$ for turbulent flow in ducts agree within 16 per cent.

8–4. FORCED CONVECTION IN LAMINAR FLOW

Although heat-transfer coefficients for laminar flow are considerably smaller than for turbulent flow, in the design of heat-exchange equipment for very viscous liquids, it is sometimes economically necessary to accept a lower unit-surface conductance in order to reduce the pumping-power requirements. In recent years, laminar gas flow has also been considered for high-temperature, compact heat exchangers, where tube diameters are very small and gas densities very low. Another potential application of laminar-flow forced convection lies in the atomic-power field, where liquid metals are used as heat-transfer mediums. Since most liquid metals have a high thermal conductivity, their heat-transfer coefficients are relatively large even in laminar flow.

The heat-flow mechanism in purely laminar flow is conduction. The rate of heat flow between the walls of a conduit and the fluid flowing in it can be obtained analytically by solving the equations of motion and of conduction heat flow simultaneously. To obtain a solution it is necessary to know or assume the velocity distribution in the duct. In fully developed laminar flow without heat transfer, the velocity distribution at any cross section has the shape of a parabola. For high-Prandtl-number fluids, such as oils, the velocity profile becomes fully established much more rapidly than the temperature profile, usually within 20 to 80 diameters from the entrance.[5] Heat-transfer equations based on the assumption of a parabolic velocity distribution will therefore not introduce serious errors for oils and other viscous fluids flowing in long ducts, if they are modified to account for effects caused by the variation of the viscosity due to the temperature gradient. For liquid metals, on the other hand, the temperature profile

[5] According to Langhaar (*Jour. Appl. Mech.*, Vol. 64, 1942, p. A–55) the length required to establish a parabolic velocity distribution in isothermal flow is 0.05 D Re$_D$.

is established much more rapidly than the velocity profile as a result of the metals' high thermal conductivity, and the assumption of a uniform velocity profile may not involve large errors for many applications.   For gases, the .temperature and velocity profiles develop nearly at equal rates along the tube, and the actual behavior of both must be considered in a heat-transfer analysis.

Effect of free convection.   An additional complication in the determination of a heat-transfer coefficient in laminar flow arises when the buoyancy forces are of the same order of magnitude as the external forces due to the forced circulation.   Such a condition may arise in oil coolers when low flow velocities are employed.   Also, in the cooling of rotating parts, such as rotor blades of gas turbines and ramjets attached to the propellers of helicopters, the free-convection forces may be so large that their effect on the velocity pattern cannot be neglected even in high-velocity flow.   When the buoyancy forces are in the same direction as the external forces, e.g., the gravitational forces superimposed on upward flow, they increase the rate of heat transfer.   When the external and buoyancy forces act in

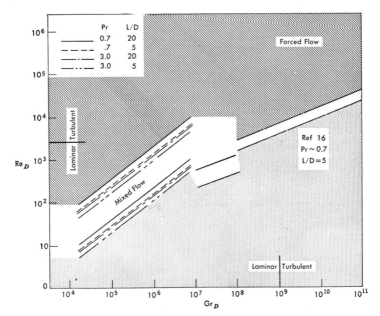

Fig. 8–11.   Forced-convection, free-convection, and mixed-flow regimes for flow in tubes at Prandtl numbers 0.7 and 3.0.   (Extracted from "Convective Heat Transfer for Mixed Free and Forced Flow Through Tubes," by R. G. Eckert and A. J. Diaguila, published in *Trans. ASME*, Vol. 76, 1954, with permission of the publishers, The American Society of Mechanical Engineers)

opposite direction, the heat transfer is reduced. Eckert (16) studied heat transfer in mixed flow in a vertical pipe, and his results are shown qualitatively in Fig. 8–11. In the darkly shaded area, the contribution of free convection to the total heat transfer is less than 10 per cent, whereas in the lightly shaded area, forced-convection effects are less than 10 per cent and free convection predominates. In the unshaded area, both free and forced convection are of the same order of magnitude. These results are only qualitative; they are presented primarily to call attention to the existence of phenomena of mixed flow. In cases where it is doubtful whether forced- or free-convection flow applies, the heat-transfer coefficient is generally calculated by using forced- and free-convection relations separately, and the larger one is used (11). The accuracy of this rule of thumb is estimated to be about 25 per cent.

Correlations and empirical equations. The details of the mathematical solutions for purely laminar flow are beyond the scope of this text. References listed at the end of this chapter, especially Refs. 17 and 18, contain the mathematical background for the engineering equations and graphs which are presented and discussed in this section.

For engineering applications it is most convenient to present the results of analytical and experimental investigations in terms of a Nusselt number defined in the conventional manner as

$$\overline{\mathrm{Nu}_D} = \frac{\bar{h}_c D}{k}$$

It was pointed out in Sec. 8–1 that the unit-convective conductance $\bar{h}_c$ varies along the tube. For practical applications the average value of the conductance is most important, and for the equations and charts presented in this section we shall use a mean Nusselt number $\overline{\mathrm{Nu}} = \bar{h}_c D/k$, averaged with respect to the length of the duct L, or

$$\overline{\mathrm{Nu}_D} = \frac{1}{L} \int_0^L \mathrm{Nu}_x dx$$

where the subscript x refers to local conditions at x. This mean Nusselt number is often termed the log-mean Nusselt number because it can be used directly in the log-mean-rate equations for heat exchangers presented in Chapter 11.

The mean Nusselt numbers for laminar flow in tubes at a uniform wall temperature have been calculated analytically by various investigators. Their results are shown in Fig. 8–12 for several velocity distributions. All of these solutions are based on the idealizations of a constant tube-wall temperature and a uniform temperature distribution at the tube inlet and apply strictly only when the physical properties are independent of temperature. The abscissa is the dimensionless quantity $\mathrm{Re}_D \mathrm{Pr} D/L$, the

reciprocal of the Graetz number Gz.   To determine the mean value of the
Nusselt number for a given tube of length L and diameter D, one evaluates
the Reynolds number Re_D, the Prandtl number Pr, forms the dimensionless
parameter $\mathrm{Re}_D\,\mathrm{Pr}D/L$, and enters the curve of Fig. 8–12.   The selection
of the curve representing the conditions which most nearly correspond to
the physical conditions depends on the nature of the fluid and the geometry
of the system.   For high-Prandtl-number fluids, such as oils, the velocity
profile is established much more rapidly than the temperature profile.

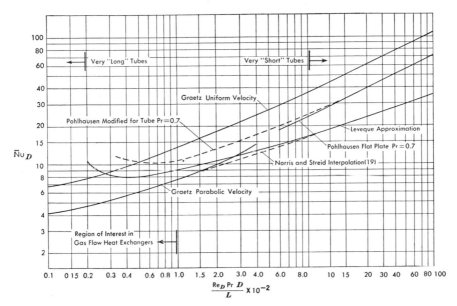

FIG. 8–12.   Curves illustrating solutions for laminar-flow heat transfer at
constant wall temperature.   (Extracted from "Numerical Solutions for Laminar Flow Heat Transfer in Circular Tubes," by W. M. Kays, published in
Trans. ASME, Vol. **77**, 1955, with permission of the publishers, The American
Society of Mechanical Engineers)

Consequently the application of the curve labeled "parabolic velocity" does
not lead to a serious error in long tubes when $\mathrm{Re}_D\mathrm{Pr}D/L$ is less than 100.
For very long tubes the Nusselt number approaches a limiting minimum
value of 3.66 when the tube temperature is uniform.   When the heat rate
instead of the tube temperature is uniform, the limiting value of $\overline{\mathrm{Nu}_D}$ is 4.36.
     For very low-Prandtl-number fluids, such as liquid metals, the tempera-
ture profile is established much more rapidly than the velocity profile.
For typical applications the assumption of a uniform velocity profile may
give satisfactory results, although experimental evidence is insufficient for
a quantitative evaluation of the possible deviation from the analytical

solution for slug flow. For very short tubes or rectangular ducts with initially uniform velocity and temperature distribution, the flow conditions along the wall approximate those along a flat plate, and the Pohlhausen analysis presented in Sec. 6–7 is expected to yield satisfactory results for liquids having Prandtl numbers between 1.0 and 15.0. The Pohlhausen solution applies (18,19) when L/D is less than 0.0048 Re_D for tubes and when L/D is less than 0.0021 Re_{D_H} for flat ducts of a rectangular cross section. For these conditions the Pohlhausen equation for flow over a flat plate can be converted to the coordinates of Fig. 8–12, or

$$\overline{\mathrm{Nu}}_D = \frac{\mathrm{Re}_D \mathrm{Pr} D}{4L} \ln\left[\frac{1}{1 - \dfrac{2.654}{\mathrm{Pr}^{0.167}\left(\mathrm{Re}_D \mathrm{Pr} D/L\right)^{0.5}}}\right] \tag{8–27}$$

An extension of Pohlhausen's analysis to longer tubes is presented in Ref. 18, and the results are shown in Fig. 8–12 for Pr = 0.73 in the range of $\mathrm{Re}_D \mathrm{Pr} D/L$ between 100 and 1500, where this approximation is most likely to be applicable.

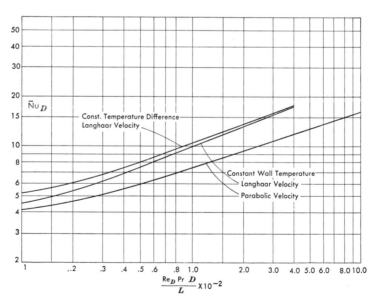

Fig. 8–13. Mean Nusselt number with respect to tube length for gases in laminar flow. (Extracted from "Numerical Solutions for Laminar Flow Heat Transfer in Circular Tubes," by W. M. Kays, published in *Trans. ASME*, Vol. **77**, 1955, with permission of the publishers, The American Society of Mechanical Engineers)

For laminar flow of gases in the range of $\mathrm{Re}\mathrm{Pr}D/L$ from 0 to 300 an extensive numerical analysis has been made by W. M. Kays (18). For laminar flow of gases whose Prandtl is approximately unity, both temperature and velocity profiles develop at an equal rate. Hence, neither the assumption of a parabolic velocity profile nor that of a uniform profile is satisfactory. Kays therefore used the actual velocity profiles, calculated earlier by Langhaar, for the analysis, whose results are shown in Fig. 8–13 for a constant wall temperature as well as for a constant temperature difference between the fluid bulk and the wall. The solution for a constant wall temperature applies to evaporators, condensers, and most parallel-flow gas-to-gas heat exchangers (see Chapter 11). The second boundary condition is approximated in gas-to-gas counterflow exchangers where both fluids have similar capacity rates and conductances. The results of Kays' analysis are in good agreement with available experimental data.

An empirical equation suggested by Sieder and Tate (12) has also been widely used to correlate experimental results for liquids. This equation can be written in the form

$$\overline{\mathrm{Nu}} = 1.86(\mathrm{Re}_D\mathrm{Pr}D/L)^{0.33}\left(\frac{\mu_b}{\mu_s}\right)^{0.14} \tag{8–28}$$

where the empirical correction factor $(\mu_b/\mu_s)^{0.14}$ is introduced to account for the effect of the temperature variation on the physical properties.

In liquids the viscosity decreases with increasing temperature, while in gases the reverse trend is observed. When a liquid is heated, the fluid near the wall is less viscous than the fluid in the center. Consequently, the velocity of the heated fluid near the wall is larger than for an unheated fluid, but less in the center. The distortion of the parabolic velocity profile for liquids when heating or cooling is shown in Fig. 8–14. For gases the conditions are reversed, but the variation of density with temperature introduces additional complications.

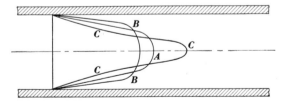

Fig. 8–14. Effect of heat transfer on velocity profiles in fully developed laminar flow. (Curve A, isothermal flow; curve B, heating of liquid or cooling of gas; curve C, cooling of liquid or heating of gas.)

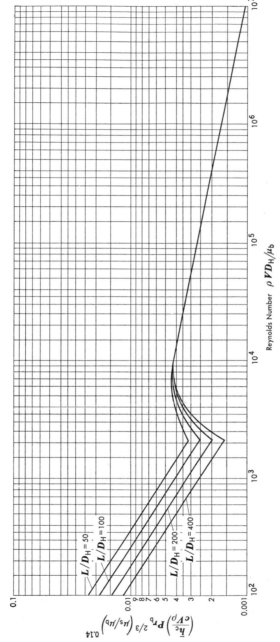

FIG. 8-15. Recommended curves for determining heat-transfer coefficient in the transition regime. (Reprinted from *Industrial and Engineering Chemistry*, Vol. 28, p. 1429, December 1936, with permission of the copyright owner, The American Chemical Society)

The empirical viscosity correction factor is merely an approximate rule of thumb, and recent data indicate that it may not be satisfactory when large temperature gradients exist. As an approximation in the absence of a more satisfactory method, it is suggested that, for liquids, the Nusselt number obtained from analytic solutions presented in Figs. 8–12 and 8–13 also be multiplied by $(\mu_s/\mu_b)^{0.14}$ to correct for the variation of properties due to the temperature gradient. For gases Kays and London (13) suggest that the Nusselt number from Fig. 8–13 be multiplied by a temperature-correction factor. If all fluid properties are evaluated at the average bulk temperature, the corrected Nusselt number is

$$\overline{\mathrm{Nu}_D} = \overline{\mathrm{Nu}_D}_{\text{Fig. 8-13}} \left(\frac{T_b}{T_s}\right)^n \tag{8-29}$$

where $n = 0.25$ for a gas heating in a tube, and 0.08 for a gas cooling in a tube.

Effect of heat transfer on the friction coefficient. The variation in physical properties also affects the friction coefficient. To evaluate the friction coefficient of fluids being heated or cooled it is suggested that, for liquids, one modifies the isothermal friction coefficient by

$$f_{\text{heat transfer}} = f_{\text{isothermal}} \left(\frac{\mu_s}{\mu_b}\right)^{0.14} \tag{8-30}$$

and for gases by

$$f_{\text{heat transfer}} = f_{\text{isothermal}} \left(\frac{T_s}{T_b}\right)^{0.14} \tag{8-31}$$

8–5. FORCED CONVECTION IN TRANSITION FLOW

The mechanisms of heat transfer and fluid flow in the transition region (Re_D between 2100 and 10,000) vary considerably from system to system. In this region the flow may be unstable, and fluctuations in pressure drop and heat transfer have been observed. There exists a large uncertainty in the basic heat-transfer and flow-friction performance, and consequently the designer is advised to design equipment, if possible, to operate outside this region. For the purpose of estimating the Nusselt number in the transition region, the curves of Fig. 8–15 may be used, but the actual performance may deviate considerably from that predicted on the basis of these curves.

REFERENCES

1. O. Reynolds, "On the Extent and Action of the Heating Surface for Steam Boilers," *Proc. Manchester Lit. Phil. Soc.*, Vol. 8 (1874).

2. L. Prandtl, "Eine Beziehung zwischen Wärmeaustausch und Strömungswiderstand der Flüssigkeiten," *Phys. Zeit.*, Vol. 11 (1910), p. 1072.

3. T. von Karman, "The Analogy between Fluid Friction and Heat Transfer," *Trans. ASME*, Vol. 61 (1939), p. 705.

4. L. M. K. Boelter, R. C. Martinelli, and F. Jonassen, "Remarks on the Analogy Between Heat and Momentum Transfer," *Trans. ASME*, Vol. 63 (1941), pp. 447–455.

5. R. C. Martinelli, "Heat Transfer to Molten Metals," *Trans. ASME*, Vol. 69 (1947), p. 947.

6. R. G. Deissler, "Investigation of Turbulent Flow and Heat Transfer in Smooth Tubes Including the Effect of Variable Properties," *Trans. ASME*, Vol. 73 (1951), p. 101.

7. R. G. Deissler, "Analysis of Turbulent Heat Transfer, Mass Transfer and Friction in Smooth Tubes at High Prandtl and Schmidt Numbers," *NACA TN* 3145, May, 1954.

8. W. F. Cope, "The Friction and Heat Transmission Coefficients of Rough Pipes," *Proc. Inst. Mech. Engrs.*, Vol. 145 (1941), p. 99.

9. J. Nikuradse, "Wiederstandsgesetz und Geschwindigkeit von turbulenten Wasserströhmungen in glatten und rauhen Rohren," *Proc. 3rd Int. Cong. Appl. Mech.*, Vol. 1 (1930), p. 239.

10. A. P. Colburn, "A Method of Correlating Forced Convection Heat Transfer Data and a Comparison with Fluid Friction," *Trans. AIChE*, Vol. 29 (1933), p. 174.

11. W. M. McAdams, *Heat Transmission*, 3d ed. (New York: McGraw-Hill Book Company, Inc., 1954.)

12. E. N. Sieder and C. E. Tate, "Heat Transfer and Pressure Drop of Liquids in Tubes," *Ind. Eng. Chem.*, Vol. 28 (1936), p. 1429.

13. W. M. Kays and A. L. London, "Compact Heat Exchangers—A Summary of Basic Heat Transfer and Flow Friction Design Data," *Tech. Rep.* 23, Stanford University, 1954.

14. R. G. Deissler, "Turbulent Heat Transfer and Friction in the Entrance Regions of Smooth Passages," *Trans. ASME*, Vol. 77 (1955), pp. 1221–1234.

15. R. N. Lyon, Ed., *Liquid Metals Handbook*, 3d ed. (Washington, D. C.: Atomic Energy Commission and Department of the Navy, 1952.)

16. R. G. Eckert and A. J. Diaguila, "Convective Heat Transfer for Mixed Free and Forced Flow Through Tubes," *Trans. ASME*, Vol. 76 (1954), pp. 497–504.

17. T. B. Drew, "Mathematical Attacks on Forced Convection Problems: A Review," *Trans. AIChE*, Vol. 26 (1931), p. 26.

18. W. M. Kays, "Numerical Solution for Laminar Flow Heat Transfer in Circular Tubes," *Trans. ASME*, Vol. 77 (1955), pp. 1265–1274.

19. R. H. Norris and D. D. Streid, "Laminar-Flow Heat-Transfer Coefficients for Ducts," *Trans. ASME*, Vol. 62 (1940), p. 525.

20. B. Lubarsky and S. J. Kaufman, "Review of Experimental Investigations of Liquid-Metal Heat Transfer," *NACA TN* 3336, 1955.

21. J. P. Hartnett, "Experimental Determination of the Thermal Entrance Length for the Flow of Water and of Oil in Circular Pipes," *Trans. ASME*, Vol. 77 (1955), pp. 1211–1234.

22. L. M. K. Boelter, D. Young, and H. W. Iverson, "An Investigation of Aircraft Heaters—XXVII Distribution of Heat Transfer Rate in the Entrance Section of a Circular Tube," *NACA TN* 1451, 1948.

23. W. Nunner, "Wärmeübergang and Druckabfall in Rauhen Rohren," *VDI Forschungsheft* No. 455, *VDI Verlag GMBM*, Duesseldorf, 1956.

PROBLEMS

8–1. Water at an average temperature of 80 F is flowing through a smooth 2-in.-ID pipe at a velocity of 3 fps. If the temperature at the inner surface of the pipe is 120 F, determine (a) the unit-surface conductance, (b) the rate of heat flow per foot of pipe, (c) the bulk-temperature rise per foot, and (d) the pressure drop per foot in psi.

Ans. (a) $\bar{h}$ = 620 Btu/hr sq ft F ($\pm 10\%$); (b) q/ft = 13,000 Btu/hr; (c) ΔT/ft = 0.89 F; (d) Δp/ft $\simeq$ 1 psi (depending on roughness)

8-2. A double-pipe heat exchanger is used to condense steam at 1 psia. Water at an average bulk temperature of 50 F flows at 10 fps through the inner pipe (copper, 1 in. ID, 1.2 in. OD). Steam at its saturation temperature flows in the annulus formed between the outer surface of the inner pipe and an outer pipe of 2 in. ID. The average unit-surface conductance of the condensing steam is 1000 Btu/hr sq ft F, and the thermal resistance of a surface scale on the outer surface of the copper pipe is 0.001 hr sq ft F/Btu. Determine (a) the over-all heat-transfer coefficient between the steam and the water based on the outer area of the copper pipe. Also sketch the thermal circuit and (b) evaluate the temperature at the inner surface of the pipe. (c) Estimate the length required to condense 1 lb of steam. *Ans.* U = 350 Btu/hr sq ft F; T_{si} = 65 F

8-3. Determine the rate of heat transfer per foot length to a light oil flowing through a 1-in.-ID, 2-ft-long copper tube at a velocity of 6 fpm. The oil enters the tube at 60 F and the tube is heated by steam condensing on its outer surface at atmospheric pressure with a unit-surface conductance of 2000 Btu/hr sq ft F. The properties of the oil at various temperatures are listed in the accompanying tabulation:

T (F)	60	80	100	150	212
ρ (lb/cu ft)	57	57	56	55	54
c (Btu/lb F)	0.43	0.44	0.46	0.48	0.51
k (Btu/hr ft F)	0.077	0.077	0.076	0.075	0.074
μ (lb/hr ft)	215	100	55	19	8
Pr	1210	577	330	116	55

Ans. $q \simeq$ 1380 Btu/hr

8-4. Atmospheric air at a velocity of 200 fps and a temperature of 60 F enters a 2-ft-long square metal duct of 8- by 8-in. cross section. If the duct wall is at 300 F, determine the *average* unit-surface conductance. Comment briefly on the L/D_H effect.

Ans. $\bar{h} \simeq$ 14 Btu/hr sq ft F ($\pm 15\%$)

8-5. Air at 60 F and atmospheric pressure enters a $\frac{1}{2}$-in.-ID tube at 100 fps. For an average wall temperature of 212 F, determine the discharge temperature of the air and the pressure drop in inches of water if the pipe is (a) 4 in. long, (b) 40 in. long. Use the average bulk temperature of the air between the inlet and the outlet to evaluate the rate of heat transfer between the wall and the air.

Ans. (a) T_{out} = 82 F, Δp = 3.8 in. H$_2$O; (b) T_{out} = 175 F, Δp = 9.1 in. H$_2$O

8-6. Evaluate the rate of heat loss per foot from superheated steam flowing at 600 F and 250-psi pressure through schedule 80 4-in. pipe at a velocity of 100 fps. The pipe is lagged with a 2-in.-thick layer of asbestos. Heat is transferred to the surroundings by free convection and radiation.

8-7. Determine the heat-transfer coefficient for liquid bismuth flowing through an annulus (2 in. ID, 2.5 in. OD) at a velocity of 15 fps. The wall temperature of the inner surface is 800 F and the bismuth is at 600 F. It may be assumed that heat losses from the outer surface are negligible.

8-8. Assume that the heat source in Prob. 8-7 is an aluminum-clad rod of uranium, 2 in. OD and 6 ft long. *Estimate* the heat flux that will raise the temperature of the bismuth 100 F and the maximum center and surface temperatures necessary to transfer heat at this rate.

8–9. Air at an average temperature of 300 F flows through a short square duct (4 by 4 by 1 in.) at a rate of 116 lb/hr. The duct-wall temperature is 800 F. Determine the average heat-transfer coefficient using duct equation with appropriate L/D correction. Compare your results with flow-over-flat-plate relations.

8–10. In a long annulus (1.0 in. ID, 1.5 in. OD), atmospheric air is heated by steam condensing at 300 F on the inner surface. If the velocity of the air is 20 fps and its bulk temperature 100 F, calculate the heat-transfer coefficient.

8–11. If the total resistance between the steam and the air (including the pipe wall and scale on the steam side) in Prob. 8–10 is 0.20 hr sq ft F/Btu, calculate the temperature difference between the outer surface of the inner pipe and the air. Show the thermal circuit.

8–12. Compute the average unit-surface conductance, $\bar{h}_c$, for 50 F water flowing at 10 fps in a long 1-in.-ID pipe (surface temperature of 102 F) by three different equations and compare your results. Also determine the pressure drop per foot length of pipe.

8–13. In a pipe within a pipe heat exchanger, water is flowing in the annulus and oil having the properties listed in Prob. 8–3 is flowing in the central pipe. The inner pipe is 0.527 in. ID, 0.625 in. OD, and the ID of the outer pipe is 0.750 in. For a water bulk temperature of 80 F and an oil bulk temperature of 175 F, determine the over-all heat-transfer coefficient based on the outer diameter of the central pipe and the frictional pressure drop per unit length of the water and the oil for the following velocities: (a) water rate 1 gpm, oil rate 1 gpm; (b) water rate 10 gpm, oil rate 1 gpm; (c) water rate 1 gpm, oil rate 10 gpm; and (d) water rate 10 gpm, oil rate 10 gpm.

8–14. Water in *turbulent* flow is to be heated in a single-pass tubular heat exchanger by steam condensing on the outside of the tubes. The flow rate of the water, its pressure drop, its inlet and outlet temperatures, and the steam pressure are fixed. Assuming that the tube-wall temperature remains constant, determine the dependence of the total required heat-exchanger area on the inside diameter of the tubes.

Ans. $A_{\text{total}} \sim (1/\text{ID})^{\frac{1}{4}}$

8–15. The following thermal-resistance data were obtained on a 50,000 sq ft condenser constructed with 1-in.-OD brass tubes, $23\frac{3}{4}$ ft long, 0.049 in. wall thickness, at various water velocities inside the tubes [*Trans. ASME*, Vol. 58 (1936), p. 672].

$\frac{1}{U_o} \times 10^{-3}$ (hr sq ft F/Btu)	Water Velocity (fps)	$\frac{1}{U_o} \times 10^{-3}$ (hr sq ft F/Btu)	Water Velocity (fps)
2.060	6.91	3.076	2.95
2.113	6.35	2.743	4.12
2.212	5.68	2.498	6.76
2.374	4.90	3.356	2.86
3.001	2.93	2.209	6.27
2.081	7.01		

Assuming that the unit-surface conductance on the steam side is 2000 Btu/hr sq ft F, determine the scale resistance. HINT: Plot U vs. $1/V^{0.8}$. (This method is called the *Wilson plot*.)

8–16. Water at 180 F is flowing through a thin copper tube (6 in. ID) at a velocity of 25 fps. The duct is located in a room at 60 F and the unit-surface conductance at the outer surface of the duct is 2.5 Btu/hr sq ft F. (a) Determine the heat-transfer coefficient at the inner surface. (b) Estimate the length of duct in which the water temperature drops 1 F.   *Ans.* (a) $\bar{h}_c \simeq 3800$ Btu/hr sq ft F; (b) $L \simeq 1500$ ft

8-17. The equation

$$\overline{\text{Nu}} = \frac{\bar{h}_c D}{k} = \left\{ 3.65 + \frac{0.0668(D/L)\ \text{Re Pr}}{1 + 0.04[(D/L)\ \text{Re Pr}]^{\frac{2}{3}}} \right\} \left(\frac{\mu_b}{\mu_s} \right)^{0.14}$$

was recommended by H. Hausen (*Zeitschr. Ver. Deut. Ing., Beiheft No.* 4, 1943) for forced convection heat transfer in fully developed laminar flow through tubes. Compare the values of the Nusselt number predicted by Hausen's equation for Re = 1000, Pr = 1, and D/L = 2, 10, and 100 respectively with those obtained from appropriate equations or graphs in the text.

8-18. The equation

$$\overline{\text{Nu}} = 0.116\ (\text{Re}^{\frac{2}{3}} - 125)\text{Pr}^{\frac{1}{3}}\ [1 + (D/L)^{\frac{2}{3}}]\ (\mu_b/\mu_s)^{0.14}$$

has been proposed by Hausen (op. cit.) for the transition range (2300 < Re < 8000) as well as for higher Reynolds numbers. Compare the values of $\overline{\text{Nu}}$ predicted by Hausen's equation for Re = 3000 and Re = 20,000 at D/L of 0.1 and 0.01 with those obtained from appropriate equation or charts in the text. Assume the fluid is water at 60 F flowing through a pipe at 200 F.

9 Forced Convection Over
Exterior Surfaces

9–1. FLOW OVER BLUFF BODIES

In this chapter we shall consider heat transfer by forced convection between the exterior surface of bluff bodies, such as spheres, wires, tubes, and tube bundles, and fluids flowing perpendicularly to the axes of these bodies. The heat-transfer phenomena for these systems, as for those in which a fluid flows inside a duct or along a flat plate, are closely related to the nature of the flow. The most important difference between the flow over a bluff body and the flow over a flat plate or a streamlined body lies in the behavior of the boundary layer. We recall that the boundary layer of a fluid flowing over the surface of a streamlined body will separate when the pressure rise along the surface becomes too large. On a streamlined body the separation, if it takes place at all, occurs near the rear. On a bluff body, on the other hand, the point of separation often lies not far from the leading edge. Beyond the point of separation of the boundary layer, the fluid in a region near the surface flows in a direction opposite to the main stream, as shown in Fig. 9–1. The local reversal in the flow

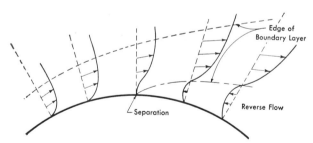

Fig. 9–1. Schematic sketch of boundary layer on a circular cylinder near separation point.

results in disturbances which produce turbulent eddies. This is illustrated in Fig. 9–2, which is a photograph of the flow pattern of a stream flowing at right angle to a cylinder. We can see that eddies from both sides of the cylinder extend downstream, so that a turbulent wake is formed in the rear of the cylinder.

Associated with the separation of the flow are large pressure losses, since the kinetic energy of the eddies which pass off into the wake can not be regained.   In flow over a streamlined body, the pressure drop is caused mainly by the skin-friction drag.   For a bluff body, on the other hand, the skin-friction drag is small compared to the form drag in the Reynolds-number range of commercial interest.   The form or pressure drag arises from the separation of the flow which prevents the closing of the streamlines and thereby induces a low-pressure region in the rear of the body.   When the pressure over the rear of the body is lower than over the front, there exists a pressure difference which produces a drag force over and above the skin friction.   The magnitude of the form drag decreases as the separation moves farther toward the rear.

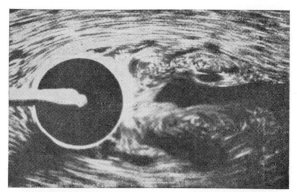

Fig. 9-2.   Flow pattern in crossflow over a
single horizontal cylinder. (Photograph by H. L.
Rubach, *Mitt. Forschungsarb*, 185, 1916)

The geometrical shapes which are most important for engineering work are the long circular cylinder and the sphere.   The heat-transfer phenomena for these two shapes in crossflow have been studied by a number of investigators, and representative data are summarized in Sec. 9-2.   In addition to the average surface conductance over a cylinder, the variation of conductance around the circumference will be considered.   A knowledge of the peripheral variation of the heat transfer associated with flow over a cylinder is important for many practical problems such as heat-transfer calculations for airplane wings, whose leading-edge contours are approximately cylindrical.   The interrelation between heat transfer and flow phenomena will also be stressed because it can be applied to the measurement of the velocity and its fluctuations in a turbulent stream by means of a hot-wire anemometer.   Heat transfer to or from spherical bodies is of importance in systems where particles suspended in a fluid stream are heated or cooled.   Examples of such systems are met in fluidization processes, settling operations, and cement preheaters.

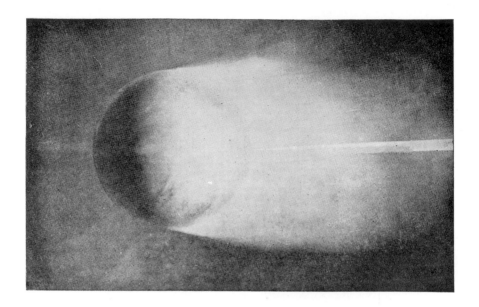

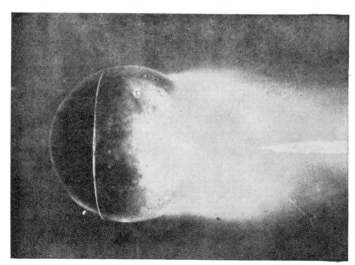

FIG. 9–3.   Photographs of air flowing over a sphere.   In lower picture a "tripping" wire induced early transition and delayed separation. (Courtesy of L. Prandtl and the *Journal of the Royal Aeronautical Society*)

Section 9–3 deals with heat transfer to or from bundles of tubes in crossflow, a configuration which is widely used in boilers, air-preheaters, and conventional shell-and-tube heat exchangers.   Representative experimental data are presented and applied to typical engineering problems.

9–2. CYLINDER AND SPHERE IN CROSSFLOW

Photographs of typical flow patterns for flow over a single cylinder and a sphere are shown in Figs. 9–2 and 9–3 respectively.   The most forward points of these bodies are called stagnation points.   Fluid particles striking there are brought to rest, and the pressure at the stagnation point p_o rises approximately one velocity head above the pressure in the oncoming free stream p_∞.   The flow divides at the stagnation point of the cylinder, and a boundary layer builds up along the surface.   The fluid accelerates when it flows past the surface of the cylinder, as can be seen by the crowding of the streamlines shown in Fig. 9–4.   This flow pattern is for a nonviscous fluid in irrotational flow, a highly idealized case called *potential flow*.   The velocity

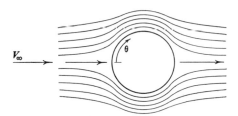

FIG. 9–4.   Streamlines for potential flow over a circular cylinder.

reaches a maximum at both sides of the cylinder, then falls again to zero at the stagnation point in the rear.   The pressure distribution around the cylinder corresponding to this idealized flow pattern is shown by the solid line in Fig. 9–5.   Since the pressure distribution is symmetrical about the vertical center plane of the cylinder, it is clear that there will be no pressure drag in irrotational flow.   However, unless the Reynolds number is very low, a real fluid will not adhere to the entire surface of the cylinder but, as mentioned previously, the boundary layer in which the flow is not irrotational will separate from the sides of the cylinder as a result of the adverse pressure gradient.   The separation of the boundary layer and the resultant wake in the rear of the cylinder give rise to pressure distributions shown for different Reynolds numbers by the dotted lines in Fig. 9–5.   It can be seen that there is fair agreement between the ideal and actual pressure distribution in the neighborhood of the forward stagnation point.   In the rear of the cylinder, however, the actual and the ideal distribution differ considerably.   The characteristics of the flow pattern and of the boundary layer depend on the Reynolds number, $V_\infty D_o \rho/\mu$, which for flow over a cylinder or a sphere is based on the velocity of the oncoming free stream V_∞ and the outside diameter of the body D_o. The flow pattern around the cylinder undergoes

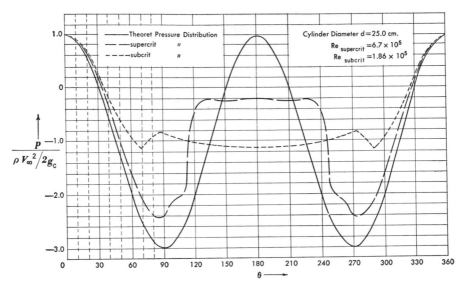

FIG. 9–5. Pressure distribution around circular cylinder in crossflow at various Reynolds numbers; p, local pressure; $\rho V_\infty^2/2g_c$, free-stream impact pressure; θ, angle measured from stagnation point. (By permission from L. Flachsbart, *Handbuch der Experimental Physik*, Vol. 4, Part 2)

a series of changes as the Reynolds number is increased, and since the heat transfer depends largely on the flow, we shall consider first the effect of Reynolds number of the flow and then interpret the heat-transfer data in the light of this information.

The sketches in Fig. 9–6 illustrate flow patterns typical of the characteristic ranges of Reynolds numbers. The letter symbols of the sketches in Fig. 9–6 correspond to the flow regimes indicated in the curve of Fig. 9–7 where the total drag coefficients of a cylinder and a sphere, C_D, are plotted as a function of the Reynolds number. The total drag coefficient is the sum of the pressure and frictional forces; it is defined by the following equation

$$C_D = \frac{\text{drag force/unit length}}{(\rho_\infty V_\infty^2/2g_c)D_o}$$

where ρ_∞ = free-stream density, in $\text{lb}_m/\text{cu ft}$;
V_∞ = free-stream velocity, in ft/sec;
D_o = outside diameter, in ft.

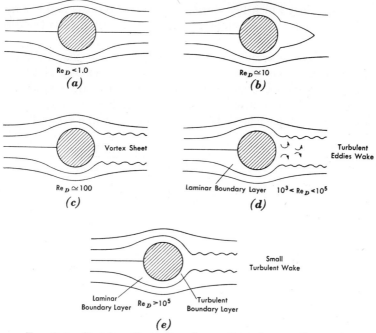

Re$_D$ < 1.0

(a)

Re$_D$ ≃ 10

(b)

Vortex Sheet

Re$_D$ ≃ 100

(c)

Turbulent
Eddies Wake

Laminar Boundary Layer   10³ < Re$_D$ < 10⁵

(d)

Small
Turbulent Wake

Laminar
Boundary Layer   Re$_D$ > 10⁵   Turbulent
Boundary Layer

(e)

FIG. 9–6. Sketches illustrating flow pattern for crossflow over
a circular cylinder at various Reynolds numbers.

The following discussion strictly applies only to long cylinders, but it also
gives a qualitative picture of the flow past a sphere. The letters a to e
refer to Figs. 9–6 and 9–7.

a) At Reynolds numbers of the order of unity or less, the flow adheres
to the surface and the streamlines follow those predicted from potential-flow
theory. The inertia forces are negligibly small and the drag is caused only
by viscous forces, since there is no flow separation. Heat is transferred
by conduction alone.

b) At Reynolds numbers of the order of 10, the inertia forces become
appreciable and two weak eddies stand in the rear of the cylinder. The
pressure drag accounts now for about one-half of the total drag.

c) At a Reynolds number of the order of 100, vortices separate alternately from both sides of the cylinder and stretch a considerable distance
downstream. These vortices are referred to as *von Karman vortex-streets*
in honor of the scientist Theodore von Karman, who studied the shedding
of vortices from bluff objects. The pressure drag now predominates.

d) In the Reynolds-number range between 10³ and 10⁵, the skin-friction
drag becomes negligible compared to the pressure drag caused by turbulent
eddies in the wake. The drag coefficient remains approximately constant
because the boundary layer remains laminar from the leading edge to the

point of separation, which lies throughout this Reynolds number range at an angular position, θ, between 80 and 85 deg measured from the direction of the flow.

e) At Reynolds numbers larger than about 10^5 (the exact value depends on the turbulence level of the stream) the kinetic energy of the fluid in the laminar boundary layer over the forward part of the cylinder is sufficient to overcome the unfavorable pressure gradient without separating. The flow in the boundary layer becomes turbulent while it is still attached,

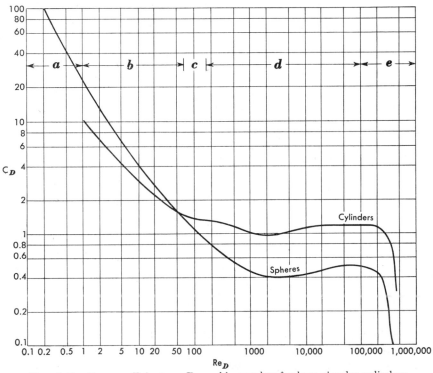

FIG. 9–7. Drag coefficient vs. Reynolds number for long circular cylinders and spheres in crossflow.

and the separation point moves toward the rear.   The closing of the streamlines reduces the size of the wake, and the pressure drag is therefore also substantially reduced.   Experiments by Fage and Falkner (1,2) indicate that, once the boundary layer has become turbulent, it will not separate before it has reached an angular position corresponding to a θ of about 130 deg.

Analyses of the boundary-layer growth and the variation of the local unit-surface conductances with angular position around circular cylinders and spheres have been only partially successful.   Squire (3) has solved the equations of motion and energy for a cylinder at constant temperature in crossflow over that portion of the surface to which a laminar boundary layer adheres. He showed that, at the stagnation point and in its immediate neighborhood, the convective unit-surface conductance can be calculated from the equation

$$\mathrm{Nu}_D = \frac{h_c D_o}{k_f} = C\sqrt{V_\infty D_o / \nu_f} \qquad (9\text{--}1)$$

where C is a constant whose numerical value at various Prandtl numbers is tabulated below:

Pr	0.7	0.8	1.0	5.0	10.0
C	1.0	1.05	1.14	2.1	1.7

Over the forward portion of the cylinder ($0 < \theta < 80$ deg), the empirical equation for $h_{c\theta}$, the local value of the unit-surface conductance at θ,

$$\frac{h_{c\theta} D_o}{k_f} = 1.14 \left(\frac{V_\infty D_o}{\nu_f} \right)^{\frac{1}{2}} \mathrm{Pr}_f^{0.4}[1 - (\theta/90)^3] \qquad (9\text{--}2)$$

has been found to agree satisfactorily (4) with experimental data. For air, Eq. 9–2 can be written in the form

$$h_{c\theta} = 0.194\, T_f^{\,0.49}\, (V_\infty\, \rho_\infty / D_o)^{0.5}\, [1 - (\theta/90)^3] \qquad (9\text{--}2a)$$

where T_f is the arithmetic average of the absolute temperatures of the free stream and of the surface in degrees Rankine R. Giedt (5) has measured the local pressures and the local unit-convective conductances over the entire circumference of a long, 4-in.-OD cylinder in an air stream over a Reynolds-number range from 90,000 to 220,000. Giedt's results are shown in Fig. 9–8, and similar data for lower Reynolds numbers are shown in Fig. 9–9. If the data shown in Figs. 9–8 and 9–9 are compared at corresponding Reynolds numbers with the flow patterns and the boundary-layer characteristics described earlier, some important observations can be made.

At Reynolds numbers below 100,000, separation of the laminar boundary layer occurs at an angular position of about 80 deg. The heat transfer and the flow characteristics over the forward portion of the cylinder resemble those for laminar flow over a flat plate which were discussed earlier. The local conductance is largest at the stagnation point and decreases with distance along the surface as the boundary-layer thickness increases. The conductance reaches a minimum on the sides of the cylinder near the separation point. Beyond the separation point the local conductance increases because considerable turbulence exists over the rear portion of the cylinder where the eddies of the wake sweep the surface. However, the conductance over the rear is no larger than over the front, because the eddies recirculate part of the fluid and, despite their high turbulence, are not as effective in mixing the fluid in the vicinity of the surface with the fluid in the main stream as a turbulent boundary layer.

At Reynolds numbers large enough to permit transition from laminar to turbulent flow in the boundary layer without separation of the laminar

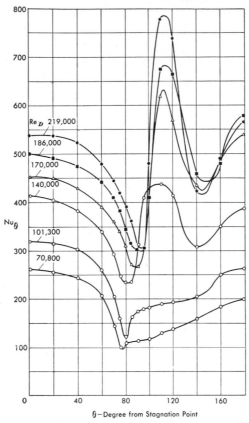

Fig. 9–8. Circumferential variation of the unit-surface conductance at high Reynolds numbers for a circular cylinder in crossflow. (Extracted from "Investigation of Variation of Point Unit-Heat-Transfer Coefficient Around a Cylinder Normal to an Air Stream," by W. H. Giedt, published in *Trans. ASME*, Vol. 71, 1949, with permission of the publishers, The American Society of Mechanical Engineers)

boundary layer, the unit-surface conductance has two minima around the cylinder. The first minimum occurs at the point of transition. As the transition from laminar to turbulent flow progresses, the unit conductance increases and reaches a maximum approximately at the point where the boundary layer becomes fully turbulent. Then the unit-surface conductance begins to decrease again and reaches a second minimum at about 130 deg, the point at which the turbulent boundary layer separates from the cylinder. Over the rear of the cylinder the unit conductance increases to another maximum at the rear stagnation point.

Example 9–1.   To design a heating system for the purpose of preventing ice formation on an aircraft wing it is necessary to know the unit-surface conductance over the outer surface of the leading edge.   The leading-edge contour may be approximated by a half cylinder of 12-in. diameter.   The ambient air is at −30 F and the surface temperature is to be no less than 32 F.   The plane is designed to fly at 25,000 ft altitude at a speed of 500 fps.   Calculate the distribution of the convective unit-surface conductance over the forward portion of the wing.

Solution: At an altitude of 25,000 ft the standard atmospheric air pressure is 785 pounds per square foot (psf) and the density of the air is 0.034 lb$_m$/cu ft (see Table A-7 in the Appendix).

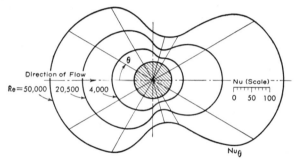

Fig. 9–9.   Circumferential   variation   of   the local Nusselt Number Nu$_\theta$-$h_{c\theta}D_o$/k_f at low Reynolds numbers for a circular cylinder in crossflow.   (According to W. Lorisch from M. ten Bosch,   "Die   Wärmeübertragung,"   3d   ed., Springer Verlag, Berlin, 1936)

The unit-surface conductance at the stagnation point, i.e., at $\theta = 0$, is, according to Eq. 9–2a,

$$h_{c0} = 0.194T_f{}^{0.49}\left(\frac{V_\infty \rho_\infty}{D_o}\right)^{0.5}$$

$$= 0.194\,(461)^{0.49}\left(\frac{500 \times 0.034}{1.0}\right)^{0.5}$$

$$= 16.2\ \text{Btu/hr sq ft F}$$

The variation of h_c with θ is obtained by multiplying the value of the unit-surface conductance at the stagnation point by $1 - (\theta/90)^3$.   The results are tabulated below.

θ (deg)	0	15	30	45	60	75
$h_{c\theta}$ (Btu/hr sq ft F)	16.2	16.1	15.6	14.2	11.4	6.88

Ans.

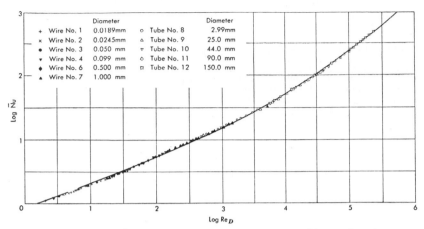

FIG. 9–10 Average heat-transfer coefficient vs. Reynolds number for a circular cylinder in crossflow. (After R. Hilbert, "Wärmeabgabe von geheizten Drähten and Rohren," *Forsch. Gebiete Ingenieurwesen*, Vol. 4, 1933, Ab.9, page 220)

It is apparent from the foregoing discussion that the variation of the unit-surface conductance around a cylinder or a sphere is a very complex problem. For many practical applications it is fortunately not necessary to know the local value $h_{c\theta}$, but sufficient to evaluate the average value of the conductance around the body. A number of observers have measured mean conductances for flow over single cylinders and spheres. Hilpert (6) accurately measured the average conductances for air flowing over cylinders of diameters ranging from 0.008 to nearly 6 in. His results are shown in Fig. 9–10, where the average Nusselt number $\bar{h}_c D_o/k_f$ is plotted as a function of the Reynolds number $V_\infty D_o/\nu_f$. The data shown in Fig. 9–10 can be correlated by the equation

$$\frac{\bar{h}_c D_o}{k_f} = C \left(\frac{V_\infty D_o}{\nu_f}\right)^n \tag{9–3}$$

where C and n are empirical constants whose numerical values vary with

TABLE 9–1

COEFFICIENTS FOR CALCULATION OF AVERAGE HEAT-TRANSFER COEFFICIENT OF A CIRCULAR CYLINDER IN A GAS FLOWING NORMAL TO ITS AXIS, BY EQ. 9–3.

Re_{Df}	C	n
0.4—4	0.891	0.330
4—40	0.821	0.385
40—4,000	0.615	0.466
4,000—40,000	0.174	0.618
40,000—400,000	0.0239	0.805

the Reynolds number as shown in Table 9–1. It should be noted that, if the turbulence level in the oncoming air is increased by placing a grid or some other type of turbulence promoter upstream of the cylinder, the surface conductance may increase by as much as 50 per cent.

For liquids flowing over a single tube or wire McAdams (9) suggests that either the right-hand side of Eq. 9–3 be multiplied by the factor $1.1\,\mathrm{Pr}_f^{0.31}$, that is,

$$\frac{\bar{h}_c D_o}{k_f} = 1.1C \left(\frac{V_\infty D_o}{\nu_f}\right)^n \mathrm{Pr}_f^{0.31} \tag{9–3a}$$

or that the equation

$$\frac{\bar{h}_c D_o}{k_f} = 0.35 + 0.56 \left(\frac{V_\infty D_o}{\nu_f}\right)^{0.5} \tag{9–3b}$$

be used to calculate the average unit conductance.

Hot-wire anemometer. The relationship between the velocity and the rate of heat transfer from a single cylinder in crossflow is used to measure velocity and velocity fluctuations in turbulent flow and in combustion processes by means of a hot-wire anemometer. This instrument consists basically of a thin (0.001 to 0.005-in.-diam) electrically heated wire stretched across the ends of two prongs. When the wire is exposed to a cooler fluid stream, it loses heat by convection. The temperature of the wire, and consequently its electrical resistance, depends on the temperature and the velocity of the fluid and the heating current. To determine the fluid velocity, the wire is either maintained at a constant temperature by adjusting the current and the fluid speed determined from the measured value of the current, or the wire is heated by a constant current and the speed deduced from a measurement of the electrical resistance or the voltage drop in the wire. In the first method the hot wire forms one arm in the circuit of a Wheatstone bridge as shown in Fig. 9–11a. The resistance of the rheostat arm R_e is adjusted to balance the bridge when the temperature, and consequently the resistance, of the wire has reached some desired value. When the fluid velocity increases, the current required to maintain the temperature and resistance of the wire constant also increases. This change in the current is accomplished by adjusting the rheostat in series with the voltage supply. When the galvanometer indicates that the bridge is in balance again, the change in current, read on the ammeter, indicates the change in speed. In the other method the fluctuations in voltage drop caused by variations in the fluid velocity are impressed across the input of an amplifier, the output of which is connected to an oscilloscope. Figure 9–11b illustrates schematically an arrangement for the voltage measurement. Additional information on the hot-wire method is given in Refs. 7 and 8.

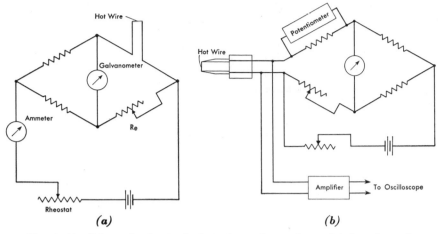

Hot Wire

Galvanometer

Ammeter

Re

Rheostat

(a)

Potentiometer

Hot Wire

Amplifier → To Oscilloscope

(b)

FIG. 9–11   Schematic circuits for hot-wire probes and associated equipment.

Example 9–2.   A 0.005-in.-diam polished platinum wire 0.25-in. long is to be used for a hot-wire anemometer to measure the velocity of 70 F air in the range between 4 and 20 fps.   The wire is to be placed into the circuit of the Wheatstone bridge shown in Fig. 9–11a.   Its temperature is to be maintained at 450 F by adjusting the current by means of the rheostat.   To design the electric circuit it is necessary to know the required current as a function of air velocity.   The electrical resistivity of platinum at 450 F is 17.1 microhms-cm.

Solution: Since the wire is very thin, conduction along the wire can be neglected; also, the temperature gradient in the wire at any cross section may be disregarded.

At the mean film temperature of 260 F the air has a thermal conductivity of 0.0195 Btu/hr ft F and a kinematic viscosity of 2.81×10^{-4} sq ft/sec.   At a velocity of 4 fps the Reynolds number is

$$\text{Re} = \frac{(4 \text{ ft/sec})(0.005/12 \text{ ft})}{2.81 \times 10^{-4} \text{ sq ft/sec}} = 5.92$$

The Reynolds-number range of interest is therefore from 6 to 30.   In this range the equation

$$\frac{\bar{h}_c D_o}{k_f} = 0.821 \text{ Re}^{0.385}$$

applies according to Table 9–1 and Eq. 9–3.   The average convective unit-surface conductance is therefore

$$\bar{h}_c = \left(\frac{0.0195 \text{ Btu/hr ft F}}{0.005/12 \text{ ft}}\right) (0.821) \left[\frac{0.005}{(12)(2.81 \times 10^{-4})}\right]^{0.385} V_\infty^{0.385}$$

$$= 44.7 \, V_\infty^{0.385} \text{ Btu/hr sq ft F}$$

At this point it is necessary to estimate the unit-surface conductance for radiant heat flow.   According to Eq. 1–6 we have

$$\bar{h}_r = \frac{q_r}{A \, (T_s - T_\infty)} = \frac{\sigma \epsilon \, (T_s{}^4 - T_\infty{}^4)}{T_s - T_\infty} = 0.173 \times 10^{-8} \, \epsilon \, (T_s{}^2 + T_\infty{}^2)(T_s + T_\infty)$$

or, since
$$(T_s + T_\infty)^2 (T_s + T_\infty) \simeq 4 \left(\frac{T_s + T_\infty}{2} \right)^3$$

we have approximately
$$\bar{h}_r = 0.173 \times 10^{-8} \, \epsilon \times 4 \left(\frac{T_s + T_\infty}{2} \right)^3$$

The emissivity of polished platinum from Table 5–1 is about 0.073, so that $\bar{h}_r$ is about 0.01 Btu/hr sq ft F. This shows that the amount of heat transferred by radiation is negligible compared to the heat transferred by forced convection. The rate at which heat is transferred from the wire is therefore

$$q = \bar{h}_c A (T_s - T_\infty) = 44.7 \, V_\infty^{0.385} \frac{(\pi)(0.005)(0.25)}{144} \, 380$$

$$= 0.46 \, V_\infty^{0.385} \text{ Btu/hr}$$

which is also the rate at which heat must be generated electrically to maintain equilibrium. The electrical resistance of the wire is

$$R_e = (17.1 \times 10^{-6} \text{ ohm cm}) \left[\frac{0.25 \text{ in.}}{(\pi) \, 0.0025^2 \text{ sq in.}} \right] \left(\frac{1}{2.54} \frac{\text{in.}}{\text{cm}} \right)$$

$$= 0.0858 \text{ ohms}$$

A heat balance with the current i in amperes gives

$$i^2 R_e \text{ watts } (3.413 \text{ Btu/watt-hr}) = 0.46 \, V_\infty^{0.385}$$

Solving for i we get the expression

$$i = \sqrt{\frac{0.46}{(0.0858)(3.413)}} \, V_\infty^{0.1925} = 1.25 \, V_\infty^{0.1925} \text{ amp}$$

from which the current can be readily calculated for any velocity within the specified range.   *Ans.*

Spheres. A knowledge of heat-transfer characteristics to or from spherical bodies is important to predict the thermal performance of systems where clouds of particles are heated or cooled in a stream of fluid. When the particles have an irregular shape, the data for spheres will yield satisfactory results if the sphere diameter is replaced by an equivalent diameter, i.e., if D_o is taken as the diameter of a spherical particle having the same surface area as the irregular particle.

The total drag coefficient of a sphere is shown as a function of the free-stream Reynolds number in Fig. 9–7[1] and corresponding data for heat transfer between a sphere and air are shown in Fig. 9–12. In the Reynolds-number range from about 25 to 100,000, the equation recommended by McAdams (9) for calculating the average unit-surface conductance for spheres heated or cooled by a gas is

$$\frac{\bar{h}_c D_o}{k_f} = 0.37 \left(\frac{V_\infty \rho_\infty D_o}{\mu_f} \right)^{0.6} \tag{9-4}$$

[1] When the sphere is dragged along by a stream, as for example a liquid droplet in a gas stream, the pertinent velocity for the Reynolds number is the velocity difference between the stream and the body.

For Reynolds numbers between 1.0 and 25, the equation

$$\bar{h}_c = c_p V_\infty \rho_\infty \left(\frac{2.2}{\mathrm{Re}_D} + \frac{0.48}{\mathrm{Re}_D^{0.5}} \right) \tag{9-5}$$

may be used for heat transfer in a gas. For heat transfer in a liquid the equation

$$\frac{\bar{h}_c D_o}{k_f} \mathrm{Pr}_f^{-0.3} = 0.97 + 0.68 \left(\frac{V_\infty \rho_\infty D_o}{\mu_f} \right)^{0.5} \tag{9-6}$$

is recommended in the Reynolds-number range between 1 and 2000.

In the limiting case when the Reynolds number is less than unity, Johnston et al. (10) have shown from theoretical considerations that the

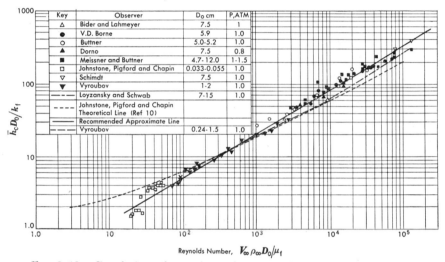

FIG. 9–12. Correlation of experimental average heat-transfer coefficients for flow over a sphere. (By permission from W. H. McAdams, *Heat Transmission*, 3d ed. New York: McGraw-Hill Book Company, Inc., 1954)

Nusselt number approaches a constant value of two for a Prandtl number of unity unless the spheres have diameters of the order of the mean free path of the molecules in the gas.

9–3. TUBE BUNDLES IN CROSSFLOW

The evaluation of the convective conductance between a bank of tubes and a fluid flowing at right angles to the tubes is an important step in the design and performance analysis of many types of commercial heat exchangers. There are, for example, a large number of gas heaters in which a hot fluid inside the tubes heats a gas passing over the outside of the tubes. Figure 9–13 shows several arrangements of tubular air heaters in

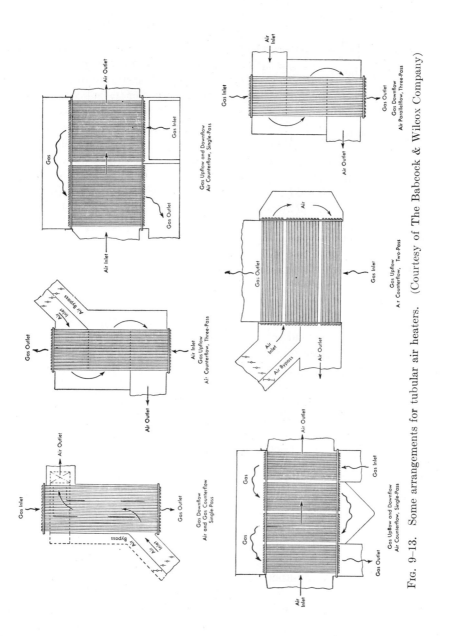

Fig. 9–13. Some arrangements for tubular air heaters. (Courtesy of The Babcock & Wilcox Company)

which the products of combustion, after they leave a boiler, economizer, or superheater, are used to preheat the air going to the steam-generating units. The shells of these gas heaters are usually rectangular and the shell-side gas flows in the space between the outside of the tubes and the shell. Since the flow cross-sectional area is continuously changing along the path, the shell-side gas speeds up and slows down periodically. A similar situation exists also in some unbaffled short-tube liquid-to-liquid heat exchangers in which the shell-side fluid flows over the tubes. In these units the tube arrangement is similar to that in a gas heater except that the shell cross-sectional area varies where a cylindrical shell is used.

The heat transfer in flow over tube bundles depends largely on the flow pattern and the degree of turbulence, which in turn are functions of the velocity of the fluid and the size and arrangement of the tubes. The photographs of Figs. 9–14 and 9–15 illustrate the flow patterns for water flowing in the low turbulent range over tubes arranged *in line* and *staggered* respectively. The photographs were obtained (11) by sprinkling fine aluminum powder on the surface of water flowing perpendicularly to the axis of vertically placed tubes. We observe that the flow patterns around tubes in the first transverse rows are similar to those for flow around single tubes. Focusing our attention on a tube in the first row of the in-line arrangement, we see that the boundary layer separates from both sides of the tube and a wake forms behind it. The turbulent wake extends to the tube located in the second transverse row. As a result of the high turbulence in the wakes, the boundary layers around tubes in the second and subsequent rows become progressively thinner. It is therefore not unexpected that, in turbulent flow, the heat-transfer coefficients of tubes in the first row are smaller than the heat-transfer coefficients of tubes in subsequent rows. In laminar flow, on the other hand, the opposite trend has been observed (14).

For a closely spaced staggered-tube arrangement (Fig. 9–15) the size of the turbulent wake behind each tube is somewhat smaller than for similar in-line arrangements, but there is no appreciable reduction in the over-all energy dissipation. Experiments on various types of tube arrangement (12) have shown that, for practical units, the relation between heat transfer and energy dissipation depends primarily on the velocity of the fluid, the size of the tubes, and the distance between the tubes. However, in the transition zone the performance of a closely spaced, staggered tube arrangement is somewhat superior to that of a similar in-line tube arrangement.

The equations available for the calculation of heat-transfer coefficients in flow over tube banks are based entirely on experimental data because the flow pattern is too complex to be treated analytically. Experiments have shown that, in flow over staggered-tube banks, the transition from

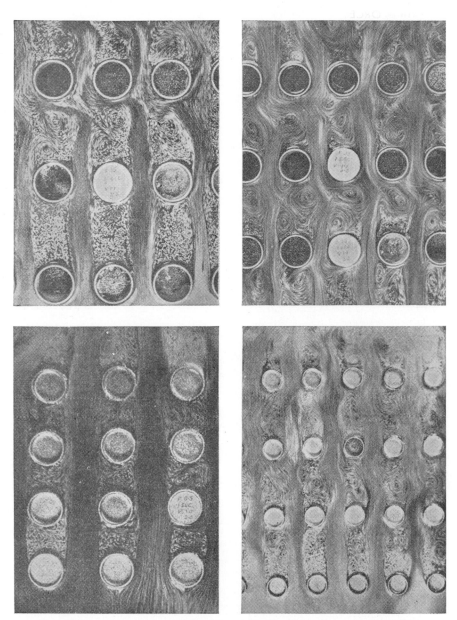

Fig. 9–14.   Flow patterns for in-line tube bundles. (By permission from R. D. Wallis, "Photographic Study of Fluid Flow Between Banks of Tubes," *Engineering*, 148, 1933)

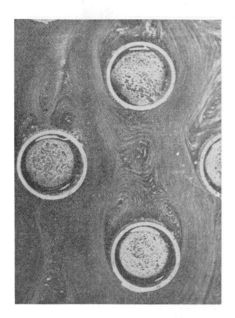

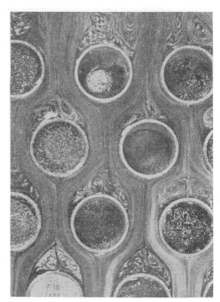

Fig. 9–15.   Flow patterns for staggered tube bundles.   (By permission from R. D. Wallis, "Photographic Study of Fluid Flow Between Banks of Tubes," *Engineering*, 148, 1933)

laminar to turbulent flow is more gradual than in flow through a pipe, whereas for in-line tube bundles the transition phenomena resemble those observed in pipe flow. In either case the transition from laminar to turbulent flow begins at a Reynolds number based on the velocity at the minimum flow area, of about 200, and the flow becomes fully turbulent at a Reynolds number of about 6000.

For engineering calculations the average heat-transfer coefficient for the entire tube bundle is of primary interest. The experimental data for heat transfer in flow over banks of tubes are usually correlated by an equation of the form $\overline{\mathrm{Nu}} = \mathrm{const}\,(\mathrm{Re})^m\,(\mathrm{Pr})^n$, which has previously been used to correlate the data for flow over a single tube. To apply this equation to flow over tube bundles it is necessary to select a reference velocity, since the speed of the fluid varies along its path. The velocity used to

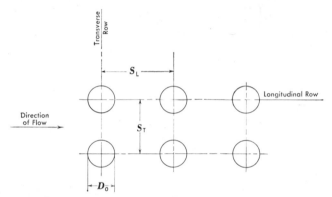

FIG. 9–16. Sketch illustrating nomenclature for in-line tube arrangements.

build the Reynolds number for flow over tube bundles is based on the *minimum free area* available for fluid flow, regardless of whether the minimum area occurs in the transverse or diagonal openings. For in-line tube arrangements (Fig. 9–16), the minimum free-flow area per unit length of tube $A_{\min}$ is always $A_{\min} = S_T - D_o$, where S_T is the distance between centers of the tubes in adjacent longitudinal rows (measured perpendicularly to the direction of flow), or the *transverse pitch*.

For staggered arrangements (Fig. 9–17) the minimum free-flow area may occur, as in the previous case, either between adjacent tubes in a row or, if S_L/S_T is so small that $\sqrt{S_T^2 + S_L^2} < 2S_T$, between diagonally opposed tubes. In the latter case, the maximum velocity, $V_{\max}$, is $2S_T/(\sqrt{S_L^2 + S_T^2} - D_o)$ times the free-flow velocity based on the shell area without tubes. The symbol S_L denotes the center-to-center distance between adjacent transverse rows of tubes or pipes (measured in the direction of flow) and is called the *longitudinal pitch*.

To account for the effect of the tube arrangement on the heat-transfer coefficient, it is convenient to write a dimensionless correlation equation either in the form

$$\frac{\bar{h}_c D_o}{k_f} = 0.33 C_H \left(\frac{G_{max}D_o}{\mu_f}\right)^m \text{Pr}_f^{\frac{1}{3}} \tag{9-7}$$

or in the form

$$j = \frac{\bar{h}_c}{c_p G_{max}} \text{Pr}_b^{\frac{2}{3}} \left(\frac{\mu_s}{\mu_b}\right)^{0.14} = \phi \left(\frac{G_{max}D_o}{\mu_b}\right) \tag{9-8}$$

where $\bar{h}_c$ is the average heat-transfer coefficient for a tube bank of 10 or more transverse rows, G_{max} is the mass flow rate per unit of minimum free area, D_o is the outer diameter of the pipes or tubes, C_H and m are empirical

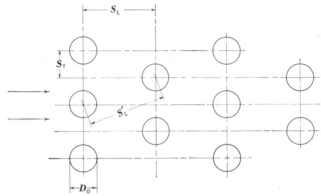

FIG. 9–17. Sketch illustrating nomenclature for staggered tube arrangements.

coefficients whose value depends on the tube arrangement, ϕ is a functional relationship dependent on the tube arrangement, and the subscripts s, f, and b refer to conditions at the wall surface, the film, and the bulk respectively.

A relation of the type represented by Eq. 9–8 has been found to correlate data in the laminar-flow range ($G_{max}D_o/\mu_b < 200$) and in the transition-flow range ($200 < G_{max} D_o/\mu_b < 6000$), whereas Eq. 9–7 is used in the turbulent range. Experimental data for oil in laminar and transition flow over several different tube arrangements have been obtained by Bergelin et al. (12,13) in a research program sponsored by the Heat Transfer Division of ASME. The averaged results of this study are shown in Fig. 9–18 where the upper series of curves represent the friction data which will be discussed later, and the lower series of curves represent the heat-transfer data. The ordinate for the lower curves in Fig. 9–18 is the dimensionless Colburn j factor of Eq. 9–8 and the abscissa is the bulk Reynolds number, $G_{max} D_o/\mu_b$. The tubes in models 1 and 4 were arranged staggered in equilateral triangles; in model 3, the tubes were arranged in staggered squares; and the tubes of models 2 and 5 were arranged in in-line squares. The outside diameter of the tubes was $\frac{3}{8}$ in.; the pitch-to-diameter ratio

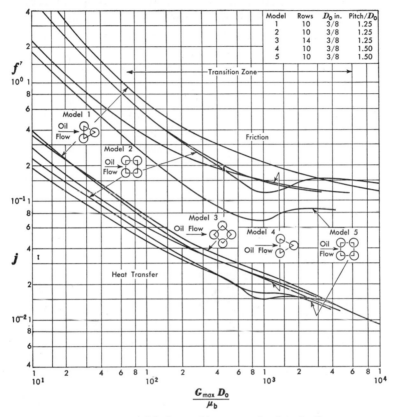

Model	Rows	D_0 in.	Pitch/D_0
1	10	3/8	1.25
2	10	3/8	1.25
3	14	3/8	1.25
4	10	3/8	1.50
5	10	3/8	1.50

FIG. 9–18. Average friction and heat-transfer data for flow over five different arrangements of $\frac{3}{8}$-in.-diameter tube bundles in the laminar and transition regime. (Extracted from "Heat Transfer and Fluid Friction During Flow Across Banks of Tubes," by O. P. Bergelin, G. A. Brown, and S. C. Doberstein, published in *Trans. ASME*, Vol. 74, 1952, with permission of the publishers, The American Society of Mechanical Engineers)

for each model is shown for each curve in Fig. 9–18. Inspection of the curves shows that, at a Reynolds number of 200, the experimental data begin to deviate markedly from the straight lines which represent the data in the viscous region. At a Reynolds number of about 5000 the heat-transfer curves for in-line and staggered tubes approach one another and the flow is assumed to be turbulent at higher values of the Reynolds number.

It will be noted that the form of the curves for in-line and staggered tubes are different in the transition zone. There is a *dip region*, similar to that observed in pipe flow, for the curves of in-line tubes, but not for staggered tubes. It is believed that the flow in the free channels between the wakes (Fig. 9–14) of in-line tubes resembles flow in a pipe or a duct and the onset of turbulence occurs throughout the tube bank. In simple cross flow over staggered tubes, on the other hand, turbulence begins at the exit end, gradually works upstream as the flow is increased, and finally spreads throughout the tube bank. These general remarks apply only to simple crossflow and may not be true for baffled arrangements where no similar experiments have as yet been performed.

The effect of the number of transverse tube rows on the heat-transfer coefficient has been investigated for the laminar regime by Meece (14) with square in-line tube arrangements having one, two, four, six, eight, and ten rows of $\frac{3}{8}$-in. tubes with a pitch-to-diameter ratio of 1.25. Meece found that, for a given Reynolds number, the average heat-transfer coefficient for a single row of tubes was 50 per cent larger than for 10 rows. For the tube arrangements used, the variation of the heat-transfer coefficient with N, the number of tube rows in the direction of flow, can be generalized by the equation

$$j_{N\text{rows}}/j_{10 \text{ rows}} = N^{0.18} \tag{9–9}$$

when the flow is laminar. Figure 9–18 shows the results for 10 rows of tubes and can be combined with Eq. 9–9 to predict the average heat-transfer coefficient at Reynolds numbers below 1000 when the number of tube rows is less than 10. For more than 10 tube rows it is suggested that no correction be applied to the value of $\bar{h}_c$, obtained from Fig. 9–18.

Experiments similar to those described above have also been performed by Kays et al. (15,16) with air flowing over banks of $\frac{1}{4}$- and $\frac{3}{8}$-in. tubes in various arrangements. The Reynolds numbers in these tests covered the transition regime and the low range of the turbulent regime, but did not extend into the laminar region. In the transition range the results obtained by Kays et al. are in fairly good agreement with those shown in Fig. 9–18 for similar geometries. A summary of the results of these tests is presented in Ref. 17.

For turbulent flow (i.e., $\text{Re}_{\max} \geq 6000$) over banks of tubes or pipes, irrespective of whether they are staggered or arranged in-line, the experimental heat-transfer data agree well with the equation

$$\frac{\bar{h}_c D_o}{k_f} = 0.33 C_H \left(\frac{G_{\max} D_o}{\mu_f} \right)^{0.6} \text{Pr}_f^{0.3} \tag{9–10}$$

if the tube bundle has 10 or more transverse rows. The value of the empirical coefficient C_H depends on the tube arrangement and the Reynolds number.   Fishenden and Saunders (18) evaluated C_H from extensive experiments by Huge (19), Pierson (20), Grimison (21), Kuznetzkof and Lokshin (22) for longitudinal and transverse pitch-to-diameter ratios ranging from 1.25 to 3.0.   They found that, for pitch-to-diameter ratios between 1.25 and 1.5, the range of practical interest for heat exchangers, the value of C_H did not deviate by more than 10 per cent from unity for any of the tube arrangements tested.   For preliminary calculations, Eq. 9–10 is therefore satisfactory.   When high accuracy is desired, it is recommended that the correlation of Kays (17) be used in the Reynolds-number range between 1000 and about 15,000 and the correlation of Grimison (18 or 21) be used for the Reynolds-number range between 10,000 and 40,000.

The variation of the average heat-transfer coefficient of a tube bank with the number of transverse rows is shown in Table 9–2 for turbulent flow.   To calculate the average heat-transfer coefficient for tube banks with less than 10 rows, the $\bar{h}_c$ obtained from Eq. 9–10 should be multiplied by the appropriate ratio $\bar{h}_c/\bar{h}_{cN}$.

TABLE 9–2

RATIO OF $\bar{h}_c$ FOR N TRANSVERSE ROWS TO $\bar{h}_c$ FOR TEN TRANSVERSE ROWS

RATIO	N									
	1	2	3	4	5	6	7	8	9	10
Staggered tubes......	0.68	0.75	0.83	0.89	0.92	0.95	0.97	0.98	0.99	1.0
In-line tubes......	0.64	0.80	0.87	0.90	0.92	0.94	0.96	0.98	0.99	1.0

SOURCE: Ref. 15.

The frictional pressure drop in lb_t/sq ft for flow over a bank of tubes Δp can be calculated from the equation

$$\Delta p = \frac{f'G_{\max}^2 N}{\rho(2.09 \times 10^8)}\left(\frac{\mu_s}{\mu_b}\right)^{0.14} \tag{9–11}$$

where $G_{\max}$ = mass velocity at the minimum area, in lb_m/hr sq ft;

ρ = mass density, in lb_m/cu ft;

N = number of transverse rows;

and f' is an empirical friction factor which can be estimated, according to Jakob (23), for values of Reynolds number larger than 1000 from the equation

$$f' = \left[0.25 + \frac{0.118}{\left(\dfrac{S_T - 1}{D_o}\right)^{1.08}}\right]\left(\frac{G_{\max}D_o}{\mu_b}\right)^{-0.16} \tag{9–12}$$

for staggered tube arrangements and by the equation

$$f' = \left[0.044 + \frac{0.08 S_L/D_o}{\left(\dfrac{S_T - 1}{D_o}\right)^{0.43 + 1.13 D_o/S_L}}\right]\left(\frac{G_{\max}D_o}{\mu_b}\right)^{-0.15} \tag{9-13}$$

for in-line tube arrangements.

For laminar flow the friction factors from the upper series of curves shown in Fig. 9–18 should be used in Eq. 9–11, but the exponent of 0.14 of the viscosity ratio (μ_s/μ_b) in Eq. 9–11 should be replaced by 0.25 (13).

Liquid metals. Experimental data for the heat-transfer characteristics of liquid metals in crossflow over a tube bank have been obtained at the Brookhaven National Laboratory (28 and 29). In these tests mercury (Pr = 0.022) was heated while flowing normal to a staggered tube bank consisting of 60 to 70 $\frac{1}{2}$-in. tubes, ten rows deep, arranged in an equilateral triangular array with a 1.375 pitch to diameter ratio. Both local and average heat-transfer coefficients were measured in turbulent flow. The average heat-transfer coefficients in the interior of the tube bank are well correlated by the equation

$$\overline{\mathrm{Nu}} = 4.03 + 0.228\,(\mathrm{Re}_{\max}\,\mathrm{Pr})_f^{0.67} \tag{9-14}$$

in the Reynolds number range from 20,000 to 80,000.

The measurements of the distribution of the local unit-surface conductance around the circumference of a tube indicate that for a liquid metal the turbulent effects in the wake upon heat transfer are small compared to the heat transfer by conduction within the fluid. Whereas with air and water a marked increase in the local heat-transfer coefficient occurs in the wake region of the tube (see Fig. 9–8), with mercury, the unit-surface conductance decreases continuously with increasing θ. At a Reynolds number of 83,000 the ratio $h_{c\theta}\sqrt{h_c}$ was found to be 1.8 at the stagnation point, 1.0 at $\theta = 90$, 0.5 at $\theta = 145$, and 0.3 at $\theta = 180$ degrees.

Grosh and Cess (30 and 31) have recently developed a theoretical and an analogical method for predicting heat-transfer coefficients for liquid metals flowing across a single cylinder on a tube bank. The procedure for obtaining these coefficients rests on the assumption that in a fluid with a small Prandtl number eddy transport of heat is negligible in comparison to molecular conduction. At low velocities this approach yields results in good agreement with measurements. At higher velocities, however, the theory yields low results because it neglects the contribution of eddy conduction.

9–4. APPLICATION TO HEAT-EXCHANGER DESIGN

In the design and selection of a stationary commercial heat exchanger, the power requirement and the initial cost of the unit must be considered.

The results obtained by Pierson (20) show that the smallest possible pitch in each direction results in the lowest power requirement for a specified rate of heat transfer. Since smaller values of pitch also permit the use of a smaller shell, the cost of the unit is reduced when the tubes are closely packed. There is little difference in performance between in-line and staggered arrangements, but the former are easier to clean. The Tubular Exchanger Manufacturers Association recommends that tubes shall be spaced with a minimum center-to-center distance of 1.25 times the outside diameter of the tube and when tubes are on a square pitch, a minimum clearance lane of $\frac{1}{4}$ in. shall be provided.

Example 9–3. Atmospheric air at 58 F is to be heated to 86 F by passing it over a bank of brass tubes inside which steam at 212 F is condensing. The unit-surface conductance on the inside of the tubes is about 1000 Btu/hr sq ft F. The tubes are 2 ft long, $\frac{1}{2}$ in. OD, BWG No. 18 (0.094-in. wall thickness). They are to be arranged in-line in a square pattern with a pitch of $\frac{3}{4}$ in. inside a rectangular shell 2 ft wide and 15 in. high. If the total mass rate of flow of the air to be heated is 32,000 lbm/hr, estimate (a) the number of transverse rows required, and (b) hte pressure drop.

Solution: (a) Since the thermal resistance on the air side will be much larger than the combined resistance of the pipe wall and the steam, we shall first assume that the outside surface of the pipe is at the steam temperature. The mean film temperature of the air T_f will then be approximately equal to

$$\frac{1}{2}\left(\frac{58 + 86}{2} + 212\right) = 142 \text{ F}$$

The mass velocity at the minimum cross-sectional area, which is between adjacent tubes, is calculated next. The shell is 15 in. high and consequently holds 20 longitudinal rows of tubes. The minimum free area is

$$A_{\min} = (20)\,(2)\,[(0.75 - 0.50)/12] = 0.833 \text{ sq ft}$$

and the maximum mass velocity is

$$G_{\max} = 32,000/0.833 = 38,400 \text{ lb}_m/\text{hr sq ft}$$

Hence, the Reynolds number is

$$\text{Re}_{\max} = \frac{G_{\max}\,D_o}{\mu_f} = \frac{(38,400 \text{ lb/hr sq ft})\,(0.5/12 \text{ ft})}{0.0485 \text{ lb/hr ft}} = 33,000$$

Assuming that more than 10 rows will be required, the unit-surface conductance is calculated from Eq. 9–10, since the flow is turbulent. We get

$$\bar{h}_c = \left(\frac{k_f}{D_o}\right)(0.33)\,(\text{Re}_{\max}{}^{0.6}\text{Pr}_f{}^{0.3})$$

$$= \left(\frac{0.016 \text{ Btu/hr ft F}}{0.5/12 \text{ ft}}\right)(0.33)\,(33,000^{0.6})\,(0.905) = 64.2 \text{ Btu/hr sq ft F}$$

We can now determine the temperature at the outer tube wall, which was originally assumed equal to the steam temperature. There are three thermal resistances in series between the steam and the air. The resistance at the steam side per tube is

$$R_1 = \frac{1}{h_i}\, \pi D_i L = \left(\frac{1}{1000}\right) 3.14 \left(\frac{0.402}{12}\right) 2 = 0.00474 \text{ hr F/Btu}$$

The resistance of the pipe wall ($k = 60$ Btu/hr ft F) is approximately

$$R_2 = \frac{0.049}{k}\, \pi \left(\frac{D_o + D_i}{2}\right) L = \left(\frac{0.049}{60}\right)(3.14)(0.451)(2) = 0.000287 \text{ hr F/Btu}$$

The resistance at the outside of the tube is

$$R_3 = \frac{1}{h_o}\, \pi D_o L = \left(\frac{1}{64.2}\right) 3.14 \left(\frac{0.5}{12}\right) 2 = 0.0595 \text{ hr F/Btu}$$

The total resistance is then

$$R_1 + R_2 + R_3 = 0.06453 \text{ hr F/Btu}$$

Since the sum of the resistance at the steam side and the resistance of the tube wall are about 8 per cent of the total resistance, about 8 per cent of the total temperature drop occurs between the steam and the outer tube wall. The mean film temperature can now be corrected and we get

$$T_f = 137 \text{ F}$$

This will not change the values of the physical properties appreciably, and no adjustment in the previously calculated value of $\bar{h}_c$ is necessary.

The mean temperature difference between the steam and the air can now be calculated. Using the arithmetic average we get

$$T_{\text{steam}} - T_{\text{air}} = 212 - \left(\frac{58 + 86}{2}\right) = 140 \text{ F}$$

The specific heat of air at constant pressure is 0.241 Btu/lb$_m$ F. Equating the rate of heat flow from the steam to the air to the rate of enthalpy rise of the air gives

$$\frac{20N\Delta T_{\text{avg}}}{R_1 + R_2 + R_3} = Gc_p(T_{\text{out}} - T_{\text{in}})_{\text{air}}$$

Solving for N, the number of transverse rows, yields

$$N = \frac{(32,000)(0.24)(86 - 58)(0.0645)}{(20)(140)} = 5$$

Since the number of tubes is less than 10, it is necessary to correct $\bar{h}_c$ in accordance with Table 9–2, or

$$\bar{h}_{c\,5\text{ rows}} = 0.92\, \bar{h}_{c\,10\text{ rows}} = (0.92)\,(64.2) = 59 \text{ Btu/hr sq ft F}$$

Repeating the calculations with the corrected value of the average unit-surface conductance on the air side we find that six transverse rows are required for heating the air according to the specifications.   *Ans.*

b) The pressure drop is obtained from Eqs. 9–11 and 9–13. We first calculate the friction factor f. For the arrangement of the heater, $S_L = 1.5\, D_o$, and we get from Eq. 9–13

$$f' = \left[0.044 + \frac{(0.08)(1.5)}{(1.5 - 1)^{0.43 + 1.13/1.5}}\right] 33,000^{-0.15} = 0.067$$

Taking the density of the air ρ at 72 F as 0.075 lb$_m$/cu ft, the pressure drop is from Eq. 9–11

$$\Delta p = \frac{(0.067)(32,000^2)(6)}{(0.075)(2.09 \times 10^8)} \, 1.2^{0.14} = 26.8 \text{ lb}_f/\text{sq ft}$$

or about 5 in. of water.   *Ans.*

In many commercial shell-and-tube heat exchangers, baffles are used to increase the velocity and consequently the heat-transfer coefficient on the shell side. Figure 9–19 is a photograph of a large baffled exchanger for vegetable-oil service. The flow of the shell-side fluid in baffled heat exchangers is partly perpendicular and partly parallel to the tubes. The

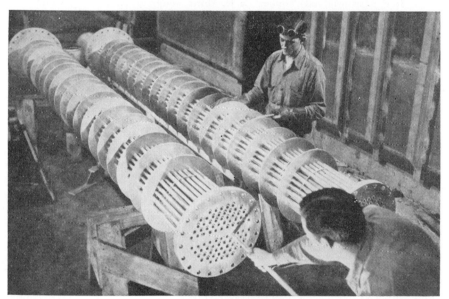

FIG. 9–19. Heat exchanger tube bundle with baffles. (Courtesy of the Aluminum Company of America)

heat-transfer coefficient on the shell side in this type of unit depends not only on the size and spacing of the tubes, the velocity and physical properties of the fluid, but also on the spacing and shape of the baffles. In addition, there is always leakage through the tube holes in the baffle and between the baffle and the inside of the shell, and there is bypassing between the tube bundle and the shell. Because of these complications, the heat-transfer coefficient can be estimated only by approximate methods or from experience with similar units. According to one approximate method which is widely used for design calculations (24), the average heat-transfer coefficient calculated for the corresponding tube arrangement in simple crossflow is multiplied by 0.6 to allow for leakage and other deviations from the simplified model. For additional information the reader is referred to Refs. 24, 25, 26, and 27.

REFERENCES

1. A. Fage, "The Air Flow Around a Circular Cylinder in the Region Where the Boundary Layer Separates from the Surface," Brit. Areo. Res. Comm., *R and M* 1179, 1929.

2. A. Fage and V. M. Falkner, "The Flow Around a Circular Cylinder," Brit. Aero Res. Comm., *R and M* 1369, 1931.

3. H. B. Squire, *Modern Developments in Fluid Dynamics*, 3d ed., Vol. 2. (Oxford: Clarendon Press, 1950.)

4. R. C. Martinelli, A. G. Guibert, E. H. Morin, and L. M. K. Boelter, "An Investigation of Aircraft Heaters VIII—A Simplified Method for Calculating the Unit-Surface Conductance over Wings," *NACA ARR*, March, 1943.

5. W. H. Giedt, "Investigation of Variation of Point Unit-Heat-Transfer Coefficient Around a Cylinder Normal to an Air Stream," *Trans. ASME*, Vol. 71 (1949), pp. 375–381.

6. R. Hilpert, "Wärmeabgabe von geheizten Drähten und Rohren," *Forsch. Gebiete Ingenieurw.*, Vol. 4 (1933), p. 215.

7. H. Dryden and A. N. Kuethe, "The Measurement of Fluctuations of Air Speed by the Hot-Wire Anemometer," *NACA Report* 320, 1929.

8. C. E. Pearson, "Measurement of Instantaneous Vector Air Velocity by Hot-Wire Methods," *J. Aero. Sci.*, Vol. 19 (1952), pp. 73–82.

9. W. H. McAdams, *Heat Transmission*, 3d ed. (New York: McGraw-Hill Book Company, Inc., 1953.)

10. H. F. Johnston, R. L. Pigford, and J. H. Chapin, "Heat Transfer to Clouds of Falling Particles," *Univ. of Ill. Bull.*, Vol. 38, No. 43 (1941).

11. R. D. Wallis, "Photographic Study of Fluid Flow Between Banks of Tubes," *Engineering*, Vol. 148 (1934), pp. 423–425.

12. O. P. Bergelin, G. A. Brown, and S. C. Doberstein, "Heat Transfer and Fluid Friction During Flow Across Banks of Tubes," *Trans. ASME*, Vol. 74 (1952), pp. 953–959.

13. O. P. Bergelin, A. P. Colburn, and H. L. Hull, "Heat Transfer and Pressure Drop During Viscous Flow Across Unbaffled Tube Banks," *Bull.* 2, Univ. of Delaware Eng. Exp. Sta. (1950).

14. W. E. Meece, *The Effect of the Number of Tube Rows Upon Heat Transfer and Pressure Drop During Viscous Flow Across In-line Tube Banks*, M.S. Thesis, Univ. of Delaware, 1949.

15. W. M. Kays and R. K. Lo, "Basic Heat Transfer and Flow Friction Design Data for Gas Flow Normal to Banks of Staggered Tubes—Use of a Transient Technique," *Tech. Rep.* 15, Navy Contract N6-onr-251 T. O. 6, Stanford Univ., 1952.

16. W. M. Kays, "Basic Heat Transfer and Flow Friction Design Data for Flow Normal to Banks of In-line Circular Tubes—Use of a Transient Technique," *Tech. Rep.* 21, Navy Contract N6-onr-251 T.O. 6, Stanford Univ., 1954.

17. W. M. Kays and A. L. London, "Compact Heat Exchangers—A Summary of Basic Heat Transfer and Flow Friction Design Data," *Tech. Rep.* 23, Navy Contract N6-onr-251, T.O. 6, Stanford Univ., 1954. (Also published in book form under same title by National Press, Palo Alto, Calif., 1955.)

18. M. Fishenden and O. A. Saunders, *An Introduction to Heat Transfer*. (Oxford: Clarendon Press, 1950.)

19. E. C. Huge, "Experimental Investigation of Effects of Equipment Size on Convection Heat Transfer and Flow Resistance in Cross Flow of Gases over Tube Banks," *Trans. ASME*, Vol. 59 (1937), pp. 573–582.

20. O. L. Pierson, "Experimental Investigation of Influence of Tube Arrangement on Convection Heat Transfer and Flow Resistance in Cross Flow of Gases over Tube Banks," *Trans. ASME*, Vol. 59 (1937), pp. 563–572.

21. E. C. Grimison, "Correlation and Utilization of New Data on Flow Resistance and Heat Transfer for Cross Flow of Gases over Tube Banks," *Trans. ASME*, Vol. 59 (1937), pp. 583–594.

22. N. V. Kuznetzkoff and V. A. Lokshin, "Conventional Heat Transfer for the Cross Flow of a Fluid over Tube Banks," *Teplo i Sila*, Vol. 13, No. 10 (1937), p. 19.

23. M. Jakob, "Heat Transfer and Flow Resistance in Cross Flow of Gases over Tube Banks," *Trans. ASME*, Vol. 60 (1938), pp. 384–386.

24. T. Tinker, "Analysis of the Fluid Flow Pattern in Shell-and-Tube Heat Exchangers and the Effect Distribution on the Heat Exchanger Performance," *Inst. Mech. Eng. and ASME Proc. of the General Discussion on Heat Transfer*, September, 1951, pp. 89–115.

25. B. E. Short, "Heat Transfer and Pressure Drop in Heat Exchangers," *Bull.* 3819, Univ. of Texas, 1938. (See also revision, *Bull.* 4324, June, 1943.)

26. D. A. Donohue, "Heat Transfer and Pressure Drop in Heat Exchangers," *Ind. Eng. Chem.*, Vol. 41 (1949), pp. 2499–2511.

27. A. C. Mueller, "Thermal Design of Heat Exchangers," *Eng. Bull.* 121, Res. Series, Purdue Univ., 1954.

28. R. J. Hoe, D. Dropkin, and O. E. Dwyer, "Heat Transfer Rates to Crossflowing Mercury in a Staggered Tube Bank—I," *Trans. ASME*, Vol. 79 (1957), pp. 899–908.

29. C. L. Richards, O. E. Dwyer, and D. Dropkin, "Heat Transfer Rates to Crossflowing Mercury in a Staggered Tube Bank—II," *ASME—AIChE* Heat Transfer Conference Paper No. 57-HT-11, 1957.

30. R. J. Grosh and R. D. Cess, "Heat Transfer to Fluids With Low Prandtl Numbers for Flow Across Plates and Cylinders of Various Cross Sections," *ASME* Paper No. 57-F-29, 1957.

31. R. D. Cess and R. J. Grosh, "Heat Transmission to Fluids With Low Prandtl Numbers for Flow Through Tube Banks," *ASME—AIChE* Heat Transfer Conference Paper No. 57-HT-12, 1957.

PROBLEMS

9–1. Determine the unit-surface conductance at the stagnation point and the average value of the conductance for a single 2-in.-OD, 24-in.-long tube in cross flow. The temperature of the tube surface is 500 F, the velocity of the fluid flowing perpendicularly to the tube axis is 20 fps, and its temperature is 100 F. The following fluids are to be considered: (a) air, (b) hydrogen, and (c) water.

9–2. A spherical water droplet of $\frac{1}{16}$-in. diam is freely falling in atmospheric air. Calculate the average convection heat-transfer coefficient when the droplet has reached its terminal velocity. Assume that the water is at 130 F, the air is at 70 F and neglect mass transfer and radiation.

9–3. A mercury-in-glass thermometer at 100 F (OD = 0.35 in.) is inserted through the duct wall into a 100 fps air stream at 150 F. Estimate the unit-convective conductance between the air and the thermometer. *Ans.* $\bar{h}_c \simeq 73$ Btu/hr sq ft F

9–4. Steam at 1 atm and 212 F is flowing across a 2-in.-OD tube at a velocity of 20 fps. Estimate the Nusselt number, the heat-transfer coefficient, and the rate of heat transfer per foot length of pipe if the pipe is at 400 F.

9–5.   Repeat Prob. 9–4 for a tube bank in which all of the tubes are spaced with their center lines 3.0 in. apart.

9–6.   Determine the average unit-surface conductance for air at 142 F flowing at a velocity of 200 fpm over a bank of 2.375-in.-OD tubes arranged as shown in the accompanying sketch.   The tube-wall temperature is 242 F.

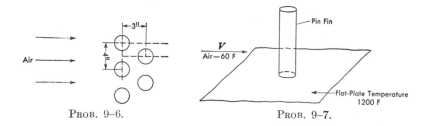

PROB. 9–6.   PROB. 9–7.

9–7.   A stainless-steel pin fin, 2-in. long, ¼-in. OD, extends from a flat plate into a 400 mph air stream as shown in the accompanying sketch.   (a) Estimate the average heat-transfer coefficient between the air and the fin.   (b) Estimate the temperature at the end of the fin.   (c) Estimate the rate of heat flow from the fin.

9–8.   Repeat Prob. 9–7 with glycerin flowing over the fin at 7 fps.

9–9.   An inventor claims that pumping power can be reduced if the tubes in a bank in crossflow are replaced by hollow streamlined bodies whose cross sections have the shape of an ellipse.   He claims that energy losses in the wake would be reduced without affecting the rate of heat transfer adversely.   See the accompanying sketch.   Present your evaluation of the inventor's claim in the form of a short report, and substantiate your conclusions by order-of-magnitude calculations.   State all of your assumptions.

PROB. 9–9.

9–10. The instruction manual for a hot-wire anemometer states that "Roughly speaking, the current varies as the fourth power of the average velocity at a fixed wire resistance." Check this statement, using the heat-transfer characteristics of a thin wire in air and water.

9–11. In a lead-shot tower, spherical $\frac{3}{8}$-in.-diam BB shots are formed by drops of molten lead which solidify as they descend in cooler air. At the terminal velocity, i.e., when the drag equals the gravitational force, estimate the total unit-surface conductance if the lead surface is at 340 F ($\epsilon = 0.63$) and the air temperature is 60 F. Assume $C_D = 0.75$ for the first trial calculation.

9–12. Water at 350 F and at 10 ft/sec enters a bare, 50 ft long, 1-in. wrought-iron pipe (1.05-in. ID, 1.32-in. OD). If air at 50 F flows perpendicular to the pipe at 40 ft/sec, determine the outlet temperature of the water. (Note that the temperature difference between the air and the water varies along the pipe.)

9–13. Estimate the unit-surface conductance for liquid sodium at 1000 F flowing over a 10-row staggered-tube bank arranged in an equilateral-triangular arrow with a 1.5 pitch to diameter ratio. The entering velocity is 10 ft/sec, based on the area of the shell, and the tube-surface temperature is 400 F. What is the outlet temperature of the sodium?

9–14. Estimate (a) the unit-surface conductance for a spherical fuel droplet injected into a diesel engine at 180 F and 300 ft/sec. The oil droplet is 0.001 in. in diam, the cylinder pressure is 700 psia, and the gas temperature is 1700 R. (b) What is the time required to heat the droplet to its self-ignition temperature of 580 F?

10 Heat Transfer with Change in Phase

10–1. FUNDAMENTALS OF BOILING HEAT TRANSFER

Heat transfer to boiling liquids is a convection process involving a change in phase from liquid to vapor. The phenomena of boiling heat transfer are considerably more complex than those of convection without phase change because, in addition to all of the variables associated with convection, those associated with the change in the phase are also relevant. Whereas in liquid-phase convection, the geometry of the system, the viscosity, the density, the thermal conductivity, the expansion coefficient, and the specific heat of the fluid are sufficient to describe the process, in boiling heat transfer, the surface characteristics, the surface tension, the latent heat of evaporation, the pressure, the density, and possibly other properties of the vapor play an important part. As a result of the large number of variables involved, neither general equations describing the boiling process nor general correlations of boiling-heat-transfer data are available to date. Considerable progress has been made, however, during the last few years in gaining a physical understanding of the boiling mechanism. By observing the boiling phenomena with the aid of high-speed photography, it has been found that there are various distinct regimes of boiling in which the heat-transfer mechanisms differ radically. To correlate the experimental data it is therefore necessary to describe and analyze each of the boiling regimes separately.

Until about fifteen years ago, processes involving heat transfer to boiling liquids were found primarily in the tubes of steam boilers, various types of kettles, in evaporators of air-conditioning and refrigeration systems, and in certain chemical processes. The emphasis in these applications is on transferring heat for the purpose of converting liquid into vapor. The over-all thermal resistance which controls the rate of heat transfer in these systems is composed of a number of individual resistances in series. Compared to the thermal resistances of single-phase fluids, especially gases or vapors, and the surface scales which usually form during operation, the thermal resistance of a boiling liquid under normal operating conditions is usually small and does not control the rate of heat flow.   A very different problem, however, has been encountered recently in high-performance machines such as nuclear reactors and rocket motors (1).   In these devices very large quantities of heat are released in relatively small volumes, and if boiling heat transfer is to be used to cool the structural components, its mechanisms and limitations must be known accurately to ensure reliable operation.   The cooling problem in these devices is illustrated by comparing the rate of heat release per unit volume in a conventional boiler with that in a rocket motor and a nuclear reactor.   A heat release of about 40,000 Btu/hr cu ft is considered good practice in a modern boiler, but in a rocket or a nuclear reactor it may be 1,000,000,000 Btu/hr cu ft.   A characteristic common to nuclear reactors and jet engines is that the rate of heat generation is essentially constant, and if the cooling is inadequate, the surface transferring the heat will fail by melting or, possibly, by very rapid corrosion caused by its high temperature.

To acquire a physical understanding of the phenomena which are characteristic of the various boiling regimes we shall first consider a simple system consisting of a heating surface, such as a flat plate or a wire, submerged in a pool of water at saturation temperature without external agitation.   This is called *pool boiling*.   A familiar example of such a system is the boiling of water in a kettle on a stove.   As long as the temperature of the surface does not exceed the boiling point of the liquid by more than a few degrees, heat is transferred to liquid near the heating surface by free convection.   The convection currents circulate the superheated liquid, and evaporation takes place at the free surface of the liquid.   The heat-transfer mechanism in this process, although some evaporation occurs, is simply free convection, because only liquid is in contact with the heating surface.

As the temperature of the heating surface is increased, a point is reached where, in certain places, the energy level of the liquid adjacent to the surface becomes so high that some of the molecules break away from the surrounding molecules, are transformed from liquid into a vapor nucleus, and finally form a vapor bubble.   This process occurs simultaneously at a number of favored spots on the heating surface.   The vapor bubbles are at first small and condense before reaching the surface, but as the temperature is raised further, they become more numerous and larger until they finally rise to the free surface.   These phenomena may be observed when boiling water in a kettle.   They are also illustrated by the sketches of Fig. 10–1 for a horizontal wire heated electrically in a pool of distilled water at atmospheric pressure and corresponding saturation temperature of 212 F (2).   In the curve accompanying the sketches of the various boiling regimes, the heat flux is plotted as a function of the temperature difference between the surface and the saturation temperature.   This temperature difference, ΔT_x, is called the *excess temperature above the boiling*

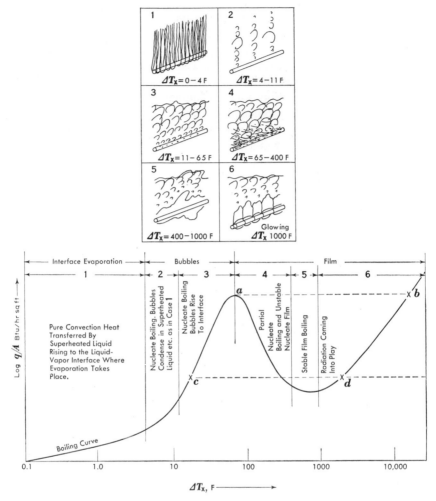

FIG. 10–1. Typical boiling data for a wire heated electrically in a pool of water at atmospheric pressure. (Extracted from "Heat Transfer to Water Boiling Under Pressure," by E. A. Farber and R. L. Scorah, published in *Trans. ASME*, Vol. 79, 1948, with permission of the publishers, The American Society of Mechanical Engineers)

point or *excess temperature* for short. We observe that, in regimes 2 and 3, the heat flux increases rapidly with increasing surface temperature. The process in these two regimes is called nucleate boiling. Most of the heat is transferred from the heating surface directly to the surrounding liquid by intense convection currents which are induced by the motion of the bubbles. As the bubbles form at the surface, they displace liquid above, which rushes back to fill the void when the vapor bubbles leave the surface.

The vapor bubbles receive only a small fraction of the total heat dissipated, but they create intense turbulence and mechanically pump hot liquid from the vicinity of the heating surface into the cooler pool.

When the excess temperature is raised to about 100 F, we observe that the heat flux reaches a maximum of about 500,000 Btu/hr sq ft, and a further increase of the temperature causes a decrease in the rate of heat flow. The reason for the inflection point in the curve may be found by examining the heat-transfer mechanism during boiling. At the onset of boiling, bubbles grow at certain favored spots on the surface until the buoyant force or currents of the surrounding liquid carry them away. Although the product of the size of the departing bubbles times the frequency of their formation at any particular spot does not vary appreciably with heat flux (3,4,5), the number of spots at which bubbles form increases nearly in direct proportion with the excess temperature (6). The increase in bubble population per unit area promotes the heat transfer by convection to the liquid, but since the thermal conductivity of the vapor is so much smaller than that of the liquid, the portion of the surface covered by vapor bubbles at any instant is effectively insulated. Thus, increasing the number of bubbles promotes the flow of heat by virtue of the agitating motion of the bubbles, but at the same time the area available for heat transfer to the liquid diminishes. As long as the agitation effects predominate, the heat flux rises with increasing surface temperature, and nucleate boiling prevails. However, when the number of spots at which bubbles form becomes so large that an appreciable portion of the surface is covered by vapor, the insulating effects overshadow the beneficial effects of fluid agitation and the heat flux decreases with increasing excess temperature. The regimes in which vapor blankets all or an appreciable portion of the heating surface are known as *film boiling*. The maximum heat flux occurs just before the transition from nucleate to film boiling takes place. The photographs in Figs. 10–2 and 10–3 illustrate the nucleate and film-boiling mechanisms on a wire submerged in water at atmospheric pressure. Note the film of vapor which completely covers the wire in Fig. 10–3. A phenomenon which closely resembles this condition is also observed when a drop of water falls on a red-hot stove. The drop does not evaporate immediately but dances on the stove because a steam film forms at the interface between the hot surface and the liquid and insulates the droplet.

The film-boiling regime is usually subdivided according to the behavior of the vapor film. Just beyond the peak heat flux, in regime 4 of Fig. 10–1, an unstable film forms over the heating surface and large vapor bubbles originate at its outer surface. The film periodically collapses and forms again under the action of circulating currents. In regime 5, vapor covers the surface continuously and only the shape of the outer film surface changes. At values of ΔT_x larger than 1000 F, radiation becomes in-

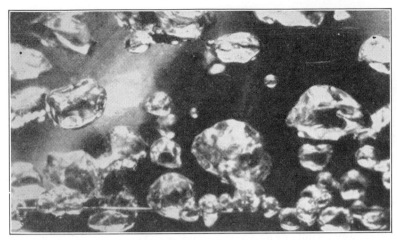

FIG. 10–2. Photograph showing nucleate boiling on a wire in water.
(Courtesy of J. T. Castles)

creasingly effective.   In this regime, 6 in Fig. 10–1, the film is very stable
and large bubbles form on its outer surface.

The characteristic boiling curve shown in Fig. 10–1 can be readily
obtained in a system when the surface temperature can be controlled.
A surface heated by hot gases or by vapors condensing at various pressures
would constitute such a system.   However, there are many applications
in which the heat flux is the independent variable and the surface temperature adjusts to provide the conditions necessary to transfer the heat from
the surface.   A wire heated by electric current, in which the heat genera-

FIG. 10–3.   Photograph showing film boiling on a wire in water.
(Courtesy of J. T. Castles)

tion is controlled by the voltage imposed, or a fuel rod of a nuclear reactor, in which the rate of heat generation is adjusted by controlling the rate of fission, are examples of systems in which the heat flux determines the excess temperature. When the peak heat flux is reached in such a system, any further increase in heat generation is accompanied by a decrease in the rate of heat flow from the surface. The difference between the energy input and the energy output causes an increase in the internal energy. This results in a rise of the temperature of the heating surface and further reduces the heat flow. Thus, a constant heat-input system is unstable in regime 4 and, unless the heat flux is quickly reduced when the peak is reached, equilibrium can be established only at point b in Fig. 10–1. The surface temperature corresponding to this operating condition is very high, since most of the heat is transferred by radiation when the surface is covered by a vapor blanket. In fact, the equilibrium temperature b generally exceeds the melting point of most metals, and the system fails usually before reaching equilibrium. The condition of maximum heat flux in the nucleate regime is often referred to as *vapor binding* or as the *burnout point*.

If the rate of heat flow from a surface is sufficiently large, local boiling in the vicinity of the surface may take place even when the bulk temperature is below the boiling point. The boiling process in a liquid whose bulk temperature is below the saturation temperature but whose boundary layer is sufficiently superheated that bubbles form next to the heating surface is usually called *heat transfer to a subcooled boiling liquid* or *surface boiling*. The mechanisms of bubble formation and heat transfer are similar to those described for liquids at saturation temperature. However, the bubbles increase in number while their size and average lifetime decrease with decreasing bulk temperature at a given heat flux (8). As a result of the increase in the bubble population, the agitation of the liquid caused by the motion of the bubbles is more intense in a subcooled liquid than in a pool of saturated liquid, and much larger heat fluxes can be attained before vapor binding occurs. The mechanism by which a typical bubble induces turbulence in subcooled and degassed water is illustrated by the sketches in Fig. 10–4, (9). The letters for the sequence of events described in the following paragraphs correspond to the designations of the sketches.

a) The liquid next to the wall is superheated.

b) A vapor nucleus of sufficient size to permit a bubble to grow has formed.

c) The bubble grows and pushes the layer of superheated liquid above it away from the wall. The resulting motion of the liquid is indicated by arrows.

d) The top of the bubble surface extends into cooler liquid. The temperature in the bubble has dropped. The bubble continues to grow by virtue of the inertia of the liquid, but at a slower rate than during stage c because it receives less heat per unit volume.

e) The inertia of the liquid has caused the bubble to grow so large that its upper surface extends far into cooler liquid. It loses more heat by evaporation and convection than it received by conduction from the heating surface.

f) The inertia forces have been dissipated and the bubble begins to collapse. Cold liquid from above follows in its wake.

g) The vapor phase has been condensed, the bubble has disappeared, and the heat wall is splashed by a stream of cold liquid at high velocity.

h) The liquid film has settled and the cycle repeats.

The foregoing description of the life cycle of a typical bubble also applies qualitatively through stage e to liquids containing dissolved gases,

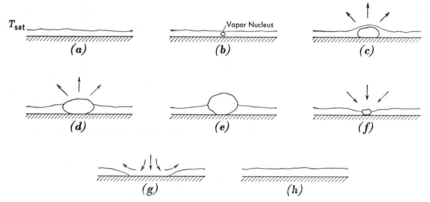

Fig. 10–4. Sketches illustrating the flow pattern induced by a bubble in a subcooled boiling liquid.

to solutions of more than one liquid, and to saturated liquids. In these cases, however, the bubble does not collapse but is carried away from the surface by buoyant forces or convection currents. A void is created all the same and the surface is swept by cooler fluid rushing in from above. What eventually happens to the bubbles, whether they collapse on the surface or are swept away, has little influence on the heat-transfer mechanism, which depends mostly on the liquid agitation.

The primary variable controlling the bubble mechanism is the excess temperature. It should be noted, however, that, in the nucleate boiling regime, the total variation of the excess temperature, irrespective of the fluid bulk temperature, is relatively small for a very large range of heat flux. For design purposes the conventional heat-transfer coefficient, which is based on the difference in temperature between the bulk of the fluid and the surface (Eq. 6–1), is therefore only of secondary interest as compared to the maximum heat flux attainable in nucleate boiling and the wall temperature at which boiling begins.

The generation of steam in the tubes of a boiler, the vaporization of fluids such as gasoline in the chemical industry, and the boiling of a refrigerant in the cooling coils of a refrigerator are processes which closely resemble those described above, except that, in these industrial applications of boiling, the fluid generally flows past the heating surface by forced convection. The heating surface is frequently the inside of a tube or a duct, and the fluid at the discharge end is a mixture of liquid and vapor. The foregoing descriptions of bubble formation and behavior also apply to forced convection, but the heat-transfer mechanism is further aided by the motion of the bulk of the fluid.

10–2. CORRELATION OF BOILING-HEAT-TRANSFER DATA

The dominant mechanism by which heat is transferred in forced convection is the turbulent mixing of hot and cold fluid particles. As shown in Chapter 6, experimental data for forced convection without boiling can be correlated by a relation of the type

$$\mathrm{Nu} = \phi \ (\mathrm{Re}) \ \psi \ (\mathrm{Pr}) \qquad [8\text{–}2]$$

where the Reynolds number Re is a measure of the turbulence and mixing motion associated with the flow. The increased heat-transfer rates attained with nucleate boiling are the result of the intense agitation of the fluid produced by the motion of vapor bubbles. In fact, the agitation caused by the bubbles in fully developed nucleate boiling is so vigorous that, in comparison, the turbulence due to ordinary convection currents is only of secondary importance.

Photographic observations (10) have shown that the latent heat required to form the bubbles represents only a very small fraction of the total energy transferred in boiling and that, despite the presence of vapor bubbles, the major portion of the heat is still transferred directly from the heating surface to the liquid by convection currents. To correlate experimental data in the nucleate-boiling regime it is, therefore, appropriate to replace the conventional Reynolds number in Eq. 8–2 by a modulus significant of the turbulence and mixing motion for the boiling process. A type of Reynolds number Re_b, which is a measure of the agitation of the liquid in nucleate-boiling heat transfer, is obtained by combining the average bubble diameter D_b, the mass velocity of the bubbles per unit area G_b, and the liquid viscosity μ_l to form the dimensionless modulus

$$\mathrm{Re}_b = \frac{D_b G_b}{\mu_l}$$

This parameter is often called the bubble Reynolds number and it takes, in nucleate boiling, the place of the conventional Reynolds. If we use the bubble diameter D_b as the significant length in the Nusselt number, Eq. 8–2 can be modified for nucleate boiling into the form

$$\mathrm{Nu}_b = \frac{h_b D_b}{k_l} = \phi(\mathrm{Re}_b)\psi(\mathrm{Pr}_l) \qquad (10\text{–}1)$$

where Pr_l is the Prandtl number of the saturated liquid and h_b is the *nucleate boiling heat-transfer coefficient* defined as

$$h_b = \frac{q/A}{\Delta T_x}$$

In nucleate boiling the excess temperature ΔT_x is the physically significant temperature potential. It replaces the temperature difference between the surface and the bulk of the fluid ΔT used in single-phase convection. Numerous experiments have shown the validity of this method, which obviates the need to know the exact temperature of the liquid and can therefore be applied to saturated as well as subcooled liquids.

Pool boiling. Using experimental data of pool boiling as a guide, Rohsenow (4) modified Eq. 10–1 by means of simplifying assumptions. The equation he found most convenient for the reduction and correlation of experimental data is

$$\frac{c_l \Delta T_x}{h_{fg} \mathrm{Pr}_l^{1.7}} = C_{sf} \left[\frac{q/A}{\mu_l h_{fg}} \sqrt{\frac{g_c \sigma}{g(\rho_l - \rho_v)}} \right]^{0.33} \qquad (10\text{–}2)$$

where c_l = specific heat of saturated liquid, in Btu/lb$_m$ F;
q/A = heat flux in Btu/hr sq ft;
h_{fg} = latent heat of vaporization, in Btu/lb$_m$;
g_c = conversion factor, 4.17×10^8 lb$_m$ ft/lb$_f$ hr^2;
g = gravitational acceleration, in ft/hr^2;
ρ_l = density of the saturated liquid, in lb$_m$/cu ft;
ρ_v = density of the saturated vapor, in lb$_m$/cu ft;
σ = surface tension of the liquid-to-vapor interface, in lb$_f$/ft;
Pr_l = Prandtl number of the saturated liquid;
μ_l = viscosity of the liquid, in lb$_m$/hr ft;

and C_{sf} is an empirical constant which depends upon the nature of the heating surface-fluid combination and whose numerical value varies from system to system. Probably the most important variable affecting C_{sf} is the angle of contact between the bubble and the heating surface, which is a measure of the wettability of a surface with a particular fluid. The sketches of Fig. 10–5 show that the contact angle decreases with greater

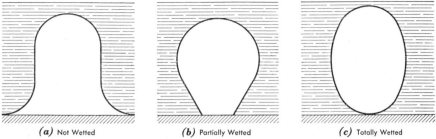

(a) Not Wetted   (b) Partially Wetted   (c) Totally Wetted

Fig. 10–5. Sketches illustrating the effect of surface wettability on the bubble contact angle.

wetting. A totally wetted surface has the smallest area covered by vapor at a given excess temperature and consequently represents the most favorable condition for efficient heat transfer. In the absence of quantitative information on the effect of wettability and surface conditions on the constant C_{sf}, its value must be determined empirically for each fluid-surface combination.

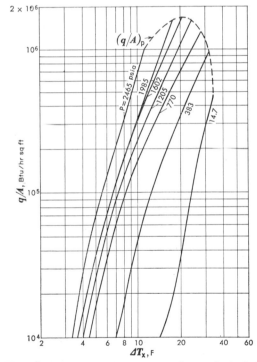

Fig. 10–6. Heat flux vs. excess temperature for nucleate boiling of water on a 0.024-in.-diam electrically-heated platinum wire. (Extracted from "A Method of Correlating Heat-Transfer Data from Surface Boiling Liquids," by W. M. Rohsenow, published in *Trans. ASME*, Vol. 74, 1955, with permission of the publishers, The American Society of Mechanical Engineers)

Figure 10–6 shows experimental data obtained by Addoms (11) for pool boiling of water on a 0.024-in.-diameter platinum wire at various saturation pressures. These data, plotted as heat flux vs. excess temperature in Fig. 10–6, are replotted in Fig. 10–7 using

$$\left[\frac{q/A}{\mu_l h_{fg}} \sqrt{\frac{g_c \sigma}{g(\rho_l - \rho_v)}} \right]$$

as the ordinate and $c_l \Delta T_x / h_{fg} \mathrm{Pr}_l^{1.7}$ as the abscissa. The slope of the

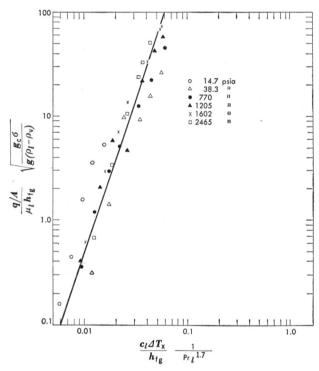

FIG. 10–7. Correlation of pool-boiling heat-transfer data by method of Rohsenow. (Extracted from "A Method of Correlating Heat-Transfer Data from Surface Boiling Liquids," by W. M. Rohsenow, published in *Trans. ASME*, Vol. 74, 1955, with permission of the publishers, The American Society of Mechanical Engineers)

straight line faired through the experimental points is 0.33; for water boiling on platinum, the value of C_{sf} is 0.013. For comparison the experimental values of C_{sf} for a number of other fluid-surface combinations are listed in Table 10–1.

TABLE 10-1

VALUES OF THE COEFFICIENT C_{sf} IN EQ. 10-2 FOR VARIOUS
LIQUID-SURFACE COMBINATIONS

Fluid-Heating Surface Combination	C_{sf}
Water–copper (12)*	0.013
Carbon tetrachloride–copper (12)	0.013
35% K_2CO_3–copper (12)	0.0054
n-Butyl alcohol–copper (12)	0.00305
50% K_2CO_3–copper (12)	0.00275
Isopropyl alcohol–copper (12)	0.00225
n-Pentane–chromium (13)	0.015
Water–platinum (11)	0.013
Benzene-chromium (13)	0.010
Water-brass (14)	0.0060
Ethyl alcohol–chromium (13)	0.0027

* Numbers in parentheses are those of references listed at end of chapter.

The principal advantage of the Rohsenow correlation is that the performance of a particular fluid-surface combination in nucleate boiling at any pressure and heat flux can be predicted from a single test. One value of the heat flux q/A and its corresponding value of the excess temperature difference ΔT_x are all that are required to evaluate C_{fs} in Eq. 10-2. It should be noted, however, that Eq. 10-2 applies only to clean surfaces. For contaminated surfaces the exponent of Pr_l has been found to vary between 0.8 and 2.0. Contamination apparently does not influence the other exponent in Eq. 10-2.

The geometrical shape of the heating surface has no appreciable effect on the nucleate-boiling mechanism (15,16). This is not unexpected, since the influence of the bubble motion on the fluid conditions is limited to a region very near the surface.

Boiling with forced convection. The foregoing method of correlating data for nucleate pool boiling has also been applied successfully to boiling of fluids flowing inside tubes or ducts by forced (4) or natural convection (12).

Figure 10-8 shows curves faired through boiling data, typical of subcooled forced convection in tubes or ducts (17,18). The system in which these data were obtained consisted of a vertical annulus containing an electrically heated stainless-steel tube placed centrally in tubes of various diameters. The heater was cooled by degassed distilled water flowing upward at velocities from 1 to 12 fps and pressures from 30 to 90 psia. The scale of Fig. 10-8 is logarithmic. The ordinate is the heat flux q/A, and the abscissa is ΔT, the temperature difference between the heating surface and the bulk of the fluid. The dotted lines represent forced-convection conditions at various velocities and various degrees of subcooling. The solid lines in-

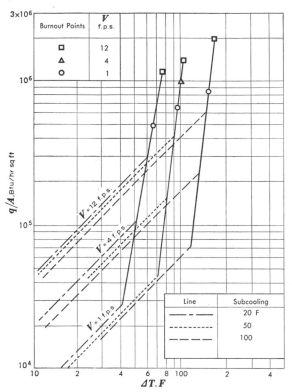

Fig. 10–8.   Typical boiling data for subcooled
forced convection—heat flux vs. temperature
difference between surface and fluid bulk.   (By
permission from W. M. McAdams, W. E. Kennel,
C. S. Minden, R. Carl, P. M. Picarnell, and J. E.
Drew from "Heat Transfer at High Rates to Water
with Surface Boiling," *Ind. Eng. Chem.*, Vol.
41, 1945)

dicate the deviation from forced convection caused by surface boiling.   We
note that the onset of boiling caused by increasing the heat flux depends on
the velocity of the liquid and the degree of subcooling below its saturation
temperature at the prevailing pressure.   At lower pressures the boiling
point at a given velocity is reached at lower heat fluxes.   An increase in
velocity increases the effectiveness of forced convection, decreases the surface temperature at a given heat flux, and thereby delays the onset of
boiling.   In the boiling region the curves are steep and the wall temperature is practically independent of the fluid velocity.   This shows that the
agitation caused by the bubbles is much more effective than turbulence in
forced convection without boiling.   The heat flux data with surface boiling
are plotted separately, in Fig. 10–9 vs. the excess temperature.   The resulting curve is similar to that for nucleate boiling in a saturated pool shown in

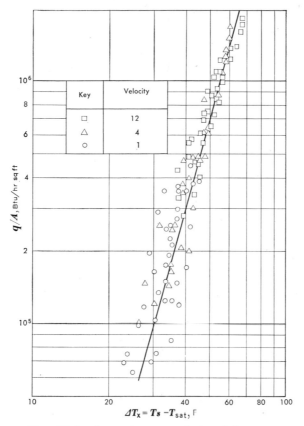

FIG. 10–9.   Approximate correlation of data for
nucleate boiling with forced-convection obtained
by plotting heat flux vs. excess temperature.
(By permission from W. M. McAdams, W. E.
Kennel, C. S. Minden, R. Carl, P. M. Picarnell,
and J. E. Drew from "Heat Transfer at High Rates
to Water with Surface Boiling," *Ind. Eng. Chem.*,
Vol. 41, 1945)

Fig. 10–1 and emphasizes the similarity of the boiling processes and their
dependence on the excess temperature.

To apply the pool-boiling correlation to forced-convection boiling, the
total heat flux must be separated into two parts, one a *boiling flux* q_b/A, the
other a *convective flux* q_c/A, or

$$q_{total} = q_b + q_c$$

The boiling heat flux is determined by subtracting the heat-flow rate,
accountable for by forced convection alone, from the total flux, or

$$q_b = q_{total} - A\bar{h}_c (T_s - T_b) \tag{10–3}$$

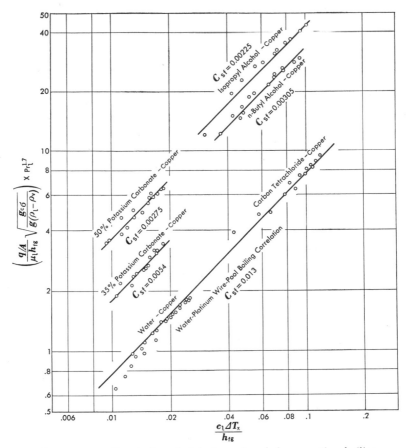

Fig. 10–10. Correlation of data for subcooled convection boiling by the Rohsenow method. (Extracted from "Recent Developments in Boiling Research," by W. H. Jens and G. Leppert, *J. Am. Soc. Naval Eng.*, Inc., Vol. 67, 1955, with permission of the publishers, The Society of Naval Engineers, Inc.)

where $\bar{h}_c$ is determined from Eq. 8–18[1] or Eq. 8–22. This value of q_b is then used in Eq. 10–3 in the same manner as the total heat flux in nucleate pool boiling. The results of this method of correlating data for boiling superimposed on convection are shown in Fig. 10–10 for a number of fluid-surface combinations. Some of the data shown in Fig. 10–10 were obtained with subcooled liquids, others with saturated liquids containing various amounts of vapor.

Maximum heat flux with nucleate boiling. The Rohsenow method unifies the correlation of data for all types of nucleate-boiling processes,

[1] If Eq. 8–18 is used, Rohsenow (4) recommends that the coefficient 0.023 be replaced by 0.019.

including pool boiling of saturated or subcooled liquids and boiling of subcooled or saturated liquids flowing by forced or natural convection in tubes or ducts. Specifically, the correlation equation (Eq. 10–2) relates the heat flux to the excess temperature, provided the relevant fluid properties and the pertinent coefficient C_{fs} are available. The correlation, although it is restricted to nucleate boiling, does not reveal the excess temperature at which the heat flux reaches a maximum; nucleate boiling breaks down, and an insulating vapor film forms. As mentioned earlier, the maximum heat flux attainable with nucleate boiling is sometimes of greater interest to the designer than the exact surface temperature because, for efficient heat transfer (19) and operating safety (1,17), particularly in high-

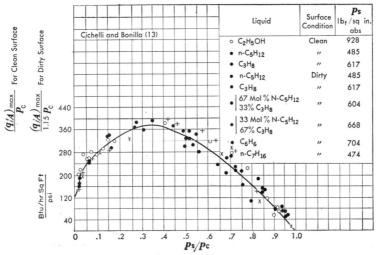

FIG. 10–11. Peak heat flux in nucleate boiling at various pressures—correlation of Ciechelli and Bonilla. (By permission from M. T. Ciechelli and C. F. Bonilla, "Heat Transfer to Liquids Boiling under Pressure," *AIChE Trans.*, Vol. 41, 1945)

performance constant-heat-input systems, operation in the film-boiling regime must be avoided. The maximum heat flux attainable with nucleate boiling depends on many factors. At the present time, the individual effects of each of the variables causing vapor binding can not be described quantitatively, but the qualitative effects of the more important variables are known from experiments.

For fluids boiling on a surface submerged in a pool of liquid at its saturation temperature, the maximum heat flux increases with increasing pressure until the pressure on the system reaches about one-third of the critical pressure. A further increase in pressure causes a decrease in the heat flux attainable with nucleate boiling. Figure 10–11 illustrates this trend for a number of different fluids at their respective saturation pressures (13).   The ordinate is the maximum heat flux $(q/A)_{max}$ in Btu/hr sq ft divided by the critical pressure p_c in psia while the abscissa is the ratio of the system pressure to the critical pressure p_s/p_c. The curve faired through the experimental points represents an average for clean surfaces. If the surface is dirty or otherwise contaminated, the maximum heat flux is increased by about 15 per cent.   All of the data shown in Fig. 10–11, as well as those presented in Refs. 11 and 20, are also correlated within about 10 per cent (21) by the dimensional equation

$$\frac{(q/A)_{max}}{\rho_v h_{fg}} = 14.3 \left(\frac{\rho_l}{\rho_v} - 1\right)^{0.6} \tag{10–4}$$

where $(q/A)_{max}$ = maximum heat flux, in Btu/hr sq ft;

ρ_v = density of the vapor, in lb_m/cu ft;

h_{fg} = latent heat of vaporization at the system pressure, in Btu/lb_m;

ρ_l = density of liquid, in lb_m/cu ft.

If the temperature of the bulk of the liquid is below the saturation temperature, considerably higher heat fluxes than those shown in Fig. 10–11 can be obtained without vapor binding. Figure 10–12 illustrates the influence of

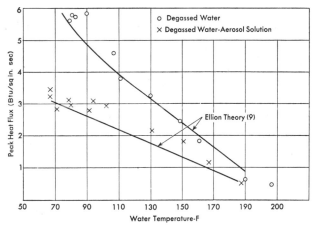

Fig. 10–12.   Effect of bulk temperature on peak heat flux in pool boiling.   (By permission from M. E. Ellion, "A Study of the Mechanism of Boiling Heat Transfer," Memo No. 20–28, Jet Propulsion Laboratory, Calif. Inst. of Tech., March, 1954)

the bulk temperature on the peak heat flux for distilled water and a 1 per cent aqueous solution of a surface-active agent boiling on a stainless-steel heater.   The addition of the surface-active agent decreased the surface tension of water from 72 to 34 dynes/cm.   This caused an appreciable decrease in the peak heat flux, an effect which is in agreement with a theoretical analysis by Ellion (9). The presence of dissolved gases also reduces the peak heat flux at a given bulk temperature.

The superposition of forced convection on boiling has a similar effect on the peak heat flux as a reduction of the bulk temperature. Table 10–2 shows a summary of some recent correlations (22) which have been pro-

TABLE 10–2

FORCED-CONVECTION BURNOUT CORRELATIONS FOR WATER

Formula*	Ref.	Range of Variables
$(q/A)_{max} = (400{,}000 + 4800\ \Delta T_{sub})u^{\frac{1}{3}}$	16	V from 1 to 20 fps p from 30 to 90 psia ΔT_{sub} from 20 to 100 F
$(q/A)_{max} = 7000u^{\frac{1}{3}}\ \Delta T_{sub}$	8	V from 5 to 40 fps p from 14 to 160 psia ΔT_{sub} from 20 to 280 F
$(q/A)_{max} = C\ (G/10^6)m\ \Delta T_{sub}^{0.22}$	22	ΔT_{sub} from 3 to 160 F

Pressure (psi)	m	C
500	0.16	0.817
1000	0.28	0.626
2000	0.50	0.445

* $(q/A)_{max}$ in Btu/hr sq ft V in fps ΔT_{sub} in F G in lb_m/hr sq ft

posed to predict the peak heat flux in forced-convection boiling. The experimental data were obtained in long heated tubes or ducts, and the burnout occurred at the outlet where the subcooling was the least. All of the correlations are based on the subcooling $\Delta T_{sub} = T_{sat} - T_b$ at the outlet. The fluid temperature is a calculated value based on the mass flow rate, heat input, and inlet temperature.

Although the experimental data are meager and the agreement between different investigators is not good, it appears that the most important variables are the velocity and the subcooling. An increase in either or both of them also increases the maximum heat flux attainable with nucleate boiling.

A moderate amount of data has also been obtained on burnout with net steam generation (22), but no general correlation of the results has so far been proposed. Heat fluxes as high as 3,000,000 Btu/hr sq ft have been obtained with exit qualities up to 30 per cent (22). It is, however, not recommended to design for such high heat fluxes, and a value of 500,000 Btu/hr sq ft is sometimes suggested as an upper limit for water with substantial vapor generation. Another factor which may impose limitations in design is the pressure drop in two-phase flow, which can be many times larger than the pressure drop calculated on the basis of liquid flowing at the same mass-flow rate. Under some extreme conditions, choking of the flow caused by compressibility effects in two-phase flow have been observed (24), and it has been suggested that these phenomena may cause burnouts (25). Complete summaries of the available information on the pressure drop and fluid-flow phenomena associated with boiling are presented in Refs. 1 and 16. The reader is referred to these sources for detailed information and a complete bibliography.

Film boiling. The unstable film-boiling region is of little practical importance, and the meager information available for this regime has not been correlated. The stable film-boiling regime, however, has been studied both experimentally and analytically by Bromley (26,27). His experimental results for stable film boiling on the outside of horizontal tubes of 0.188 and 0.35 in. in diameter can be correlated with satisfactory accuracy by the equation

$$\bar{h}_b = 0.62 \left[\frac{k_v^3 \rho_v (\rho_l - \rho_v) g \lambda'}{D_o \mu_v \Delta T_x} \right]^{\frac{1}{4}} \tag{10-5}$$

where k_v = thermal conductivity of saturated vapor, in Btu/hr ft F;

D_o = outside diameter of tube, in ft;

μ_v = viscosity of saturated vapor, in lb_m/hr ft;

while, except for λ', the other symbols are the same as those used in Eq. 10–2. The symbol λ' is defined as

$$\lambda' = h_{fg} \left(1 + \frac{0.4 \Delta T_x c_{pv}}{h_{fg}} \right) \tag{10-6}$$

where c_{pv} is the specific heat of the saturated vapor.

The average unit-surface conductance $\bar{h}_b$ in Eq. 10–5 accounts only for the heat which is transferred by conduction through the vapor film and by boiling convection from the surface of the film to the surrounding liquid. Superimposed on this heat-flow path is the contribution of radiation to the total heat transfer. Since the heat transfer by radiation causes an increase in the thickness of the film, the coefficient h_b for conduction and convection in the presence of appreciable radiation is less than in the absence of radiation. The total surface conductance when radiation is appreciable can be estimated from the empirical relation

$$\bar{h} = \bar{h}_b \left(\frac{\bar{h}_b}{\bar{h}} \right)^{\frac{1}{3}} + \bar{h}_r \tag{10-7}$$

by trial and error. The radiation conductance $\bar{h}_r$ can be evaluated with the aid of Eq. 1–11. To determine the heat-transfer coefficient when the liquid is flowing past the surface of the tube, Bromley (27) suggests the equation

$$\bar{h}_b = 2.7 \sqrt{\frac{V_\infty k_v \rho_v \lambda'}{D_o \Delta T_x}} \tag{10-8}$$

if the velocity V_∞ is larger than $2\sqrt{gD_o}$. The total conductance, including radiation, is then

$$\bar{h} = \bar{h}_b + \tfrac{7}{8}\bar{h}_r \tag{10-9}$$

under these conditions. At velocities less than $2\sqrt{gD_o}$, the flow is not fully developed turbulent and the conductance may be evaluated from data in Ref. 27.

Practical aspects of boiling heat transfer. As mentioned before, in most industrial applications it is desirable to avoid film boiling. This is accomplished by providing adequate circulation and by keeping the heat flux below the maximum value attainable with nucleate boiling. It is, however, advantageous in many cases to allow the formation of a limited number of vapor bubbles in order to reduce the surface temperature with a minimum of pressure drop. An important application of this technique is the regenerative cooling of rocket motors, where the combustion chamber is cooled by its own fuel or oxidizer. In this application the liquid is pumped past the hot wall at a velocity which is low enough to permit surface boiling, but high enough to keep the bulk of the liquid sufficiently subcooled to condense the vapor and prevent failure by burnout.

Several industrial applications of forced convection with progressive vaporization have been cited previously. A few conventional high-pressure boilers are also designed on this principle, but natural circulation is more common. Boiling and progressive vaporization of a liquid flowing by natural circulation is a very complicated process, and despite considerable research that has been done on this problem, natural-circulation systems can not be analyzed without making simplifying assumptions of questionable validity. An extensive review of the experimental and theoretical work in the field is given by McAdams (16), and a simplified method of analysis with particular emphasis on the design of conventional boilers is presented in Ref. 19. We shall restrict our discussion here to a qualitative analysis of a natural-convection evaporator typical of the type used in conventional boilers (Fig. 10–13).

In natural circulation the difference in density of the fluids in the *downcomer* (i.e., the unheated downflow pipe) and the *riser* (i.e., the heated upflow pipe) produces the motion. Ideally, the water in the downcomer is slightly below its saturation temperature, and the water entering the upflow pipe at the bottom is subcooled. As it flows upward the water is heated and brought to saturation conditions by two mechanisms: (1) the temperature of the liquid increases as a result of the heat transferred to it, and (2) the saturation temperature decreases because the pressure on the fluid diminishes as a result of wall friction and reduction in the hydrostatic head.   In the lower part of the tube the heat-transfer mechanism is simple convection unless the heat flux is high enough to cause surface boiling.   In the upper portion of the riser, the fluid is saturated, heat is transferred to the fluid by nucleate boiling, and vaporization occurs progressively.   A two-phase mixture of water and steam emerges at the top, where the steam is removed and make-up water is added to maintain steady flow.   When the

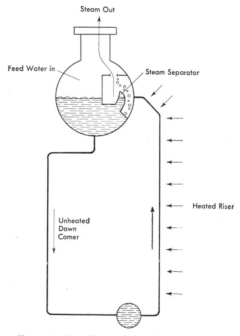

Fig. 10–13.   Natural circulation system.

system is in equilibrium, the mass flow rates and the pressure drops in the downcomer and in the riser are equal.   The rate of flow depends on the difference of the densities of the respective fluids in the riser and down-comer.   Since the density of the fluid in the riser is a function of the heat transfer, there exists a complicated interaction between the pressure drop and the heat transfer.

The heat-transfer coefficient at any point in the riser depends on the local temperature, the pressure, and the velocity.   The rate of heat transfer is therefore not only a function of these quantities but also of the source temperature and the thermal resistances at the outer surface of the pipe and the pipe itself. As the rate of heat transfer to the riser is increased, more of the water evaporates. This, in turn, increases the density difference of the fluids in the riser and the downcomer, which tends to accelerate the rate of flow. However, as more of the fluid turns into vapor, the velocity of the mixture increases and, for a given mass flow rate, a larger pressure gradient is necessary to overcome the frictional drag. Since the pressure losses increase with the square of the velocity, a point will be reached where a further increase in heat flux causes the pressure losses to increase faster than the available pressure difference. When the heat flux is increased beyond this point, the flow rate begins to decrease and the system may become unstable. A properly designed natural-circulation system should therefore operate in the region where the flow rate rises with an increase in heat flow (19).

10-3. HEAT TRANSFER IN CONDENSATION

When a saturated vapor comes in contact with a surface at a lower temperature, condensation occurs. Under normal conditions a continuous flow of liquid is formed over the surface and the condensate flows downward under the influence of gravity. Unless the velocity of the vapor is very high or the liquid film very thick, the motion of the condensate is laminar and heat is transferred from the vapor-liquid interface to the surface merely by conduction. The rate of heat flow depends, therefore, primarily on the thickness of the condensate film, which in turn depends on the rate at which vapor is condensed and the rate at which the condensate is removed. On a vertical surface the film thickness increases continuously from top to bottom, as shown in Fig. 10-14. As the plate is inclined from the vertical position, the drainage rate decreases and the liquid film becomes thicker. This, of course, causes a decrease in the rate of heat transfer.

Filmwise condensation. Theoretical relations for calculating the heat-transfer coefficients for filmwise condensation of pure vapors on tubes and plates were first obtained by Nusselt (28), in 1916. To illustrate the classical Nusselt approach we shall consider a plane vertical surface at a constant temperature T_s on which a pure vapor at saturation temperature, T_{sv} is condensing. As shown in Fig. 10-14, a continuous film of liquid flows downward under the action of gravity, and its thickness increases as more and more vapor condenses at the liquid-vapor interface. At a distance x from the top of the plate the thickness of the film is δ. If the flow of the liquid is laminar and is caused by gravity alone, we can estimate the velocity of the liquid by means of a force balance on the element $dx\delta 1$. The downward force acting on the liquid at a distance greater than y from the surface is $(\delta - y) \, dx\rho g$. The force retarding the downward motions consists of the drag of the vapor at the liquid-vapor interface and the drag at the inner boundary of the element. Unless the vapor flows at a very

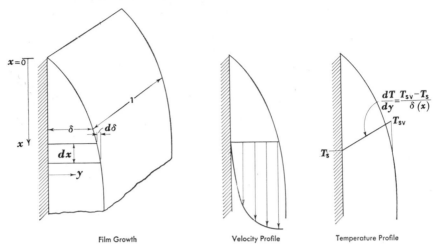

Film Growth   Velocity Profile   Temperature Profile

Fɪɢ 10–14. Filmwise condensation on a vertical surface—film growth, temperature distribution, and velocity profile.

high velocity, the shear at the free surface is quite small and may be neglected. The retarding force will then simply be the viscous shear ($\mu\, du/dy$)-dx at the vertical plane y. Under equilibrium conditions the upward and downward forces are equal, or

$$(\delta - y)\rho g = \mu\, \frac{du}{dy} \tag{10–10}$$

The velocity u at y is obtained by separating the variables in Eq. 10–10 and integrating. This yields the expression

$$u(y) = \frac{\rho g}{\mu}\,(\delta y - \frac{1}{2}y^2) + \text{const} \tag{10–11}$$

The constant of integration is zero because the velocity u is zero at the surface, i.e., $u = 0$ at $y = 0$.

The mass rate of flow of condensate per unit breadth Γ_c is obtained by integrating the local mass flow rate at the elevation x, $\rho u(y)$, between the limits $y = 0$ and $y = \delta$, or

$$\Gamma_c = \int_0^\delta \rho\, \frac{\rho g}{\mu}\left(\delta y - \frac{y^2}{2}\right) dy = \frac{\rho^2 g \delta^3}{3\mu} \tag{10–12}$$

Since heat is transferred through the condensate film solely by conduction, the rate of heat flow through the element of liquid $1dx\delta$ to the wall is

$$kdx\, \frac{T_{sv} - T_s}{\delta} \tag{10–13}$$

where k is the thermal conductivity of the condensate. Equation 10–13 assumes that there is no temperature difference between the vapor and the liquid at their interface. Actually the temperature of the liquid has to be slightly below the saturation temperature to allow energy transfer, but because of the very intense molecular motion at the interface, the temperature difference is negligible under ordinary conditions (29).

The film thickness $\delta(x)$ is zero at the top and increases in a downward direction. Between the distances x and $x + dx$ the film thickness increases by an amount $d\delta$ as a result of condensation. The liquid condensed in the distance dx increases the flow rate by the amount

$$\frac{\partial}{\partial \delta}\left(\frac{\rho^2 g \delta^3}{3\mu}\right) = \frac{\rho g \delta^2 d\delta}{\mu}$$

At the same time there must be maintained a rate of heat flow to the cold wall equal to

$$\frac{\rho g h_{fg}}{\mu}\, \delta^2 d\delta$$

the rate at which latent heat of condensation is released between x and $x + dx$. An energy balance between the rate of heat liberation as a result of condensation at the free surface of the film and the rate of heat conduction through the film gives the equation

$$\frac{\rho g h_{fg}}{\mu}\, \delta^2 d\delta = k(T_{sv} - T_s)\frac{dx}{\delta} \qquad (10\text{–}14)$$

Integration between the limits $\delta = 0$ at $x = 0$ and $\delta = \delta$ at $x = x$ yields

$$k(T_{sv} - T_s)x = \frac{\rho g h_{fg}}{\mu}\left(\frac{\delta^4}{4}\right) \qquad (10\text{–}15)$$

Solving for the film thickness δ at a distance x from the top we get

$$\delta = \left[\frac{4\mu k x(T_{sv} - T_s)}{g h_{fg}\rho^2}\right]^{\frac{1}{4}} \qquad (10\text{–}16)$$

According to Eq. 6–6, the local heat-transfer coefficient h_x is k/δ. Substituting in Eq. 6–6 the expression for δ from Eq. 10–16 gives the unit-surface conductance as

$$h_x = \left[\frac{\rho^2 g h_{fg}k^3}{4\mu x(T_{sv} - T_s)}\right]^{\frac{1}{4}} \qquad (10\text{–}17)$$

and from Eq. 6–4 the dimensionless local Nusselt number at x is

$$\mathrm{Nu}_x = \frac{h_x x}{k} = \left[\frac{\rho^2 g h_{fg}x^3}{4\mu k(T_{sv} - T_s)}\right]^{\frac{1}{4}} \qquad (10\text{–}18)$$

Inspection of Eq. 10–17 shows that the unit conductance for condensation decreases with increasing distance from the top as the film thickens.   The thickening of the condensate film is similar to the growth of a boundary layer over a flat plate in convection.   At the same time it is also interesting to observe that an increase in the temperature difference $(T_{sv} - T_s)$ causes a decrease in the surface conductance.   This is caused by the increase in the film thickness as a result of the increased rate of condensation.   No comparable phenomenon occurs in simple convection.

The average value of the conductance $\bar{h}$ for a vapor condensing on a plate of height L is obtained by integrating the local value h_x over the plate and dividing by the area.   For a vertical plate of unit width and height L we obtain by this operation

$$\bar{h}_c = \frac{1}{L} \int_0^L h_x dx = \frac{4}{3} h_{x=L} \qquad (10\text{–}19)$$

or

$$\bar{h}_c = 0.94 \left[\frac{\rho^2 g h_{fg} k^3}{\mu L (T_{sv} - T_s)} \right]^{\frac{1}{4}} \qquad (10\text{–}20)$$

It can easily be shown that, for a surface inclined by an angle ψ with the horizontal, the average conductance is

$$\bar{h}_c = 0.94 \left[\frac{\rho^2 g h_{fg} k^3 \sin \psi}{\mu L (T_{sv} - T_s)} \right]^{\frac{1}{4}} \qquad (10\text{–}21)$$

The corresponding equation for the average conductance of a pure saturated vapor condensing on the outside of a single horizontal tube of diameter D is

$$\bar{h}_c = 0.725 \left[\frac{\rho^2 g h_{fg} k^3}{\mu D (T_{sv} - T_s)} \right]^{\frac{1}{4}} \qquad (10\text{–}22)$$

If condensation occurs on N horizontal tubes so arranged that condensate from one tube flows directly onto the tube below, the average unit-surface conductance for the system can be estimated by replacing the tube diameter D in Eq. 10–22 by (DN).   This method will in general yield conservative results because a certain amount of turbulence is unavoidable in this type of system (31).

In the preceding equations the unit-surface conductance will be in Btu/hr sq ft F if the other quantities are evaluated in the units listed below:

k, thermal conductivity of liquid, in Btu/hr ft F.
ρ, density of liquid, in lb_m/cu ft.
g, gravitational force, in ft/hr² (4.17 × 10⁸ ft/hr² under normal conditions).
h_{fg}, latent heat of condensation or vaporization, in Btu/lb_m.
μ, viscosity of the liquid, in lb_m/hr ft.

D, tube diameter, in ft.

L, length of plane surface, in ft.

T_{sv}, temperature of saturated vapor, in **F**.

T_s, wall surface temperature, in F.

The physical properties of the liquid film in Eqs. 10–16 to 10–22 should be evaluated at the arithmetic average of the vapor and wall temperature. When used in this manner, Nusselt's equations are satisfactory for estimating surface conductances for condensing vapors. Experimental data are in general agreement with Nusselt's theory when the physical conditions comply with the assumptions inherent in the analysis. Deviations from Nusselt's film theory occur when the condensate flow becomes turbulent, when the vapor velocity is very high, or when a special effort is made to render the surface nonwettable. All of these factors tend to increase the surface conductance, and the Nusselt film theory will therefore always yield conservative results.

Example 10–1. A $\frac{1}{2}$-in.-OD, 5-ft-long tube is to be used to condense steam at 6 psia. Estimate the unit-surface conductances for this tube in the (a) horizontal and (b) vertical positions. Assume that the average tube-wall temperature is 130 F.

Solution: (a) At the average temperature of the condensate film [$T_f = (170 + 130)/2 = 150$ F], the physical-property values pertinent to the problem are

$$k = 0.383 \text{ Btu/hr ft F}$$
$$\rho = 61.2 \text{ lb}_m/\text{cu ft}$$
$$h_{fg} = 996.3 \text{ Btu/lb (from steam tables)}$$
$$\mu_f = 1.06 \text{ lb/hr ft}$$
$$T_{sv} = 170 \text{ F}$$

For the tube in the horizontal position Eq. 10–22 applies and the unit-surface conductance is

$$\bar{h}_c = 0.725 \left[\frac{(0.383^3)(61.2^2)(4.17 \times 10^8)(996.3)}{(0.5/12)(1.06)(170 - 130)} \right]^{\frac{1}{4}}$$

$$= 1920 \text{ Btu/hr sq ft F} \qquad\qquad Ans.$$

b) In the vertical position the tube may be treated as a vertical plate of area πDL and, according to Eq. 10–20, the average unit-surface conductance is

$$\bar{h}_c = 0.94 \left[\frac{(61.2^2)(4.17 \times 10^8)(996.3)(0.383^3)}{(1.06)(5)(170 - 130)} \right]^{\frac{1}{4}}$$

$$= 730 \text{ Btu/hr sq ft F} \qquad\qquad Ans.$$

Effect of turbulence in the film. The results of the preceding calculations show that, for a given temperature difference, the average unit conductance is considerably larger when the tube is placed in a horizontal position where the path of the condensate is shorter and the film thinner than in the vertical position where the path is longer and the film thicker. This conclusion is generally valid when the length of the vertical tube is larger than 2.87 times the outer diameter, as can be seen by a comparison of Eqs. 10–21 and 10–22. However, both of these equations are based on the assumption that the flow of the condensate film is laminar and consequently do not apply when the flow of the condensate is turbulent. Turbulent flow is hardly ever reached on a horizontal tube but may be established over the lower portion of a vertical surface. When this occurs, the average heat-transfer coefficient becomes larger as the length of the condensing surface is increased because the condensate no longer offers as high a thermal resistance as it does in laminar flow. This phenomenon is somewhat analogous to the behavior of a boundary layer.

Just as a fluid flowing over a surface undergoes a transition from laminar to turbulent flow, so the motion of the condensate becomes turbulent when its Reynolds number exceeds a critical value of about 2000. The Reynolds number of the condensate film Re_δ, when based on the hydraulic diameter (Eq. 8–1), can be written as $Re_\delta = 4A\Gamma_c/P\mu_f$, where P is the wetted perimeter equal to πD for a vertical tube and A is the flow cross-sectional area equal to $P\delta$. According to an analysis by Colburn (30) the local heat-transfer coefficient for turbulent flow of the condensate can be evaluated from the equation

$$h_x = 0.056 \left(\frac{4\Gamma_c}{\mu_f} \right)^{0.2} \left(\frac{k^3 \rho^2 g}{\mu^2} \right)^{\frac{1}{3}} Pr_f^{\frac{1}{3}} \qquad (10\text{–}23)$$

To obtain average values of the conductance, integration of h_x over the surface by means of Eq. 10–17 for values of $(4\Gamma_c/P\mu_f)$ less than 2000 and Eq. 10–23 for values larger than 2000 is necessary. The results of such calculations for two values of the Prandtl number are plotted as solid lines in Fig. 10–15, where some experimental data obtained with diphenyl in turbulent flow are also shown (31). The heavy dashed line shown on the same graph is an empirical curve recommended by McAdams (16) for evaluating the average unit-surface conductance of single vapors condensing on vertical surfaces.

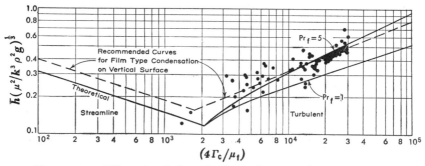

Fig. 10–15.   Effect of turbulence in film on heat transfer with condensation.

Example 10-2. Determine whether or not the flow of the condensate in Example 10-1b is laminar or turbulent at the lower end of the tube.

Solution: The Reynolds number of the condensate at the lower end of the tube can be written with the aid of Eq. 10-12 as

$$\text{Re}_\delta = \frac{4\Gamma_c}{P\mu_f{}^2} = \frac{4\rho^2 g\delta^3}{3\mu_f{}^2}$$

Substituting Eq. 10-16 for δ yields

$$\text{Re}_\delta = \frac{4\rho^2 g}{3\mu_f{}^2}\left[\frac{4\mu kL(T_{sv} - T_s)}{gh_{fg}\rho^2}\right]^{\frac{3}{4}}$$

$$= \frac{4}{3}\left[\frac{4kL(T_{sv} - T_s)\rho^{\frac{1}{3}}g^{\frac{1}{3}}}{\mu^{\frac{5}{3}}h_{fg}}\right]^{\frac{3}{4}}$$

Inserting in the expression above the numerical values for the problem yields

$$\text{Re}_\delta = \frac{4}{3}\left[\frac{(4 \times 0.383 \text{ Btu/hr ft F}) (10 \text{ ft}) (40 \text{ F}) (61.2 \text{ lb}_m/\text{cu ft})^{\frac{2}{3}} (4.17 \times 10^8 \text{ ft/hr}^2)^{\frac{1}{3}}}{(1.06 \text{ lb}_m/\text{hr ft})^{\frac{5}{3}}(996 \text{ Btu/lb}_m)}\right]^{\frac{3}{4}}$$

$$= 960 \text{ (dimensionless)}$$

Since the Reynolds number at the lower edge of the tube is below 2000, the flow of the condensate is laminar and the result obtained from Eq. 10-20 is valid.   *Ans.*

Effect of high vapor velocity. One of the approximations made in Nusselt's film theory is that the frictional drag between the condensate and the vapor is negligible (Eq. 10-10). This approximation ceases to be valid when the velocity of the uncondensed vapor is substantial compared with the velocity of the liquid at the vapor-condensate interface. When the vapor flows upward, it adds a retarding force to the viscous shear and causes the film thickness to increase. With downward flow of vapor, the film thickness decreases, and surface conductances substantially larger than those predicted from Eq. 10-20 can be obtained. In addition, the transition from laminar to turbulent flow occurs at condensate Reynolds numbers of the order of 300 when the vapor velocity is high. Carpenter and Colburn (33) determined the heat-transfer coefficients for condensation of pure vapors of steam and several hydrocarbons in a vertical tube, 8 ft long and $\frac{1}{2}$ in. ID, with inlet vapor velocities at the top up to 500 fps. Their data are correlated reasonably well by the equation

$$\frac{\bar{h}_c}{c_p G_m}\,\text{Pr}_l{}^{\frac{1}{2}} = 0.046\sqrt{\frac{\rho_l}{\rho_v}}\,f \qquad\qquad (10\text{-}24)$$

where Pr_l = Prandtl number of liquid;
$\quad\rho_l$ = density of liquid, in $\text{lb}_m/\text{cu ft}$;
$\quad\rho_v$ = density of vapor, in $\text{lb}_m/\text{cu ft}$;
$\quad c_p$ = specific heat of liquid, in Btu/lb_m F;

$\bar{h}$ = average unit conductance, in Btu/hr sq ft F;

f = Fanning pipe-friction coefficient evaluated at the average vapor velocity;

G_m = mean value of the mass velocity of the vapor, in lb_m/hr sq ft.

The value of G_m in Eq. 10–24 can be taken as

$$G_m = \sqrt{\frac{G_1{}^2 + G_1 G_2 + G_2{}^2}{3}}$$

where G_1 = mass velocity at top of tube;

G_2 = mass velocity at bottom of tube.

All physical properties of the liquid in Eq. 10–24 are to be evaluated at a reference temperature equal to $0.25\ T_{sv} + 0.75\ T_s$. These results have not been verified on other systems but may be used generally as an indication of the influence of vapor velocity on the heat-transfer coefficient of condensing vapors when the vapor and the condensate flow in the same direction.

Condensation of superheated vapor. Although all of the preceding equations strictly apply only to saturated vapors, they can also be used with reasonable accuracy for condensation of superheated vapors. The rate of heat transfer from a superheated vapor to a wall at T_s will therefore be

$$q = A\bar{h}\ (T_{sv} - T_s) \tag{10–25}$$

where $\bar{h}$ = average value of unit conductance determined from equation appropriate to the geometrical configuration with same vapor at saturation conditions;

T_{sv} = *saturation temperature* corresponding to the prevailing system pressure.

Dropwise condensation. When a condensing surface is contaminated with a substance which prevents the condensate from wetting the surface, the vapor will condense in drops rather than as a continuous film (34). This is known as dropwise condensation. A large part of the surface is not covered by an insulating film under these conditions, and the heat-transfer coefficients are four to eight times as high as in filmwise condensation. So far, dropwise condensation has been reliably obtained only with steam. For the purpose of calculating the unit conductance in practice, it is recommended that filmwise condensation be assumed because, even with steam, dropwise condensation can be expected only under carefully controlled conditions which can not always be maintained in practice. Dropwise condensation of steam may, however, be a useful technique in experimental work when it is desirable to reduce the thermal resistance on one side of a surface to a negligible value.

Condenser design. The evaluation of the surface conductance of condensing vapors, as can be seen from Eqs. 10–20, 10–21, and 10–22, presupposes a knowledge of the temperature of the condensing surface. In practical problems this temperature is generally not known because its value depends on the relative order of magnitudes of the thermal resistances in the entire system. The type of problem usually encountered in practice, whether it be a performance calculation on an existing piece of equipment or the design of equipment for a specific process, requires simultaneous evaluation of thermal resistances at the inner and outer surfaces of a tube or the wall of a duct. In most cases the geometric configuration is either specified, as in the case of an existing piece of equipment, or assumed, as in the design of new equipment. When the desired rate of condensation is specified, the usual procedure is to estimate the total surface area required and then to select a suitable arrangement for a combination of size and number of tubes that meets the preliminary area specification. The performance calculation can then be made as though one were dealing with an existing piece of equipment, and the results can later be compared with the specifications. The flow rate of the coolant is usually determined by the allowable pressure drop or the allowable temperature rise. Once the flow rate is known, the thermal resistances of the coolant and the tube wall can be computed without difficulty. The unit-surface conductance of the condensing fluid, however, depends on the condensing-surface temperature, which can be computed only after the conductance is known. A trial-and-error solution is therefore necessary. One either assumes a surface temperature or, if more convenient, estimates the unit conductance on the condensing side and calculates the corresponding surface temperature. With this first approximation of the surface temperature, the unit-surface conductance is then recalculated and compared with the assumed value. A second approximation is usually sufficient for satisfactory accuracy.

The orders of magnitude of unit-thermal conductances for various vapors listed in Table 10–3 will aid in the initial estimates and reduce the amount of trial and error. We note that, for steam, the thermal resistance is very small, whereas for organic vapors it is of the same order of magnitude as the resistance offered to the flow of heat by water at a low turbulent Reynolds number. In the refrigeration industry and in some chemical processes, finned tubes have been used to reduce the thermal resistance on the condensing side. A method for dealing with condensation on finned tubes and tube banks is presented in Ref. 32. We shall here consider only a simple example to illustrate the trial-and-error approach. When repeated calculations of the conductance for condensation of pure

TABLE 10–3

Approximate Values of Unit-Surface
Conductances for Condensation of Pure Vapors

Vapor	System	Approximate Range of $T_{sv} - T_s$	Approximate Range of Average Unit Conductance (Btu/hr sq ft F)
Steam......	Horizontal tubes, 1–3 in. OD	5–40	2000–4000
Steam......	Vertical surface 10 ft high	5–40	1000–2000
Ethanol....	Vertical surface ½ ft high	20–100	200–340
Benzene....	Horizontal tube, 1 in. OD	30–80	250–350
Ethanol....	Horizontal tube, 2 in. OD	10–40	300–450
Ammonia...	Horizontal 2-to-3-in. annulus	2–7	250–450*

* Over-all heat-transfer coefficient U for water velocities between 4 and 8 fps (35) inside the tube.

vapors are to be made, alignment charts devised by Chilton, Colburn, Genereaux, and Vernon, reproduced in Ref. 15, are convenient.

Example 10–3. Estimate (a) the heat-transfer surface area required and (b) suggest a suitable arrangement for the condenser of a 10-ton refrigeration machine. The working fluid is ammonia condensing on the outside of horizontal pipes at a pressure of 170 psia. The condenser is to be constructed with 1-in. steel pipes (1.00-in. OD, 0.834-in. ID), cooling water is available at 79 F, and the average water velocity in the pipes is not to exceed 6 fps.

Solution: (a) Ten tons of refrigeration are equivalent to 10×200 (Btu/min) = 2000 Btu/min of heat removal in the system. Neglecting losses, this is also the steady-state rate of heat flow from the ammonia to the water in the condenser. The rise in the temperature of the cooling water is therefore

$$\Delta T = \frac{q}{\rho V A c N} = \frac{(2000)(144)}{(62.3)(6)(0.546)(1.0)(60)(N)} = \frac{23.6}{N}$$

where N is the number of condenser tubes in parallel. For a preliminary estimate, assume that there are 10 parallel tubes arranged in 2 rows. The bulk Reynolds number of the water is

$$\mathrm{Re}_D = \frac{VD\rho}{\mu} = \frac{(6)(0.0695)(62.3)(3600)}{2.22} = 42{,}200$$

The average water temperature is about 80 F, the Prandtl number is 2.3, and the heat-transfer coefficient, according to Eq. 8–20, is

$$\bar{h}_c = \frac{k}{D} \, \mathrm{Re}_D{}^{0.8} \, \mathrm{Pr}_l{}^{\frac{1}{3}} = 760 \text{ Btu/hr sq ft F}$$

The thermal resistance of the pipe wall, based on the outer surface area, is

$$R_{th} = \frac{D_o \ln (D_o/D_i)}{2\,k} = \frac{1.0 \times \ln 1.2}{(12)(2)(25.8)} = 0.000294 \text{ hr sq ft F/Btu}$$

To estimate the temperature at the outer surface of the tube, refer to Table 10–3 and assume that the over-all heat-transfer coefficient is 400 Btu/hr sq ft F, or

$$\frac{1}{U} = \frac{1}{400} = \frac{1}{\bar{h}_{\text{ammonia}}} + R_{th \text{ pipe}} + \frac{1}{\bar{h} \text{ water } D_i/D_o}$$

The unit-surface conductance of the condensing ammonia (saturation temperature = 86.3 F) is therefore approximately

$$\bar{h}_{\text{ammonia}} = \frac{1}{0.0025 - 0.000294 - 0.00158} = 1600 \text{ Btu/hr sq ft F}$$

The temperature drop between the ammonia and the wall surface is

$$T_{sv} - T_{\text{surf}} = \frac{(T_{sv} - T_{\text{water}})1/\bar{h}_{\text{ammonia}}}{1/U} = \frac{(6.3)(400)}{1600} = 2.1 \text{ F}$$

Now apply Eq. 10–22 to calculate the unit-surface conductance on the outside of the tubes. Using property values of ammonia at 85 F, Eq. 10–22 for 2 tube rows gives

$$\bar{h}_c = 0.725 \left[\frac{(37.2^2)(4.18 \times 10^8)(493.6)(0.29^3)}{(0.24)(2)(1.0/12)(2.1)} \right]^{\frac{1}{4}} = 2200 \text{ Btu/hr sq ft F}$$

Since this value is larger than that assumed in the first approximation, we correct the calculations and obtain

$$\frac{1}{U} = \frac{1}{2200} + 0.000294 + \frac{1}{630} = 0.00234 \text{ hr sq ft F/Btu}$$

$$T_{sv} - T_s = 1.22 \text{ F}$$

$$\bar{h}_{\text{ammonia}} = 2500 \text{ Btu/hr sq ft F}$$

The second iteration will not change the value of the over-all heat-transfer coefficient appreciably because the thermal resistance at the condensing side is less than one-fifth of the total resistance. It yields

$$U = 440 \text{ Btu/hr sq ft F}$$

and with this value of the over-all heat-transfer coefficient, the required total area is

$$A_o = \frac{q}{U(T_{sv} - T_{\text{water}})} = \frac{(2000)(60)}{(440)(6.3)} = 43.5 \text{ sq ft} \qquad Ans.$$

b) If there are 10 pipes, each must have a length of

$$L = \frac{4.35}{\pi D} = \frac{(4.35)(12)}{(3.14)(1)} = 16.5 \text{ ft}$$

The shell of such a condenser is probably too long. The large surface area–to–volume ratio would make it difficult to insulate the shell and give a clumsy appearance. It is therefore suggested that 30 parallel tubes be arranged in 5 rows. This will reduce the length of the unit to about 6 ft. *Ans.*

The details of this calculation are left as an exercise to the reader.

Mixtures of vapors and noncondensable gases. The analysis of a condensing system containing a mixture of vapors, or a pure vapor mixed with noncondensable gas, is considerably more complicated than the analysis of a pure-vapor system. The presence of appreciable quantities of a noncondensable gas will in general reduce the rate of heat transfer. If high rates of heat transfer are desired, it is considered good practice to vent the noncondensable gas, which otherwise will blanket the cooling surface and add considerably to the thermal resistance. It will also be shown in Chapter 13 that non-condensable gases inhibit the mass transfer by offering a diffusional resistance. A complete treatment of problems involving condensation of mixtures is beyond the scope of this text, and the reader is referred to Refs. 16 and 30 for a comprehensive summary of available information on these topics.

10–4. FREEZING AND MELTING

Problems involving the solidification or melting of materials are of considerable importance in many technical fields. Typical examples in the field of engineering are the making of ice, the freezing of foods, or the solidification and melting of metals in casting processes. In geology the solidification rate of the earth has been used to estimate the age of our planet. Whatever the field of application, the problem of central interest is the rate at which solidification or melting occurs.

We shall here consider only the problem of solidification, and it is left for the reader as an exercise to show that a solution of this problem is also a solution to the corresponding problem in melting. Figure 10–16 shows

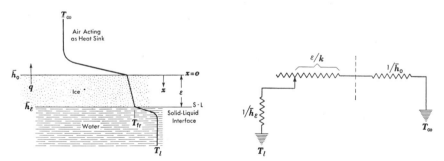

FIG. 10–16. Temperature distribution for ice forming on water with air acting as heat sink, and simplified thermal circuit for the system with heat capacity of solid considered to be negligible.

the temperature distribution in an ice layer on the surface of a liquid. The upper face is exposed to air at subfreezing temperature. Ice formation occurs progressively at the solid-liquid interface as a result of heat transfer through the ice to the cold air. Heat flows by convection from the water to the ice, by conduction through the ice, and by convection to the sink. The ice layer is subcooled except for the interface in contact with the liquid, which is at the freezing point. A portion of the heat transferred to the sink is used to cool the liquid at the interface SL to the freezing point and to remove its latent heat of solidification. The other portion serves to subcool the ice. Cylindrical or spherical systems may be described in a similar manner, but solidification may proceed either inward (as for freezing of water inside a can) or outward (as for water freezing on the outside of a pipe).

The freezing of a slab can be formulated as a boundary-value problem in which the governing equation is the general conduction equation for the solid phase

$$\frac{\partial^2 T}{\partial x^2} = \frac{1}{a}\frac{\partial T}{\partial \theta}$$

subject to the boundary conditions that

at $x = 0$
$$-k\frac{\partial T}{\partial x} = \bar{h}_o(T_{x=0} - T_\infty)$$

at $x = \epsilon$
$$-k\frac{\partial T}{\partial x} = \rho L_f\frac{d\epsilon}{d\theta} + \bar{h}_\epsilon(T_l - T_{fr})$$

where ϵ = distance to the solid-liquid interface which is a function of time, θ;

L_f = latent heat of fusion of the material;

a = thermal diffusivity of the solid phase $(c\rho/k)$;

ρ = density of the solid phase;

T_l = temperature of the liquid;

T_∞ = temperature of the heat sink;

T_{fr} = freezing point temperature;

$\bar{h}_o$ = unit conductance at $x = 0$, the air-ice interface;

$\bar{h}_\epsilon$ = unit conductance at $x = \epsilon$, the water-ice interface.

The analytic solution of this problem is very difficult and has only been obtained for special cases. The reason for the difficulty is that the governing equation is a partial-differential equation for which the particular solutions are unknown when physically realistic boundary conditions are imposed.

An approximate solution of practical value can however be obtained by considering the heat capacity of the subcooled solid phase as negligible relative to the latent heat of solidification. To simplify our analysis further we shall assume that the physical properties of the ice, ρ, k, and c, are uniform, that the liquid is at the solidification temperature (i.e., $T_l = T_{fr}$ and

$1/\bar{h}_\epsilon = 0$), and that $\bar{h}_o$ and T_∞ are constant during the process.

The rate of heat flow per unit area through the resistances offered by the ice and the air, acting in series, as a result of the temperature potential $(T_{fr} - T_\infty)$ is

$$\frac{q}{A} = \frac{T_{fr} - T_\infty}{1/\bar{h}_o + \epsilon/k} \tag{10-26}$$

This is the heat-flow rate which removes the latent heat of fusion necessary for freezing at the surface $x = \epsilon$, or

$$\frac{q}{A} = \rho L_f \frac{d\epsilon}{d\theta} \tag{10-27}$$

where $(d\epsilon/d\theta)$ is the volume rate of ice formation per unit area at the growing surface in cu ft/hr sq ft, and ρL_f is the latent heat in Btu/cu ft. Combining of Eqs. 10–26 and 10–27 to eliminate the rate of heat flow yields the equation

$$\frac{T_{fr} - T_\infty}{1/\bar{h}_o + \epsilon/k} = \rho L_f \frac{d\epsilon}{d\theta} \tag{10-28}$$

which relates the depth of ice to the freezing time. The variables ϵ and θ can now be separated and we get

$$d\epsilon \left(1/\bar{h}_o + \epsilon/k\right) = [(T_{fr} - T_\infty)/\rho L] \, d\theta \tag{10-29}$$

To make this equation dimensionless let

$$\epsilon^+ = \frac{\bar{h}_o \epsilon}{k}$$

and

$$\theta^+ = \theta \bar{h}_o^2 \frac{T_{fr} - T_\infty}{\rho L_f k}$$

Substituting these dimensionless parameters in Eq. 10–29 yields

$$d\epsilon^+ \left(1 + \epsilon^+\right) = d\theta^+ \tag{10-30}$$

If the freezing process starts at $\theta = \theta^+ = 0$ and continues for a time θ, the solution of Eq. 10–30, obtained by integration between the specified limits, is

$$\epsilon^+ + (\epsilon^+)^2/2 = \theta^+ \tag{10-31}$$

or

$$\epsilon^+ = -1 + \sqrt{1 + 2\theta^+} \tag{10-32}$$

When the temperature of the liquids T_l is above the fusion temperature and the convective resistance at the liquid-to-solid interface is $\bar{h}_\epsilon$, the dimensionless equation corresponding to Eq. 10–30 in the foregoing simplified treatment becomes

$$\frac{(1 + \epsilon^+)d\epsilon^+}{1 + R^+T^+(1 + x^+)} = d\theta^+ \tag{10-33}$$

where $R^+ = \bar{h}_\epsilon/\bar{h}_o$;
$T^+ = (T_l - T_{fr})/(T_{fr} - T_\infty)$;

while the other symbols represent the same dimensionless quantities used previously in Eq. 10–30.

For the boundary conditions that, at $\theta^+ = 0$, $\epsilon^+ = 0$ and, at $\theta^+ = \theta^+$, $\epsilon^+ = \epsilon^+$, the solution of Eq. 10–33 becomes

$$\theta^+ = -\frac{1}{(R^+T^+)^2} \ln \left(1 - \frac{R^+T^+\epsilon^+}{1 - R^+T^+} \right) - \frac{\epsilon^+}{R^+T^+} \tag{10-34}$$

The results are shown graphically in Fig. 10–17 where the generalized thickness ϵ^+ is plotted vs. generalized time θ^+ with the generalized potential-resistance ratio R^+T^+ as parameter.

Example 10-4. In the production of "Flakice," ice forms in thin layers on a horizontal rotating drum which is partly submerged in water. The cylinder is internally

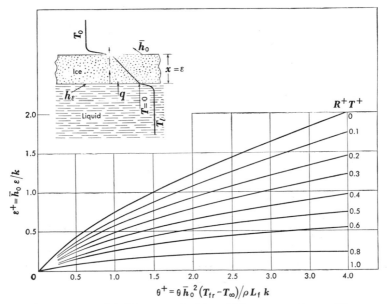

FIG. 10–17. Solidification of slab—thickness vs. time. (Extracted from "Rates of Ice Formation," by A. L. London and R. A. Seban, *Trans. ASME*, Vol. 65, 1943, with permission of the publishers, The American Society of Mechanical Engineers)

refrigerated with a brine spray at 12 F.   Ice formed on the exterior surface is peeled off as the revolving-drum surface emerges from the water.

For the operating conditions listed below, estimate the time required to form an ice layer 0.1 in. thick.

> Water liquid temperature. . . .40 F
> Liquid-surface conductance. . . .10 Btu/hr sq ft F
> Conductance between brine and
>   ice (including metal wall). . . . . .100 Btu/hr sq ft F

Solution: For the conditions stated above we have

$$R^+ = \frac{\bar{h}_\epsilon}{\bar{h}_o} = \frac{10}{100} = 0.1$$

$$T^+ = \frac{T_l - T_{fr}}{T_{fr} - T_\infty} = \frac{40 - 32}{32 - 12} = 0.4$$

$$\epsilon^+ = \frac{\bar{h}_o \epsilon}{k_{\text{ice}}} = \frac{(100 \text{ Btu/hr sq ft})(0.1/12 \text{ ft})}{1.34 \text{ Btu/hr sq ft F/ft}} = 0.622$$

We assume now that the ice is a sheet.   This is justified because the thickness of the ice is very small compared to the radius of curvature of the drum.   The boundary conditions of this problem are then the same as those assumed in the solution of Eq. 10–33.   Hence, Eq. 10–34 is the solution to the problem at hand.   Substituting numerical values for R^+, T^+, and ϵ^+ in Eq. 10–34 yields

$$\theta^+ = -\frac{1}{(0.04)^2} \ln \left(1 - \frac{0.0245}{1 - 0.04} \right) - \frac{0.622}{0.04} = 0.615$$

From the definition of θ^+, the time θ is

$$\theta = 0.615 \times \rho L_f k / h_o^2 \, (T_{fr} - T_\infty)$$

$$= (0.615)\,(57.3)\,(143.6)\,(1.34)/(10{,}000)\,(20)$$

$$= 0.034 \text{ hr or about 2 min} \qquad\qquad Ans.$$

Equations for the rate of ice formation on the inside and outside of cylinders of radius r_o have been solved by London and Seban (36) under the same assumptions used to derive Eq. 10–33 for the slab.   Their results are shown in Fig. 10–18 for freezing outside a long cylinder containing a heat sink and in Fig. 10–19 for freezing of a liquid in a long circular cylindrical container immersed in a medium at a temperature below the freezing point of the liquid.   The dimensionless time for complete solidification of the liquid in the latter case corresponds to the abscissa intercept $r^+ = r/r_o = 0$ at the appropriate value of the system parameter $\bar{h}_o r_o / k$.   The dimensionless time parameter θ^* plotted as the abscissa in Figs. 10–18 and 10–19 is defined as

$$\theta^* = \frac{(T_{fr} - T_\infty)k\theta}{L_f \rho r_o^2}$$

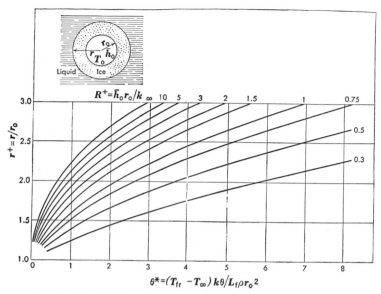

FIG. 10–18. Solidification on outside of cylinder. (Extracted from "Rates of Ice Formation," by A. L. London and R. A. Seban, *Trans. ASME*, Vol. 65, 1943, with permission of the publishers, The American Society of Mechanical Engineers)

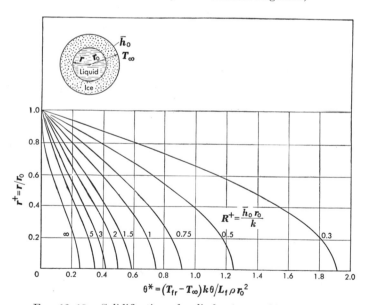

FIG. 10–19. Solidification of cylinder in a colder medium. (Extracted from "Rates of Ice Formation," by A. L. London and R. A. Seban, *Trans. ASME*, Vol. 65, 1943, with permission of the Publishers, The American Society of Mechanical Engineers)

An estimate of the error caused by neglecting the heat capacity of the solidified portion has been obtained by means of an electrical network simulating the freezing of a slab originally at the fusion temperature (37). It was found that the error is not appreciable when $\bar{\epsilon} h_o/k$ is less than 0.1 (37) or when $[L_f/(T_{fr} - T_\infty)c]$ is larger than 1.5 (38). In the intermediate range, the freezing rates predicted by the simplified analysis are too large. The solutions presented here are valid for ice and other substances which have heats of fusion which are large compared to their specific heats. An approximate method for predicting the freezing rate of steel and other metals, where $[L_f/(T_{fr} - T_\infty)c]$ may be less than 1.5, is presented in Ref. 38.

REFERENCES

1. W. H. Jens and G. Leppert, "Recent Developments in Boiling Research," Parts I, II. *J. Am. Soc. Naval Engrs.*, Vol. 67 (1955), pp. 137–155; Vol. 66 (1955), pp. 437–456.

2. E. A. Farber and R. L. Scorah, "Heat Transfer to Water Boiling under Pressure," *Trans. ASME*, Vol. 70 (1948), pp. 369–384.

3. M. Jakob, *Heat Transfer*, Vol. 1. (New York: John Wiley & Sons, Inc., 1949.)

4. W. M. Rohsenow, "A Method of Correlating Heat Transfer Data for Surface Boiling Liquids," *Trans. ASME*, Vol. 74 (1952), pp. 969–975.

5. M. Jakob, "Kondensation und Verdampfung," *Z. Ver. Deutsch. Ing.*, Vol. 76 (1932), pp. 1161–1170.

6. M. Jakob, "Local Temperature Differences as Occurring in Evaporation, Condensation, and Catalytic Reactions," *Temperature, Its Measurement and Control and Science and Industry*, (New York: Reinhold Publishing Corporation, 1941), p. 834.

7. J. T. Castles, *S. M. Thesis in Chem. Eng.*, Massachusetts Institute of Technology, 1947.

8. F. C. Gunther, "Photographic Study of Surface Boiling Heat Transfer with Forced Convection," *Trans. ASME*, Vol. 73 (1951), pp. 115–123.

9. M. E. Ellion, "A Study of the Mechanism of Boiling Heat Transfer," *Memorandum 20–88*, Jet Propulsion Laboratory, Calif. Inst. of Tech., March, 1954.

10. F. C. Gunther and F. Kreith, "Photographic Study of Bubble Formation in Heat Transfer to Subcooled Water," *Prog. Rept.* 4–120, Jet Propulsion Lab., Calif. Inst. of Tech., March, 1950.

11. J. N. Addoms, *Heat Transfer at High Rates to Water Boiling Outside Cylinders*, *D.Sc. Thesis*, Dept. of Chem. Engrg., Massachusetts Institute of Technology, 1948.

12. E. L. Piret and H. S. Isbin, "Natural Circulation Evaporation Two-phase Heat Transfer," *Chem. Eng. Progress*, Vol. 50 (1954), p. 305.

13. M. T. Cichelli and C. F. Bonilla, "Heat Transfer to Liquids Boiling under Pressure," *Trans. AIChE*, Vol. 41 (1945), pp. 755–787.

14. D. S. Cryder and A. C. Finalbargo, "Heat Transmission from Metal Surfaces to Boiling Liquids: Effect of Temperature of the Liquid on Film Coefficient," *Trans. AIChE*, Vol. 33 (1937), pp. 346–362.

15. W. H. McAdams et al., "Heat Transfer from Single Horizontal Wires to Boiling Water," *Chem. Eng. Progress*, Vol. 44 (1948), pp. 639–646.

16. W. H. McAdams, *Heat Transmission*, 3d ed. (New York: McGraw-Hill Book Company, Inc., 1954.)

17. F. Kreith and M. J. Summerfield, "Heat Transfer to Water at High Flux Densities With and Without Surface Boiling," *Trans. ASME*, Vol. 71 (1949), pp. 805–815.

18. W. H. McAdams et al., "Heat Transfer at High Rates to Water with Surface Boiling," *Ind. Eng. Chem.*, Vol. 41 (1949), pp. 1945–1953.

19. *Steam—Its Generation and Use.* (New York: The Babcock & Wilcox Company, 1955.)

20. E. A. Kazekov, "Maximum Heat Transfer to Boiling Water at High Pressures," *Izvestia Adakmii Nauk USSR*, September, 1950, pp. 1377–1387. (Reviewed in *Engrg. Digest*, Vol. 12 (1951), pp. 81–85.)

21. W. Rohsenow and P. Griffith, "Correlation of Maximum Heat Flux Data for Boiling of Saturated Liquids." (Preprint, Heat Transfer Symposium, *Am. Inst. Chem. Engrs.*, Louisville, Ky., March, 1955.)

22. W. H. Jens and P. A. Lottes, "Analysis of Heat Transfer, Burnout, Pressure Drop and Density Data for High-Pressure Water," *Argonne Nat. Lab. Rpts.* ANL—4627, May, 1951.

23. W. H. Jens and P. A. Lottes, "Two Phase Pressure Drop and Burnout Using Water Flowing in Round and Rectangular Channels," *Argonne Nat. Lab. Rpts.* ANL—4915, October, 1952.

24. J. L. Schweppe and A. S. Foust, "The Effect of Forced Circulation Rate on Boiling Heat Transfer and Pressure Drop in a Short Vertical Tube," *Chem. Eng. Progress Symp.*, Series No. 5, Vol. 1944 (1953).

25. F. Kreith and A. S. Foust, "Remarks on the Stability and Mechanism of Surface Boiling Heat Transfer," *ASME Paper* 54-A-16, August, 1954.

26. L. A. Bromley, "Heat Transfer in Stable Film Boiling," *Chem. Eng. Progress*, Vol. 46 (1950), pp. 221–227.

27. L. A. Bromley et al., "Heat Transfer in Forced Convection Film Boiling," *Ind. Eng. Chem.*, Vol. 45 (1953), pp. 2639–2646.

28. W. Nusselt, "Die Oberflächenkondensation des Wasserdampfes," *Z. Ver. Deutsch. Ing.*, Vol. 60 (1916), pp. 541, 569.

29. A. P. Colburn, "Problems in Design on Research on Condensers of Vapours and Vapour Mixtures," Inst. Mech. Eng. and ASME, *Proc. General Discussion on Heat Transfer*, September, 1951, pp. 1–11.

30. A. P. Colburn, "The Calculation of Condensation where a Portion of the Condensate Layer is in Turbulent Flow," *Trans. Am. Inst. Chem. Engrs.*, Vol. 30 (1933), p. 187.

31. C. G. Kirkbridge, "Heat Transfer by Condensing Vapors on Vertical Tubes," *Trans. Am. Inst. Chem. Engrs.*, Vol. 30 (1933), p. 170.

32. D. L. Katz, E. H. Young, and G. Bolekjian, "Condensing Vapors on Finned Tubes," *Petroleum Refiner* (November, 1954), pp. 175–178.

33. E. F. Carpenter and A. P. Colburn, "The Effect of Vapor Velocity on Condensation-inside Tubes," Inst. Mech. Eng. ASME, *Proc. General Discussion on Heat Transfer*, 1951, pp. 20–26.

34. T. B. Drew, W. M. Nagle, and W. Q. Smith, "The Conditions for Dropwise Condensation of Steam," *Trans. Am. Inst. Chem. Engrs.*, Vol. 31 (1935), pp. 605–621.

35. A. P. Katz, H. J. Macintire, and R. E. Gould, "Heat Transfer in Ammonia Condensers," *Bull.* 209. Univ. Ill., Eng. Expt. Sta., 1930.

36. A. L. London and R. A. Seban, "Rate of Ice Formation," *Trans. ASME*, Vol. 65 (1943), pp. 771–778.

37. F. Kreith and F. E. Romie, "A Study of the Thermal Diffusion Equation with Boundary Conditions Corresponding to Freezing or Melting of Materials at the Fusion Temperature," *Proc. Phys. Soc.*, Vol. 68 (1955), pp. 277–291.

38. D. L. Cochran, "Solidification Application and Extension of Theory," *Tech. Rep.* 24, Navy Contract N6-onr-251, Stanford Univ., 1955.

39. W. H. McAdams, W. E. Kennel, C. S. Minden, R. Carl, P. M. Picornell, and J. E. Dew, "Heat Transfer at High Rates to Water with Surface Boiling," *Ind. Eng. Chem.*, Vol. 41 (1944), pp. 1945–1953.

10–1. Show that the dimensionless equation for ice formation at the outside of a tube of radius r_o is

$$\theta^* = \frac{r^{*^2}}{2} \ln r^* \left(\frac{1}{2R^*} + \frac{1}{4} \right) (r^{*^2} - 1)$$

where $r^* = \dfrac{\epsilon + r_o}{r_o}$ $R^* = \dfrac{h_o r_o}{k}$ $\theta^* = \dfrac{(T_f - T_\infty)\, k\theta}{\rho L r_o^2}$

Assume that the water is originally at the freezing temperature T_f, that the cooling medium inside the tube surface is below the freezing temperature at a uniform temperature T_∞, and that h_o is the total conductance between the cooling medium and the pipe-ice interface. Also show the thermal circuit.

10–2. In the manufacture of can ice, cans having inside dimensions of 11 by 22 by 50 in. with 1-in. inside taper are filled with water and immersed in brine having a temperature of 10 F. [For details of the process see *The Refrigerating Data Book*, ASRE, Vol. II (1940), pp. 9,56]. For the purpose of a preliminary analysis, the actual ice can may be considered as an equivalent cylinder having the same cross-sectional area as the can, and end effects may be neglected. The over-all conductance between the brine and the inner surface of the can is 40 Btu/hr sq ft F. Determine the time required to freeze the water and compare with the time necessary if the brine-circulation rate would be increased to reduce the thermal resistance of the surface to one-tenth of the value specified above.

10–3. Estimate the time required to freeze vegetables in thin, tin, cylindrical containers of 6-in. diameter. Air at 10 F is blowing at 15 fps over the cans, which are stacked to form one long cylinder. The physical properties of the vegetables may be taken as those of water and ice respectively.

10–4. Develop the Nusselt film-condensation relation for condensation inside small vertical tubes where the film builds up an annulus.

10–5. Consider a ½-in.-ID vertical tube at a surface temperature of 150 F with atmospheric saturated steam inside. Determine the tube length at which the condensate fills the tube and chokes the flow.

10–6. Calculate the average heat-transfer coefficient for film-type condensation of water at pressures of 1 in. Hg abs and 14.7 psia for (a) a vertical surface 5 ft high; (b) the outside surface of a ⅝-in.-OD vertical tube 5 ft long; (c) the outside surface of a ⅝-in.-OD horizontal tubes 5 ft long; and (d) a 10-tube vertical bank of ⅝-in.-OD horizontal tubes 5 ft long. In all cases, assume that the vapor velocity is negligible and that the surface temperatures are constant at 20 F below saturation temperature.

10–7. Predict the nucleate-boiling heat-transfer coefficient for water boiling at atmospheric pressure on the outside surface of a ⅝-in.-OD vertical tube 5 ft long. Assume the tube-surface temperature constant at 20 F above the saturation temperature.

10–8. Estimate the maximum heat flux obtainable with nucleate pool boiling on a clean surface for (a) water at 1 atm on brass, (b) water at 10 atm on brass, and (c) *n*-butyl alcohol at 3 atm on copper.

10–9. Determine the excess temperature at one-half of the maximum heat flux for the fluid-surface combinations in Prob. 10–8.

10–10. Estimate the time required to freeze a 1-in. thickness of water due to nocturnal radiation with ambient air and initial water temperatures at 40 F. Neglect evaporation effect.

11 Heat Exchangers

11-1. DESIGN AND SELECTION

A heat exchanger is a device which effects the transfer of heat from one fluid to another. The simplest type of heat exchanger is a container in which a hot and a cold fluid are mixed directly. In such a system both fluids will reach the same final temperature, and the amount of heat transferred can be estimated by equating the energy lost by the hotter fluid to the energy gained by the cooler one. Open feed-water heaters, desuperheaters, and jet condensers are examples of heat-transfer equipment employing direct mixing of fluids. More common, however, are heat exchangers in which one fluid is separated from the other by a wall or a partition through which the heat flows. These types of exchangers are called *recuperators*. There are many forms of such equipment ranging from a simple pipe-within-a-pipe with a few square feet of heat-transfer surface up to complex surface condensers and evaporators with many thousands of square feet of heat-transfer surface. In between these extremes is a broad field of common shell-and-tube exchangers. These units are widely used because they can be constructed with large heat-transfer surfaces in a relatively small volume, can be fabricated from alloys to resist corrosion, and are suitable for heating, cooling, evaporating, or condensing all kinds of fluids.

The complete design of a heat-exchanger can be broken down into three major phases:
1. The thermal analysis.
2. The preliminary mechanical design.
3. Design for manufacture.

The emphasis in this chapter will be on the thermal design. This phase of the design is primarily concerned with the determination of the heat-transfer surface area required to transfer heat at a specified rate for given flow rates and temperatures of the fluids.

The mechanical design involves considerations of the operating temperatures and pressures, the corrosive characteristics of one or both fluids, the relative thermal expansions and accompanying thermal stresses, and the relation of the heat exchanger to other equipment concerned.

The design for manufacture requires the translation of the physical

characteristics and dimensions into a unit which can be built at a low cost.
Selections of materials, seals, enclosures, and the optimum mechanical
arrangement have to be made and the manufacturing procedures must be
specified.

To achieve maximum economy the majority of manufacturers have
adopted standard lines of heat exchangers. The standards establish tube
diameters and pressure ratings and promote the use of standard drawings
and standard fabrication procedures. Standardization does not mean, however, that heat exchangers can be delivered off the shelf, because service
requirements vary too much. Some engineering design is necessary for
almost every exchanger, but if service conditions permit, the use of exchangers built to standard lines saves money. The engineer concerned
with the installation of heat exchangers in power plants and process equipment is therefore often called upon to select a heat-exchanger unit which
is suitable for a particular application. The selection requires a thermal
analysis to determine whether a standard unit of specified size and geometry
can meet the requirements of heating or cooling a given fluid at a specified
rate. In this type of analysis the initial cost must be weighed against such
factors as life of equipment, ease of cleaning, and space required. It is
also important that the requirements of the safety codes of ASME be met,
and for this purpose the Standards of the Tubular Exchanger Manufacturers Association (TEMA) should be consulted.

11-2. BASIC TYPES OF HEAT EXCHANGER

The simplest type of shell-and-tube heat exchanger is shown in Fig. 11–1.
It consists of a tube or a pipe located concentrically inside another tube
which forms the shell for this arrangement. One of the fluids flows
through the inner tube, the other through the annulus formed between the
inner and the outer tube. Since both fluid streams traverse the exchanger
only once, this arrangement is called a *single-pass* heat exchanger. If both
fluids flow in the same direction, the exchanger is a *parallel-flow* type; if
the fluids move in opposite directions, the exchanger is of the *counterflow*

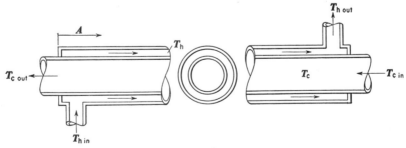

FIG. 11–1.   Diagram of a simple tube-within-a-tube counterflow heat exchanger.

type. The temperature difference between the hot and the cold fluid is, in general, not constant along the tube, and the rate of heat flow will vary from section to section. To determine the rate of heat flow one must therefore use an appropriate mean-temperature difference, as shown in Sec. 11–3.

When the two fluids flowing along the heat-transfer surface move at right angles to each other, the heat exchanger is of the *crossflow* type. Three separate arrangements of this type of exchanger are possible. In the first case each of the fluids is *unmixed* as it passes through the exchanger and, therefore, the temperatures of the fluids leaving the heater section are not uniform, being hotter on one side than on the other. A flat-plate type heater (Fig. 11–2), a design used for turbine regenerators to reclaim the energy of the exhaust gases, or an automobile radiator approximates this type of exchanger. In the second case, one of the fluids is *unmixed* and

Gas

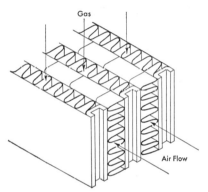

Air Flow

Fig. 11–2. Flat-plate type heat exchanger illustrating crossflow with both fluids unmixed.

the other is perfectly *mixed* as it flows through the exchanger. The temperature of the mixed fluid will be uniform across any section and will vary only in the direction of flow. An example of this type is the crossflow air heater shown schematically in Fig. 11–3. The air flowing over the bank of tubes is mixed, while the hot gases inside the tubes are confined and therefore do not mix. In the third case, both of the fluids are *mixed* as they flow through the exchanger; that is, the temperature of both fluids will be uniform across the section and will vary only in the direction of flow. This type of arrangement is less important than the other two and will not be discussed here.

In order to increase the effective heat-transfer surface area per unit volume, most commercial heat exchangers provide for more than a single pass through the tubes, and the fluid flowing outside the tubes in the shell is routed back and forth by means of baffles. Figure 11–4 is a cross section

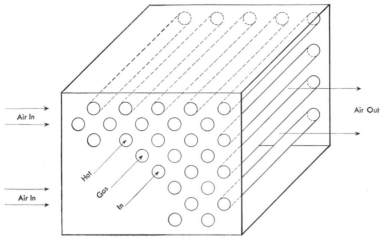

Fig. 11–3. Crossflow air heater illustrating crossflow with one fluid mixed, the other unmixed.

of a heat exchanger with two tube passes and one cross-baffled shell pass. The baffles are of the segmental type This and other typical types of baffles are shown in Fig. 11–5. In a baffled exchanger, the flow pattern on the shell side is complex. As shown by the arrows, part of the time the flow is perpendicular, and part of the time parallel, to the tube.

The heat exchanger illustrated in Fig 11–4 has fixed tube plates at each end and the tubes are welded or expanded into the plates. This type of construction has the lowest initial cost but can only be used for small temperature differences between the hot and the cold fluid because no provision is made to prevent thermal stresses due to the differential expansion between the tubes and the shell. Another disadvantage is that the tube bundle can not be removed for cleaning. These drawbacks can be overcome by the modification of the basic design as shown in Fig. 11–6. In this arrangement one tube plate is fixed but the other is bolted to a floating-head cover which permits the tube bundle to move relative to the

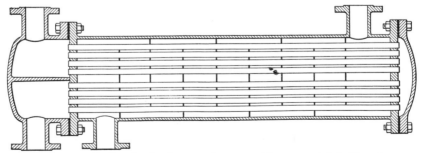

Fig. 11–4. Shell-and-tube heat exchanger with segmental baffles: two tube passes, one shell pass.

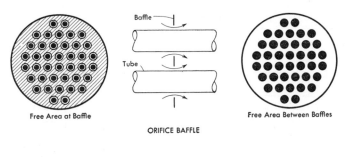

ORIFICE BAFFLE

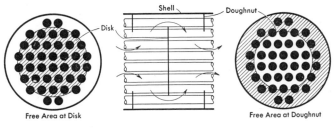

DISK-AND-DOUGHNUT BAFFLE

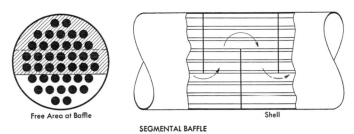

SEGMENTAL BAFFLE

Fig. 11–5. Three types of baffles used in shell-and-tube heat exchangers. (After C. B. Cramer, *Heat Transfer*, 2d ed. International Textbook Company, Scranton, Pa.)

shell. The floating tube sheet is clamped between the floating head and a flange so that it is possible to remove the tube bundle for cleaning. The heat exchanger shown in Fig. 11–6 has one shell pass and two tube passes.

For certain special applications such as regenerators for aircraft or automobile gas turbines, the rate of heat transfer per unit weight and unit volume is the prime consideration. Compact, lightweight heat exchangers for this type of service have been investigated by Kays and London (1). A typical design is shown in Fig. 11–7. For a complete description and analysis of compact heat exchangers, especially for the application of fins to increase the effectiveness of such units, the reader is referred to the original papers (1,2,3,4,5).

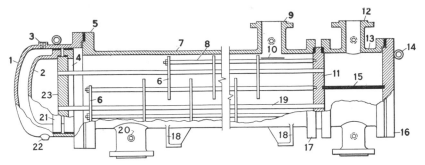

1. Shell cover	8. Tie rods and	17. Shell channel—
2. Floating head	spacers	end flange
3. Vent connection	9. Shell nozzle	18. Support saddles
4. Floating-head	10. Impingement baffle	19. Heat-transfer
backing device	11. Stationary tube	tube
5. Shell cover—end	sheet	20. Test connection
flange	12. Channel nozzle	21. Floating-head
6. Transverse baf-	13. Channel	flange
fles or support	14. Lifting ring	22. Drain connection
plates	15. Pass partition	23. Floating tube
7. Shell	16. Channel cover	sheet

FIG. 11–6.   Shell-and-tube heat exchanger with floating head.   (Courtesy of the Tubular Exchange Manufacturer's Association)

FIG. 11–7.   Typical compact heat-exchanger section.   (Courtesy of the Harrison Radiator Division, General Motors Corp.)

11–3. MEAN TEMPERATURE DIFFERENCE

The temperatures of fluids in a heat exchanger are generally not constant, but vary from point to point as heat flows from the hotter to the colder fluid. Even for a constant thermal resistance, the rate of heat flow will therefore vary along the path of the exchangers because its value depends on the temperature difference between the hot and the cold fluid at the section. Figures 11–8, 11–9, 11–10, and 11–11 illustrate the changes in temperature that may occur in either or both fluids in a simple shell-and-tube exchanger (Fig. 11–1). The distances between the solid lines are proportional to the temperature differences ΔT between the two fluids.

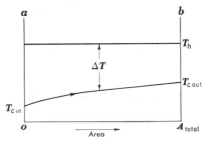

Fig. 11–8. Temperature distribution in single-pass condenser.

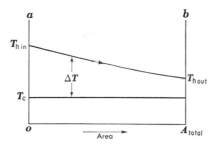

Fig. 11–9. Temperature distribution in single-pass evaporator.

Figure 11–8 illustrates the case where a vapor is condensing at a constant temperature while the other fluid is being heated. Figure 11–9 is representative of a case where a liquid is evaporated at constant temperature while heat is flowing from a warmer fluid whose temperature decreases as it passes through the heat exchanger. For both of these cases the direction of flow of either fluid is immaterial and the constant-temperature medium may also be at rest. Figure 11–10 represents conditions in a parallel-flow exchanger, and Fig. 11–11 applies to counterflow. No change of phase occurs in the latter two cases. Inspection of Fig. 11–10 shows that, no matter how long the exchanger is, the final temperature of the colder fluid can never reach the exit temperature of the hotter fluid in parallel flow. For counterflow on the other hand, the final temperature of the cooler fluid may exceed the outlet temperature of the hotter fluid, since a favorable temperature gradient exists all along the heat exchanger. An additional advantage of the counterflow arrangement is that, for a given rate of heat flow, less surface area is required than in parallel flow.

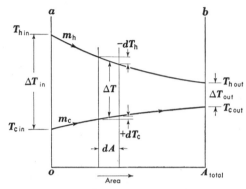

FIG. 11–10. Temperature distribution in single-pass parallel-flow heat exchanger.

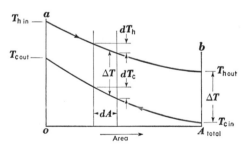

FIG. 11–11. Temperature distribution in single-pass counterflow heat exchanger.

To determine the rate of heat transfer in any of the aforementioned cases the equation

$$dq = U dA \Delta T \qquad (11\text{-}1)$$

must be integrated over the heat-transfer area A along the length of the exchanger. If the over-all unit conductance U is constant, if changes in kinetic energy are neglected, and if the shell of the exchanger is insulated, Eq. 11–1 can easily be integrated analytically for parallel or counterflow. An energy balance over a differential area dA yields

$$dq = -m_h c_{ph}\, dT_h = \pm\, m_c c_{pc}\, dT_c = U dA\, (T_h - T_c) \qquad (11\text{-}2)$$

where m is the mass rate of flow in lb_m/hr, c_p is the specific heat at constant pressure in Btu/lb_mF, and T is the average bulk temperature of the fluid in F. The subscripts h and c refer to the hot and cold fluid respectively; the plus sign in the third term applies to parallel flow, and the minus sign to counterflow. If the specific heats of the fluids do not vary with temperature, we can write a heat balance from the inlet to an arbitrary cross section in the exchanger, or

$$- C_h(T_h - T_{h \ in}) = C_c \ (T_c - T_{c \ in}) \qquad \textbf{(11-3)}$$

where $C_h = m_h c_{ph}$, the hourly heat-capacity flow rate of the hotter fluid in Btu/hr F;

$C_c = m_c c_{pc}$, the hourly heat-capacity flow rate of the colder fluid in Btu/hr F.

Solving Eq. 11–3 for T_h gives

$$T_h = T_{h \ in} - \frac{C_c}{C_h} (T_c - T_{c \ in}) \qquad \textbf{(11-4)}$$

from which we obtain

$$T_h - T_c = -\left(1 + \frac{C_c}{C_h}\right)T_c + \frac{C_c}{C_h} T_{c \ in} + T_{h \ in} \qquad \textbf{(11-5)}$$

Substituting Eq. 11–5 for $T_h - T_c$ in Eq. 11–2 yields after some rearrangement

$$\frac{dT_c}{-[1 + (C_c/C_h)] \ T_c + (C_c/C_h) \ T_{c \ in} + T_{h \ in}} = \frac{UdA}{C_c} \qquad \textbf{(11-6)}$$

Integrating Eq. 11–6 over the entire length of the exchanger (i.e., from $A = 0$ to $A = A_{\text{total}}$) yields

$$\ln \left\{ \frac{- [1 + (C_c/C_h)] \ T_{c \ out} + (C_c/C_h) \ T_{c \ in} - T_{h \ in}}{- [1 + (C_c/C_h)] \ T_{c \ in} + (C_c/C_h) \ T_{c \ in} - T_{h \ in}} \right\}$$

$$= - \left(\frac{1}{C_c} + \frac{1}{C_h}\right) UA \qquad \textbf{(11-7)}$$

Equation 11–7 can be simplified to read

$$\ln \left[\frac{(1 + C_c/C_h)(T_{c \ in} - T_{c \ out}) + T_{h \ in} - T_{c \ in}}{T_{h \ in} - T_{c \ in}} \right]$$

$$= -\left(\frac{1}{C_c} + \frac{1}{C_h}\right) UA \qquad \textbf{(11-8)}$$

From Eq. 11–3 we obtain for the total length of the exchanger

$$\frac{C_c}{C_h} = - \frac{T_{h \ out} - T_{h \ in}}{T_{c \ out} - T_{c \ in}} \qquad \textbf{(11-9)}$$

which can be used to eliminate the hourly heat capacities in Eq. 11–8. After some rearrangement we get

$$\ln \left(\frac{T_{h\ out} - T_{c\ out}}{T_{h\ in} - T_{c\ in}} \right)$$

$$= [(T_{h\ out} - T_{c\ out}) - (T_{h\ in} - T_{c\ in})] \frac{UA}{q} \qquad \textbf{(11–10)}$$

since $\qquad q = C_c(T_{c\ out} - T_{c\ in}) = C_h(T_{h\ in} - T_{h\ out})$

Letting $T_h - T_c = \Delta T$, Eq. 11–10 can be written

$$q = UA \frac{\Delta T_a - \Delta T_b}{\ln(\Delta T_a / \Delta T_b)} \qquad \textbf{(11–11)}$$

where the subscripts a and b refer to the respective ends of the exchanger (see Figs. 11–10 and 11–11). In practice it is convenient to use an average effective temperature difference $\overline{\Delta T}$ for the entire heat exchanger defined by

$$q = UA\overline{\Delta T} \qquad \textbf{(11–12)}$$

Comparing Eqs. 11–12 and 11–11, one finds that, for parallel or counterflow

$$\overline{\Delta T} = \frac{\Delta T_a - \Delta T_b}{\ln(\Delta T_a / \Delta T_b)} \qquad \textbf{(11–13)}$$

which is called the logarithmic mean over-all temperature difference often designated by LMTD. The LMTD also applies when the temperature of one of the fluids is constant, as shown in Figs. 11–8 and 11–9. When $m_h c_{ph} = m_c c_{pc}$, the temperature difference is constant in counterflow and $\overline{\Delta T} = \Delta T_a = \Delta T_b$.

The use of the logarithmic mean temperature is only an approximation in practice because U is generally not constant. In design work, however, the over-all conductance is usually evaluated at a mean section, usually halfway between ends, and treated as constant. If U varies considerably, a numerical step-by-step integration of Eq. 11–1 may be necessary.

If the temperature difference ΔT_a is not more than 50 per cent greater than ΔT_b, the arithmetic mean temperature difference will be within 1 per cent of the LMTD and may be used to simplify calculations.

For more complex heat exchangers such as the shell-and-tube arrangements with several tube or shell passes and with crossflow exchangers having mixed and unmixed flow, the mathematical derivation of an expression for the mean temperature difference becomes quite complex. The usual procedure is to modify the simple LMTD by correction factors which have been published in chart form by Bowman, Mueller, and Nagle (6) and by the Tubular Exchanger Manufacturer's Association (7).

Four of these graphs[1] are shown in Figs. 11–12, 11–13, 11–14, and 11–15. The ordinate of each is the correction factor F. To obtain the true mean temperature for any of these arrangements, the LMTD calculated for *counterflow* must be multiplied by the appropriate correction factor, that is,

$$\Delta T_{\text{true mean}} = \text{LMTD} \times F \qquad (11\text{–}14)$$

The values shown on the abscissa are for the dimensionless temperature-difference ratio

$$P = (T_{t\text{ out}} - T_{t\text{ in}})/(T_{s\text{ in}} - T_{t\text{ in}}) \qquad (11\text{–}15)$$

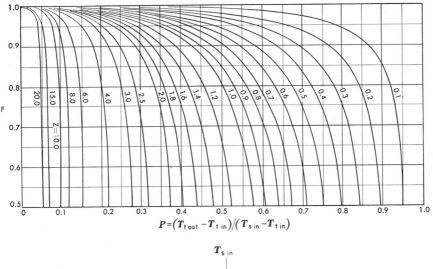

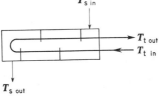

FIG. 11–12. Correction factor to counterflow LMTD for heat exchanger with one shell pass and two, or a multiple of two, tube passes. (Courtesy of the Tubular Exchange Manufacturer's Association)

where the subscripts t and s refer to the tube and shell fluid respectively, and the subscripts *in* and *out* refer to the inlet and outlet conditions respectively. The ratio P is an indication of the heating or cooling effectiveness and can vary from zero for a constant temperature of one of the fluids to unity for the case when inlet temperature of the hotter fluid equals the outlet temperature of the colder fluid. The parameter for each of the curves Z is equal to the ratio of the products of the mass-flow rate times

[1] Correction factors for several other arrangements are presented in Ref. 6.

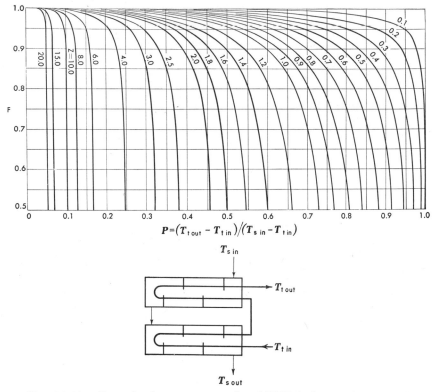

$$P = \left(T_{t\,out} - T_{t\,in}\right) / \left(T_{s\,in} - T_{t\,in}\right)$$

Fig. 11–13. Correction factor to counterflow LMTD for heat exchanger with two shell passes and a multiple of two tube passes. (Courtesy of the Tubular Exchange Manufacturer's Association)

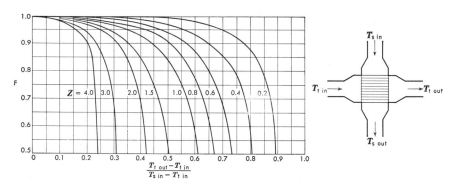

$$\frac{T_{t\,out} - T_{t\,in}}{T_{s\,in} - T_{t\,in}}$$

Fig. 11–14. Correction factor to counterflow LMTD for crossflow heat exchangers, fluid on shell side mixed, other fluid unmixed, one tube pass. (Extracted from "Mean Temperature Difference in Design," by R. A. Bowman, A. C. Mueller, and W. M. Nagel, published in *Trans. ASME*, Vol. 62, 1940, with permission of the publishers, The American Society of Mechanical Engineers)

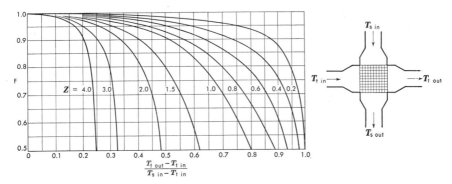

Fig. 11–15. Correction factor to counterflow LMTD for crossflow heat exchanger, both fluids unmixed, one tube pass. (Extracted from "Mean Temperature Difference in Design," by R. A. Bowman, A. C. Mueller, and W. M. Nagel, published in *Trans. ASME*, Vol. 62, 1940, with permission of the publishers, The American Society of Mechanical Engineers)

the heat capacity of the two fluids $m_t c_{pt}/m_s c_{ps}$. This ratio is also equal to the temperature change of the shell fluid divided by the temperature change of the fluid in the tubes, or

$$Z = \frac{m_t c_{pt}}{m_s c_{ps}} = \frac{T_{s\ in} - T_{s\ out}}{T_{t\ out} - T_{t\ in}} \tag{11–16}$$

In the application of the correction factors it is immaterial whether the warmer fluid flows through shell or tubes. If the temperature of either of the fluids remains constant, the direction of flow is also immaterial, since F equals 1 and the LMTD applies directly.

Example 11–1. Determine the heat-transfer surface area required for a heat exchanger constructed from 1-in.-OD tube to cool 55,000 lb/hr of a 95 per cent ethyl alcohol solution ($c_p = 0.91$ Btu/lb F) from 150 to 103 F, using 50,000 lb/hr of water available at 50 F. Assume that the over-all coefficient of heat transfer based on the outer-tube area is 400 Btu/hr sq ft F and consider each of the following arrangements:

    a) Parallel-flow tube and shell;
    b) Counterflow tube and shell;
    c) Reversed-current exchanger with two shell passes and 72 tube passes, the alcohol flowing through the shell and the water flowing through the tubes;
    d) Crossflow, with one tube pass and one shell pass, shell-side fluid mixed.

Solution: (a) The outlet temperature of the water for any of the four arrangements can be obtained from an over-all energy balance, assuming that the heat loss to the atmosphere is negligible. Writing the energy balance as

$$m_h c_{ph} (T_{h\ in} - T_{h\ out}) = m_c c_{pc} (T_{c\ out} - T_{c\ in})$$

and substituting the data in the above equation we obtain

$$(55,000)\ (0.91)\ (150 - 103) = (50,000)\ (1.0)\ (T_{c\ out} - 50)$$

from which the outlet temperature of the water is found to be 97 F. The rate of heat flow from the alcohol to the water is therefore

$$q = m_h c_{ph}(T_{h\ in} - T_{h\ out}) = (55{,}000)\ (0.91)\ (150 - 103) = 2{,}350{,}000\ \text{Btu/hr}$$

From Eq. 11–13, the LMTD for parallel flow is

$$\text{LMTD} = \frac{\Delta T_a - \Delta T_b}{\ln\ (\Delta T_a/\Delta T_b)} = \frac{100 - 6}{\ln\ (100/6)} = 33.4\ \text{F}$$

From Eq. 11–12 the heat-transfer surface area is

$$A = \frac{q}{(U)(\text{LMTD})} = \frac{2{,}350{,}000}{(100)(33.4)} = 703\ \text{sq ft}$$

The length of the exchanger for a 1-in.-OD tube would be too great to be practical.   *Ans.*

b) For the counterflow arrangement, the appropriate mean temperature difference is $150 - 97 = 53$ F because $m_c c_{pc} = m_h c_{ph}$. The required area is

$$A = \frac{q}{(U)(\text{LMTD})} = \frac{2{,}350{,}000}{(100)(53)} = 444\ \text{sq ft}$$

which is 40 per cent less than the area necessary for parallel flow.   *Ans.*

c) For the reversed-current arrangement, we determine the appropriate mean temperature difference by applying the correction factor found from Fig. 11–13 to the mean temperature for counterflow.

$$P = \frac{T_{c\ out} - T_{c\ in}}{T_{h\ in} - T_{c\ in}} = \frac{97 - 50}{150 - 50} = 0.47$$

and the hourly heat capacity ratio is

$$Z = \frac{m_c c_{pc}}{m_h c_{ph}} = 1$$

From the chart of Fig. 11–13, $F = 0.97$ and the heat-transfer area is

$$A = \frac{444}{0.97} = 460\ \text{sq ft} \qquad\qquad Ans.$$

The length of the exchanger for 72 1-in.-OD tubes in parallel would be

$$L = \frac{A/72}{\pi D} = \frac{6.4}{(\pi)(1/12)} \simeq 24.4\ \text{ft}$$

This length is not unreasonable, but if it is desirable to shorten the exchanger, more tubes could be used.

d) For the crossflow arrangement (Fig. 11–3), the correction factor is found from the chart of Fig. 11–14 to be 0.88. The required surface area is thus 504 sq ft, about 10 per cent larger than that for the reversed-current exchanger.   *Ans.*

11–4. HEAT-EXCHANGER EFFECTIVENESS

In the thermal analysis of the various types of heat exchanger presented in the preceding section, an equation of the type

$$q = UA\Delta T_{\text{mean}} \qquad\qquad\qquad \textbf{[11–12]}$$

was used. This form will be found convenient when all of the terminal temperatures necessary for the evaluation of the appropriate mean temperature are known, and Eq. 11–12 is widely employed in the design of heat exchangers to given specifications.   There are, however, numerous occasions when the performance of a heat exchanger (i.e., U) is known, or can at least be estimated, but the temperatures of the fluids leaving the exchanger are not known.   This type of problem is encountered in the selection of a heat exchanger or when the unit has been tested at one flow rate but service conditions require different flow rates for one or both fluids.   The outlet temperatures and the rate of heat flow can only be found by a rather tedious trial-and-error procedure if the charts presented in the preceding section are used.   In such cases it is desirable to circumvent entirely any reference to the logarithmic or any other mean temperature difference.   A method which accomplishes this has been proposed by Nusselt (8) and Ten Broeck (9).

To obtain an equation for the rate of heat transfer which does not involve any of the outlet temperatures, we introduce the *heat-exchanger effectiveness* $\mathcal{E}$.   The heat-exchanger effectiveness is defined as the ratio of the actual rate of heat transfer in a given heat exchanger to the maximum possible rate of heat exchange.   The latter would be obtained in a counter-flow heat exchanger of infinite heat-transfer area.   In this type of unit, if there are no external heat losses, the outlet temperature of the colder fluid equals the inlet temperature of the hotter fluid when $m_c c_{pc} < m_h c_{ph}$; when $m_h c_{ph} < m_c c_{pc}$, the outlet temperature of the warmer fluid equals the inlet temperature of the colder one.   In other words, the effectiveness compares the actual heat-transfer rate to the maximum rate whose only limit is the second law of thermodynamics.   Depending on which of the hourly heat capacities is smaller, the effectiveness is

$$\mathcal{E} = \frac{C_h(T_{h\ in} - T_{h\ out})}{C_{min}(T_{h\ in} - T_{c\ in})} \tag{11–17a}$$

or

$$\mathcal{E} = \frac{C_c(T_{c\ out} - T_{c\ in})}{C_{min}(T_{h\ in} - T_{c\ in})} \tag{11–17b}$$

where C_{min} is the smaller of the $m_h c_{ph}$ and $m_c c_{pc}$ magnitudes.

Once the effectiveness of a heat exchanger is known, the rate of heat transfer can be determined directly from the equation

$$q = \mathcal{E}C_{min} (T_{h\ in} - T_{c\ in}) \tag{11–18}$$

since

$$\mathcal{E}C_{min} (T_{h\ in} - T_{c\ in}) = C_h (T_{h\ in} - T_{h\ out}) = C_c (T_{c\ out} - T_{c\ in})$$

Equation 11–18 is the basic relation in this analysis because it expresses the rate of heat transfer in terms of the effectiveness, the smaller hourly heat capacity, and the difference between the inlet temperatures.   It replaces Eq. 11–12 in the LMTD analysis but does not involve the outlet temperatures.   Equation 11–18 is of course also suitable for design purposes instead of Eq. 11–12.

We shall illustrate the method of deriving an expression for the effectiveness of a heat exchanger by applying it to a parallel-flow arrangement.   The effectiveness can be introduced into Eq. 11–8 by replacing $(T_{c\ in} - T_{c\ out})/(T_{h\ in} - T_{c\ in})$ by the effectiveness relation from Eq. 11–17. We obtain

$$\ln\left[1 - \varepsilon\left(\frac{C_{\min}}{C_h} + \frac{C_{\min}}{C_c}\right)\right] = -\left(\frac{1}{C_c} + \frac{1}{C_h}\right)UA$$

or

$$1 - \varepsilon\left(\frac{C_{\min}}{C_h} + \frac{C_{\min}}{C_c}\right) = e^{-(1/C_c + 1/C_h)UA}$$

Solving for ε yields

$$\varepsilon = \frac{1 - e^{-[1+(C_h/C_c)]UA/C_h}}{(C_{\min}/C_h) + (C_{\min}/C_c)} \tag{11-19}$$

When C_h is less than C_c, the effectiveness becomes

$$\varepsilon = \frac{1 - e^{-[1+(C_h/C_c)]UA/C_h}}{1 + (C_h/C_c)} \tag{11-20}$$

and when $C_c < C_h$, we obtain

$$\varepsilon = \frac{1 - e^{-[1+(C_c/C_h)]UA/C_c}}{1 + (C_c/C_h)} \tag{11-20a}$$

The effectiveness for both cases can therefore be written in the form

$$\varepsilon = \frac{1 - e^{-[1+(C_{\min}/C_{\max})]UA/C_{\min}}}{1 + (C_{\min}/C_{\max})} \tag{11-21}$$

The foregoing derivation illustrates how the effectiveness for a given flow arrangement can be expressed in terms of two dimensionless parameters, the hourly heat-capacity ratio $C_{\min}/C_{\max}$ and the ratio of the over-all conductance to the smaller hourly heat capacity, $UA/C_{\min}$.   The latter of the two parameters is called the *number of heat-transfer units*, or NTU for short.   The number of heat-transfer units is a measure of the heat-transfer size of the exchanger.   The larger the value of NTU, the closer the heat exchanger approaches its thermodynamic limit.   By analyses which in principle are similar to the one presented here for parallel flow, effectivenesses may be evaluated for most flow arrangements of practical interest.   The results have been put by Kays and London (1) into convenient graphs from which the effectiveness can be determined for given values of NTU and $C_{\min}/C_{\max}$.

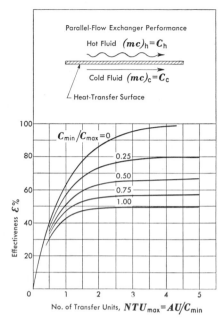

Fig. 11–16. Heat-exchanger effectiveness for parallel flow. (By permission from W. M. Kays and A. L. London, *Compact Heat Exchangers*, National Press, 1955)

The effectiveness curves for some common flow arrangements are shown in Figs. 11–16 to 11–20. The abscissas of these figures are the NTU's of the heat exchangers. The constant parameter for each curve is the hourly heat capacity ratio C_{min}/C_{max}, and the effectiveness is read on the ordinate. Note that, for an evaporator or condenser, $C_{min}/C_{max} = 0$, because if one fluid remains at constant temperature throughout the exchanger, its effective specific heat, and thus its capacity rate, is by definition equal to infinity.

Example 11–2. From a performance test on a well-baffled single-shell, two-tube-pass heat exchanger, the following data are available: oil ($c_p = 0.5$ Btu/lb F) in turbulent flow inside the tubes entered at 160 F at the rate of 5000 lb/hr and left at 100 F; water flowing on the shell side entered at 60 F and left at 80 F. A change in service conditions requires the cooling of a similar oil from an initial temperature of 200 F but at three fourths of the flow rate used in the performance test. Estimate the outlet temperature of the oil for the same water rate and inlet temperature as before.

Solution: The test data may be used to determine the hourly heat capacity of the water and the over-all conductance of the exchanger. The hourly heat capacity of the water is from Eq. 11–9

$$C_c = C_h \frac{T_{h\ \text{in}} - T_{h\ \text{out}}}{T_{c\ \text{out}} - T_{c\ \text{in}}} = (5000)(0.5)\left(\frac{160 - 100}{80 - 60}\right) = 7500 \text{ Btu/hr}$$

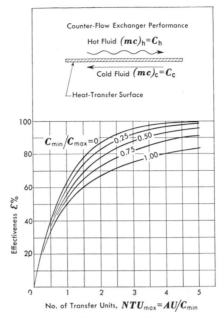

FIG. 11–17. Heat-exchanger effectiveness for counterflow. (By permission from W. M. Kays and A. L. London, *Compact Heat Exchangers*, National Press, 1955)

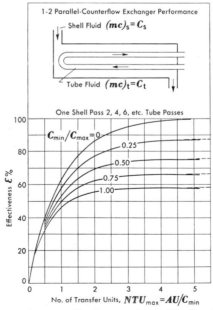

FIG. 11–18. Heat-exchanger effectiveness for shell-and-tube heat exchanger with one well-baffled shell pass and two, or a multiple of two, tube passes. (By permission from W. M. Kays and A. L. London, *Compact Heat Exchangers*, National Press, 1955)

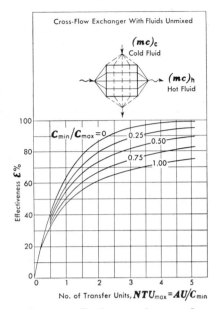

Fig. 11–19. Heat-exchanger effectiveness for crossflow with both fluids unmixed. (By permission from W. M. Kays and A. L. London, *Compact Heat Exchangers*, National Press, 1955)

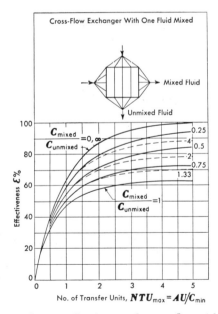

Fig. 11–20. Heat-exchanger effectiveness for crossflow with one fluid mixed, the other unmixed. When $C_{mixed}/C_{unmixed} > 1$, NTU_{max} is based on $C_{unmixed}$. (By permission from W. M. Kays and A. L. London, *Compact Heat Exchangers*, National Press, 1955)

and the temperature ratio P is from Eq. 11–15

$$P = \frac{T_{t\ out} - T_{t\ in}}{T_{s\ in} - T_{t\ in}} = \frac{60}{100} = 0.6 \qquad Z = \frac{20}{60} = 0.33$$

From Fig. 11–12, $F = 0.94$ and the mean temperature difference is

$$\overline{\Delta T} = F \times \text{LMTD} = 0.94 \frac{80 - 40}{\ln (80/40)} = 54.2 \text{ F}$$

From Eq. 11–12 the over-all conductance is

$$UA = q/\overline{\Delta T} = (7500)\ (20)/54.2 = 2760 \text{ Btu/hr F}$$

Since the thermal resistance on the oil side is controlling, a decrease in velocity to 75 per cent of the original value will increase the thermal resistance roughly by the velocity ratio raised to the 0.8 power. This can be verified by reference to Eq. 8–17. Under the new conditions the conductance, the NTU, and the hourly heat capacity ratio will therefore be approximately

$$UA \simeq (2760)\ (0.75^{0.8}) = 2190 \text{ Btu/hr F}$$

$$\text{NTU} = \frac{UA}{C_{\text{oil}}} = \frac{2190}{(0.75)(2500)} = 1.17$$

and
$$C_{\text{oil}}/C_{\text{water}} = C_{\min}/C_{\max} = (0.75)\ (2500)/7500 = 0.25$$

From Fig. 11–18 the effectiveness is equal to 0.63. Hence from the definition of ε, the oil outlet temperature is

$$T_{\text{oil out}} = T_{\text{oil in}} - \frac{C_{\text{oil}}}{C_{\text{water}}} \varepsilon \Delta T_{\max} = (160 - 0.25)(0.63)(100) = 144.3 \text{ F} \quad Ans.$$

Example 11–3. A flat-plate-type heater (Fig. 11–21) is to be used to heat air with the hot exhaust gases from a turbine. The required air-flow rate is 6000 lb/hr, entering at 60 F; the hot gases are available at a temperature of 1600 F and at a rate of 5000 lb/hr. Determine the temperature of the air leaving the heat exchanger.

Solution: Inspection of Fig. 11–21 shows that the unit is of the cross-flow type, both fluids unmixed. As a first approximation the end effects will be neglected. The flow systems for the air and gas streams are similar to flow in straight ducts having the following dimensions:

> Length of air duct, $L_a = 0.583$ ft
> Hydraulic diameter of air duct $D_{Ha} = 4A_a/P_a = 0.0427$ ft
> Length of gas duct $L_g = 1.13$ ft
> Hydraulic diameter of gas duct $D_{Hg} = 4A_g/P_g = 0.0516$ ft
> Heat-transfer surface area $A = 23.6$ ft

The unit conductances may be evaluated from Eqs. 8–23a and 8–18 for flow in ducts ($L_a/D_{Ha} = 0.583/0.0427 = 13.7$, $L_g/D_{Hg} = 1.13/0.0516 = 21.9$). A difficulty arises, however, because the temperatures of both fluids vary along the duct. It is therefore necessary to estimate an average temperature and refine the calculations after the outlet temperatures have been found. Selecting the average air temperature at 160 F and the average gas temperature at 1500 F, the absolute viscosities at those temperatures are from Table A–3:

$$\mu_{air} = 1.4 \times 10^{-5} \text{ lb}_m/\text{ft sec}$$
$$\mu_{gas} \text{ (assuming air properties)} = 3.0 \times 10^{-5} \text{ lb}_m/\text{ft sec}$$

The mass rates per unit area are:

$$(m/A)_{air} = (6000/19)\,(0.0246) = 12{,}840 \text{ lb/hr sq ft}$$
$$(m/A)_{gas} = (5000/18)\,(0.0158) = 17{,}550 \text{ lb/hr sq ft}$$

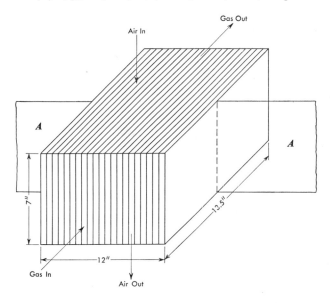

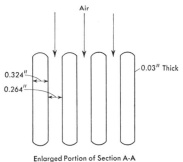

Enlarged Portion of Section A-A
(Not to Scale)

FIG. 11–21.   Flat-plate-type heater.

Dimensions at Section A–A

P_a = Wetted perimeter on air side	2.3 ft	
P_g = Wetted perimeter on gas side	1.22 ft	
A_a = Cross-sectional area of air passage (per passage)	0.0246 sq ft	
A_g = Cross-sectional area of gas passage (per passage)	0.0158 sq ft	
Heat-transfer area	23.6 sq ft	
Air passages	19	
Gas passages	18	

The Reynolds numbers are:

$$\mathrm{Re}_{\mathrm{air}} = \frac{(m/A)_a D_{Ha}}{\mu_a} = \frac{(12{,}840 \text{ lb}_m/\text{hr sq ft})(0.0427 \text{ ft})}{(3600 \text{ sec/hr})(1.4 \times 10^{-5} \text{ lb}_m/\text{ft sec})} = 11{,}100$$

$$\mathrm{Re}_{\mathrm{gas}} = \frac{(m/A)_g D_{Hg}}{\mu_g} = \frac{(17{,}550 \text{ lb}_m/\text{hr sq ft})(0.0516 \text{ ft})}{(3600 \text{ sec/hr})(3.0 \times 10^{-5} \text{ lb}_m/\text{ft sec})} = 8200$$

Using Eqs. 8–18 and 8–23a the average unit conductances are:

$$\bar{h}_{\mathrm{air}} = \left[(0.023) \left(\frac{k_a}{D_{Ha}} \right) (\mathrm{Re}_D{}^{0.8} \, \mathrm{Pr}^{0.33}) \right] \left[1 + \left(\frac{D_{Ha}}{L} \right)^{0.7} \right]$$

$$= \left[(0.023) \left(\frac{0.0185}{0.0427} \right) (1720)(0.87) \right] (1 + 0.16) = 17.3 \text{ Btu/hr sq ft F}$$

$$\bar{h}_{\mathrm{gas}} = \left[(0.023) \left(\frac{0.048}{0.0516} \right) (1340)(0.84) \right] (1 + 0.116) = 26.8 \text{ Btu/hr sq ft F}$$

If the thermal resistance of the metal wall is neglected, the over-all conductance is

$$UA = \frac{1}{\dfrac{1}{\bar{h}_a A} + \dfrac{1}{\bar{h}_g A}} = \frac{1}{\left(\dfrac{1}{17.3 \times 23.6} \right) + \left(\dfrac{1}{26.8 \times 23.6} \right)} = 250 \text{ Btu/hr F}$$

The number of transfer units, based on the warmer fluid which has the smaller heat capacity rate, are

$$\mathrm{NTU} = UA/C_{1\,\mathrm{min}} = (250/5000)\,(0.24) = 0.208$$

the hourly heat capacity ratio is

$$\frac{C_g}{C_a} = \frac{(5000)(0.24)}{(6000)(0.24)} = 0.833$$

and from Fig. 11–19 the effectiveness is 0.15. Finally, the average outlet temperature of the air is

$$T_{\mathrm{air\ out}} = T_{\mathrm{air\ in}} + \frac{C_g}{C_a} \varepsilon \Delta T_{\max} = 60 + (0.833)(0.15)(1540) = 247 \text{ F} \qquad Ans.$$

A check on the mean air temperature gives

$$T_{\mathrm{mean}} = \frac{247 + 60}{2} = 153.5 \text{ F}$$

which is sufficiently close to the assumed value of 160 F to make a second approximation unnecessary. To appreciate the usefulness of the approach based on the concept of heat-exchanger effectiveness, it is suggested that this same problem be worked out by trial and error, using Eq. 11–12 and the chart of Fig. 11–15.

The effectiveness of the heat exchanger in Example 11–3 is very low (15 per cent) because the heat-transfer area is too small to utilize the available energy efficiently. The relative gain in heat-transfer performance which can be achieved by increasing the heat-transfer area is well represented on the effectiveness curves. A fivefold increase in area would raise the effectiveness to 60 per cent. If, however, a particular design falls near or above the knee of these curves, increasing the surface area will not improve the performance appreciably, but may cause an undue increase in the frictional pressure drop.

11–5. FOULING FACTORS

The performance of heat exchangers under service conditions, especially in the process industry, cannot often be predicted from a thermal analysis alone. During operation with most liquids and some gases, a dirt film gradually builds up on the heat-transfer surface. This deposit may be rust, boiler scale, silt, coke, or any number of things. Its effect, which is referred to as *fouling*, is to increase the thermal resistance. The manufacturer cannot usually predict the nature of the dirt deposit, nor the rate of fouling. Therefore, only the performance of clean exchangers can be guaranteed. The thermal resistance of the deposit can generally be obtained only from actual tests or from experience. If performance tests are made on a clean exchanger and repeated later after the unit has been in service for some time, the thermal resistance of the deposit can be determined from the relation

$$R_d = \frac{1}{U_a} - \frac{1}{U}$$

where U = unit conductance of the clean exchanger;
   U_a = conductance after fouling has occurred;
   R_d = thermal resistance of the scale.

Fouling factors for various applications have been compiled by the Tubular Exchanger Manufacturers Association and are available in their publication (7). A few samples are given in Table 11–1. The fouling factors

TABLE 11–1

TABLE OF NORMAL FOULING FACTORS

Types of Fluid	Fouling Resistance (hr F sq ft/Btu)
Sea water below 125 F	0.0005
Sea water above 125 F	0.001
Treated boiler feed water above 125 F	0.001
East River water below 125 F	0.002–0.003
Fuel oil	0.005
Quenching oil	0.004
Alcohol vapors	0.0005
Steam, non-oil-bearing	0.0005
Industrial air	0.002
Refrigerating liquid	0.001

SOURCE: Ref. 7.

should be applied as indicated in the following equation for the over-all design heat-transfer coefficient U_d of *unfinned* tubes:

$$U_d = \frac{1}{\dfrac{1}{\bar{h}_o} + R_o + R_k + \dfrac{R_i A_o}{A_i} + \dfrac{A_o}{\bar{h}_i A_i}} \qquad (11\text{-}22)$$

where U_d = design over-all coefficient of heat transfer in Btu/hr F sq ft outside tube surface;

$\bar{h}_o$ = average unit-surface conductance of the fluid on the outside of tubing, in Btu/hr F sq ft;

$\bar{h}_i$ = average unit-surface conductance of fluid inside tubing, in Btu/hr F sq ft;

R_o = fouling resistance on outside of tubing, in hr F sq ft/Btu;

R_i = fouling resistance on inside of tubing, in hr F sq ft/Btu;

R_k = resistance of tubing in hr F sq ft outside tube surface/Btu;

A_o/A_i = ratio of outside tube surface to inside tube surface.

For preliminary estimates of heat-exchanger sizes and performance parameters, it is often sufficient to know the order of magnitude of the over-all transmittance under average service conditions.

Typical values of over-all heat-transfer coefficients recommended for preliminary estimates by Mueller (13) are given in Table 11–2.

11–6. CLOSURE

In this chapter we have studied the thermal design of heat exchangers in which two fluids at different temperatures flow in spaces separated by a wall and exchange heat by convection at and conduction through the wall. Such heat exchangers, sometimes called recuperators, are by far the most common and industrially important heat-transfer devices. In addition to recuperators there are, however, two other general types of heat exchangers in use. In both of these types the hot and cold fluid streams occupy the same space, a channel with or without solid inserts. In one type, the *regenerator*, the hot and the cold fluid pass alternately over the same heat-transfer surface. In the other type, the *cooling tower*, both fluids flow through the same passage simultaneously.

In a cooling tower the transfer of heat is accompanied by simultaneous transfer of mass. The discussion of the transfer mechanism will therefore be taken up in Chapter 13 in conjunction with the principles of mass transfer.

Periodic flow regenerators have been used in practice only with gases. The regenerator consists of one or more flow passages which are partially

TABLE 11–2

ApproximateOver-allCoefficients for
Preliminary Estimates

Duty	Over-all Coefficient (Btu/hr sq ft F)
Steam to water	
Instantaneous heater	400–600
Storage-tank heater	175–300
Steam to oil	
Heavy fuel	10–30
Light fuel	30–60
Light petroleum distillate	50–200
Steam to aqueous solutions	100–600
Steam to gases	5–50
Water to compressed air	10–30
Water to water, jacket water coolers	150–275
Water to lubricating oil	20–60
Water to condensing oil vapors	40–100
Water to condensing alcohol	45–120
Water to condensing Freon-12	80–150
Water to condensing ammonia	150–250
Water to organic solvents, alcohol	50 150
Water to boiling Freon-12	50–150
Water to gasoline	60–90
Water to gas oil or distillate	35–60
Water to brine	100–200
Light organics to light organics	40–75
Medium organics to medium organics	20–60
Heavy organics to heavy organics	10–40
Heavy organics to light organics	10 60
Crude oil to gas oil	30–55

source: Ref. 13.

filled either with solid pellets or with metal matrix inserts. During one part of the cycle the inserts store internal energy as the warmer fluid flows over their surfaces. During the other part of the cycle internal energy is released as the colder fluid passes through the regenerator and is heated. Thus, heat is transferred in a cyclic process. The principal advantage of the regenerator is a high heat-transfer effectiveness per unit weight and space. The major problem is to prevent leakage between the warmer and cooler fluids at elevated pressures. Regenerators have been used successfully as air preheaters in open-hearth and blast furnaces and in gas liquification processes.

The theories of the regenerators are very difficult and involved. The reader interested in the design and operation of these units is referred to Refs. 14 to 16 for detailed information. Reference 14 contains a summary of the design theory with particular emphasis on the exhaust-gas thermal-energy regenerator in gas turbine power plants. Reference 15 presents calculated values for the effectiveness of regenerators and Ref. 16 gives a complete and detailed treatment of regenerator theory and practice.

REFERENCES

1. W. M. Kays and A. L. London, *Compact Heat Exchangers.* (Palo Alto, Calif.: National Press, 1955.)

2. W. M. Kays, A. L. London, and D. W. Johnson, "Gas Turbine Plant Heat Exchangers," *ASME Research Publication*, April, 1951.

3. W. M. Kays and A. L. London, "Remarks on the Behavior and Application of Compact High-Performance Heat Transfer Surfaces," Inst. Mech. Eng. and ASME, *Proc. General Discussion on Heat Transfer*, 1951, pp. 127–132.

4. L. M. K. Boelter, R. C. Martinelli, F. E. Romie, and E. H. Morrin, "An Investigation of Aircraft Heaters XVIII—A Design Manual for Exhaust Gas and Air Heat Exchangers," *NACA Wartime Report*, ARR 5 AO6, August, 1945.

5. A. L. London and W. M. Kays, "The Gas Turbine Regenerator—the Use of Compact Heat Transfer Surfaces," *Trans. ASME*, Vol. 72 (1950), p. 611.

6. R. A. Bowman, A. C. Mueller, and W. M. Nagle, "Mean Temperature Difference in Design," *Trans. ASME*, Vol. 62 (1940), pp. 283–294.

7. Tubular Exchanger Manufacturers Association, *Standards TEMA*, 3d ed. (New York, 1952.)

8. W. Nusselt, "A New Heat Transfer Formula for Cross-Flow," *Technische Mechanik and Thermodynamik*, Vol. 12 (1930).

9. H. Ten Broeck, "Multipass Exchanger Calculations," *Ind. Eng. Chem.*, Vol. 30 (1938), pp. 1041–1042.

10. K. A. Gardner, "Efficiency of Extended Surface," *Trans. ASME*, Vol. 67 (1945), pp. 621–631.

11. W. P. Harper and D. R. Brown, "Mathematical Equations for Heat Conduction in the Fins of Air Cooled Engines," *NACA Report* 158, 1922.

12. Townsend Tinker, "Shell Side Characteristics of Shell and Tube Heat Exchangers," Inst. Mech. Eng. and ASME, *Proc. General Discussion on Heat Transfer*, 1951, pp. 89–116.

13. A. C. Mueller, "Thermal Design of Shell-and-Tube Heat Exchangers for Liquid-to-Liquid Heat Transfer," *Eng. Bull.*, Res. Ser. 121, Purdue Univ. Eng. Exp. Sta., 1954.

14. J. E. Coppage and A. L. London, "The Periodic-Flow Regenerator—A Summary of Design Theory," *Trans. ASME*, Vol. 75, 1953, pp. 779–787.

15. T. J. Lambertson, "Performance Factors of a Periodic-Flow Heat Exchanger," M. S. Thesis, USN Postgraduate School, Monterey, Calif., 1957, also *ASME* Paper No. 57-SA-13, 1957.

16. M. Jakob, *Heat Transfer*, Vol. 2. (New York: John Wiley & Sons, Inc., 1957.)

PROBLEMS

NOTE. The problems marked * require the direct or indirect evaluation of heat-transfer coefficients *before* the heat exchanger can be analyzed.

11-1. In a tubular heat exchanger with two shell passes and eight tube passes, 100,000 lb/hr of water are heated from 180 to 300 F. Hot exhaust gases having roughly the same physical properties as air enter at 650 F and leave at 350 F. The total surface, based on the outer tube surface is 10,000 sq ft. Determine (a) the log-mean temperature if the heat exchanger were a simple counterflow type, (b) the correction factor F for the actual arrangement, (c) the effectiveness of the heat exchanger, (d) the average over-all heat-transfer coefficient.

11-2.* Design (i.e., determine the over-all area and a suitable arrangement of shell and tube passes) for a tubular feed-water heater capable of heating 5000 lb/hr of water from 70 to 190 F. The following specifications are given: (a) saturated steam at 134 psia is condensing on the outer tube surface, (b) unit-surface conductance on steam side is 1200 Btu/hr sq ft F, (c) tubes are of copper, 1-in. OD, 0.9-in. ID, 8-ft long, and (d) water velocity is 3 fps.

11-3.* Repeat Prob. 11-2, but assume that the design should contain a safety factor to allow for scale formation on the steam side which could add an additional thermal resistance of 0.02 hr sq ft F/Btu.

11-4.* A small space heater is constructed of $\frac{1}{2}$-in., 18-gauge brass tubes, 2 ft long. The tubes are arranged in isosceles, staggered triangles on $1\frac{1}{2}$-in. centers, four rows of 15 tubes each. A fan blows 2000 cfm of atmospheric air at 70 F uniformly over the tubes (see sketch). Estimate: (a) heat-transfer rate; (b) exit temperature of the air; (c) rate of steam condensation, assuming that saturated steam at 2 psig inside the tubes is the heat source. State your assumptions. NOTE. Work parts a, b, and c of this problem by two methods. First use the LMTD, which requires a trial-and-error or graphical solution; then use the effectiveness method. (d) Also, estimate pressure drop of the air, in inches of water; (e) size motor required to drive the fan.

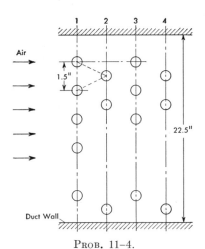

PROB. 11-4.

11-5.* Calculate the over-all conductance and the rate of heat flow from the hot gases to the cold air in the cross-flow tube-bank type of heat exchanger shown in the accompanying illustration for the following operating conditions:

> Air flow rate = 3000 lb/hr.
> Hot-gas flow rate = 5000 lb/hr.
> Temperature of hot gases entering exchanger = 1600 F.
> Temperature of cold air entering exchanger = 100 F.
> Both gases are approximately at atmospheric pressure.

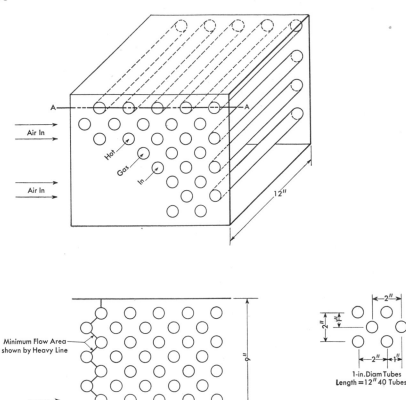

Prob. 11–5.

11–6. In a single-pass counterflow heat exchanger, 10,000 lb/hr of water enter at 60 F and cool 20,000 lb/hr of an oil having a specific heat of 0.50 Btu/lb F from 200 to 150 F. If the over-all heat-transfer coefficient is 50 Btu/hr sq ft F, determine the surface area required.

11–7. Determine the outlet temperature of the oil in Prob. 11–6 for the same initial temperatures of the fluids if the flow arrangement is one shell pass and two tube passes, but with the same total area and average over-all heat-transfer coefficient as the unit in Prob. 11–6.

11–8. Carbon dioxide at 800 F is to be used to heat 100,000 lb/hr of water from 100 F to 300 F while the gas temperature drops 400 F. For an over-all heat-transfer coefficient of 10 Btu/hr sq ft F, compute the required area of the exchanger in square feet for (a) parallel flow, (b) counterflow, (c) a 4–8 reversed current exchanger, and (d) cross flow, gas mixed.

11-9.* A double-pipe oil-water heat exchanger is constructed of a 10-ft-long brass tube, BWG No. 18 (0.527 in. ID, 0.625 in. OD), concentric within a well-insulated standard $\frac{3}{4}$-in. wrought-iron pipe (0.824 in. ID). Water flows in the annulus, entering at 60 F. A light oil flows in the tube, entering at 200 F. The flow arrangement is counterflow. For the velocities specified, determine (a) the exit temperature of the oil, (b) the rate of heat flow, and (c) the frictional pressure losses of the water and the oil.

The velocities specified are: (1) water rate = 1 gpm, oil rate = 1 gpm; (2) water rate = 10 gpm, oil rate = 1 gpm; (3) water rate = 1 gpm, oil rate = 20 gpm; (4) water rate = 10 gpm, oil rate = 20 gpm.

11-10. An economizer is to be purchased for a power plant. The unit is to be large enough to heat 60,000 lb/hr of water from 160 to 360 F. There are 100,000 lb/hr of flue gases (c_p = 0.24 Btu/lb F) available at 800 F. Estimate (a) the outlet temperature of the flue gases, (b) the heat-transfer area required for a counterflow arrangement if the over-all heat-transfer coefficient is 10 Btu/hr sq ft F.

11-11. Saturated steam at 5 psi condenses on the outside of an 8.5-ft length of copper tubing heating 0.6 gpm of water flowing in the tube. The water temperatures, measured at 10 equally spaced stations along the tube length are:

Station	1	2	3	4	5	6	7	8	9	10	11
Temperature (F)	65	109	135	152	163	172	179	186	190	195	198

Calculate (a) average over-all heat-transfer coefficient U_o based on the outside tube area; (b) average water-side heat-transfer coefficient $\bar{h}_w$ (assume steam-side coefficient at $\bar{h}_s$ = 2000 Btu/sq ft hr F), (c) local over-all coefficient U_x based on the outside tube area for each of the 10 sections between temperature stations, and (d) local water-side coefficients h_{wx} for each of the 10 sections.

Plot all items vs. tube length. Tube dimensions: ID = 0.790 in., OD = 0.985 in., length = 8.5 ft. Temperature station 1 is at tube entrance and station 11 at tube exit.

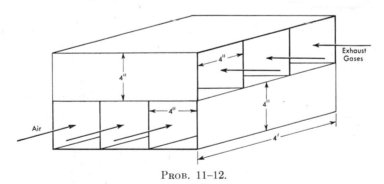

PROB. 11-12.

11-12.* A one-tube pass cross-flow heat exchanger is considered for recovering energy from the exhaust gases of a turbine-driven engine. The heat exchanger is constructed of flat plates, forming an egg-crate pattern. The velocities of the entering air (50 F) and exhaust gases (800 F) are both equal to 200 fps. Assuming that the properties of the exhaust gases are the same as those of the air, estimate, for a path length of 4 ft the over-all heat-transfer coefficient U, neglecting the thermal resistance of the intermediate metal wall. Then determine the outlet temperature of the air, comment on the suitability of the proposed design, and if possible, suggest improvements.

11–13. Water is heated while flowing through a pipe by steam condensing on the outside of the pipe. (a) Assuming a uniform over-all conductance along the pipe, derive an expression for the water temperature as a function of distance from the entrance. (b) For an over-all conductance of 100 Btu/hr sq ft F, based on the inside diameter of 2 in., a steam temperature of 220 F, and a water-flow rate of 500 lb_m/min, calculate the length required to raise the water temperature from 60 F to 150 F.   *Ans.* 475 ft

11–14. An oil having a specific heat of 0.50 Btu/lb_m F enters an oil cooler at 180 F at the rate of 20,000 lb_m/hr. The cooler is a counter-flow unit with water as the coolant, the transfer area being 300 sq ft and the over-all heat-transfer coefficient being 100 Btu/ sq ft F hr. The water enters the exchanger at 80 F. Determine the water rate required if the oil is to leave the cooler at 100 F.

11–15. Steam is to be condensed at atmospheric pressure in a shell-and-tube heat exchanger consisting of 72 eight-foot lengths of standard 1-in. 18 BWG copper condenser tubing (0.902 in. ID, 0.049 in. wall thickness). Water is available at a rate of 500,000 lb_m/hr; it flows inside the tubes, entering at 60 F. For the average unit-surface conductances listed below, estimate the pounds of steam per hour condensed. The unit-surface conductances (based on actual area) are:

Water side	800 Btu/hr sq ft F
Steam side	2000 Btu/hr sq ft F
Scale on steam side	1800 Btu/hr sq ft F
Scale of water side	2000 Btu/hr sq ft F

11–16. Show that the effectiveness for a counter flow arrangement is

$$\varepsilon = \frac{1 - e^{-[1 - (C_{min}/C_{max})]\, NTU_{max}}}{1 - (C_{min}/C_{max})\, e^{-[1 - (C_{min}/C_{max})]\, NTU_{max}}}$$

11–17.* The following data were obtained with an experimental parallel-flow heat exchanger that consisted of a horizontal steel tube (0.053 in. ID and 1.002 in. OD) surrounded by a concentrically-arranged steel tube (1.263 in. ID) well insulated externally. A high pressure steam (2400 lb/hr) at an absolute pressure of 1643 lb/sq in. and at 821 F entered the inner tube and left with an absolute pressure of 1523 lb/sq in. and a temperature of 722 F; 953 lb/hr of low pressure steam at an absolute pressure of 189 lb/sq in. at 424 F entered the annular space and left at an absolute pressure of 122 lb/sq in. with a temperature of 744 F. Predict the heat-transfer rate if the steam flow in the inner tube were reversed, the entering temperatures remaining the same as before.

11–18. One hundred thousand lb/hr of benzene are to be cooled continuously from 180 to 130 F by 80,000 lb/hr of water available at 60 F. Using Table 11–2 estimate the surface area required for (a) cross flow, six tube passes, one-shell pass, neither of the fluids mixed; (b) reversed current exchanger, two-shell passes and eight tube passes, colder fluid inside of tubes.

11–19.* An oil is being cooled by water in a double-pipe parallel-flow heat exchanger. The water enters the center pipe at a temperature of 60 F and is heated to 120 F. The oil which flows in the annulus is cooled from 270 to 150 F. It is proposed to cool the oil to a lower final temperature by increasing the length of the exchanger. Neglecting external heat loss from the exchanger, determine: (a) the minimum temperature to which the oil may be cooled; (b) the exit-oil temperature as a function of the fractional increase in the exchanger length; (c) the exit temperature of each stream if the existing exchanger were switched to counterflow operation; (d) the lowest temperature to which the oil could be cooled with counterflow operation; (e) the ratio of the required length for counterflow to that for parallel flow as a function of the exit-oil temperature.

$Ans.$ (a) 130 F, (b) $270 - 140 (1 - e^{5.84x})$, (e) $\frac{1}{3} \left(\ln \dfrac{75 + 0.5\,T_{h2}}{T_{h2} - 60} \middle/ \ln \dfrac{210}{75 + 1.5\,T_{h2}} \right)$

11-20. In gas turbine recuperators the exhaust gases are used to heat the incoming air and C_{min}/C_{max} is therefore approximately equal to unity. Show that for this case $\varepsilon = 1 - e^{-NTU}$ for counterflow and $\varepsilon = \frac{1}{2}(1 - e^{-2\,NTU})$ for parallel flow.

11-21. In most gas turbine regenerators the heat capacity ratio C_{min}/C_{max} is near unity. For rapid cost estimates it is desirable to have performance curves for this condition showing the effectiveness, ε, as a function of the Number of Transfer Units, NTU. Prepare a series of such curves on one graph for counterflow, parallel-flow, 1 shell–2 tube passes, and unmixed cross flow. What conclusions can you draw?

11-22. It is proposed to preheat the water for a boiler with flue gases from the stack ($c_p = 0.24$ Btu/lb$_m$ F). The flue gases are available at 300 F, at the rate of 2000 lb$_m$/hr. The water entering the exchanger at 60 F at the rate of 400 lb$_m$/hr is to be heated to 200 F. The heat exchanger is to be of the reversed current type, one shell pass and 4 tube passes. The water flows inside the tubes which are made of copper (1 in. ID, 1.25 in. OD). The heat-transfer coefficient at the gas side is 20 Btu/hr sq ft F, while the heat-transfer coefficient on the water side is 200 Btu/hr sq ft F. A scale on the water side offers an additional thermal resistance of 0.01 hr sq ft F/Btu. (a) Determine the over-all heat-transfer coefficient based on the *outer* tube diameter. (b) Determine the appropriate mean temperature difference for the heat exchanger. (c) Estimate the required tube length. (d) What would be the improvement in the effectiveness if the water flow rate would be doubled, giving an average-unit conductance of 320 Btu/hr sq ft F?

11-23. The heater arrangement of Prob. 9–6 is to heat air from 65 to 220 F with steam at 11 psig condensing inside the tubes. If the bank is 40 rows deep with 30 pipes in each row, estimate the capacity of the heater in pounds per hour of air and the pressure drop in inches of water. The pipes are 6 ft long and the free cross-sectional flow area is 60 ft? *Ans.* 83,000 lb$_m$/hr

12　Heat Transfer in High-Speed Flow

12-1. AERODYNAMIC HEATING

Problems related to heat transfer in high-speed flow have become important in recent years as speeds of airplanes and missiles have reached and exceeded sonic velocity and satellites circle the globe at speeds of the order of 20,000 ft/sec. In fact, the thermal barrier is at present the major obstacle to high-speed flight and to the safe re-entry of satellite vehicles. The term "thermal barrier" includes problems associated with physical properties of aircraft material at elevated temperatures and the temperature limitations on personnel and instruments in the aircraft, but it refers primarily to the problems related to the dissipation of the energy generated in the boundary layer at high speeds. As mentioned previously, the viscous stresses within the boundary layer do shearing work on the fluid and at high velocities raise its temperature appreciably. This process, often called aerodynamic heating, also raises the surface temperatures of bodies placed in a high-speed fluid stream or of bodies moving at high speed through a stagnant fluid. An example of the latter is the heating of the skins of high-speed airplanes and missiles. Aerodynamic heating becomes a serious problem at very high speeds because the rate of heat flow to the skin increases roughly in proportion to the flight velocity if the surface is maintained at a constant temperature. At a Mach number of 2 for example, the rate of heat flow to a surface at 120 F has been estimated to be as high as 10,000 Btu/hr sq ft at 30,000 ft altitude. At the satellite velocity of 26,000 ft/sec the stagnation point heat-transfer rate is of the order of 100,000 Btu/hr sq ft at an altitude of 300,000 ft, giving rise to a surface temperature of about 3000 R according to Kemp and Ridell (24).

For the flow of most liquids and gases in commercial heat exchangers, the Mach numbers are low and aerodynamic heating is negligible. On the other hand, at Mach numbers of the order of 1 and larger, the aerodynamic heating of the boundary layer affects the heat transfer and the friction appreciably, and it becomes necessary to re-examine the definition of the unit-surface conductance used heretofore. Additional complications arise

470

when the temperatures become so high that the gas dissociates (19) or when the gas is so rarefied, as for example at very high altitudes, that the mean free path of the molecules becomes of the order of magnitude of the boundary-layer thickness.

12–2. FLOW REGIMES

In convectional analyses of heat transfer by forced convection the nature of the flow can be described by the Reynolds number which is a measure of the ratio of inertial to viscous forces.   In high speed flow at least two additional parameters must be considered.   As soon as the velocity of a gas becomes comparable in magnitude to the local sound speed a_∞, a new dimensionless parameter must be introduced to describe the influence of compressibility on heat transfer and flow phenomena.   This parameter is the Mach number M_∞, defined as the ratio of the gas or flight velocity V_∞ to the local speed of sound in the gas, a_∞.   When the Mach number reaches a value of about 0.5, compressibility phenomena exert appreciable influence on the flow pattern and on the heat transfer by convection.

The Reynolds, Prandtl, and Mach numbers are the parameters governing the convective-heat transfer as long as the transferring medium may be treated as a continuum.   This is permissible as long as the mean free molecular path is small when compared with significant dimensions of the body to whom the heat is transferred.   Under normal conditions even in gases where the distances between molecules are much larger than in liquids and solids, the mean free molecular path is very small when compared with those dimensions which are of immediate concern in heat-transfer calculations.   The condition of a small mean free-path length to significant body-dimension ratio is therefore usually satisfied.

A continuum treatment may fail, however, when the gas is at very low pressure as, for example, at extremely high altitudes.   Then the effect of the coarseness of the molecular structure on the flow and heat transfer must be considered.   Under such conditions, i.e., when the *molecular mean free path*[1] λ is of the same order of magnitude as some significant dimension of a body in the flow field L, the flow is called *rarefied*.   The ratio λ/L, called the *Knudsen number* K, is a measure of the degree of rarefaction.   It is related (10) to the Reynolds number and Mach number by the equation

$$K = 1.26\sqrt{\gamma M/Re}$$

where K and Re are both based on the same characteristic length.

Tentative limits for a subdivision of gas dynamics into various flow regimes, based on characteristic ranges of values of an appropriate Knudsen number, were originally proposed by Tsien (10) and later revised by Schaaf

[1] The mean free path is the average distance travelled by a molecule between collisions—it is not the distance between molecules.

and Chambre (16).   The subdivisions are shown in Fig. 12–1 as solid lines
while the dotted lines indicate the corresponding altitudes for a body having
a characteristic dimension L of unity.

The conventional continuum regime of fluid mechanics and gas dynamics
is limited to $M/\sqrt{Re} < 0.1$ and $Re \gg 1.0$.   At the other end of the scale, for
values of M/Re larger than 3, the mean free path is much larger than L.
This is called the *free-molecule flow* regime in which molecule to molecule
collisions can be neglected in comparison with molecule to body-surface
collisions.   No boundary layer exists in this regime.

In the *transition regime* the collisions between molecules and the
collisions between molecules and the body are of equal importance.   The
regime of small, but not negligible Knudsen numbers is called the *slip flow
regime*.   As the name implies, in this regime the molecules immediately

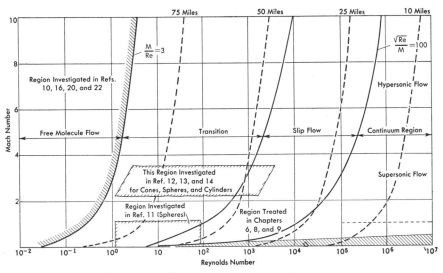

FIG. 12–1.   The flow regimes of gas dynamics.

adjacent to a surface do not stick to it, but slide over it with a definite
tangential velocity.   The mean free path in slip flow is of the order of 1 to
10 per cent of the boundary layer thickness or the characteristic body
dimension L.   The flow and heat transfer phenomena in the transition and
slip flow regimes are exceedingly complex.   Our knowledge about them is
still limited and they will not be discussed here.   Figure 12–1 shows those
ranges in which data have been obtained and the pertinent references.

In addition to the subdivisions cited above, the field of gas dynamics is
also subdivided according to the value of the Mach number.   If the Mach
number is less than unity, the flow is subsonic.   When the Mach number exceeds unity, the flow is supersonic, but at extremely high Mach numbers we

speak of hypersonic flow.   Hypersonic flow is defined (7) as supersonic flow with small perturbations for which $M_\infty \, t/L$ is of the order of unity or greater, t/L being the thickness to length ratio of the body in the flow field.

Recent experiments have shown that at hypersonic speeds all bodies must be blunt-nosed to reduce heat-transfer rates and to allow for sufficient internal heat conduction.   Otherwise the forward section is likely to melt as a result of the large temperature rise caused by the shock at or in front of the leading edge.   A detached bow shock wave just ahead of a blunt-nosed body in hypersonic flight converts most of the kinetic energy associated with the flight velocity into thermal and chemical energy.   At the satellite escape velocity of 26,400 ft/sec, for example, this energy amounts to about 14,000 Btu/lb air (19), which is sufficient to dissociate almost all of the nitrogen and oxygen molecules.

For the case of laminar heat transfer over blunt-nosed bodies at hypersonic speeds, Lees (19) and Stalder (18) have calculated the rate of heat transfer under extreme conditions.   First it was assumed that complete thermodynamic equilibrium in which the gas properties and concentrations of atoms, molecules, and ions correspond to their equilibrium values at each point in the flow exists; then (19), that diffusion across streamlines (see Chapter 13) is the rate governing mechanism; and finally (18), that the air is a perfect gas.   In the absence of experimental data it is not clear which of these assumptions is most realistic; but since the results do not differ by more than 50 per cent they are satisfactory for preliminary estimates of the heat-transfer rates as hypersonic speeds.   The details of the calculations are quite involved and the reader interested in them is referred to the original papers.   The preceding comments are only intended to call attention to some of the complicated phenomena encountered in hypersonic flow which are at present under intensive study.

The subdivisions shown in Fig. 12–1 are of course not rigid, but the transition from one regime into the next will always be gradual.   For example, a missile having a characteristic length of 10 ft and flying at a Mach number of 4 away from the earth will gradually encounter slip phenomena at an altitude of 30 miles and will reach the free molecule flow region at about 100 miles elevation.

A complete treatment of heat transfer in supersonic flow requires a previous knowledge of supersonic gasdynamics, in particular an understanding of shock phenomena.   The reader interested in this field is referred to Refs. 7, 17, and 18 for a detailed treatment of these problems.   However, as far as heat transfer analyses for forced convection in a continuum are concerned, they depend mostly on the flow near the surface and are applicable to subsonic as well as supersonic flow.   The following presentation will be restricted to an analysis of heat transfer in high speed flow to or from a gas flowing over a shock free surface.   To simplify the treatment we shall assume, that the gas behaves as an ideal gas which has a constant specific heat and obeys the perfect gas law.

12–3. FRICTION AND HEAT TRANSEFER IN LAMINAR HIGH-SPEED FLOW

To gain a qualitative picture of high-speed flow in a continuum, consider first a laminar boundary layer in high-speed flow over an insulated plate. The velocity distribution is qualitatively similar to that observed at low Mach numbers but the temperature profile (Fig. 12–2) is quite different.

We observe that the temperature increases in a direction toward the insulated surface and reaches at the wall a value only slightly less than the total temperature of the free stream. This temperature rise is a result of the viscous forces in the boundary layer which slow down the gas and dissipate the kinetic energy of the free stream. The shape of the temperature profile depends on the relation between rate at which shear work increases the internal energy of the fluid and the rate at which heat is conducted toward the free stream.

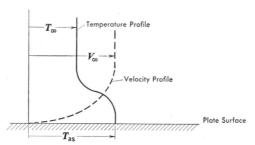

FIG. 12–2. Velocity and temperature distribution in high-speed flow over an insulated plate.

Although the processes in the boundary layer are not adiabatic, it is general practice to relate them to adiabatic processes because the latter are much simpler to analyze. According to basic thermodynamic principles, when a flowing gas is slowed down adiabatically to zero velocity, its temperature rises to the stagnation temperature $T_{o\infty}$. The stagnation or total temperature in a gas having a constant specific heat c_p is related to the local temperature T_∞ and velocity V_∞ by the equation

$$T_{o\infty} = T_\infty + \frac{V_\infty^2}{2Jg_c c_p} \tag{12–1}$$

where the last term is called the free-stream *dynamic-temperature rise*. Using the definition of the Mach number of the flowing gas M_∞ and the specific heat ratio $\gamma = c_p/c_v$, Eq. 12–1 can be written

$$T_{o\infty} = T_\infty \left(1 + \frac{\gamma - 1}{2} M_\infty^2\right) \tag{12–2}$$

where $M_\infty = V_\infty/a_\infty$, and

a_∞ = velocity of sound, equal to $\sqrt{\gamma \Re g_c T_\infty}$ in a perfect gas.

When a gas flows past an insulated or adiabatic surface, the temperature at the surface will rise above the temperature of the gas, but will not quite reach the total temperature. The temperature at an adiabatic surface T_{as} is called the *adiabatic wall temperature*.

In practice it has been found convenient to relate T_{as} and $T_{o\,\infty}$ by the *recovery factor* R_T, which is a measure of the fraction of the free-stream dynamic-temperature rise recovered at the wall. We define R_T as

$$R_T = \frac{T_{as} - T_\infty}{V_\infty{}^2/2c_p J g_c} = \frac{T_{as} - T_\infty}{T_{o\,\infty} - T_\infty} = \frac{2}{(\gamma - 1)M_\infty{}^2}\left(\frac{T_{as}}{T_\infty} - 1\right) \quad (12\text{-}3)$$

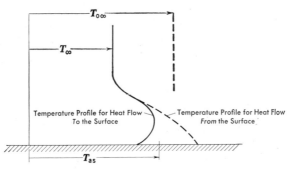

FIG. 12-3.   Temperature profiles in high-speed boundary layer for heating and cooling.

Experiments with air in laminar flow (1) have shown that, for practical purposes,

$$R_T \simeq \sqrt{\mathrm{Pr}} \quad (12\text{-}4)$$

over wide ranges of velocity and temperature, whereas for turbulent boundary layers, the recovery factor can be approximated (1) by the relation

$$R_T \simeq \sqrt[3]{\mathrm{Pr}} \quad (12\text{-}5)$$

When a surface is not insulated, the rate of heat flow between the gas and the solid surface q_s is governed by

$$q_s/A = -k \left.\frac{\partial T}{\partial y}\right|_{y=0}$$

The influence of heat transfer to or from the plate on the temperature distribution is illustrated in Fig. 12-3. We observe that, at high speeds, heat can flow to the surface even when the surface temperature is *higher* than the free-stream temperature. This rather unexpected phenomenon is a result of the aerodynamic heating in the boundary layer. To calculate heat-transfer coefficients in high-speed flow we must therefore re-examine the analysis of the boundary layer for low-speed flow, taking into account the effects of the viscous shearing work and heat conduction.

As shown in Sec. 6–7, the energy equation for a laminar boundary layer can be written in the form

$$\rho u \left(c_p \frac{\partial T_o}{\partial x} \right) + \rho v \left(c_p \frac{\partial T_o}{\partial y} \right) = \frac{\partial}{\partial y} \left(k \frac{\partial T}{\partial y} \right) + \frac{1}{Jg_c} \frac{\partial}{\partial y} \left(\mu u \frac{\partial u}{\partial y} \right) \quad [\mathbf{6\text{--}22}]$$

If c_p and k are assumed constant and the approximation that $u \gg v$ is introduced, we have

$$c_p T_o = c_p T + \frac{u^2 + v^2}{2Jg_c} \simeq c_p T + \frac{u^2}{2Jg_c}$$

and

$$\frac{u}{Jg_c} \frac{\partial u}{\partial y} = \frac{\partial}{\partial y} \left(\frac{u^2}{2Jg_c} \right) = c_p \left(\frac{\partial T_o}{\partial y} - \frac{\partial T}{\partial y} \right)$$

Rearranging Eq. 6–22 with the aid of the above relations and dividing by c_p yields

$$\rho u \frac{\partial T_o}{\partial x} + \rho v \frac{\partial T_o}{\partial y} = \frac{\partial}{\partial y} \left(\mu \frac{\partial T_o}{\partial y} \right) + \frac{\partial}{\partial y} \left[\left(\frac{k}{c_p \mu} - 1 \right) \mu \frac{\partial T}{\partial y} \right] \quad (12\text{--}6)$$

The energy equation in this form may be used to illustrate, at least qualitatively, the effect of high velocities on the heat transfer and the temperature distribution in a laminar-boundary layer. Since high-speed-flow phenomena are of practical importance only in gases where the Prandtl number $c_p \mu/k$ is not too far from unity, we shall further simplify Eq. 12–6 by assuming that Pr = 1. This will make it possible to point out important practical results with a minimum of mathematical difficulties.

Making this simplification, the energy equation takes the form

$$\rho u \frac{\partial T_o}{\partial x} + \rho v \frac{\partial T_o}{\partial y} = \frac{\partial}{\partial y} \left(\mu \frac{\partial T_o}{\partial y} \right) \quad (12\text{--}7)$$

for which one particular solution is

$$T_o = T + \frac{u^2}{2Jg_c c_p} = T_{o\,\infty} = \text{constant} \quad (12\text{--}8)$$

Physically, Eq. 12–8 states that the total temperature equals the free-stream stagnation temperature throughout the boundary layer. The temperature at the wall is therefore equal to $T_{o\,\infty}$, since $u = 0$ at $y = 0$. The rate of heat flow from the wall to the fluid is zero for the solution given by Eq. 12–8 since, at $y = 0$

$$q_s/A = -\ k\ \frac{\partial T}{\partial y}\bigg|_{y\,=\,0} = \frac{ku}{c_p J g_c}\frac{\partial u}{\partial y}\bigg|_{y\,=\,0} = 0$$

This condition is satisfied when the wall is insulated. We note, however, that the temperature gradient for $y > 0$ is finite, and heat flows from fluid in the vicinity of the wall toward the outer edge of the boundary layer. According to Eq. 12–8 this is only possible when the rate of heat conduction in the fluid across any plane parallel to the wall is equal to the rate at which shear work crosses this plane in the opposite direction, or

$$-k\ \frac{\partial T}{\partial y}\bigg|_{\text{at } y} = \frac{\mu u}{J g_c}\frac{\partial u}{\partial y}\bigg|_{\text{at } y} = \mu\frac{\partial}{\partial y}\left(\frac{u^2}{2J g_c}\right)$$

Dividing by k and rearranging gives

$$\frac{\partial}{\partial y}\left(T + \text{Pr}\ \frac{u^2}{2J g_c c_p}\right) = 0 \qquad\qquad (12\text{–}9)$$

Equation 12–9 shows that the stagnation temperature in the boundary layer is constant when $\text{Pr} = 1$ and the wall is insulated. The term $\text{Pr}\ u^2/2J g_c c_p$ represents physically the kinetic energy "recovered" in the boundary layer where the viscous forces slow down the fluid particles from the free-stream velocity u_∞ to zero at the wall. It is apparent from Eq. 12–9 that, for a Prandtl number less than unity, not all of the kinetic energy is converted into enthalpy and the temperature at an adiabatic wall T_{as} is therefore less than the total free-stream temperature $T_{o\,\infty}$. However, for $\text{Pr} = 1$ the total energy is constant throughout the boundary layer even when the flow is not frictionless and the energy equation for adiabatic temperature changes applies. This simplification is a result of that particular combination of c_p, μ, and k for which the Prandtl number is unity. Results obtained from this analysis apply, however, qualitatively to air with $\text{Pr} = 0.7$. Hence, the analysis confirms the observation made previously that the temperature at the surface of a body in high-speed flight is much closer to the free-stream stagnation temperature than to the free-stream static temperature.

To avoid unnecessary complications we shall restrict our subsequent consideration to parallel flow over a flat plate at a constant temperature T_s. The results obtained from this analysis apply approximately to flow over curved surfaces as long as the pressure gradient is not so large that it causes separation of the boundary layer.

The momentum equation developed in Sec. 6–7 applies also to high-speed flow, but the frictional-work term cannot be neglected. For flow over a flat plate we have

$$\rho u \frac{\partial u}{\partial x} + \rho v \frac{\partial u}{\partial y} = \frac{\partial}{\partial y}\left(\mu \frac{\partial u}{\partial y}\right) \qquad [6\text{-}16]$$

Inspection of Eqs. 6–16 and 12–7 shows that they are quite similar. They can be reduced to the same equation if we assume that the total temperature is related to the velocity by the relation

$$T_o = T + \frac{u^2}{2c_p g_c J} = a + bu \qquad (12\text{-}10)$$

where a and b are constants. The boundary conditions demand that

$$\text{at } y = 0, \text{ where } u = 0 \qquad T_o = T_s$$
$$\text{at } y = \delta, \text{ where } u = V_\infty \qquad T_o = T_{o\,\infty}$$

Substituting these conditions into Eq. 12–10 yields

$$\frac{T_o - T_s}{T_{o\,\infty} - T_s} = \frac{u}{V_\infty}$$

or in terms of the static temperature, T, we get

$$T = T_s + (T_{o\,\infty} - T_s)\frac{u}{V_\infty} - \frac{\gamma - 1}{2} M_\infty^2 T_\infty \left(\frac{u}{V_\infty}\right)^2 \qquad (12\text{-}11)$$

This solution applies only to a constant wall temperature since at the wall, where the velocity u is zero, the temperature must be constant to satisfy the boundary conditions. A physical interpretation of this solution shows that the dimensionless temperature profile $(T_o - T_s)/(T_{o\,\infty} - T_s)$ and the dimensionless velocity profile u/V_∞ are similar.

The rate of heat flow from the plate is now obtained by applying the conduction equation at the wall. With the aid of Eq. 12–10 we get

$$\frac{q_s}{A} = -k\left.\frac{\partial T}{\partial y}\right|_{y=0} = -k\left.\frac{\partial T}{\partial u}\frac{\partial u}{\partial y}\right|_{y=0}$$

$$= \frac{k}{V_\infty}\frac{\partial u}{\partial y}\left[T_s - T_{o\,\infty} + (\gamma - 1)M_\infty^2 T_\infty \frac{u}{V_\infty}\right]_{y=0} \qquad (12\text{-}12)$$

but at the wall (i.e., at $y = 0$) the velocity u is zero and the last term drops out. Since by definition

$$g_c \tau_s = \mu\left.\frac{\partial u}{\partial y}\right|_{y=0}$$

the velocity gradient in Eq. 12–12 can be eliminated by substituting $g_c \tau_s / \mu$ for it and we obtain

$$\frac{q_s}{A} = \frac{g_c \tau_s}{V_\infty} \frac{k}{\mu} (T_s - T_{o\infty}) = \frac{g_c \tau_s}{V_\infty} c_p (T_s - T_{o\infty})/\text{Pr} \qquad (12\text{–}13)$$

Since for $\text{Pr} = 1$, $T_{o\infty} = T_{as}$, the above equation can also be written as

$$\frac{q_s}{A} = \frac{g_c \tau_s}{V_\infty} c_p (T_s - T_{as}) \qquad (12\text{–}14)$$

Experiments have verified that, in high-speed flow, the direction of heat flow at the surface does *not* depend on the difference *between* the wall temperature and the free-stream temperature as in low-speed flow, but rather on the *difference between the wall temperature and the adiabatic wall temperature*. To correlate experimental data it is therefore convenient to define the unit-surface convective conductance for high-speed flow $\bar{h}_c$ as

$$\bar{h}_c = \frac{q_c}{A(T_s - T_{as})} \qquad (12\text{–}15)$$

Substituting the unit-surface conductance defined by Eq. 12–15 in Eq. 12–14 yields

$$\bar{h}_c = \frac{g_c \tau_s}{V} c_p$$

or in dimensionless form

$$\frac{\bar{h}_c}{V_\infty c_p \rho_\infty} = \text{St} = \frac{1}{2} \frac{g_c \tau_s}{\rho_\infty V_\infty^2/2} = \frac{C_f}{2} \qquad (12\text{–}16)$$

We recognize that also for high-speed flow the Stanton number equals one-half the skin friction coefficient if (1) the unit-surface conductance is defined according to Eq. 12–15 and if (2) the physical properties remain constant. Figure 12–4 shows the variation of the skin-friction coefficient with Mach number, Reynolds number, and heat transfer as calculated by Van Driest (9). The factor T_s/T_∞ is an indication of the effect of heat transfer on the friction by virtue of the property variations with temperature. The last assumption in Eq. 12–16 is obviously unreasonable for high-speed flow, but the relation between skin friction and heat transfer expressed by Eq. 12–16 is still useful even when the property values vary with temperature because it yields results of acceptable accuracy if the properties are evaluated at an appropriate reference temperature T^*.

Rubesin and Johnson (6) have shown that the local Nusselt number for laminar flow over a plane surface can be calculated from the equation

$$\text{Nu}_x = 0.332 \, \text{Re}_x^{\frac{1}{2}} \, \text{Pr}^{\frac{1}{3}} \qquad (12\text{–}17)$$

if the properties are introduced at the reference temperature T^* defined by

$$T^* = T_\infty + 0.58 \,(T_s - T_\infty) + 0.19 \,(T_{as} - T_\infty) \qquad \textbf{(12–18)}$$

The same reference temperature should also be used (4) for the specific heat in Eq. 12–3 to obtain the appropriate value for the recovery factor. The average value of the surface conductance over a surface of length L is obtained by integration of the local value of h_{cx}, or

$$\bar{h}_c = 2 \, h_{c(x\,=\,L)} \qquad \textbf{(12–19)}$$

With a slight modification, Eq. 12–17 can also be used to calculate the heat-transfer coefficient for a conical nose at supersonic speed. In level flight there will be a shock in front of the cone. As long as this shock is attached to the nose (7), the boundary conditions for flow over a cone and

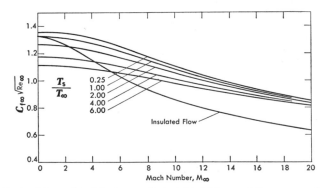

Fig. 12–4. Mean skin-friction coefficient for high-speed flow over a flat plate with heat transfer, based on calculations of Van Driest (9) for Pr = 0.75 and a viscosity-temperature relation of the type $\mu/\mu_\infty = 1.505(T/T_\infty)^{\frac{3}{2}}/[(T/T_\infty) + 0.505]$. (Courtesy of the National Advisory Committee for Aeronautics, TN 597)

for flow over a flat plate are similar. Hantsche and Wendt (8) showed that the laminar-flow flat-plate heat-transfer coefficient equations apply when modified by a multiplication factor determined by the geometry of the flow. The factors are $\sqrt{3}$ and $2/\sqrt{3}$ for the local and average heat-transfer coefficients, respectively. From Eqs. 12–17 and 12–19 we obtain therefore the relations

$$\mathrm{Nu}_x = 0.575 \, \mathrm{Re}_x^{\frac{1}{2}}\mathrm{Pr}^{\frac{1}{3}} \qquad \textbf{(12–20)}$$

and

$$\overline{\mathrm{Nu}}_L = 0.767 \, \mathrm{Re}_L^{\frac{1}{2}}\mathrm{Pr}^{\frac{1}{3}} \qquad \textbf{(12–21)}$$

for the local and the average Nusselt number respectively for a cone with an attached shock if x and L are measured along the surface from the tip. The physical properties and the velocity in the dimensionless parameters of

Eqs. 12–20 and 12–21 must be based on the conditions behind the shock. The flow conditions behind the shock can be determined from charts or tables (e.g., see Ref. 7).

The equations for laminar flow are appropriate only up to the transition point where the flow becomes turbulent. The problem of determining the transition point is a very difficult one, and the information available to date is insufficient for accurate predictions. Gazley (5) has surveyed the available data and theories and Fig. 12–5 presents a summary of some experimental results on the effect of the Mach number on the transition Reynolds number. Other factors such as heat transfer, shocks, pressure gradients, and surface roughness influence the transition phenomena.

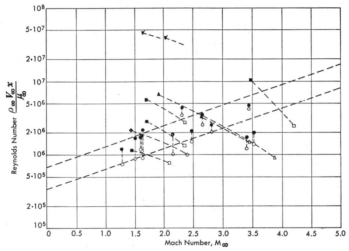

Fig. 12–5. The effect of Mach number on boundary-layer transition in firing range ($T_s \simeq T_\infty$) and in rocket flight ($T_s \simeq 1.3 T_\infty$). o = cones in firing range; □, ▽, △ = V-2 flights (3); and ◇ rocket flight. Open points denote beginning, solid points, end of transition region. (By permission from Carl Gazley, Jr., *Journal of the Aeronautical Sciences*, Vol. 20, 1953, p. 26)

Figure 12–5 is therefore only useful for a qualitative estimate of the transition Reynolds number. For additional information the reader is referred to Refs. 5 and 7.

12–4. FRICTION AND HEAT TRANSFER IN TURBULENT HIGH-SPEED FLOW

Our knowledge of flow and heat-transfer phenomena in turbulent boundary layers is not yet sufficient to calculate the friction and heat-transfer coefficients by a direct analysis. To arrive at relations for the skin friction, heat transfer, and the boundary-layer thickness, it is necessary to resort to semi-empirical relations describing the behavior of fluid in the boundary layer. Analyses available to date usually employ the basic concept of a mixing length which is outlined in Sec. 6–9 for incompressible flow. For engineering calculations it is preferable to rely on experimental results. Eckert (4) has made an extensive survey of the available data, and his recommendations for calculating the skin friction and heat transfer in turbulent high-speed flow are summarized below.

The local skin friction coefficient for flow over a plane surface at T_s can be calculated at Reynolds numbers up to 10^9 and Mach numbers below 5 from the equation

$$C_{fx} = \frac{0.370}{(\log_{10} \mathrm{Re}_{x\infty})^{2.58}}$$

and the average value from

$$\overline{C}_{fL} = \frac{0.0296}{(\log_{10} \mathrm{Re}_{L\infty})^{2.58}} \left(\frac{\mu^*}{\mu_\infty}\right)^{0.2} \left(\frac{\rho^*}{\rho_\infty}\right)^{0.8} \tag{12-22}$$

where the subscript ∞ denotes that the properties are to be evaluated at the free-stream temperature T_∞ and the superscript $*$ denotes that the properties are to be evaluated at the temperature T^*, which is defined by Eq. 12–18. The average heat-transfer coefficient can be estimated from the equation

$$\left(\frac{\overline{\mathrm{Nu}^*}_L}{\mathrm{Re}^*_L \mathrm{Pr}^*}\right) \mathrm{Pr}^{*\frac{2}{3}} = \frac{\overline{C}_{fL}}{2} \tag{12-23}$$

where all property values are to be introduced at the reference temperature T^*. The heat-transfer coefficient in the Nusselt number is defined by the same equation used previously for laminar flow, that is

$$\bar{h}_c = \frac{q_c}{A\,(T_{as} - T_s)}$$

where

$$T_{as} = R^*_T(T_{o\infty} - T_\infty) + T_\infty$$

$$R^*_T = \frac{T_{as} - T_\infty}{V_\infty^2 / 2c_p^* J g_c} \simeq \sqrt[3]{\mathrm{Pr}}$$

for turbulent flow.

The foregoing relations are strictly applicable only to flat plates at constant temperature, but they will also yield results of acceptable accuracy when the wall temperature is variable and the surface is curved. Calculations made with these relations are also useful as approximations of sufficient accuracy for a slender body at zero or small angles of attack. For the same values of the free-stream Mach number, the Reynolds number, the wall temperature, and free-stream temperature, the local friction coefficient and the Nusselt number for a cone are approximately 15 per cent larger than the corresponding values for the flat plate.

Turbulent heat transfer and friction in fully developed high speed subsonic flow through tubes have been investigated by Lelchuk (23). The results of his experiments, involving simultaneous heat transfer and friction, with the Mach number varying along the length of the tube, are in good agreement with Reynolds analogy. The pipe friction coefficient for diameter Reynolds numbers up to 10^5 can be represented with satisfactory accuracy by

$$f = 0.079 \ \mathrm{Re}_D^{-0.25} \tag{12-24}$$

Reynolds analogy yields therefore

$$\overline{\mathrm{Nu}} = 0.0395 \ \mathrm{Re}_D^{0.75} \ \mathrm{Pr} \tag{12-25}$$

which can be written for air ($\mathrm{Pr} = 0.72$) in the form

$$\overline{\mathrm{Nu}} = 0.0364 \ (\mathrm{Re}_D \mathrm{Pr})^{0.75} \tag{12-26}$$

Experimental results for Mach numbers varying between 0 and 1 (23) are in good agreement with Eq. 12–26, thus indicating that the Reynolds analogy is not appreciably influenced by compressibility if the heat-transfer coefficient is evaluated in accordance with Eqs. 12–5 and 12–15.

12–5. CONVECTIVE HEAT TRANSFER IN FREE MOLECULE FLOW

In the free-molecule flow regime the relations governing the convective heat transfer to or from a body in the gas can be deduced from fundamental principles. When the molecular mean-free path is much larger than the characteristic dimension of the body, molecules which impinge on the body and are then re-emitted will on the average travel a long distance before colliding with other molecules. It is therefore permissible to assume that the incident stream of molecules is completely unaffected by the presence of the body. Consequently one can treat the flow of incident and reflected or re-emitted molecules separately. Detailed calculations presuppose familiarity with the kinetic theory of gases (21) but one can gain a physical understanding of the method of approach used in these calculations and apply the results in practice, without following the details.

The convective rate of heat transfer to a body in a free-molecular flow is governed by the energy balance

$$q/A = \dot{e}_i - \dot{e}_r \tag{12-27}$$

where $\dot{e}_i$ is the energy transport rate of the incident molecules per unit area and $\dot{e}_r$ is the energy transport rate of the re-emitted molecules per unit area. The number of re-emitted molecules depends on the interaction process between the impinging particles and the surface. This interaction process can be described quantitatively by defining the *thermal accommodation efficient* as

$$\alpha = (\dot{e}_i - \dot{e}_r)/(\dot{e}_i - \dot{e}_s) \qquad (12\text{–}28)$$

where $\dot{e}_s$ is the energy flux which would be reflected from the surface if all the incident molecules were re-emitted with Maxwellian distribution (17) at the body surface temperature T_s. Values of α can be determined only by experiment and Table 12–2 lists some of them for various air-surface combinations.

TABLE 12–2

THERMAL ACCOMMODATION COEFFICIENTS α FOR AIR*

Surface	α
Flat lacquer on bronze	0.88–0.89
Polished bronze	0.91–0.94
Machined bronze	0.89–0.93
Polished cast iron	0.87–0.93
Polished aluminum	0.87–0.95
Machined aluminum	0.95–0.97
Etched aluminum	0.89–0.97

* From M. L. Wiedmann and P. R. Trumpler, "Thermal Accommodation Coefficients," *Trans. ASME*, Vol. 68 (1946), pp. 57–64.

Combining Eqs. 12–27 and 12–28 yields

$$q/A = \alpha(\dot{e}_s - \dot{e}_i) \qquad (12\text{–}29)$$

The incident and re-emitted energy fluxes have been calculated, among others, by Stalder and Jukoff (22), Oppenheim (20), and Tsien (10). For the purpose of these calculations the energy fluxes are broken up into two components. The first is due to the translational motion of the molecules, the second is due to the internal degrees of freedom such as rotation or vibration, if present. Assuming a Maxwellian distribution of velocities for the incident molecules and making use of other concepts derived from the kinetic theory of gases the number of the molecules incident on and issuing from the surface, as well as their energies can be calculated as shown in detail in Refs. 10, 16, 20, and 22. The results of these calculations are summarized in Figs. 12–6 and 12–7 for a number of geometrical configurations of bodies at uniform surface temperature T_s. Figure 12–6 shows the recovery factor R_T multiplied by $(\gamma + 1)/\gamma$ as a function of the *molecular speed ratio* s, defined as the ratio of the flight speed V_∞ to the most probable molecular speed V_m. Since according to kinetic theory $V_m = \sqrt{2g_c \Re T}$, it can easily be shown that $s = M_\infty \sqrt{\gamma/2}$. In Fig. 12–7 the high-speed Stanton number multiplied by $\gamma/\alpha(\gamma + 1)$ is plotted as a function of s. In both figures

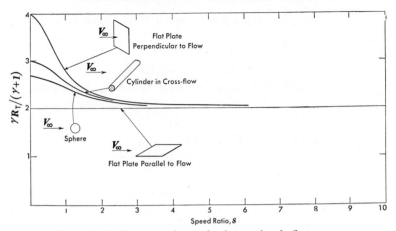

FIG. 12–6. Recovery factor for free-molecule flow.

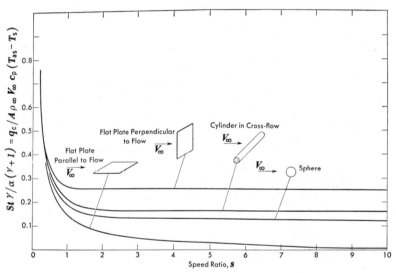

FIG. 12–7. High-speed Stanton number for free-molecule flow.

curves for a flat plate, parallel and perpendicular to the flow, a cylinder in cross flow, and a sphere are shown.   It will be observed that in free molecular flow, in contrast to a continuum flow, the recovery factors are larger than unity and consequently the adiabatic surface temperature is larger than the local stagnation temperature of the gas.

Example 12–1. Estimate the equilibrium temperature of an aluminum sphere having a diameter of 0.2 ft and travelling at a Mach number of 12 at an altitude of 390,000 ft where the molecular mean free path is about 1.0 ft, the temperature about 200 F, and the density of the air 2.4×10^{-8} lb$_m$/ cu ft.

Solution: Since the ratio λ/L is greater than 3, free molecule flow prevails. The molecular speed ratio is

$$s = M_\infty \sqrt{\gamma/2} = 10$$

and from Fig. 12-7 $\qquad St\gamma/\alpha\,(\gamma + 1) = 0.125$

For aluminum α is about 0.9 according to Table 12-2. The flight velocity is $M_\infty \sqrt{\gamma \Re g_c T} = 15{,}000$ ft/sec and the unit-surface convective conductance is therefore

$$\bar{h}_c = 0.125\alpha(\gamma + 1)\rho V c_p/\gamma$$

$$= 0.125 \times 0.9 \times 2.4 \times 2.4 \times 10^{-8}\ (\text{lb}_m/\text{cu ft}) \times 15{,}000 \times 3.600$$
$$(\text{ft/hr}) \times 0.24\ (\text{Btu/lb F})/1.4$$

$$= .06\ \text{Btu/hr sq ft F}$$

The adiabatic surface temperature is obtained with the aid of Eqs. 12-3 and Fig. 12-6 from which

$$R_T = 2 \times 1.4/2.4 = 1.16$$

as

$$T_{as} = 660(1 + 1.16 \times 0.2 \times 12^2) = 22{,}600\ \text{R}$$

A heat balance for the incoming convection and outgoing radiation yields

$$\bar{h}_c(T_{as} - T_s) = \epsilon\sigma T_s^4$$

if it is assumed that the incident radiation is negligible. From Table 5-1, ϵ is about 0.9 for anodized aluminum so that at equilibrium we have

$$\sigma T_s^4(\epsilon/\bar{h}_c) + T_s = 22{,}600\ \text{R}$$

Solving for T_s by trial and error gives 955 R or 495 F for the equilibrium temperature.

12-6. CLOSURE

In this chapter we have surveyed briefly some phenomena associated with heat transfer at very high speeds. It is important to emphasize that the material presented is merely a cursory introduction into a vast and important area of heat transfer. The field of heat transfer at high speeds has only recently become of practical significance and is therefore still in its infancy. It is apparent from an inspection of Fig. 12-1 that there are many ranges of Knudsen, Mach, and Reynolds number combinations in which no experimental data are available. Numerous experimental studies are, however, in progress and their results will in the near future supply the information necessary for the thermal design of ultra high-speed missiles and satellites. Since the problems arising from aerodynamic heating are at the present time the major obstacles to high speed flight and the safe re-entry of satellites and space ships, their solution is a challenge to science which undoubtedly will soon be met successfully.

A complete analysis of problems associated with heat transfer at high speeds requires consideration of the dynamics and thermodynamics simultaneously with the phenomena of heat transfer. In the region of conventional aerodynamics shock and rarefaction waves play an important role. In the free-molecule and hypersonic flow regimes an understanding of the kinetic theory of gases, the dissociation and ionization of gas molecules, and of the catalytic interaction between the molecules and the body surface is necessary for a complete analysis. Readers interested in following the development in these fields are referred to the current literature, in particular to the Journal of the American Rocket Society, the Journal of the Aeronautical Sciences, and the publications of the National Advisory Committee for Aeronautics. An up-to-date survey is presented in the High-Speed Aerodynamics and Jet Propulsion Series of the Princeton University Press.

REFERENCES

1. J. Kaye, "Survey of Friction Coefficients, Recovery Factors, and Heat Transfer Coefficients for Supersonic Flow," *J. Aeronautical Sci.*, Vol. 21, No. 2 (1954), pp. 117–129.

2. E. R. Van Driest, "Turbulent Boundary Layer in Compressible Fluids," *J. Aeronautical Sci.*, Vol. 18, No. 3 (1951), pp. 145–161.

3. W. W. Fisher and R. M. Norris, "Supersonic Convective Heat Transfer Correlation from Skin Temperature Measurements on a V-2 Rocket in Flight," *Trans. ASME*, Vol. 71 (1949), pp. 457–469.

4. E. R. A. Eckert, "Engineering Relations for Heat Transfer and Friction in High-Velocity Laminar and Turbulent Boundary Layer Flow over Surface with Constant Pressure and Temperature," *Trans. ASME*, Vol. 78 (1956), pp. 1273–1281.

5. Carl Gazley, "Boundary-Layer Stability and Transition in Subsonic and Supersonic Flow," *J. Aeronautical Sci.*, Vol. 20, No. 1 (1953), pp. 19–28.

6. M. W. Rubesin and H. A. Johnson, "A Critical Review of Skin-Friction and Heat-Transfer Solutions of the Laminar Boundary Layer of a Flat Plate," *Trans. ASME*, Vol. 71 (1949), pp. 383–388.

7. A. H. Shapiro, *Compressible Fluid Flow*, Vol. II. (New York: The Ronald Press Company, 1954.)

8. W. Hantsche and H. Wendt, "The Laminar Boundary Layer of a Circular Cone in Supersonic Flow at Zero Angle of Attack," *Jahrbuch der Deutschen Luftfahrtforschung*, 1941, Part 1, pp. 76–77.

9. E. R. Van Driest, "Investigation of Laminar Boundary Layer in Compressible Fluids Using the Crocco Method," *NACA TN* 597, 1952.

10. H. S. Tsien, "Supraerodynamics, Mechanics of Rarefied Gases," *J. of the Aero. Sci.*, Vol. 13 (1946), pp. 653–664.

11. L. L. Kavanau, "Heat Transfer from Sphere to a Rarefied Gas in Subsonic Flow," *Trans. ASME*, Vol. 77 (1955).

12. R. M. Drake and G. H. Backer, "Heat Transfer from Spheres to a Rarefied Gas in Supersonic Flow," *Trans. ASME*, Vol. 74 (1952).

13. F. M. Sauer, "Convective Heat Transfer from Spheres in Free Molecule Flow," *J. of the Aero Sci.*, Vol. 18 (1951), pp. 353–354.

14. J. R. Stalder, G. Goodwin and M. O. Creager, "Heat Transfer to Bodies in a High Speed Rarefied Gas Stream," *NACA TN* 2438, 1951.

15. R. M. Drake and G. J. Maslach, "Heat Transfer from Right Circular Cones to a Rarefied Gas in Supersonic Flow," *Univ. of Calif. Inst. Eng. Res. Rep. M.E.*, (1952) pp. 150–191.

16. S. A. Schaaf and P. L. Chambre, *Flow of Rarefied Gases*, High Speed Aerodynamics and Jet Propulsion Series, Vol. IV, Part G, Princeton University Press, 1956.

17. M. W. Liepman and A. Roshko, *Elements of Gasdynamics*. (New York: John Wiley & Sons, Inc.)

18.   J. R. Stalder, "A Survey of Heat Transfer Problems Encountered by Hypersonic Aircraft," *Jet Propulsion*, Vol. 27 (1957), pp. 1178–1188.

19.   L. Lees, "Laminar Heat Transfer over Blunt-Nosed Bodies at Hypersonic Speeds," *Jet Propulsion*, Vol. 26 (1956), pp. 259–264.

20.   A. K. Oppenheim, "Generalized Theory of Convective Heat Transfer in a Free-Molecule Flow," *J. of the Aero. Sci.*, Vol. 20 (1953), pp. 49–57.

21.   E. M. Kennard, *Kinetic Theory of Gases.* (New York: McGraw-Hill Book Company, Inc., 1938.)

22.   J. R. Stalder and D. Jukoff, "Heat Transfer to Bodies Travelling at High Speeds in the Upper Atmosphere," *NACA Rep.* No. 944, 1944.

23.   V. L. Lelchuk, "Heat Transfer and Hydraulic Flow Resistance for Streams of High Velocity," *NACA TM* 1054, 1943.

24.   N. H. Kemp and F. R. Ridell, "Heat Transfer to Satellite Vehicles Re-entering the Atmosphere," *Jet Propulsion*, Vol. 27 (1957), pp. 132–139.

13 Mass Transfer

by L. Bryce Andersen

13–1. INTRODUCTION

The transport of one constituent of a fluid solution from a region of higher concentration to a region of lower concentration is called mass transfer. The mechanism of mass transfer can be most readily understood by drawing an analogy to heat transfer. Heat is transferred in a direction which reduces an existing temperature gradient; mass is transferred in a direction which reduces an existing concentration gradient. Heat transfer ceases when there is no longer a temperature difference; mass transfer ceases when the concentration gradient is reduced to zero. The rates of both heat and mass transfer depend on a driving potential and a resistance. Other similarities between heat and mass transfer will be discussed in connection with mass transfer theory. This chapter will develop the basic concepts of mass transfer and apply these concepts to a few typical problems. The detailed design of industrial mass transfer equipment will not be considered. Those readers who wish to pursue the subject of mass transfer further are referred to the references listed at the end of this chapter.

Mass transfer may occur either within the gas phase or within the liquid phase. In many chemical engineering unit operations, transfer of mass takes place between two different phases. In *gas absorption*, a soluble gas is removed from a gaseous mixture with an insoluble gas by transfer to a liquid phase. In *adsorption*, one constituent of a fluid phase is transferred to the surface of a solid adsorbent. In *distillation*, mass transfer takes place simultaneously in two directions: from the liquid to the vapor, and vice versa. The net effect is to increase the concentration of the more volatile constituent in the vapor phase and to deplete the liquid phase. *Liquid extraction* involves the transfer of a constituent from one liquid phase to another liquid phase. The two liquid phases must be immiscible to some extent, or no separation is possible. *Leaching*, or solid-liquid extraction, is an operation in which the soluble component of a solid phase is dissolved and transferred to a liquid solvent. An everyday example of leaching is the making of coffee, where the soluble component of the ground coffee is dissolved out by a hot-water phase.

In certain mass transfer operations, simultaneous heat transfer must be considered. For example, *humidification* is an operation in which a pure liquid is evaporated into a bulk gas phase. In the humidification of air, water is transferred from the liquid phase to the bulk air phase. Sufficient energy to supply the latent heat of vaporization of the water must be provided. This energy can be supplied by transferring heat from the gas to the liquid. Under this condition heat is transferred in a direction opposite to that of the mass transfer. Thermal effects are often important in distillation, since the liquid is continually vaporized and the vapor continually condensed. Other common mass-transfer operations are drying, evaporation, and condensation.

The mechanism of mass transfer, just as that of heat transfer, depends largely on the dynamics of the fluid phases. Mass can be transferred not only by random molecular motion in quiescent or laminar-flowing fluids, but also by eddy currents through fluids in turbulent motion. The former is analogous to conduction heat transfer, the latter, to convection. Before interphase mass transfer is considered, molecular and turbulent mass diffusion will be discussed.

13–2. MASS TRANSFER BY MOLECULAR DIFFUSION

Mass transfer by molecular diffusion is directly analogous to conduction heat transfer or to momentum transfer in laminar flow. Mass transfer by molecular diffusion may occur in a stagnant fluid or in a fluid in laminar flow. The transient one-dimensional mass-transfer equation can be written in a form identical to the Fourier heat-transfer equation,

$$\frac{\partial c_A}{\partial \theta} = D_v \frac{\partial^2 c_A}{\partial y^2} \qquad (13\text{–}1)$$

where c_A = concentration of component A in a mixture of A and B, in lb-moles/cu ft;

θ = time, in hr;

D_v = mass diffusivity, in sq ft/hr;

y = distance in the direction of diffusion, in ft.

In the steady state the concentration at any point does not vary with time, and

$$\frac{N_A}{A} = -D_v \frac{dc_A}{dy} \qquad (13\text{–}2)$$

where N_A/A is the mass flux in lb-moles/hr sq ft. The negative sign appears because the concentration gradient is negative in the direction of mass transfer.

The equivalent expression for heat transfer is

$$\frac{q}{A} = -k\frac{dT}{dy} = -\frac{k}{c_p\rho}\frac{d(c_p\rho T)}{dy} = -a\frac{d(c_p\rho T)}{dy} \qquad (13\text{-}3)$$

where q/A = heat flux, in Btu/hr sq ft;
k = thermal conductivity, in Btu/hr ft F;
c_p = heat capacity, in Btu/lb$_m$;
ρ = density, in lb$_m$/cu ft;
T = temperature, in F;
a = thermal diffusivity, in sq ft/hr.

Similarly, the equation for momentum transfer in laminar flow is

$$\tau g_c = -\mu\frac{du}{dy} = -\frac{\mu}{\rho}\frac{d(u\rho)}{dy} = -\nu\frac{d(u\rho)}{dy} \qquad (13\text{-}4)$$

where τg_c = momentum flux, in ft lb$_m$/hr sq ft hr;
μ = absolute viscosity, in lb$_m$/ft hr;
u = velocity in the x-direction;
ν = momentum diffusivity (kinematic viscosity), in sq ft/hr.

An examination of Eqs. 13–2, 13–3, and 13–4 shows that they are all of the form: Flux = diffusivity × concentration gradient. Equation 13–2 is written for a mass concentration, c_A, Eq. 13–3 for a thermal concentration, $c_p\rho T$, and Eq. 13–4 for a momentum concentration, $u\rho$. All three diffusivities, D_v, a, ν, have the same dimensions and the concentration gradients are linear for a uniform medium at steady state.

Equation 13–2 states that mass will be transferred between two points in a fluid if a difference in concentration exists between the points. Mass transfer occurs at an appreciable rate only in gases and liquids. In solids, mass transfer is suppressed by the relative immobility of the molecules.

In the gas phase, concentrations are usually expressed as partial pressures. If the perfect gas law,

$$p_A = \frac{n_A \Re T}{V} = c_A \Re T \qquad (13\text{-}5)$$

where p_A = partial pressure of gas A in a mixture, in atm;
n_A = number of moles of gas, in lb-moles;
$\Re$ = gas constant, in cu ft atm/lb-mole F;
V = gas volume, in cu ft;

is assumed to hold, Eq. 13–2 becomes

$$\frac{N_A}{A} = \frac{-D_v}{\Re T}\frac{dp_A}{dy} \qquad (13\text{-}6)$$

Integration of Eq. 13–6 between any two planes in the fluid gives

$$\frac{N_A}{A} = \frac{-D_v(p_{A_2} - p_{A_1})}{\Re T(y_2 - y_1)} \tag{13-7}$$

where p_{A_1} is the partial pressure at y_1 and p_{A_2} is the partial pressure at y_2. Equation 13–7 is rigorously correct only for equimolar counter diffusion. In equimolar counter diffusion gases A and B diffuse simultaneously in opposite directions through each other. The rates of diffusion are equal but in opposite directions, i.e., $N_A = -N_B$. This situation has no counterpart in heat transfer, since heat can be transferred only in one direction at a time. Of course, gas B will be transferred only if a concentration gradient

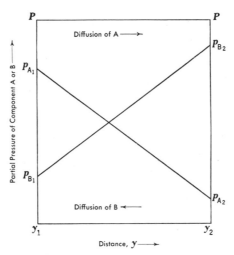

Fig. 13–1. Partial pressure gradients in equimolar counterdiffusion of two gases.

for B exists. This is shown schematically in Fig. 13–1. For equimolar counterdiffusion the partial pressure gradients must be equal but of opposite sign. Diffusion of this type can occur in distillation.

Diffusion of a gas through a second stationary gas often occurs in industrial mass-transfer equipment. For example, in the humidification of air, water vapor must diffuse from the air-water interface through an air layer which is stationary. Conversely, in the dehumidification of air, water vapor must diffuse from the bulk of the gas phase through stationary air to reach the surface at which it condenses.

Consider the case of gas A diffusing through a stationary gas B to a gas-liquid interface where gas A is absorbed but gas B is not (Fig. 13–2). Since gas A is diffusing toward the interface, there must be a partial-

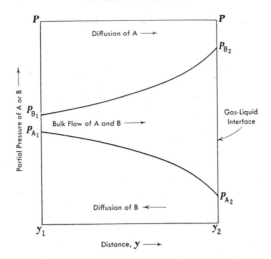

FIG. 13–2. Partial pressure gradients
in the diffusion of a gas through a
stationary gas.

pressure gradient for A in the direction of diffusion. The rate of transfer
of A is given by Eq. 13–6

$$\frac{N_A}{A} = \frac{-D_v}{\Re T} \frac{dp_A}{dy}$$

Since there is a continuous gas phase, the total pressure P must be constant
throughout the gas. Since $p_A + p_B = P$, a gradient in p_A will cause a
gradient of p_B in the opposite direction. This gradient will force diffusion
of gas B away from the interface, at the rate

$$\frac{N_B}{A} = \frac{-D_v}{\Re T} \frac{dp_B}{dy} = \frac{D_v}{\Re T} \frac{dp_A}{dy} \qquad (13\text{–}8)$$

since $dp_B/dy = -dp_A/dy$. Since gas B is not being produced at the interface, even though it is diffusing away from the interface, some other mechanism must supply gas B to maintain a constant concentration of gas B at
the interface. A bulk flow of gas toward the interface replenishes the gas
B which is diffusing away. The bulk flow will consist of a mixture of A and
B. The bulk flow of B toward the interface must equal $-N_B/A$ to balance
the diffusion of B in the opposite direction. The presence of A in the bulk
flow will effectively increase the rate of transfer of A toward the interface.
Since the bulk flow rate of B toward the interface equals $-N_B/A$, the bulk
flow rate of A toward the interface equals

$$\frac{\text{moles } A \text{ in bulk flow}}{\text{moles } B \text{ in bulk flow}} \times \text{bulk flow of } B = \frac{p_A}{p_B}\left(\frac{-N_B}{A}\right) = \frac{p_A}{P - p_A}\left(\frac{-N_B}{A}\right)$$

The total bulk flow rate equals the sum of bulk flow rates of A and B

$$\frac{-N_B}{A}\left(1 + \frac{p_A}{P - p_A}\right)$$

The total flux of A toward the interface is the sum of the diffusion of A and the bulk flow of A, or

$$\frac{N_{At}}{A} = \frac{-D_v}{\mathfrak{R}T}\frac{dp_A}{dy} + \frac{p_A}{P - p_A}\left(\frac{-N_B}{A}\right) \tag{13-9}$$

Substitution for N_B from Eq. 13–8 yields

$$\frac{N_{At}}{A} = \frac{-D_v}{\mathfrak{R}T}\left(1 + \frac{p_A}{P - p_A}\right)\frac{dp_A}{dy} \tag{13-10}$$

Integration gives

$$\frac{N_{At}}{A} = \frac{D_v}{\mathfrak{R}T}\frac{P}{y_2 - y_1}\ln\frac{P - p_{A2}}{P - p_{A1}} \tag{13-11}$$

but since $p_B = P - p_A$,

$$\frac{N_{At}}{A} = \frac{D_v P}{\mathfrak{R}T(y_2 - y_1)}\ln\frac{p_{B2}}{p_{B1}} \tag{13-12}$$

The definition of the logarithmic mean partial pressure of B is

$$p_{Bm} = \frac{p_{B2} - p_{B1}}{\ln\dfrac{p_{B2}}{p_{B1}}} \tag{13-13}$$

Since $p_{B2} = P - p_{A2}$ and $p_{B1} = P - p_{A1}$,

$$p_{B2} - p_{B1} = p_{A1} - p_{A2} \tag{13-14}$$

Combination of Eqs. 13–12, 13–13, and 13–14 yields

$$\frac{N_{At}}{A} = \frac{-D_v P(p_{A2} - p_{A1})}{\mathfrak{R}T\, p_{Bm}(y_2 - y_1)} \tag{13-15}$$

Comparison of Eq. 13–15 with Eq. 13–7 shows that the factor P/p_{Bm} is introduced when diffusion through a stationary gas is considered. For a dilute mixture of A in B, p_{Bm} is approximately equal to P and Eq. 13–15 reduces to Eq. 13–7. It should be noted that the "stationary" characteristic of B does not imply that B is not moving, but refers to the *net* behavior of B. Since B is supplied by bulk flow at the same rate it diffuses away, there is no *net* movement of B.   The partial-pressure gradients for diffusion through a stationary gas are not linear with distance, contrasted to the linear gradients in equimolar counterdiffusion.

Mass diffusivities must be evaluated experimentally.   Selected values for gases and liquids are given in Table 13-1.

TABLE 13-1

Mass Diffusivities for Gases and Liquids

Gases at 77 F, 1 atm	
System	Diffusivity (sq ft/hr)
Ammonia-air	1.08
Water vapor-air	0.99
Ethanol-air	0.46
CO_2-air	0.64
O_2-air	0.80
H_2-air	1.60
Benzene-air	0.34
Liquid Phase at 68 F, Dilute Solutions	
Oxygen in water	7.0×10^{-5}
Ammonia in water	6.8×10^{-5}
Ethanol in water	3.8×10^{-5}
CO_2 in water	6.9×10^{-5}
H_2 in water	20.0×10^{-5}
HCl in water	10.0×10^{-5}
Sucrose in water	1.8×10^{-5}
NaCl in water	5.3×10^{-5}
CO_2 in ethanol	13.2×10^{-5}

The coefficients for gases in Table 13-1 are for either component diffusing through the other.   The liquid-phase diffusivities are several orders of magnitude smaller than the gaseous diffusivities.   This is due to the smaller molecular mobilities in liquids.   Diffusivities for systems where no direct experimental data are available may be predicted by semiempirical equations (see Refs. 2,6,7).   Diffusion coefficients for gases and vapors vary approximately with the 3/2 power of the absolute temperature and inversely with the total pressure.

Example 13-1.   Calculate the rate of diffusion of water vapor from a pool of water at the bottom of a 20-ft well to dry air flowing over the top of the well.   Assume the air in the well is stagnant and that the entire system is at 77 F and 1 atm.

Solution: This is the case of a gas diffusing through a second, stationary, gas. The bottom of the well is taken as point 1 and the top as point 2, and Eq. 13-15 is applied.   Air is nearly insoluble in water, so diffusion of air into water can be ignored. The diffusivity of water vapor in air is taken from Table 13-1: $D_v = 0.99$ sq ft/hr. The partial pressure of water vapor at the water surface at the bottom of the well is equal to the saturated vapor pressure of water at 77 F.   Therefore, from vapor pressure tables, $p_{A1} = 0.031$ atm. Since the air at the top of the well is dry, $p_{A2} = 0$. The gas constant $\mathfrak{R}$ is 0.730 cu ft atm/lb-mole R.

$$p_{B_1} = P - p_{A_1} = 0.969 \qquad p_{B_2} = P - p_{A_2} = 1.0$$

$$p_{Bm} = \frac{p_{B2} - p_{B1}}{\ln p_{B2}/p_{B1}} = \frac{1 - 0.969}{\ln \dfrac{1}{0.969}} = 0.983$$

$$\frac{N_A}{A} = \frac{-(0.99)(1)(0 - 0.031)}{(0.730)(460 + 77)(0.983)(20 - 0)}$$

$$= 3.99 \times 10^{-6} \text{ lb-moles/hr sq ft of well cross section} \qquad Ans.$$

Since the water vapor partial pressure is small, Eq. 13–7 may be used as an approximation. It yields $N_A/A = 4.03 \times 10^{-6}$ lb-moles/hr sq ft. The difference is only about 1 per cent.

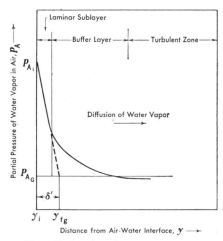

Fig. 13–3. Steady-state concentration gradient of water vapor in air flowing over a horizontal water surface.

13–3. MASS TRANSFER BY CONVECTION

The mechanism of mass transfer in turbulent flow is similar to that of heat transfer in turbulent flow. Consider, for example, an air stream flowing over the surface of a pool of water. The velocity distribution in the air is the same as for flow over a plate (Chapter 6). Near the surface there is a laminar sublayer, followed by a buffer layer, and a turbulent main stream (Fig. 13–3). The rate of mass transfer of water vapor to the air is given by the equation

$$\frac{N_A}{A} = \frac{-D_v P}{\mathfrak{R} T p_{Bm}} \frac{(p_{AG} - p_{Ai})}{(y_{fg} - y_i)} \tag{13–16}$$

where p_{A_G} = average partial pressure of the water vapor in the bulk gas phase (Fig. 13–3);

p_{A_i} = partial pressure of water vapor at the gas-liquid interface;

$y_{f_g} - y_i$ = effective boundary-layer thickness for mass transfer, δ'_m, discussed previously in Sec. 6–3. Its resistance to molecular diffusion is the same as that offered to total diffusion by the sublayer, buffer layer, and turbulent region combined.

While simple theory predicts that the effective film thicknesses for mass and heat transfer should be the same, the experimental data available show that this is only an approximation.

Since the effective film thickness cannot be measured directly, Eq. 13–9 is rewritten

$$\frac{N_A}{A} = k_G(p_{A_i} - p_{A_G}) \tag{13–17}$$

where k_G is the gas-phase mass-transfer coefficient, defined by

$$k_G = \frac{D_v P}{\Re T p_{Bm}(y_{f_g} - y_i)} \text{ lb-moles/hr sq ft atm} \tag{13–18}$$

The mass transfer coefficient k_G is analogous to the heat-transfer coefficient $\bar{h}_c$.

For mass transfer in the liquid phase

$$\frac{N_A}{A} = \frac{-D_v c_t(c_{A_i} - c_{A_L})}{c_{Bm}(y_i - y_{fl})} = k_L(c_{A_i} - c_{A_L}) \tag{13–19}$$

where c_{A_i} = concentration of the diffusing component at the interface;

c_{A_L} = concentration of the diffusing component in the bulk liquid phase;

c_t = total concentration $(c_A + c_B)$;

c_{Bm} = log-mean concentration of component B

$y_{fl} - y_i$ = thickness of the effective liquid film;

k_L = liquid-phase mass-transfer coefficient; defined by

$$k_L = \frac{D_v c_t}{c_{Bm}(y_{fl} - y_i)} \text{ lb-moles/hr sq ft (lb-mole/cu ft)} \tag{13–20}$$

The mass-transfer coefficients defined by Eqs. 13–18 and 13–20 apply to diffusion of one component through a second *stationary* component. Coefficients for equimolar counterdiffusion may be obtained similarly (see Prob. 13–9). In the humidification of air there is no resistance to diffusion of water in the liquid phase, since only water is present. Therefore, the liquid-phase mass-transfer coefficient is infinite, and only the gas-phase resistance need be considered.

and

$$j_M = \frac{\text{Sh}}{\text{ReSc}^{0.33}} = \left(\frac{k_G \Re T p_{Bm}}{VP}\right)\left(\frac{\mu}{\rho D_v}\right)^{0.67} = \frac{1}{2} f \qquad \text{(13–30)}$$

where j_H is the j factor for heat transfer and j_M is the j factor for mass transfer. Combination of Eq. 13–27 with Eq. 13–29 gives

$$j_H = 0.023 \text{ Re}^{-0.2} \qquad \text{(13–31)}$$

and combination of Eq. 13–28 with Eq. 13–30 gives

$$j_M = 0.023 \text{ Re}^{-0.17} \qquad \text{(13–32)}$$

Experimental data for flow in tubes show that $j_H = \frac{1}{2} f = j_M$ within the accuracy of the data. This correlation considers only skin friction. In flow past blunt objects and in typical industrial mass-transfer equipment, separation of the boundary layer often induces additional pressure losses, and j_H and j_M are not equal to $\frac{1}{2} f$. However, in many cases, j_H is still approximately equal to j_M, and mass-transfer coefficients can be predicted by the relation

$$j_H = j_M$$

or

$$\left(\frac{\bar{h}_c}{V \rho c_p}\right)\left(\frac{c_p \mu}{k}\right)^{0.67} = \left(\frac{k_G \Re T}{V}\right)\left(\frac{p_{Bm}}{P}\right)\left(\frac{\mu}{\rho D_v}\right)^{0.67}$$

So that

$$k_G = \left(\frac{\bar{h}_c}{c_p \rho}\right)\left(\frac{P}{\Re T p_{Bm}}\right)\left[\left(\frac{c_p \mu}{k}\right)\left(\frac{\rho D_v}{\mu}\right)\right]^{0.67} \qquad \text{(13–33)}$$

If the Prandtl and Schmidt numbers are equal, Eq. 13–33 reduces to Eq. 13–26. Where direct mass-transfer data for a new system are not available, Eq. 13–33 may be used to predict mass-transfer coefficients from heat-transfer data taken in a system of identical geometry and flow characteristics.

Example 13–2. Predict the mass-transfer coefficient for liquid ammonia vaporizing into air at 77 F and 1 atm, knowing that the heat-transfer coefficient in the same equipment, at the same gas and liquid flow rates, is 800 Btu/hr sq ft F.

Solution: Equation 13–28 cannot be used, since equipment size and flow rates are not given. In any event, Eq. 13–28 is valid only for a wetted-wall column. Equation 13-33 will therefore be used.

For ammonia at 77 F, $D_v = 1.08$ sq ft/hr. The physical properties of the gas phase will be evaluated assuming a dilute mixture of ammonia in air. For air at 77 F and 1 atm:

$$\mu = 0.018 \text{ centipoise} = 0.044 \text{ lb}_m/\text{ft hr}$$
$$\rho = 0.074 \text{ lb/cu ft}$$

$$c_p = 0.25 \text{ Btu/lb F}$$
$$k = 0.015 \text{ Btu/hr ft F}$$
$$\mathcal{R} = 0.730 \text{ cu ft atm/lb-mole F}$$
$$T = 460 + 77 = 537 \text{ R}$$

For a dilute gas $p_{Bm} = P$, and

$$k_G = \left(\frac{800}{0.25 \times 0.074}\right)\left(\frac{1}{0.730 \times 537}\right)\left(\frac{0.25 \times 0.044}{0.015} \times \frac{0.074 \times 1.08}{0.044}\right)^{0.67}$$

$$= 134 \text{ lb-moles/hr sq ft atm}$$

As an exercise, the dimensions of the above equation should be checked. If Eq. 13–26 is used

$$k_G = \frac{\bar{h}_c}{c_p \rho \mathcal{R} T} = \frac{800}{0.25 \times 0.074 \times 0.73 \times 537}$$

$$= 110 \text{ lb-moles/hr sq ft atm} \qquad Ans.$$

The difference in the two values of k_G is 18 per cent.

13–5. INTERPHASE MASS TRANSFER

All industrial mass-transfer operations involve the transfer of material from one phase to another. The total resistance to mass transfer in the two phases may be expressed in terms of an over-all mass-transfer coefficient similar to an over-all heat-transfer coefficient. There is, however, an important difference in the evaluation of over-all mass- and heat-transfer coefficients.

To illustrate the difference between the two over-all coefficients, consider first the transfer of heat from a hot gas to a cold liquid. The gas is insoluble in the liquid, and the liquid does not vaporize. The gas is flowing countercurrent to the liquid. The temperature gradient for this system is shown in Fig. 13–4. The driving potential for heat transfer in the gas phase is $(T_G - T_i)$, and in the liquid phase, $(T_i - T_L)$. The over-all driving potential, $(T_G - T_L)$, is the sum of the two. The over-all heat-transfer coefficient is given by

$$\frac{1}{U} = \left(\frac{1}{h_{\text{gas}}} + \frac{1}{h_{\text{liquid}}}\right) \qquad (13\text{–}34)$$

and the heat flux by

$$q/A = U(T_G - T_L)$$

Now consider the transfer of mass from a gas to a liquid, as for example, the absorption of ammonia from an air-ammonia mixture by water. In heat transfer the interfacial temperature T_i is identical for each phase, but as shown in Fig. 13–5, there is an apparent discontinuity in concentration at the gas-liquid interface which remains even when the concentrations in each phase are expressed in the same dimensions. If there is no resistance to heat transfer at the interface, the potentials are equal. In mass transfer, on the other hand, even if the two phases are assumed to be at equilibrium at the interface, the interfacial concentrations are not equal. The explanation of this apparent discrepancy lies in the choice of concentration as the driving potential for mass transfer. Strictly speaking the concentration is the driving potential for mass transfer within a phase, but not *between* phases. The correct driving potential between phases is a property called the *chemical potential*. In a single phase, the chemical potential is related to the concentration, but this relationship may change from one phase to another. Since the chemical potential is difficult to evaluate for industrial applications, it is seldom used in engineering calculations. It will not be

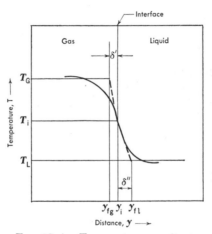

FIG. 13–4. Temperature gradient for heat transfer from a hot gas to a cold liquid.

considered in detail here, but it should be noted that when the chemical potentials of two phases are equal, they are in equilibrium. Thus, the chemical potentials at the interface in mass transfer are equal.

A simple illustration will show the possible great difference in mass concentration of two phases in thermodynamic equilibrium. Consider air at 77 F and 1 atm in equilibrium with water at the same temperature. If the air is saturated with water vapor, the partial pressure of the water vapor is 0.031 atm and the mole fraction of water vapor in the gas phase is 0.031. In the liquid phase the mole fraction of water is 1.0, since only water is present. (Actually a very small quantity of air would be dissolved in the water, but this will be ignored here.) Obviously, the concentrations of the two phases at equilibrium are not equal.

Experimental data for phase equilibria must be gathered for each system separately. Fortunately, groups of systems follow general laws, which facilitate the prediction of the equilibrium concentrations. For example, Henry's law adequately describes the equilibrium between a gas and a liquid phase for many gases and liquids,

$$p_A = mc_A \tag{13-35}$$

where p_A = partial pressure of component A in the gas phase, in atm;
c_A = concentration of component A in the liquid phase in equilibrium with the gas, in lb-moles/cu ft;
m = Henry's law constant, experimentally determined, in atm cu ft/lb-mole.

Values for the Henry's law constant for many gases, such as oxygen, nitrogen, and carbon dioxide dissolved in water, are given in Table 13–2. Gases such as sulfur dioxide and ammonia do not follow Henry's law, but data for these gases are tabulated in Ref. 4.

TABLE 13–2

HENRY'S LAW CONSTANTS FOR VARIOUS GASES IN WATER AT MODERATE PRESSURES
$m \times 10^{-4}$, atm/(lb mole/cu ft)

T C	Air	O_2	N_2	CO_2
0	1.25	0.736	1.53	0.021
10	1.58	0.944	1.93	0.030
20	1.92	1.16	2.32	0.041
30	2.24	1.38	2.68	0.054
40	2.52	1.56	3.02	0.067
50	2.76	1.72	3.30	0.083
60	2.96	1.85	3.52	0.100
70	3.10	1.96	3.69	.....
80	3.18	2.04	3.74	.....
90	3.23	2.09	3.77	.....
100	3.22	2.11	3.79	.....

An expression for the over-all mass-transfer coefficient may now be derived for systems that follow Henry's law. Since it is not practical to measure concentrations at the gas-liquid interface, p_{A_i} and c_{A_i} are unknown. However, Henry's law can be used to determine the partial pressure of a constituent of a gas in equilibrium with a given bulk liquid concentration

$$p_A{}^* = mc_{A_L} \tag{13-36}$$

where the * denotes that p_A is the gas-phase concentration in equilibrium with c_{A_L}. Similarly,

$$c_A{}^* = \frac{p_{A_G}}{m} \tag{13-37}$$

where $c_A{}^*$ is the liquid-phase concentration in equilibrium with a gas of concentration p_{AG}. It should be noted that c_{AL} and p_{AG} are actual concentrations (see Fig. 13–5), while $p_A{}^*$ and $c_A{}^*$ are fictitious concentrations, when mass transfer occurs.

Equations 13–17 and 13–19 may be written for mass transfer from the gas to liquid phase in the form

$$\frac{N_A}{A} = k_G(p_{AG} - p_{A_i}) \qquad\qquad [\textbf{13–17}]$$

$$\frac{N_A}{A} = k_L(c_{A_i} - c_{AL}) \qquad\qquad [\textbf{13–19}]$$

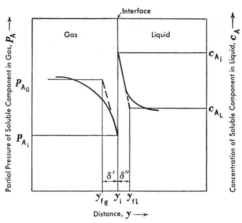

Fig. 13–5.   Concentration gradient for mass transfer from a gas to a liquid.

Since the interfacial concentrations cannot be evaluated, it is convenient to define over-all coefficients

$$N_A = K_G(p_{AG} - p_A{}^*) \qquad\qquad (\textbf{13–38})$$

and

$$N_A = K_L(c_A{}^* - c_{AL}) \qquad\qquad (\textbf{13–39})$$

where K_G = over-all mass-transfer coefficients based on the gas phase concentrations, in lb-moles/hr sq ft atm;

$\quad\;\; K_L$ = over-all mass-transfer coefficient based on the liquid-phase concentrations, lb-moles/hr sq ft (lb mole/cu ft).

In the steady state the rate of mass transfer for 1 sq ft of transfer area N_A is the same in the gas and liquid films.

Solving Eq. 13–17 for p_{Ai} and Eq. 13–19 for c_{Ai} gives

$$p_{Ai} = p_{AG} - \frac{N_A}{k_G} \tag{13-40}$$

and

$$c_{Ai} = c_{AL} + \frac{N_A}{k_L} \tag{13-41}$$

or

$$mc_{Ai} = mc_{AL} + \frac{mN_A}{k_L} \tag{13-42}$$

Since $p_{Ai} = mc_{Ai}$, Eq. 13–40 may be subtracted from Eq. 13–42, and

$$p_{AG} - \frac{N_A}{k_G} = mc_{AL} + \frac{mN_A}{k_L} \tag{13-43}$$

Since $mc_{AL} = p_A^*$,

$$p_{AG} - p_A^* = N_A \left(\frac{1}{k_G} + \frac{m}{k_L} \right) \tag{13-44}$$

Eliminating $p_{AG} - p_A^*$ between Eq. 13–38 and Eq. 13–44 gives the relation

$$\frac{1}{K_G} = \frac{1}{k_G} + \frac{m}{k_L} \tag{13-45}$$

which is equivalent to Eq. 13–34 for heat transfer. In a similar manner, an expression for the over-all liquid-phase mass-transfer coefficient can be derived:

$$\frac{1}{K_L} = \frac{1}{mk_G} + \frac{1}{k_L} \tag{13-46}$$

Combining Eq. 13–45 and Eq. 13–46 gives

$$K_L = mK_G \tag{13-47}$$

The over-all coefficient based on either phase may be determined and used in calculations. The interrelation given in Eq. 13–47 is analogous to the interrelation of over-all heat-transfer coefficients based on different areas. It is conventional to use the over-all mass-transfer coefficient based on the phase where the major resistance to mass transfer lies.

In many cases the major resistance to mass transfer lies in one phase. For example, slightly soluble gases like oxygen and nitrogen have very large values of m. For systems having a large value of m, Eq. 13–46 reduces to $K_L \cong k_L$. Absorption of a slightly soluble gas is therefore said to be "liquid-phase controlling." Similarly, for a very soluble gas, m

is very small and by Eq. 13–45, $K_G \cong k_G$. Therefore, the absorption of a very soluble gas is said to be "gas-phase controlling." Many systems are approximately either gas- or liquid-phase controlled. This approximation is made whenever possible, since calculations then require knowledge of only one individual phase coefficient. However, in certain systems resistance to mass transfer is appreciable in both phases, and both of the individual coefficients must be evaluated to calculate the mass-transfer rate. An example of a system where the resistance to mass transfer appears to be appreciable in both phases is the absorption of sulfur dioxide in water. The system has an additional complication of a chemical reaction between the sulfur dioxide and water in the liquid phase. The rate of such a chemical reaction may also influence the rate of absorption in such cases.

In cases of mass transfer where a pure phase is involved, no resistance to mass transfer exists in the pure phase. For example, in the humidification of air by water, the liquid is pure water and all resistance to mass transfer lies in the gas phase where there is a mixture of air and water vapor. If this concept is applied to mass transfer between two pure phases, one concludes that there is no resistance to mass transfer at all for such a case. An example of this would be the vaporization of water into pure steam, with no air present. In this case the rate of vaporization is determined by the rate at which heat is supplied to the liquid.

13–6. SIMULTANEOUS HEAT AND MASS TRANSFER

Simultaneous heat and mass transfer must be considered in vaporization and condensation operations. Operations of particular interest to mechanical engineers are humidification and dehumidification of air. This discussion will be limited to the air-water system, but the theory also applies to any system of a condensing and a noncondensing gas.

When air is humidified in contact with liquid water, the latent heat of the water which is vaporized must be supplied by the gas, the liquid, or an outside source. Conversely, in condensation, heat must be removed by one of these agents. A number of cases will be considered from a theoretical viewpoint.

Humidification where equilibrium is established between water and air which is at a constant temperature. This is the case of water-cooling towers in power-plant installations. A limited quantity of liquid water is contacted with a stream of air. The quantity of air is sufficiently large so that the air temperature and humidity do not change appreciably, and it is assumed that no heat is supplied from the surroundings. If the air and water are initially at the same temperature, vaporization will tend to lower the temperature of the remaining water. This will establish a temperature gradient and heat will be transferred from the bulk gas phase to the water. The water will decrease in temperature until it reaches the temperature where the heat transferred to the water just balances the heat removed in vaporization. This temperature T_{wb} is known as the wet-bulb temperature of the gas. The expression for the equality of the heat transferred to the water and the heat supplied for vaporization is

$$\frac{q}{A} = \lambda_M N_A / A \qquad (13\text{–}48)$$

where q/A = heat transferred per unit of interfacial area, in Btu/hr sq ft;
N_A/A = water vaporized, in lb-moles/hr sq ft;
λ_M = molar latent heat of vaporization evaluated at T_{wb}, the wet-bulb temperature, in Btu/lb-mole.

At equilibrium, the liquid phase will be at a uniform temperature T_{wb}. The rate of heat transfer is

$$\frac{q}{A} = h_G(T_G - T_{wb}) \qquad (13\text{–}49)$$

where h_G = gas-phase heat-transfer coefficient, in Btu/hr sq ft F;
T_G = dry-bulb temperature of the bulk of the gas, in F;
T_{wb} = temperature of the water at steady state, in F.

The resistance to heat and mass transfer lies only in the gas phase, since the liquid water is a pure phase, and the rate of mass transfer is

$$\frac{N_A}{A} = k_G(p_{wb} - p_G) \qquad (13\text{–}50)$$

where k_G = gas-phase mass-transfer coefficient, in lb-moles/hr sq ft atm;
p_{wb} = partial pressure of water vapor at the air-water interface; in this case it is the vapor pressure of water at temperature T_{wb}, in atm;
p_G = partial pressure of water vapor in the bulk gas phase, in atm.

Substitution of Eqs. 13–49 and 13–50 in Eq. 13–48 gives

$$p_{wb} - p_G = \frac{h_G}{\lambda_M k_G} (T_G - T_{wb}) \qquad (13\text{–}51)$$

Since mass and heat are transferred by similar mechanisms, one might expect the ratio h_G/k_G to be constant. It is essentially constant for the conditions usually encountered in humidification. Equation 13–51 relates the wet- and dry-bulb temperatures for any mixture of water vapor and air. It is often written in terms of humidity

$$Y_{wb} - Y_G = \frac{1}{\lambda} \frac{h_G}{k_G M_G P} (T_G - T_{wb}) \qquad (13\text{–}52)$$

where Y = absolute humidity of the air, in lb_m water vapor/lb_m dry air;

λ = specific latent heat of vaporization of water, in Btu/lb_m;

M_G = molecular weight of the gas phase—in this case air, in lb/lb-mole;

P = total pressure, in atm.

Equation 13–52 follows from Eq. 13–51 when the humidity is defined as

$$Y = \frac{M_w}{M_G} \frac{p_w}{P - p_w} \qquad (13\text{--}53)$$

where M_w = molecular weight of water;

p_w = partial pressure of water vapor in the gas phase.

Usually p_w is small compared to P and

$$Y = \frac{M_w p_w}{M_G P} \qquad (13\text{--}54)$$

may be substituted in Eq. 13–51 to obtain Eq. 13–52.

The group $h_G/k_G M_G P$ has been evaluated for a limited number of systems. Selected values are given in Table 13–3.

TABLE 13–3

VALUES OF $h_G/k_G M_G P$ FOR VARIOUS VAPORS IN AIR

Vapor	$h_G/k_G M_G P$
Water	0.26
Benzene	0.41
Carbon tetrachloride	0.44
Methyl alcohol	0.35

Where direct experimental values are not available, the j factor relation can be used to calculate the group. Rearrangement of Eq. 13–33 gives

$$\left(\frac{h_G}{k_G \rho \Re T}\right)\left(\frac{P}{p_{B_m}}\right) = c_p \left(\frac{\mu/\rho D_v}{c_p \mu/k}\right)^{0.67} \qquad (13\text{--}55)$$

where the physical properties are those of the gas. For most humidification problems $p_{B_m}/P \simeq 1$. From the perfect gas law, $\rho \Re T = M_G P$. Equation 13–55 then becomes

$$\frac{h_G}{k_G M_G P} = c_p \left(\frac{\mu/\rho D_v}{c_p \mu/k}\right)^{0.67} = c_p \left(\frac{\text{Sc}}{\text{Pr}}\right)^{0.67} \qquad (13\text{--}56)$$

Equation 13–56 gives a value of $h_G/k_G M_G P$ of 0.21 for the air-water system, compared to the experimental value of 0.26.

Humidification where equilibrium is established between water at a constant temperature and air. In this case the supply of air is limited and its temperature is lowered as heat is transferred to the liquid. This is the case usually approached in industrial air humidification towers when air is humidified and cooled. The final equilibrium temperature T_{as} is called the *adiabatic saturation temperature* and the operation is called *adiabatic humidification*. This implies that no heat is supplied to the air-water system from the surroundings.

An enthalpy balance can be written around the air and water, since adiabatic operation is assumed. Assume that the water enters at temperature T_{as}. The quantity of water supplied is large and the quantity vaporized is small so that its final temperature will also be T_{as}. Therefore, there is essentially no change in enthalpy of the water phase. An enthalpy balance for the gas phase gives semantically

$$\left(\begin{array}{c}\text{Enthalpy of entering dry air}\\ +\text{ water vapor}\end{array}\right) = \left(\begin{array}{c}\text{enthalpy of leaving dry air}\\ +\text{ water vapor}\end{array}\right)$$

or

$$\left(\begin{array}{c}\text{enthalpy of entering dry air}\\ -\text{enthalpy of leaving dry air}\end{array}\right) = \left(\begin{array}{c}\text{enthalpy of leaving water vapor}\\ -\text{enthalpy of entering water vapor}\end{array}\right)$$

Then

$$c_a(T_G - T_{as}) = -Y_G c_w(T_G - T_{as}) - \lambda(Y_G - Y_{as}) \qquad \textbf{(13–57)}$$

where c_a = specific heat of air, in Btu/lb_m;

$\quad c_w$ = specific heat of water, in Btu/lb_m;

$\quad T_G$ = initial air temperature, in F;

$\quad T_{as}$ = final equilibrium air temperature, in F;

$\quad Y_G$ = absolute humidity of the initial air, in lb_m H_2O/lb_m dry air;

$\quad Y_{as}$ = absolute humidity of the air at T_{as}, in lb_m H_2O/lb_m dry air.

Rearrangement of Eq. 13–57 gives

$$Y_{as} - Y_G = \frac{1}{\lambda}(c_a + Y_G c_w)(T_G - T_{as}) \qquad \textbf{(13–58)}$$

Comparison of Eq. 13–58 with Eq. 13–52 shows that if $h_G/k_G M_G P = (c_a + Y_G c_w)$, the adiabatic saturation temperature T_{as} is identical to the wet-bulb temperature T_{wb}. For air-water systems, the quantities are essentially equal and, therefore, $T_{as} = T_{wb}$. However, for any other vapor in air the temperatures are considerably different. The group $(c_a + Y_G c_w)$ is called the "humid heat," although a more appropriate term would be the humid heat capacity, which is designated by c_s. For the air-water vapor system $c_s = 0.24 + 0.45 Y_G$.

Example 13–3. A stream of air has a dry-bulb temperature of 120 F and a wet-bulb temperature of 90 F. What is the humidity of the air?

Solution: At 120 F, $Y_s = 0.08$ lb water vapor/lb dry air (from the saturation curve on a humidity chart, Ref. 4) and $\lambda = 1025$ Btu/lb. From Table 13–2, $h_G/k_G M_G P = 0.26$. With Eq. 13–52

$$Y_G = 0.080 - \frac{1(0.26)(120 - 90)}{1025} = 0.072 \text{ lb H}_2\text{O/lb dry air} \qquad Ans.$$

If the air has a dry-bulb temperature of 120 F and an adiabatic saturation temperature of 90 F, Y_G may be evaluated from Eq. 13–58

$$Y_G = \frac{Y_{as} - c_a(T_G - T_{as})/\lambda}{1 + c_w(T_G - T_{as})/\lambda} = \frac{0.080 - 0.24(120 - 90)/1025}{1 + 0.45(120 - 90)/1025}$$

$$= 0.072 \text{ lb H}_2\text{O/lb dry air} \qquad Ans.$$

Within the limits of accuracy of the calculation in Example 13–3, the answers are identical and $T_{as} = T_{wb}$ for water. This coincidence simplifies calculations for the air-water system. However, the adiabatic saturation temperature and the wet-bulb temperature are generally not equal for other systems.

Both of these cases are for conditions existing at the equilibrium of an air stream flowing past a water stream. In actual humidification and water-cooling equipment, equilibrium is only approached. An infinitely high tower would be required to give true equilibrium between the two streams. The wet-bulb temperature and the adiabatic saturation temperature may be considered as limiting values beyond which no equipment can go.

Adiabatic humidification—cooling. The calculation of the size of industrial equipment for adiabatically humidifying and cooling an air stream requires integration of the rate equation over the height or length of the equipment. Usually in such equipment the quantity of water recirculated is large, so that the water remains constant at the adiabatic saturation temperature of the air, T_{as}.

The rate equation for mass transfer can be rewritten in terms of humidity

$$\frac{N_A'}{A} = k_Y(Y_{as} - Y) \qquad (13\text{–}59)$$

where k_Y = gas-phase mass-transfer coefficient, in lb of water transferred /hr sq ft unit ΔY;

N_A' = mass flux, in lb/hr sq ft of transfer area;

Y = absolute humidity of the air, in lb H$_2$O/lb dry air.

Since the water temperature is constant at T_{as}, and since there is no resistance to mass transfer in a pure water phase, the driving potential is

($Y_{as} - Y$), in which Y_{as} is the saturated humidity of air at the water-air interface where the temperature is T_{as}.

To determine the rate of mass transfer, it is necessary to know the air-water interfacial area A. It is often impossible to estimate accurately the interfacial area available in industrial equipment. The water flows or is sprayed downward over wood slats or irregular packing to achieve a large interfacial area. This interfacial area may vary with liquid or gas flow rate. Because of the difficulty in estimating interfacial area for mass transfer, it is usually redefined as

$$A = aV = aSZ \qquad (13\text{--}60)$$

where A = total interfacial area for mass transfer in the humidification tower, in sq ft;

a = interfacial area per unit volume of tower packing, in sq ft/cu ft;

S = cross-sectional area of the tower, in sq ft;

Z = height of the tower, in ft.

Combination of Eqs. 13–59 and 13–60 gives

$$N_A' = k_Y a(Y_{as} - Y)SZ \qquad (13\text{--}61)$$

Since a is difficult to evaluate, it is combined with k_Y to form a new mass-transfer coefficient, $k_Y a$, which can be evaluated experimentally for a given tower packing and fluid flow rates.

Figure 13–6 is a schematic picture of a humidification tower. The water L_2 enters at the top of the tower and flows downward over packing to the bottom. The air G with a humidity Y_1 enters at the bottom of the tower, flows countercurrent to the water, and leaves the top of the tower at humidity Y_2. The mass velocity of air G is expressed as the lb dry air/hr sq ft of tower cross section; therefore it is constant through the tower, even though the humidity varies. The mass velocity of water L is given as lb water/hr sq ft of tower cross section, and it varies from L_2 at the top of the tower to L_1 at the bottom. A material balance on the water over the total height of the tower gives

$$L_2 - L_1 = G(Y_2 - Y_1) \qquad (13\text{--}62)$$

i.e., the rate of vaporization from the liquid phase equals the rate of mass transfer to the gas.

Consider a differential height dZ as shown in Fig. 13–6. The change in humidity in the height dZ is dY and therefore the rate of transfer of water to the gas per square foot of tower cross-section is given by the equation

$$dL = G\,dY \qquad (13\text{--}63)$$

Therefore, the rate of mass transfer across height dZ is

$$dN_A' = SGdY \qquad \text{(13–64)}$$

since G is based on a square foot of tower cross section.

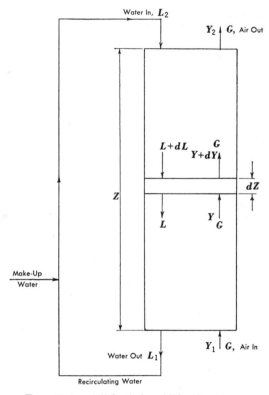

FIG. 13–6.   Adiabatic humidification tower.

Combining Eqs. 13–61 and 13–64 yields

$$GdY = k_Y a(Y_{as} - Y)dZ \qquad \text{(13–65)}$$

Integration from the bottom to the top of the tower, assuming $k_Y a$ is constant, gives

$$\int_0^Z dZ = \frac{G}{k_Y a} \int_{Y_1}^{Y_2} \frac{dY}{Y_{as} - Y}$$

$$Z = \frac{G}{k_Y a} \ln \frac{Y_{as} - Y_1}{Y_{as} - Y_2} \qquad \text{(13–66)}$$

Equation 13–66 may be used to calculate the height of an adiabatic humidification tower required to humidify air from Y_1 to Y_2. The coefficient $k_Y a$ must be evaluated experimentally or by an empirical correlation.

Example 13–4. Three thousand cu ft/min of air at 100 F and an absolute humidity of 0.003 lb water/lb dry air is to be adiabatically humidified and cooled in a packed tower by contacting it with 20 gal/min of recirculated water. The fluid flow rates dictate a cross-sectional area of 25 sq ft and the $k_Y a$ for the packing used has been determined as $k_Y a = 0.45\,GL^{0.2}$ (Ref. 8). (a) Calculate the height required to cool the air to 70 F (corresponding to a humidity of 0.016 lb/lb). (b) Calculate the height of tower required to cool the gas of (a) to 62 F (corresponding to a humidity of 0.019).

Solution: (a) First calculate $k_Y a$. Neglecting the humidity of the incoming air,

$$G = \left(3000\,\frac{\text{cu ft}}{\text{min}}\right)\left(\frac{60\,\text{min}}{1\,\text{hr}}\right)\left(\frac{492\,\text{R}}{560\,\text{R}}\right)\left(\frac{1\,\text{lb mole}}{359\,\text{cu ft at STP}}\right)\left(29\,\frac{\text{lb air}}{\text{lb mole air}}\right)\left(\frac{1}{25\,\text{sq ft}}\right)$$

= 513 lb dry air/hr sq ft of tower cross section

$$L = \left(20\,\frac{\text{gal}}{\text{min}}\right)\left(\frac{60\,\text{min}}{1\,\text{hr}}\right)\left(\frac{8.34\,\text{lb}_\text{m}\,\text{H}_2\text{O}}{\text{gal}}\right)\left(\frac{1}{25\,\text{sq ft}}\right)$$

= 400 lb$_\text{m}$/hr sq ft of tower cross section

$$k_Y a = (0.45)\,(513)(400)^{0.2}$$

Therefore

$$= 764\ \text{lb}_\text{m}/\text{hr cu ft unit } \Delta Y$$

The adiabatic saturation temperature T_{as} and humidity Y_{as} may be evaluated from Eq. 13–58 or from a humidity chart; $T_{as} = 62$ F and $Y_{as} = 0.019$. Use of Eq. 13–66 gives a height of

$$Z = \frac{513}{764}\,\ln\,\frac{0.019 - 0.003}{0.019 - 0.016} = 1.1\ \text{ft}$$

b) For cooling to 62 F,

$$Z = \frac{513}{764}\,\ln\,\frac{0.019 - 0.003}{0.019 - 0.019} = \infty \qquad\qquad Ans.$$

This shows that an infinitely tall tower is required to reach the equilibrium condition of saturation.

Adiabatic humidification is a simple case of the more general humidification problem. In adiabatic humidification the enthalpies of both the liquid and gas are nearly constant; but, in general, this is not the case and energy transfer across an enthalpy potential must be considered. An equation similar to Eq. 13–65 can be written with enthalpy driving forces and it may be integrated graphically. A discussion of this method, with examples, is given in Ref. 3. Use of the enthalpy potential is necessary whenever the enthalpy of either phase changes appreciably. For example, it would be required in the calculation of a water-cooling tower.

Dehumidification. Air conditioning often involves the removal of water vapor from air by direct cooling with cold water or by indirect cooling by contact with a cold metal wall. Although spray towers are widely used for direct cooling, little data have been published on their performance.

The contact of humid air with a cold metal wall results in mass and heat transfer from the air to the liquid layer flowing down the metal wall. The heat transferred across the liquid layer must equal the heat transferred across the gas film plus the latent heat given up at the gas-liquid interface

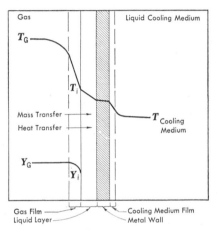

FIG. 13-7. Simultaneous heat and mass transfer in the dehumidification of air by indirect cooling.

on condensation of the mass transferred across the gas film. Figure 13-7 represents such a system. An expression for the heat transferred across a unit area is

$$h_L(T_i - T_L) = h_G(T_G - T_i) + \lambda k_Y(Y_G - Y_i) \qquad (13\text{-}67)$$

where T_i = temperature at the gas-liquid interface;
T_G = temperature in the bulk-gas phase;
T_L = temperature in the liquid layer;
h_L = liquid-phase heat-transfer coefficient;
h_G = gas-phase heat-transfer coefficient;
k_Y = gas-phase mass-transfer coefficient.

The use of this equation for dehumidification calculations involves a trial-and-error procedure, since the interface conditions are not known. The method of calculation is outlined in Ref. 2.

13–7. MASS-TRANSFER EQUIPMENT

The theoretical relationships which have been discussed can be applied to the design of industrial equipment. However, the calculations are usually complex and are beyond the scope of this brief discussion. Detailed design methods and illustrations of industrial equipment can be found in Refs. 4, 5, 6, and 7.

Mass-transfer equipment can be classified as batch or continuous flow. The tendency in industry has been toward continuous-flow equipment, where steady state is reached and material is fed and withdrawn continuously. Calculation of batch equipment involves the consideration of transient mass transfer.

Continuous-flow equipment can be further classified as to whether it is stage-contact or continuous-contact. In stage-contacting, the two phases are brought together, mass is transferred between the phases, and finally the phases are mechanically separated. In continuous countercurrent stage-contacting, the resultant two phases are then sent in opposite directions to other stages for further contacting. Usually calculations are based on the assumption that the two phases leaving a stage are in equilibrium with each other. The number of *equilibrium stages* required to give the specified purity and recovery of product is determined from equilibrium and stoichiometric relationships. In such a calculation the *rate* of mass transfer is not considered, since it is assumed that transfer was rapid enough to establish equilibrium.

In an *actual* stage, for example a plate in a distillation column, the two phases are not usually in contact long enough to reach equilibrium. Therefore, more *actual* stages are required than *equilibrium* stages. A *stage efficiency* is applied to the number of equilibrium stages calculated to obtain the number of actual stages required. Stage efficiencies depend on many factors, including the physical configuration of the equipment, the phase-flow rates, and the rate of mass transfer. Experimental data on stage efficiencies for many systems are available. Correlations have been made on certain systems, such as petroleum distillation columns. (Refs. 5 and 7.)

An example of a continuous countercurrent stage-contacting device is a multiple-stage petroleum distillation column. A typical crude petroleum distillation column is shown with its accessory equipment in Fig. 13–8. A schematic diagram of the column, Fig. 13–9, shows the individual stages, the crude oil intake, and the points of withdrawal of the various products. The withdrawn products increase in volatility from the bottom to the top of the tower. Since the less volatile components may decompose when heated to their boiling points at atmospheric pressure, the lower part of the column may be operated at less than atmospheric pressure to reduce the temperatures required for vaporization. The column shown in Fig.

13–8 has been split into two parts which are placed side by side to reduce the over-all height of the unit.

In equipment such as packed absorption, distillation, or humidification towers the contact between the liquid and gas is *continuous* through the

Fig. 13–8. Crude petroleum distillation unit. The taller tower in the center of the picture separates the lighter components of the crude petroleum. It is the upper part of the column shown in Fig. 13–9. The shorter tower at the left separates the heavier components and is represented by the lower part of the column shown in Fig. 13–9. Also of interest is the group of large shell-and-tube heat exchangers to the right of the taller tower. They are used to cool the product streams. (Courtesy of Standard Oil Company of California and California Research Corporation)

equipment. There is no mechanical separation of phases as occurs in stage equipment. For this case, differential forms of the rate equations are integrated over the height of the tower to determine the total mass transfer, as illustrated in Sec. 13–6. Problems encountered in calculating packed towers include variation in mass-transfer coefficients with flow rates and tower packing size and shape, unknown interfacial area for mass transfer, and variations in the flow pattern through the equipment. A natural-draft water-cooling tower is shown in Fig. 13–10. Water-cooling towers are used to conserve water by permitting reuse of cooling water. Warm water is distributed across the top of the tower. It flows downward through wood-slat gratings, continuously contacting air which is flowing upward by

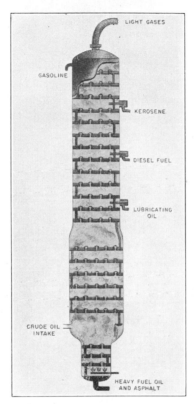

FIG. 13–9. Crude petroleum distillation column. (Courtesy of Standard Oil Company of California and California Research Corporation)

natural convection. As the water contacts the air, it humidifies the air and is cooled.

In many cases existing mass-transfer equipment is evaluated to determine its performance under new operating conditions or for a new separation. The principles involved are identical with those required for design of new equipment.

Fig. 13–10. Natural-draft water-cooling tower. (Courtesy of Standard Oil Company of California and California Research Corporation)

REFERENCES

1. W. L. Badger and J. T. Banchero, *Introduction to Chemical Engineering.* (New York: McGraw-Hill Book Company, Inc., 1955.)

2. A. P. Colburn and O. A. Hougen, *Ind. Eng. Chem.*, Vol. 26 (1934), pp. 1178–1182.

3. H. S. Mickley, *Chem. Eng. Prog.*, Vol. 45 (1949).

4. J. H. Perry, Ed., *Chemical Engineers' Handbook*, 3d ed. (New York: McGraw-Hill Book Company, Inc., 1950.)

5. C. S. Robinson and E. R. Gilliland, *Elements of Fractional Distillation*, 4th ed. (New York: McGraw-Hill Book Company, Inc., 1950.)

6. T. K. Sherwood and R. L. Pigford, *Absorption and Extraction*, 2d ed. (New York: McGraw-Hill Book Company, Inc., 1952.)

7. R. E. Treybal, *Mass Transfer Operations.* (New York: McGraw-Hill Book Company, Inc., 1955.)

8. F. Yoshida and T. Janaka, *Ind. Eng. Chem.*, Vol. 43 (1951), p. 1467.

PROBLEMS

13-1. An open circular tank 10 ft in diameter which contains ethanol is exposed to the open air at 77 F and atmospheric pressure. Assuming that there is a stagnant layer of air 6 in. thick over the surface of the ethanol, calculate the weight of ethanol lost by evaporation in 24 hr. Vapor pressure of ethanol at 77 F = 58 mm Hg.

13-2. Calculate the rate of diffusion of ammonia across a water film 0.1 in. thick at 77 F. The concentration of ammonia is 2 per cent (by weight) on one side of the film and 1 per cent (by weight) on the other side.

13-3. Calculate the mass-transfer coefficient for the vaporization of water into air in a wetted-wall column under the following conditions.

Column diameter = 1.0 in.

Air and water temperature = 77 F

Average partial pressure of water vapor in air = 5 mm Hg

Total pressure = 753 mm Hg

Air flow rate = 2 cu ft/min

Calculate the effective film thickness for mass transfer.

13-4. Air at 100 C flows over a streamlined naphthalene body. Naphthalene sublimes into air and its vapor pressure at 100 C is 20 mm Hg. The heat-transfer coefficient for this system was previously found to be 3 Btu/hr sq ft F. The mass diffusivity of naphthalene vapor in air at 100 C is 0.32 sq ft/hr. The concentration of naphthalene in the bulk air stream is negligibly small. Calculate the mass-transfer coefficient and the mass flux for the system.

13-5. Ammonia is being absorbed from air by water at 77 F in an absorption column. At a point in the column the following conditions exist:

k_L = 0.95 lb-mole/hr sq ft (lb-mole/cu ft)

k_G = 0.15 lb-mole/hr sq ft atm

Gas composition = 1 per cent ammonia (by volume)

Total pressure = 1500 mm Hg

Liquid composition = 0.02 lb-moles NH_3/cu ft

p_{NH_3} = 0.38 c_{NH_3} at 77 F for dilute solutions

Calculate: (a) over-all gas-phase mass-transfer coefficient; (b) over-all liquid-phase mass-transfer coefficient; (c) percentage of total resistance to mass transfer which lies in the gas phase; (d) interfacial compositions of both phases; (e) mass flux of ammonia; (f) effective film thickness for each phase.

13-6. Air at 200 F and 1 atm has a humidity of 0.12 lb H_2O/lb dry air. Calculate: (a) the wet-bulb temperature; (b) the adiabatic saturation temperature.

13-7. Air at 100 F and 1 atm contains carbon tetrachloride vapor such that the wet-bulb temperature is 85 F. What is the adiabatic saturation temperature? At 100 F the vapor pressure of carbon tetrachloride is 200 mm Hg and the latent heat of vaporization is 83 Btu/lb.

13-8. Air at 120 F dry bulb and 70 F wet bulb is to be cooled and humidified adiabatically in a tower filled with packing which is the same as that in Example 13-4. The tower has a cross-sectional area of 17 sq ft. Air is supplied at a rate of 110 lb/min and water at 10 gal/min. Calculate and plot the height of tower required to cool the air to final temperatures between 70 F and 80 F.

13-9. Derive expressions for the liquid and gas phase mass-transfer coefficients for equimolar counterdiffusion. How do they differ from those for diffusion through a stagnant film?

13-10. Derive Eq. 13-22a by dimensionless analysis.

13-11. Derive Eq. 13-23 by dimensionless analysis.

13-12. Derive Eq. 13-46.

Appendix I

NOMENCLATURE

Symbol	Quantity	Preferred Units

LETTER SYMBOLS

a velocity of sound — ft/sec

a thermal diffusivity $= k/c\rho$ — sq ft/hr

a interfacial area per unit volume of tower packing in Chapter 13 — sq ft/cu ft

A area; A_c, cross-sectional area; A_p, projected area of a body normal to the direction of flow; A_q, area through which rate of heat flow is q; A_s, surface area; A_o, outside surface area; A_i, inside surface area; $\bar{A}$, logarithmic mean area defined by Eq. 3–8 — sq ft

A azimuth of the sun — deg

b breadth or width — ft

c specific heat; c_p, specific heat at constant pressure; c_v, specific heat at constant volume; c_s, humid heat capacity in Chapter 13 — Btu/lb$_m$ F

c_A concentration of component A in Chapter 13 — lb-moles/cu ft

C constant

C thermal capacity — Btu/F

C hourly heat capacity rate in Chapter 11; C_c, hourly heat capacity rate of colder fluid in a heat exchanger; C_h, hourly heat capacity rate of warmer fluid in a heat exchanger — Btu/hr F

C_e electrical capacitance — farads

C_D total drag coefficient

C_f skin friction coefficient; C_{fx}, local value of C_f at distance x from leading edge; $\bar{C}_f$, average value of C_f defined by Eq. 6–20

D diameter; D_H, hydraulic diameter; D_o, outside diameter; D_i, inside diameter — ft

D_v mass diffusivity — sq ft/hr

e base of Natural or Napierian logarithm

E electric potential — volt

E emissive power of a radiating body; E_b, emissive power

521

Symbol	Quantity	Preferred Units

of a black body; E_λ, monochromatic emissive power per micron at wavelength λ — Btu/hr sq ft

ε heat exchanger effectiveness defined by Eq. 11–17

f Fanning friction coefficient for flow through a pipe or a duct, defined by Eq. 8–12

f' friction coefficient for flow over banks of tubes, defined by Eq. 9–11

F force — lb$_f$

F_T temperature factor defined by Eq. 5–33

$F_{1\text{-}2}$ geometrical shape factor for radiation from one black body to another defined by Eq. 5–19

$\mathfrak{F}_{1\text{-}2}$ geometric shape and emissivity factor for radiation from one gray body to another

g acceleration of gravity — ft/sec^2 or ft/hr^2

g_c dimensional conversion factor—32.2 ft lb$_m$/lb$_f$ sec^2 or 4.18×10^8 ft lb$_m$/lb$_f$ hr^2

G mass velocity or flow rate per unit area $(G = \rho V)$ — lb$_m$/hr sq ft

G irradiation incident upon unit surface in unit time — Btu/hr sq ft

h enthalpy per unit mass — Btu/lb$_m$

$\bar{h}$ combined unit-surface conductance, $\bar{h} = \bar{h}_c + \bar{h}_r$; h_b, unit-surface conductance of a boiling liquid, defined by Eq. 10–1; h_c, local unit convective conductance; $\bar{h}_c$, average unit convective conductance; $\bar{h}_r$, average unit conductance for radiation — Btu/hr sq ft F

h_{fg} latent heat of condensation or evaporation — Btu/lb$_m$

h_G gas-phase heat-transfer coefficient in Chapter 13 — Btu/hr sq ft F

h_L liquid-phase heat-transfer coefficient in Chapter 13 — Btu/hr sq ft F

H total hour angle from noon to sunrise or sunset — deg

i angle between sun direction and surface normal in Chapter 5 — deg

i electric current flow rate — amp

I intensity of radiation; I_λ, intensity per micron at wavelength λ — Btu/hr unit solid angle

J radiosity — Btu/hr sq ft

k thermal conductivity; k_s, thermal conductivity of a solid; k_f, thermal conductivity of a fluid evaluated at the mean film temperature — Btu/hr ft F

k_G mass-transfer coefficient for the gas phase defined by Eq. 13–18 — lb-moles/hr sq ft atm

k_L mass-transfer coefficient for the liquid phase defined by Eq. 13–20 — lb-moles/hr sq ft (lb-moles/cu ft)

K thermal conductance; K_k, thermal conductance for conduction heat transfer; K_c, thermal convective conductance; K_r, thermal conductance for radiation heat transfer — Btu/hr F

K_e electrical conductance — amp/volt

Symbol	Quantity	Preferred Units

K_G over-all mass-transfer coefficient based on the gas phase | lb-moles/hr sq ft atm

K_L over-all mass-transfer coefficient based on the liquid phase | lb-moles/hr sq ft (lb-mole/cu ft)

log logarithm to the base 10

ln logarithm to the base e

l length, general | ft or in.

L length along a heat flow path or characteristic length of a body | ft or in.

L_f latent heat of solidification | Btu/lb

m mass flow rate | lb_m/sec or lb_m/hr

m Henry's law constant in Chapter 13 | atm cu ft/lb-mole

M mass | lb_m

m_A mass of gas A in Chapter 13 | lb-mole

M_G molecular weight of the gas phase in Chapter 13 | lb/lb-mole

N number in general; number of tubes, etc.

p static pressure; p_c, critical pressure; p_A, partial pressure of gas A in Chapter 13 | psi/or lb_f/sq ft or atm

P wetted perimeter | ft

P total pressure in Chapter 13

q rate of heat flow; q_k, rate of heat flow by conduction; q_r, rate of heat flow by radiation; q_c, rate of heat flow by convection; q_b, rate of heat flow by nucleate boiling | Btu/hr

$\tilde{q}$ rate of heat flow per unit area or heat flux | Btu/hr sq ft

$\dot{q}$ rate of heat generation per unit volume | Btu/hr cu ft

Q quantity of heat | Btu

$\dot{Q}$ volumetric rate of fluid flow | cu ft/hr

Q_e electric charge of condenser | coulomb

r radius; r_H, hydraulic radius; r_i, inner radius; r_o, outer radius | ft

R thermal resistance; R_c, thermal resistance to convection heat transfer; R_k, thermal resistance to conduction heat transfer; R_r, thermal resistance to radiation heat transfer | hr F/Btu

R_e electrical resistance | ohm

R_T temperature recovery factor defined by Eq. 12–3

$\mathfrak{R}$ perfect gas constant | 1545.4 ft lb/lb-mole F or 0.730 cu ft atm/lb-mole F

s molecular speed ratio

S cross-sectional area of mass-transfer tower in Chapter 13 | sq ft

S shape factor for conduction heat flow

S_L distance between centerlines of tubes in adjacent longitudinal rows | ft

S_T distance between centerlines of tubes in adjacent transverse rows | ft

T temperature; T_b, temperature of bulk of fluid; T_f, mean film temperature; T_s, surface temperature; T_∞, temperature of fluid far removed from heat source or sink; T_m, mean bulk temperature of fluid flowing in a duct; T_{abs}, temperature on absolute scale; T_s, temperature at surface of a wall; T_{sv}, temperature of saturated vapor; T_{sl}, temperature of a saturated liquid; T_{fr}, freezing temperature; T_l, liquid temperature; T_o, total temperature; T_{as}, adiabatic wall temperature or adiabatic saturation temperature in Chapter 13; T_{wb}, wet bulb temperature .... F or R

u internal energy per unit mass .... Btu/lb$_m$

u time average velocity in x direction; u', instantaneous fluctuating x component of velocity; u_∞, free stream velocity .... ft/sec or ft/hr

U over-all unit conductance, over-all heat-transfer coefficient, or over-all transmittance .... Btu/hr sq ft F

v specific volume .... cu ft/lb$_m$

v time average velocity in y direction; v', instantaneous fluctuating y component of velocity .... ft/sec or ft/hr

V volume .... cu ft

V average velocity; V_l, velocity of light; V_∞, free stream or flight velocity .... ft/sec or ft/hr

x distance from the leading edge; x_c, critical distance from the leading edge where flow becomes turbulent ... ft

x coordinate

y coordinate

y distance from a solid boundary measured in direction normal to surface .... ft

Y absolute humidity in Chapter 13 .... lb$_m$/lb$_m$

z zenith distance .... deg

z coordinate

Z ratio of hourly heat capacity rates in heat exchangers

Z height of mass-transfer equipment .... ft

GREEK LETTERS

α absorptivity for radiation; α_λ, monochromatic absorptivity at wavelength λ

α thermal accommodation coefficient defined by Eq. 12–28

β temperature coefficient of volume expansion 1/F

β_k temperature coefficient of thermal conductivity 1/F

γ specific heat ratio, c_p/c_r

Γ body force per unit mass .... lb$_f$/lb$_m$

Γ_c mass rate of flow of condensate per unit breadth $= m/\pi D$ for a vertical tube .... lb$_m$/hr ft

δ boundary layer thickness; δ_h, hydrodynamic boundary layer thickness; δ_{th}, thermal boundary layer thickness; δ_m', effective boundary layer thickness for mass transfer ... ft

Symbol	Quantity	Preferred Units

δ solar declination in Chapter 5 — deg
Δ difference between values
ϵ emissivity for radiation; ϵ_λ, monochromatic emissivity at wavelength λ; ϵ_ϕ, emissivity in direction of ϕ
ϵ_H thermal eddy diffusivity — sq ft/hr or sq ft/sec
ϵ_M momentum eddy diffusivity — sq ft/hr or sq ft/sec
ζ ratio of thermal to hydrodynamic boundary layer thickness, δ_{th}/δ_h
η_f fin efficiency
θ time — hr or sec
λ wavelength; λ_{max}, wavelength at which monochromatic emissivity $E_{b\lambda}$ is a maximum (see Eq. 5–6) — micron
λ latent heat of vaporization in Chapter 13; λ_M, molar latent heat of vaporization — Btu/lb$_m$ or Btu/lb-mole
λ molecular mean free path in Chapter 12 — ft
μ absolute viscosity — lb$_m$/ft sec or lb$_m$/ft hr
ν kinematic viscosity, μ/ρ — sq ft/hr or sq ft/sec
ν_r frequency of radiation — 1/sec
ρ mass density, $1/v$; ρ_l, density of liquid; ρ_v, density of vapor — lb$_m$/cu ft
ρ reflectivity for radiation
τ shearing stress; τ_s, shearing stress at surface; τ_w, shear at wall of a tube or a duct — lb$_f$/sq ft
τ transmissivity for radiation
σ Stefan-Boltzmann constant — Btu/hr sq ft R^4
σ surface tension — lb$_f$/ft
ϕ phase lag angle — radians
ϕ latitude of location in Chapter 5 — deg
ψ inclination from horizontal — deg
ω angular velocity — 1/sec
ω solid angle — steradian

DIMENSIONLESS GROUPS[1]

Bi   Biot number $= \bar{h}L/k_s$ or $\bar{h}r_o/k_s$

Fo   Fourier modulus $= a\theta/L^2$ or $a\theta/r_o^2$

Gz   Graetz number $= mc_p/k_f L$

Gr   Grashof number $= \beta g L^3 \Delta T/\nu$

j Colburn j factor for heat transfer $= (\text{Nu}/\text{Re Pr})\, \text{Pr}^{\frac{2}{3}}$; j_M, j factor for mass transfer $= (\text{Sh}/\text{Re Sc})\, \text{Sc}^{\frac{2}{3}}$

K   Knudsen number $= \lambda/L$

M   Mach number $= V/a$

Nu   Nusselt number $= h_c L/k_f$; Nu$_x$, local value of Nu at point x

$\overline{\text{Nu}}$ average value of Nu over surface $= \bar{h}_c\, L/k_f$; $\overline{\text{Nu}_D}$, diameter Nusselt number $= \bar{h}_c\, D/k_f$

Pe   Peclet number $= \text{Re Pr}$

Pr   Prandtl number $= c_p\mu/k_f$ or ν/a

Re   Reynolds number $= V\rho L/\mu$; Re_x, local value of Re at a distance x from leading edge; Re_D, diameter Reynolds number; Re_b, bubble Reynolds number

θ Boundary Fourier modulus $= \bar{h}^2 a\theta/k_s^2$

Sh   Sherwood number $= k_G\mathfrak{R}T p_{Bm}L$

Sc   Schmidt number $\mu/\rho D_v$

St   Stanton number $= h_c/\rho V c_p$ or Nu/RePr

[1] The symbols used in this book for the dimensionless groups are generally in accordance with present day engineering usage, but differ slightly from those recommended recently by some committees of engineering societies who propose to use a capital N to denote any dimensionless group and then to identify the specific group by a subscript, e.g., N_{Nu} instead of Nu. It is, however, necessary to distinguish between local and average quantities and identify a significant length dimension as well as a temperature at which physical properties are to be evaluated. If these characteristics are indicated in the usual manner, that is, by sub- and superscripts attached to the symbol identifying the dimensionless group, combinations of symbols become clumsy and difficult to read. In order to avoid the use of a double subscript notation, the author decided, although not without serious misgivings, to omit the capital N from the symbols denoting the dimensionless groups.

MISCELLANEOUS

$a > b$	a greater than b	$\propto$	proportional sign
$a \gg b$	a much greater than b	$\simeq$	approximately equal sign
$a < b$	a smaller than b	∞	infinity sign
$a \ll b$	a much smaller than b	Σ	summation sign

Appendix II

UNITS, DIMENSIONS, AND CONVERSION FACTORS

Numerical calculations in heat transfer, as in all other branches of engineering, require a consistent system of units. In the field of heat transfer a great variety of different units are encountered because contributions, to this field have been made not only by engineers, but also by physicists and chemists of various countries. Many of the physical properties measured in the laboratory have been reported in CGS (cm-gm-sec) units, but engineers in this country generally use the engineering or technical system of units. Before one can proceed with numerical calculations, it is absolutely necessary to express all quantities in a consistent system. Several systems exist, each of them is equally correct. The choice is largely a matter of convenience but confusion between systems must be avoided.

A dimension is a name describing a geometrical or physical property which can be measured, observed or defined. It would be possible to assign a separate dimension to each property of interest, but it is more convenient to limit the number of dimensions to a few basic or primary dimensions and to express all other dimensions in terms of these fundamental quantities. The number of primary dimensions must of course be sufficient to express all derived or secondary dimensions in terms of them.

The physicist usually selects length, time and mass as his primary set of dimensions. In engineering, force and temperature are generally added to this set, and in heat transfer the dimension of the energy in transit due to a temperature difference, i.e., heat, is also included.

Dimensions differ from units of measurement. Dimensions describe a property *qualitatively* while units give a *quantitative* specification. For example, the length of a bar may be specified in feet, inches, or centimeters. All of these units are a quantitative specification of the primary dimension of length, L.

To familiarize the reader with the dimensions and units used in heat transfer, relations between some of the primary dimensions and the units associated with them will be briefly reviewed.

Time, θ, is the dimension of duration. The basic engineering unit is the second (sec), but in heat-transfer work the hour (hr) is frequently used.

Length, L, is the dimension of distance. The basic engineering unit is the foot (ft).

Mass, M, is the dimension of quantity of matter. The basic engineering unit is the pound (lb_m).

Temperature, T, is the dimension which describes the thermal potential of a system. It must be referred to an arbitrary datum, being somewhat analogous to the height above some reference level for gravitational action. The basic engineering unit is the degree Fahrenheit (F), which is closely equal to 1/180 of the temperature difference between the boiling and freezing temperature level of water at atmospheric pressure. For radiation phenomena the temperature is measured above absolute zero and is expressed in degrees Rankine (R). One Rankine degree equals one Fahrenheit degree, but the relation between the absolute values of the Fahrenheit and Rankine scales is

$$\text{degrees Rankine} = 459.7 + \text{degrees Fahrenheit}$$

Force, F, is the dimension describing the action which tends to produce a change in the motion of a body. The basic engineering unit is the standard pound (lb_f) force, defined as the force necessary to support one pound mass under standard gravity conditions, corresponding to a gravitational force which accelerates one pound (lb_m) mass at the rate of 32.1739 ft/sec^2. Misunderstandings often arise because the work pound is used to denote the fundamental units of both mass and force. It is obvious of course that a pound of mass is an entirely different sort of thing from a pound force.

Heat, Q, is the dimension of energy in transit by virtue of a temperature difference. The basic engineering unit is the British thermal unit or Btu, defined as the amount of heat required to raise the temperature of one pound mass of water at atmospheric pressure from 59.5 to 60.5 F.

Since heat is a form of energy it can be expressed in terms of its mechanical equivalent by means of the first law of thermodynamics. For a system whose state is not changed during a process the amount of heat added to the system Q must equal the work done by the system W, or

$$W = JQ$$

where J is a dimensional conversion factor. Since work has the dimensions FL, J must have the dimensions FL/Q. For the system of units given here the experimentally measured value of the energy conversion factor J is

$$J = 778.161 \text{ ft-lb}_f/\text{Btu}$$

which is often called "the mechanical equivalent of heat."

Newton's second law of motion relates the independent physical quantities, force, mass, length and time, just as the first law of thermodynamics relates force, length, and heat. According to the second law of motion the net force F acting on a body of mass M is proportional to the product of the mass M and the acceleration a, or

$$F = \frac{1}{g_c} Ma$$

where g_c is an experimentally determined constant whose dimensions are always $ML/F\theta^2$, but whose magnitude depends on the units of force, mass, length, and time as shown in the following tabulation.

Mass	Length	Time	Force	g_c
lb$_m$	ft	sec	lb$_f$	32.1739 lb$_m$ ft/lb$_f$ sec^2
slug	ft	sec	lb$_f$	1.0 slug ft/lb$_f$ sec^2
slug	ft	hr	lb$_f$	1.296×10^7 slug ft/lb$_f$ hr^2
lb$_m$	ft	sec	poundal	1.0 lb$_m$ ft/poundal sec^2
g	cm	sec	dyne	1.0 g-cm/dyne-sec^2

In the engineering system which is used in this text and is shown in the first line of the tabulation, g_c equals 32.1739 lb$_m$ ft/lb$_f$ sec^2, but a value of 32.2 is a satisfactory approximation in practice. It is important to note that g_c is a universal constant entirely different from the acceleration of gravity which has the dimensions L/θ^2 and whose numerical value depends on the location.

Once Newton's second law of motion, including the proportionality constant g_c, is known, it is possible to redefine any one of the units of measure in terms of the other three, thus reducing the number of primary quantities by one. For example, if the mass M is divided by g_c, we obtain a new mass unit, the *slug*. In equation form we have then

$$M' = \frac{M}{g_c}$$

where M' is the mass of the body expressed in slugs. The slug has the dimension $F\theta^2/L$ in a force-time-length system. The equation of motion becomes in this case

$$F = M'a$$

and we note that now the dimension of mass has been eliminated as a primary dimension.

TABLE OF CONVERSION FACTORS

Length:	1 in. = 0.08333 ft
	1 cm = 0.03281 ft
	1 mile = 5280 ft
	1 μ (micron) = 3.281×10^{-6} ft
	1 A (angstrom unit) = 10^{-8} cm
Mass:	1 kg (kilogram) = 2.205 lb_m
	1 g (gram) $\quad$ = 2.205×10^{-3} lb_m
	1 slug $\qquad$ = 32.1739 lb_m
Force:	1 poundal $\quad$ = 0.03108 lb_f
	1 dyne $\qquad$ = 2.248×10^{-6} lb_f
	1 kg $\qquad$ = 2.205 lb_f
Energy:	1 ft-lb_f $\quad$ = 0.001285 Btu
	1 kw-hr (kilowatt-hour) = 3413 Btu
	1 hp (horsepower) = 2544 Btu
	1 kcal (kilocalorie) = 3.968 Btu
	1 joule $\qquad$ = 9.478×10^{-4} Btu
Heat flow rate per unit area:	1 cal/sec sq cm = 13,272 Btu/hr sq ft
	1 watt/sq cm $\quad$ = 3171 Btu/hr sq ft
	1 cal/hr sq cm $\quad$ = 3.687 Btu/hr sq ft
Pressure:	1 atm $\qquad$ = 2116 psf
	1 dyne/sq cm $\quad$ = 0.00209 psf
	1 cm Hg $\qquad$ = 27.85 psf
	1 in. Hg $\qquad$ = 70.73 psf
	1 in. water $\qquad$ = 5.20 psf
	1 ft water $\qquad$ = 62.43 psf
Density:	1 gm/cu cm = 62.43 lb_m/cu ft
	1 lb_m/gallon = 7.481 lb_m/cu ft
	1 lb_m/cu in. = 1728 lb_m/cu ft
Temperature:	1 R (degree Rankine) $\quad$ = 1 F (degree Fahrenheit)
	1 C (degree Centigrade) = 1.8 F
	1 K (degree Kelvin) $\quad$ = 1.8 F
Specific energy per degree:	1 cal/g C $\qquad$ = 1 Btu/lb_m F
Thermal conductivity:	1 cal/sec sq cm (C/cm) = 241.9 Btu/hr sq ft (F/ft)
	1 watts/sq cm (C/cm) $\quad$ = 57.79 Btu/hr sq ft (F/ft)
	1 Btu/hr sq ft (F/in.) $\quad$ = 0.08333 Btu/hr sq ft (F/ft)
Unit thermal conductance:	1 cal/sec sq cm C = 7373 Btu/hr sq ft F
	1 watt/sq cm C $\quad$ = 1761 Btu/hr sq ft F
	1 cal/hr sq cm C $\quad$ = 2.048 Btu/hr sq ft F
Viscosity:	1 cp (centipoise) = 0.000672 lb_m/sec ft
	1 cp = 2.42 lb_m/hr ft
	1 lb_f sec/sq ft = 32.174 lb_m/sec ft
Volume:	1 gal (U.S.) = 0.1337 cu ft

NOTE: To convert a given quantity from one set of units to another:

1. Write after the magnitude of the quantity the names of the units in which it is measured.

2. Replace each name by its equivalent in the new units, and arithmetically combine all numbers in the new expression.

For example, to change the density of water from slugs per cubic foot into pounds-mass per cubic foot, we have (to three significant figures)

$$\rho = 1.94 \text{ slugs/cu ft} = (1.94 \text{ slugs/cu ft}) (32.2 \text{ } lb_m/\text{slug})$$
$$= 1.94 \times 32.2 \text{ } lb_m/\text{cu ft} = 62.4 \text{ } lb_m/\text{cu ft}$$

$$1 \frac{BTU}{HR} = 2.93 \times 10^{-4} \text{ KWatts}$$

Alternately, the dimension of force can be eliminated as a primary dimension by defining a new force unit, the poundal, and writing

$$F' = Fg_c$$

The poundal F' has the dimension ML/θ^2 in a mass-time-length system and the equation of motion becomes

$$F' = Ma$$

When one is in doubt which system of dimensions and units is used in a reference, it is suggested that all of the dimensions and units in one of the equations be written out and the equation checked dimensionally. The procedure is illustrated in Sec. 6–6.

In heat transfer calculations it is most convenient to express all quantities in terms of feet, hours (or seconds), Btu, pound-mass, and degrees Fahrenheit. This choice of units does not cause trouble until one encounters problems in which fluid dynamics is involved. In fluid dynamics both force and mass are used as primary dimensions. The density of fluids is commonly expressed in pounds-mass per cubic foot, but the viscosity is often given in pound-force-second per square foot. The pressure drop and the shear are always given in pound-force units. Since all physical properties in this book, including the viscosity, are expressed in pound-mass units, it is necessary to include the conversion factor g_c in equations derived from Newton's second law.

The Table of Conversion Factors will be helpful in converting the units of a given quantity into the units used in this text.

Appendix III

The following tables have been compiled to facilitate the solution of the problems at the end of each chapter and are not intended to take the place of a handbook. Whenever answers to problems are given, they have been obtained with the aid of these tables.

Table A–1 gives the properties of metals and alloys. Table A–2 lists physical properties of nonmetals such as insulating and building materials. Table A–3 presents the property values of several gases at atmospheric pressure, of some liquids, and of three liquid metals. The property values have been extracted from various sources. The bibliography following Table A–3 lists these sources with the exception of some manufacturers' catalogs which may not be readily available. The reader interested in additional information on physical properties should consult the publications listed in the bibliography.

In Table A–4 the radiation functions described in Chapter 5 are tabulated. Tables A–5 and A–6 list the dimensions of tubes and steel pipes respectively. It should be noted that the schedule number is now used exclusively to characterize the pipe-wall thickness which was previously designated by "standard" or "extra strong."

Table A–7 contains selected physical properties of the atmosphere at altitudes up to 900,000 ft. The values above 300,000 are likely to be revised at the end of the International Geophysical Year.

TABLE A–1

THERMAL CONDUCTIVITY k, SPECIFIC HEAT c, DENSITY ρ, AND THERMAL DIFFUSIVITY a
OF METALS AND ALLOYS

MATERIAL	k (Btu/hr ft F)				c (Btu/lb$_m$F)	ρ(lb$_m$/cu ft)	a (sq ft/hr)
	32 F	212 F	572 F	932 F	32 F	32 F	32 F
Metals							
Aluminum..........	117	119	133	155	0.208	169	3.33
Bismuth............	4.9	3.9	....	....	0.029	612	0.28
Copper, pure........	224	218	212	207	0.091	558	4.42
Gold..............	169	170	....	....	0.030	1203	4.68
Iron, pure..........	35.8	36.6	....	....	0.104	491	0.70
Lead..............	20.1	19	18	....	0.030	705	0.95
Magnesium.........	91	92	....	....	0.232	109	3.60
Mercury...........	4.8	....	....	....	0.033	849	0.17
Nickel.............	34.5	34	32	....	0.103	555	0.60
Silver.............	242	238	....	....	0.056	655	6.6
Tin...............	36	34	....	....	0.054	456	1.46
Zinc..............	65	64	59	....	0.091	446	1.60
Alloys							
Admiralty metal.....	65	64					
Brass, 70% Cu,							
30% Zn..........	56	60	66	....	0.092	532	1.14
Bronze, 75% Cu,							
25% Sn..........	15	....	....	....	0.082	540	0.34
Cast iron							
Plain...........	33	31.8	27.7	24.8	0.11	474	0.63
Alloy...........	30	28.3	27	....	0.10	455	0.66
Constantan, 60% Cu,							
40% Ni	12.4	12.8	....	....	0.10	557	0.22
18–8 stainless steel,							
Type 304.......	8.0	9.4	10.9	12.4	0.11	488	0.15
Type 347.......	8.0	9.3	11.0	12.8	0.11	488	0.15
Steel, mild, 1% C....	26.5	26	25	22	0.11	490	0.49

PHYSICAL PROPERTIES OF SOME NONMETALS

Material	Average Temperature (F)	k (Btu/hr ft F)	c (Btu/lb$_m$F)	ρ (lb$_m$/cu ft)	a (sq ft/hr)
Insulating Materials					
Asbestos	32	0.087	0.25	36	~0.01
	392	0.12	....	36	~0.01
Cork	86	0.025	0.04	10	~0.006
Cotton, fabric	200	0.046			
Diatomaceous earth,					
powdered	100	0.030	0.21	14	~0.01
	300	0.036	....		
	600	0.046	....		
Molded pipe covering	400	0.051	....	26	
	1600	0.088	....		
Glass wool					
Fine	20	0.022	....		
	100	0.031	....	1.5	
	200	0.043	....		
Packed	20	0.016	....		
	100	0.022	....	6.0	
	200	0.029	....		
Hair felt	100	0.027	....	8.2	
Kaolin insulating					
brick	932	0.15	....	27	
	2102	0.26	....		
Kaolin insulating					
firebrick	392	0.05	....	19	
	1400	0.11	....		
85% magnesia	32	0.032	....	17	
	200	0.037	....	17	
Rock wool	20	0.017	....	8	
	200	0.030	....		
Rubber	32	0.087	0.48	75	0.0024
Building Materials					
Brick					
Fire-clay	392	0.58	0.20	144	0.02
	1832	0.95			
Masonry	70	0.38	0.20	106	0.018
Zirconia	392	0.84	....	304	
	1832	1.13	....		
Chrome brick	392	0.82	....	246	
	1832	0.96			
Concrete					
Stone	~70	0.54	0.20	144	0.019
10% moisture	~70	0.70	....	140	~0.025
Glass, window	~70	~0.45	0.2	170	0.013
Limestone, dry	70	0.40	0.22	105	0.017
Sand					
Dry	68	0.20	....	95	
10% H$_2$O	68	0.60	....	100	
Soil					
Dry	70	~0.20	0.44	......	~0.01
Wet	70	~1.5	....	......	~0.03
Wood					
Oak ⊥ to grain	70	0.12	0.57	51	0.0041
‖ to grain	70	0.20	0.57	51	0.0069
Pine ⊥ to grain	70	0.06	0.67	31	0.0029
‖ to grain	70	0.14	0.67	31	0.0067
Ice	32	1.28	0.46	57	0.048

TABLE A–3

Physical Properties of Gases, Liquids, and Liquid Metals
(All Gas Properties Are for Atmospheric Pressure)

GASES

T (F)	ρ (lbm/cu ft)	c_p (Btu/ lbm F)	$\mu \times 10^5$ (lbm/ ft sec)	$\nu \times 10^3$ (sq ft/ sec)	k (Btu/ hr ft F)	Pr	a (sq ft/hr)	$\beta \times 10^3$ (1/F)	$\dfrac{g\beta\rho^2}{\mu^2}$ (1/F cu ft)
				Air					
0	0.086	0.239	1.110	0.130	0.0133	0.73	0.646	2.18	4.2×10^6
32	0.081	0.240	1.165	0.145	0.0140	0.72	0.720	2.03	3.16
100	0.071	0.240	1.285	0.180	0.0154	0.72	0.905	1.79	1.76
200	0.060	0.241	1.440	0.239	0.0174	0.72	1.20	1.52	0.850
300	0.052	0.243	1.610	0.306	0.0193	0.71	1.53	1.32	0.444
400	0.046	0.245	1.750	0.378	0.0212	0.689	1.88	1.16	0.258
500	0.0412	0.247	1.890	0.455	0.0231	0.683	2.27	1.04	0.159
600	0.0373	0.250	2.000	0.540	0.0250	0.685	2.68	0.943	0.106
700	0.0341	0.253	2.14	0.625	0.0268	0.690	3.10	0.862	70.4×10^3
800	0.0314	0.256	2.25	0.717	0.0286	0.697	3.56	0.794	49.8
900	0.0291	0.259	2.36	0.815	0.0303	0.705	4.02	0.735	36.0
1000	0.0271	0.262	2.47	0.917	0.0319	0.713	4.50	0.685	26.5
1500	0.0202	0.276	3.00	1.47	0.0400	0.739	7.19	0.510	7.45
2000	0.0161	0.286	3.45	2.14	0.0471	0.753	10.2	0.406	2.84
2500	0.0133	0.292	3.69	2.80	0.051	0.763	13.1	0.338	1.41
3000	0.0114	0.297	3.86	3.39	0.054	0.765	16.0	0.289	0.815
				Steam					
212	0.0372	0.451	0.870	0.234	0.0145	0.96	0.864	1.49	0.877×10^6
300	0.0328	0.456	1.000	0.303	0.0171	0.95	1.14	1.32	0.459
400	0.0288	0.462	1.130	0.395	0.0200	0.94	1.50	1.16	0.243
500	0.0258	0.470	1.265	0.490	0.0228	0.94	1.88	1.04	0.139
600	0.0233	0.477	1.420	0.610	0.0257	0.94	2.31	0.943	82×10^3
700	0.0213	0.485	1.555	0.725	0.0288	0.93	2.79	0.862	52.1
800	0.0196	0.494	1.700	0.855	0.0321	0.92	3.32	0.794	34.0
900	0.0181	0.50	1.810	0.987	0.0355	0.91	3.93	0.735	23.6
1000	0.0169	0.51	1.920	1.13	0.0388	0.91	4.50	0.685	17.1
1200	0.0149	0.53	2.14	1.44	0.0457	0.88	5.80	0.603	9.4
1400	0.0133	0.55	2.36	1.78	0.053	0.87	7.25	0.537	5.49
1600	0.0120	0.56	2.58	2.14	0.061	0.87	9.07	0.485	3.38
1800	0.0109	0.58	2.81	2.58	0.068	0.87	10.8	0.442	2.14
2000	0.0100	0.60	3.03	3.03	0.076	0.86	12.7	0.406	1.43
2500	0.0083	0.64	3.58	4.30	0.096	0.86	18.1	0.338	0.603
3000	0.0071	0.67	4.00	5.75	0.114	0.86	24.0	0.289	0.293
				Oxygen					
0	0.0955	0.2185	1.215	0.127	0.0131	0.73	0.627	2.18	4.33×10^6
100	0.0785	0.2200	1.420	0.181	0.0159	0.71	0.880	1.79	1.76
200	0.0666	0.2228	1.610	0.242	0.0179	0.722	1.20	1.52	0.84
400	0.0511	0.2305	1.955	0.382	0.0228	0.710	1.94	1.16	0.256
600	0.0415	0.2390	2.26	0.545	0.0277	0.704	2.79	0.943	0.103
800	0.0349	0.2465	2.53	0.725	0.0324	0.695	3.76	0.794	48.5×10^3
1000	0.0301	0.2528	2.78	0.924	0.0366	0.690	4.80	0.685	25.8
1500	0.0224	0.2635	3.32	1.480	0.0465	0.677	7.88	0.510	7.50

T (F)	ρ (lbm/cu ft)	c_p (Btu/ lbm F)	$\mu \times 10^5$ (lbm/ ft sec)	$\nu \times 10^3$ (sq ft/ sec)	k (Btu/ hr ft F)	Pr	a (sq ft/hr)	$\beta \times 10^3$ (1/F)	$\dfrac{g\beta\rho^2}{\mu^2}$ (1/F cu ft)
				Nitrogen					
0	0.0840	0.2478	1.055	0.125	0.0132	0.713	0.635	2.18	4.55×10^6
100	0.0690	0.2484	1.222	0.177	0.0154	0.71	0.898	1.79	1.84
200	0.0585	0.2490	1.380	0.236	0.0174	0.71	1.20	1.52	0.876
400	0.0449	0.2515	1.660	0.370	0.0212	0.71	1.88	1.16	0.272
600	0.0364	0.2564	1.915	0.526	0.0252	0.70	2.70	0.943	0.110
800	0.0306	0.2623	2.145	0.702	0.0291	0.70	3.62	0.794	52.0×10^3
1000	0.0264	0.2689	2.355	0.891	0.0330	0.69	4.65	0.685	27.7
1500	0.0197	0.2835	2.800	1.420	0.0423	0.676	7.58	0.510	8.12
				Carbon Monoxide					
0	0.0835	0.2482	1.065	0.128	0.0129	0.75	0.621	2.18	4.32×10^6
200	0.0582	0.2496	1.390	0.239	0.0169	0.74	1.16	1.52	0.860
400	0.0446	0.2532	1.670	0.374	0.0208	0.73	1.84	1.16	0.268
600	0.0362	0.2592	1.910	0.527	0.0246	0.725	2.62	0.943	0.109
800	0.0305	0.2662	2.134	0.700	0.0285	0.72	3.50	0.794	52.1×10^3
1000	0.0263	0.2730	2.336	0.887	0.0322	0.71	4.50	0.685	28.0
1500	0.0196	0.2878	2.783	1.420	0.0414	0.70	7.33	0.510	8.13
				Helium					
0	0.012	1.24	1.140	0.950	0.078	0.67	5.25	2.18	77800
200	0.00835	1.24	1.480	1.77	0.097	0.686	9.36	1.52	15600
400	0.0064	1.24	1.780	2.78	0.115	0.70	14.5	1.16	4840
600	0.0052	1.24	2.02	3.89	0.129	0.715	20.0	0.943	2010
800	0.00436	1.24	2.285	5.24	0.138	0.73	25.5	0.794	932
1000	0.00377	1.24	2.520	6.69	......	.....	....	0.685	494
1500	0.0028	1.24	3.160	11.30	......	.....	....	0.510	129
				Hydrogen					
0	0.0060	3.39	0.540	0.89	0.094	0.70	4.62	2.18	86600
100	0.0049	3.42	0.620	1.26	0.110	0.695	6.56	1.79	36600
200	0.0042	3.44	0.692	1.65	0.122	0.69	8.45	1.52	18000
500	0.0028	3.47	0.884	3.12	0.160	0.69	16.5	1.04	3360
1000	0.0019	3.51	1.160	6.2	0.208	0.705	31.2	0.685	591
1500	0.0014	3.62	1.415	10.2	0.260	0.71	51.4	0.510	161
2000	0.0011	3.76	1.64	14.4	0.307	0.72	74.2	0.406	59
3000	0.0008	4.02	1.72	24.2	0.380	0.66	118.0	0.289	20
				Carbon Dioxide					
0	0.132	0.184	0.88	0.067	0.0076	0.77	0.313	2.18	15.8×10^6
100	0.108	0.203	1.05	0.098	0.0100	0.77	0.455	1.79	6.10
200	0.092	0.216	1.22	0.133	0.0125	0.76	0.63	1.52	2.78
500	0.063	0.247	1.67	0.266	0.0198	0.75	1.27	1.04	0.476
1000	0.0414	0.280	2.30	0.558	0.0318	0.73	2.75	0.685	71.4×10^3
1500	0.0308	0.298	2.86	0.925	0.0420	0.73	4.58	0.510	19.0
2000	0.0247	0.309	3.30	1.34	0.050	0.735	6.55	0.406	7.34
3000	0.0175	0.322	3.92	2.25	0.061	0.745	10.8	0.289	1.85

LIQUIDS

T (F)	ρ (lb$_m$/cu ft)	c_p (Btu/ lb$_m$ F)	$\mu \times 10^3$ (lb$_m$/ ft sec)	$\nu \times 10^5$ (sq ft/ sec)	k (Btu/ hr ft F)	Pr	$a \times 10^3$ (sq ft/hr)	$\beta_T \times 10^4$ (1/F)	$\dfrac{g\beta\rho^2}{\mu^2}$ (1/F cu ft)
					Water				
32	62.4	1.01	1.20	1.93	0.319	13.7	5.07	−0.37	
40	62.4	1.00	1.04	1.67	0.325	11.6	5.21	0.20	2.3×10^6
50	62.4	1.00	0.88	1.40	0.332	9.55	5.33	0.49	8.0
60	62.3	0.999	0.76	1.22	0.340	8.03	5.47	0.85	18.4
70	62.3	0.998	0.658	1.06	0.347	6.82	5.57	1.2	34.6
80	62.2	0.998	0.578	0.93	0.353	5.89	5.68	1.5	56.0
90	62.1	0.997	0.514	0.825	0.359	5.13	5.79	1.8	85.0
100	62.0	0.998	0.458	0.740	0.364	4.52	5.88	2.0	118×10^6
150	61.2	1.00	0.292	0.477	0.384	2.74	6.27	3.1	440.0
200	60.1	1.00	0.205	0.341	0.394	1.88	6.55	4.0	1.11×10^9
250	58.8	1.01	0.158	0.269	0.396	1.45	6.69	4.8	2.14
300	57.3	1.03	0.126	0.220	0.395	1.18	6.70	6.0	4.00
350	55.6	1.05	0.105	0.189	0.391	1.02	6.69	6.9	6.24
400	53.6	1.08.	0.091	0.170	0.381	0.927	6.57	8.0	8.95
450	51.6	1.12	0.080	0.155	0.367	0.876	6.34	9.0	12.1
500	49.0	1.19	0.071	0.145	0.349	0.87	5.99	10.0	15.3
550	45.9	1.31	0.064	0.139	0.325	0.93	5.05	11.0	17.8
600	42.4	1.51	0.058	0.137	0.292	1.09	4.57	12.0	20.6

T (F)	ρ (lb$_m$/ cu ft)	c_p (Btu/ lb$_m$ F)	$\mu \times 10^5$ (lb$_m$/ ft sec)	$\nu \times 10^5$ (sq ft/ sec)	k (Btu/ hr ft F)	Pr	$a \times 10^3$ (sq ft/hr)	$\beta_T \times 10^3$ (1/F)	$\dfrac{g\beta\rho^2}{\mu^2}$ (1/F cu ft)
					Commercial Aniline				
60	64.0	0.48	325.0	5.08	0.10	56.0	3.25		
100	63.0	0.49	170.0	2.70	0.10	30.0	3.24	0.49	21.6×10^6
150	61.5	0.505	96.5	1.57	0.098	18.0	3.16	0.492	64.5
200	60.0	0.515	61.1	1.02	0.096	11.8	3.11		
300	57.5	0.54	32.5	0.565	0.093	6.8	3.00		
					Ammonia (Saturated Liquid)				
−20	42.4	1.07	17.6	0.417	0.317	2.15	6.94		
0	41.6	1.08	17.1	0.410	0.316	2.09	7.04		
10	40.8	1.09	16.6	0.407	0.314	2.07	7.08		
32	40.0	1.11	16.1	0.402	0.312	2.05	7.03	1.2	238×10^6
50	39.1	1.13	15.5	0.396	0.307	2.04	6.95	1.3	266
80	37.2	1.17	14.5	0.386	0.293	2.01	6.73		
120	35.2	1.22	13.0	0.355	0.275	1.99	6.40		
					Freon 12, CCl$_2$F$_2$, (Saturated Liquid)				
−40	94.8	0.211	28.4	0.300	0.040	5.4	2.00		
−20	93.0	0.214	25.0	0.272	0.040	4.8	2.01	1.03	4.6×10^9
0	91.2	0.217	23.1	0.253	0.041	4.4	2.07	1.05	5.27
20	89.2	0.220	21.0	0.238	0.042	4.0	2.14	1.34	7.80
32	87.2	0.223	20.0	0.230	0.042	3.8	2.16	1.72	10.5
60	83.0	0.231	18.0	0.213	0.042	3.5	2.19	2.1	14.4
100	78.5	0.240	16.0	0.206	0.040	3.5	2.12	2.5	19.4
120	75.9	0.244	15.5	0.204	0.039	3.5	2.12		

T (F)	ρ (lbm/ cu ft)	c_p (Btu/ lbm F)	$\mu \times 10^5$ (lbm/ ft sec)	$\nu \times 10^5$ (sq ft/ sec)	k (Btu/ hr ft F)	Pr	$a \times 10^3$ (sq ft/hr)	$\beta \times 10^3$ (1/F)	$\dfrac{g\beta\rho^2}{\mu^2}$ (1/F cu ft)
				n-Butyl Alcohol					
60	50.5	0.55	226	4.48	0.097	46.6	3.49		21.5×10^6
100	49.7	0.61	129	2.60	0.096	29.5	3.16	0.45	80
150	48.5	0.68	67.5	1.39	0.095	17.4	2.88	0.48	
200	47.2	0.77	38.6	0.815	0.094	11.3	2.58		
300	.....	.....	19.0						
				Benzene					
60	55.1	0.40	46.0	0.835	0.093	7.2	4.22	0.60	0.3×10^9
80	54.6	0.42	39.6	0.725	0.092	6.5	4.01		
100	54.0	0.44	35.1	0.650	0.087	5.1	3.53		
150	53.5	0.46	26.0	0.480	.....	4.5			
200	.....	.....	20.3	.....	.....	4.0			
				Light Oil					
60	57.0	0.43	5820	102	0.077	1170	3.14	0.38	1.17×10^4
80	56.8	0.44	2780	49	0.077	570	3.09	0.38	5.1
100	56.0	0.46	1530	27.4	0.076	340	2.95	0.39	16.7
150	54.3	0.48	530	9.8	0.075	122	2.88	0.40	1.34×10^6
200	54.0	0.51	250	4.6	0.074	62	2.69	0.42	6.4
250	53.0	0.52	139	2.6	0.074	35	2.67	0.44	21.0
300	51.8	0.54	83	1.6	0.073	22	2.62	0.45	56.5

T (F)	ρ (lbm/ cu ft)	c_p (Btu/ lbm F)	$\mu \times 10^2$ (lbm/ ft sec)	$\nu \times 10^2$ (sq ft/ sec)	k (Btu/ hr ft F)	Pr	$a \times 10^3$ (sq ft/hr)	$\beta \times 10^3$ (1/F)	$\dfrac{g\beta\rho^2}{\mu^2}$ (1/F cu ft)
				Glycerin					
50	79.3	0.554	256	3.23	0.165	31×10^3	3.76		
70	78.9	0.570	100	1.27	0.165	12.5	3.67	0.28	56
85	78.5	0.584	42.4	0.54	0.164	5.4	3.58	0.30	332
100	78.2	0.600	18.8	0.24	0.163	2.5	3.45		
120	77.7	0.617	12.4	0.16	.....	$\simeq 1.6$			

LIQUID METALS

T (F)	ρ (lbm/ cu ft)	c_p (Btu/ lbm F)	$\mu \times 10^3$ (lbm/ ft sec)	$\nu \times 10^6$ (sq ft/ sec)	k (Btu/ hr ft F)	Pr	a (sq ft/hr)	$\beta_T \times 10^3$ (1/F)	$\dfrac{g\beta_T\rho^2}{\mu^2}$ (1/F cu ft)
				Bismuth					
600	625	0.0345	1.09	1.74	9.5	0.014	0.44	0.065	0.687×10^9
800	616	0.0357	0.90	1.5	9.0	0.013	0.41	0.068	
1000	608	0.0369	0.74	1.2	9.0	0.011	0.40	0.070	
1200	600	0.0381	0.62	1.0	9.0	0.009	0.39		
1400	591	0.0393	0.53	0.9	9.0	0.008	0.39		

T (F)	ρ (lbm/ cu ft)	c_p (Btu/ lbm F)	$\mu \times 10^3$ (lbm/ ft sec)	$\nu \times 10^6$ (sq ft/ sec)	k (Btu/ hr ft F)	Pr	a (sq ft/hr)	$\beta_T \times 10^3$ (1/F)	$\dfrac{g\beta_T\rho^2}{\mu^2}$ (1/F cu ft)

Mercury

T (F)	ρ	c_p	$\mu \times 10^3$	$\nu \times 10^6$	k	Pr	a	$\beta_T \times 10^3$	$\dfrac{g\beta_T\rho^2}{\mu^2}$
50	847	0.033	1.07	1.2	4.7	0.027	0.17	0.1	2.02×10^9
200	834	0.033	0.84	1.0	6.0	0.016	0.22	0.1	2.02
300	826	0.033	0.74	0.9	6.7	0.012	0.25		
400	817	0.032	0.67	0.8	7.2	0.011	0.27		
600	802	0.032	0.58	0.7	8.1	0.008	0.31		

Sodium

T (F)	ρ	c_p	$\mu \times 10^3$	$\nu \times 10^6$	k	Pr	a	$\beta_T \times 10^3$	$\dfrac{g\beta_T\rho^2}{\mu^2}$
200	58.0	0.33	0.47	8.1	49.8	0.011	2.6	0.150	73.5×10^6
400	56.3	0.32	0.29	5.1	46.4	0.007	2.6	0.20	243
700	53.7	0.31	0.19	3.5	41.8	0.005	2.5		
1000	51.2	0.30	0.14	2.7	37.8	0.004	2.4		
1300	48.6	0.30	0.12	2.5	34.5	0.004	2.4		

BIBLIOGRAPHY FOR PHYSICAL PROPERTIES

1. *International Critical Tables*, New York: McGraw-Hill Book Company, Inc., 1929.

2. L. S. Marks, et al., *Mechanical Engineers' Handbook*, ed. New York: McGraw-Hill Book Company, Inc.

3. J. H. Perry, ed., *Chemical Engineers' Handbook*, 3rd ed., McGraw-Hill Book Company, Inc., 1950.

4. J. L. Everhart, W. E. Lindlief, J. Kanegis, P. G. Weissler, and F. Siegel, *Mechanical Properties of Metals and Alloys*, Circular C447, U. S. Department of Commerce, National Bureau of Standards, Washington, D. C., 1943.

5. J. H. Keenan and F. G. Keyes, *Thermodynamic Properties of Steam*, New York: John Wiley & Sons, Inc., 1936.

6. J. H. Keenan and J. Kaye, *Gas Tables*, New York: John Wiley & Sons, Inc., 1945.

7. W. H. McAdams, *Heat Transmission*, 3rd ed., McGraw-Hill Book Company, Inc., 1954.

8. E. Schmidt, *Thermodynamics*, Oxford at the Claredon Press, 1949.

9. J. Hilsenrath, C. W. Beckett, W. S. Benedict, L. Fano, H. M. Hoge, J. F. Masi, R. L. Nuttall, Y. S. Touloukian, and H. W. Woolley, *Tables of the Thermal Properties of Gases*, National Bureau of Standards Circular 564, Washington, D. C., 1955.

10. F. B. Rowley and A. B. Algren, *Thermal Conductivity of Building Materials*, Bulletin No. 12, Eng. Exp. St., Univ. of Minnesota, 1937.

11. L. S. Kowalczyk, "Thermal Conductivity and its Variability with Temperature and Pressure," *Trans. ASME*, Vol. 77 (1955) p. 1021.

12. *Liquid-Metals Handbook*, 2d ed., U. S. Govt. Printing Office, Washington, D. C., 1952.

13. C. L. Mantell, ed., *Engineering Materials Handbook*, McGraw-Hill Book Company., Inc., 1958

APPENDIX III

TABLE A–4
RADIATION FUNCTIONS*

λT	$\dfrac{E\lambda b \times 10^5}{\sigma T^5}$	$\dfrac{E_{b(0-\lambda T)}}{\sigma T^4}$	λT	$\dfrac{E\lambda b \times 10^5}{\sigma T^5}$	$\dfrac{E_{b(0-\lambda T)}}{\sigma T^4}$	λT	$\dfrac{E\lambda b \times 10^5}{\sigma T^5}$	$\dfrac{E_{b(0-\lambda T)}}{\sigma T^4}$
1000	.0000394	0	7200	10.089	.4809	13400	2.714	.8317
1200	.001184	0	7400	9.723	.5007	13600	2.605	.8370
1400	.01194	0	7600	9.357	.5199	13800	2.502	.8421
1600	.0618	.0001	7800	8.997	.5381	14000	2.416	.8470
1800	.2070	.0003	8000	8.642	.5558	14200	2.309	.8517
2000	.5151	.0009	8200	8.293	.5727	14400	2.219	.8563
2200	1.0384	.0025	8400	7.954	.5890	14600	2.134	.8606
2400	1.791	.0053	8600	7.624	.6045	14800	2.052	.8648
2600	2.753	.0098	8800	7.304	.6195	15000	1.972	.8688
2800	3.872	.0164	9000	6.995	.6337	16000	1.633	.8868
3000	5.081	.0254	9200	6.697	.6474	17000	1.360	.9017
3200	6.312	.0368	9400	6.411	.6606	18000	1.140	.9142
3400	7.506	.0506	9600	6.136	.6731	19000	.962	.9247
3600	8.613	.0667	9800	5.872	.6851	20000	.817	.9335
3800	9.601	.0850	10000	5.619	.6966	21000	.702	.9411
4000	10.450	.1051	10200	5.378	.7076	22000	.599	.9475
4200	11.151	.1267	10400	5.146	.7181	23000	.516	.9531
4400	11.704	.1496	10600	4.925	.7282	24000	.448	.9589
4600	12.114	.1734	10800	4.714	.7378	25000	.390	.9621
4800	12.392	.1979	11000	4.512	.7474	26000	.341	.9657
5000	12.556	.2229	11200	4.320	.7559	27000	.300	.9689
5200	12.607	.2481	11400	4.137	.7643	28000	.265	.9718
5400	12.571	.2733	11600	3.962	.7724	29000	.234	.9742
5600	12.458	.2983	11800	3.795	.7802	30000	.208	$.976_5$
5800	12.282	.3230	12000	3.637	.7876	40000	.0741	$.988_1$
6000	12.053	.3474	12200	3.485	.7947	50000	.0326	$.994_1$
6200	11.783	.3712	12400	3.341	.8015	60000	.0165	$.996_3$
6400	11.480	.3945	12600	3.203	.8081	70000	.0092	$.998_1$
6600	11.152	.4171	12800	3.071	.8144	80000	.0055	$.998_7$
6800	10.808	.4391	13000	2.947	.8204	90000	.0035	$.999_0$
7000	10.451	.4604	13200	2.827	.8262	100000	.0023	$.999_2$
						∞	0	1.000_0

* From Dunkle, R. V., *Trans. ASME*, **76**, 549 (1954).

TABLE A-5
AVERAGE PROPERTIES OF TUBES

DIAMETER		THICKNESS		EXTERNAL			INTERNAL				Length of Tube Containing One Cu Ft
Ex-ternal (in.)	In-ternal (in.)	BWG Gage	NOM Wall (in.)	Circum-ference (in.)	Surface per Lineal Foot (sq ft)	Lineal Feet of Tube per Square Foot of Surface	Trans-verse Area (sq in.)	Volume or Capacity per Lineal Foot			
								Cu In.	Cu Ft	U.S. Gal	
⅝	0.527	18	.049	1.9635	0.1636	6.1115	0.218	2.616	0.0015	0.011	661
	0.495	16	.065				0.193	2.316	0.0013	0.010	746
	0.459	14	.083				0.166	1.992	0.0011	0.009	867
¾	0.652	18	.049	2.3562	0.1963	5.0930	0.334	4.008	0.0023	0.017	431
	0.620	16	.065				0.302	3.624	0.0021	0.016	477
	0.584	14	.083				0.268	3.216	0.0019	0.014	537
	0.560	13	.095				0.246	2.952	0.0017	0.013	585
1	0.902	18	.049	3.1416	.2618	3.8197	0.639	7.668	0.0044	0.033	225
	0.870	16	.065				0.595	7.140	0.0041	0.031	242
	0.834	14	.083				0.546	6.552	0.0038	0.028	264
	0.810	13	.095				0.515	6.180	0.0036	0.027	280
1¼	1.152	18	.049	3.9270	.3272	3.0558	1.075	12.90	0.0075	0.056	134
	1.120	16	.065				0.985	11.82	0.0068	0.051	146
	1.084	14	.083				0.923	11.08	0.0064	0.048	156
	1.060	13	.095				0.882	10.58	0.0061	0.046	163
	1.032	12	.109				0.836	10.03	0.0058	0.043	172
1½	1.402	18	.049	4.7124	.3927	2.5465	1.544	18.53	0.0107	0.080	93
	1.370	16	.065				1.474	17.69	0.0102	0.076	98
	1.334	14	.083				1.398	16.78	0.0097	0.073	103
	1.310	13	.095				1.343	16.12	0.0093	0.070	107
	1.282	12	.109				1.292	15.50	0.0090	0.067	111
1¾	1.620	16	.065	5.4978	.4581	2.1827	2.061	24.73	0.0143	0.107	70
	1.584	14	.083				1.971	23.65	0.0137	0.102	73
	1.560	13	.095				1.911	22.94	0.0133	0.099	75
	1.532	12	.109				1.843	22.12	0.0128	0.096	78
	1.490	11	.120				1.744	20.92	0.0121	0.090	83
2	1.870	16	.065	6.2832	.5236	1.9099	2.746	32.96	0.0191	0.143	52
	1.834	14	.083				2.642	31.70	0.0183	0.137	55
	1.810	13	.095				2.573	30.88	0.0179	0.134	56
	1.782	12	.109				2.489	29.87	0.0173	0.129	58
	1.760	11	.120				2.433	29.20	0.0169	0.126	59

TABLE A–6

STEEL-PIPE DIMENSIONS*

Nominal pipe size, in.	Outside diam, in.	Schedule No.	Wall thick-ness, in.	Inside diam, in.	Cross-sectional area metal, sq in.	Inside cross-sectional area sq ft
⅛	0.405	40†	0.068	0.269	0.072	0.00040
		80‡	0.095	0.215	0.093	0.00025
¼	0.540	40†	0.088	0.364	0.125	0.00072
		80‡	0.119	0.302	0.157	0.00050
⅜	0.675	40†	0.091	0.493	0.167	0.00133
		80‡	0.126	0.423	0.217	0.00098
½	0.840	40†	0.109	0.622	0.250	0.00211
		80‡	0.147	0.546	0.320	0.00163
		160	0.187	0.466	0.384	0.00118
¾	1.050	40†	0.113	0.824	0.333	0.00371
		80‡	0.154	0.742	0.433	0.00300
		160	0.218	0.614	0.570	0.00206
1	1.315	40†	0.133	1.049	0.494	0.00600
		80‡	0.179	0.957	0.639	0.00499
		160	0.250	0.815	0.837	0.00362
1¼	1.660	40†	0.140	1.380	0.699	0.01040
		80‡	0.191	1.278	0.881	0.00891
		160	0.250	1.160	1.107	0.00734
1½	1.900	40†	0.145	1.610	0.799	0.01414
		80‡	0.200	1.500	1.068	0.01225
		160	0.281	1.338	1.429	0.00976
2	2.375	40†	0.154	2.067	1.075	0.02330
		80‡	0.218	1.939	1.477	0.02050
		160	0.343	1.689	2.190	0.01556
2½	2.875	40†	0.203	2.469	1.704	0.03322
		80‡	0.276	2.323	2.254	0.02942
		160	0.375	2.125	2.945	0.02463
3	3.500	40†	0.216	3.068	2.228	0.05130
		80‡	0.300	2.900	3.016	0.04587
		160	0.437	2.626	4.205	0.03761
3½	4.000	40†	0.226	3.548	2.680	0.06870
		80‡	0.318	3.364	3.678	0.06170
4	4.500	40†	0.237	4.026	3.173	0.08840
		80‡	0.337	3.826	4.407	0.07986
		120	0.437	3.626	5.578	0.07170
		160	0.531	3.438	6.621	0.06447

* Based on A.S.A. Standards B36.10.
† Designates former "standard" sizes
‡ Former "extra strong."

Nominal pipe size, in.	Outside diam, in.	Schedule No.	Wall thick- ness, in.	Inside diam, in.	Cross- sectional area metal, sq in.	Inside cross- sectional area, sq ft
5	5.563	40†	0.258	5.047	4.304	0.1390
		80‡	0.375	4.813	6.112	0.1263
		120	0.500	4.563	7.953	0.1136
		160	0.625	4.313	9.696	0.1015
6	6.625	40†	0.280	6.065	5.584	0.2006
		80‡	0.432	5.761	8.405	0.1810
		120	0.562	5.501	10.71	0.1650
		160	0.718	5.189	13.32	0.1469
8	8.625	20	0.250	8.125	6.570	0.3601
		30†	0.277	8.071	7.260	0.3553
		40†	0.322	7.981	8.396	0.3474
		60	0.406	7.813	10.48	0.3329
		80‡	0.500	7.625	12.76	0.3171
		100	0.593	7.439	14.96	0.3018
		120	0.718	7.189	17.84	0.2819
		140	0.812	7.001	19.93	0.2673
		160	0.906	6.813	21.97	0.2532
10	10.75	20	0.250	10.250	8.24	0.5731
		30†	0.307	10.136	10.07	0.5603
		40†	0.365	10.020	11.90	0.5475
		60‡	0.500	9.750	16.10	0.5185
		80	0.593	9.564	18.92	0.4989
		100	0.718	9.314	22.63	0.4732
		120	0.843	9.064	26.24	0.4481
		140	1.000	8.750	30.63	0.4176
		160	1.125	8.500	34.02	0.3941
12	12.75	20	0.250	12.250	9.82	0.8185
		30†	0.330	12.090	12.87	0.7972
		40	0.406	11.938	15.77	0.7773
		60	0.562	11.626	21.52	0.7372
		80	0.687	11.376	26.03	0.7058
		100	0.843	11.064	31.53	0.6677
		120	1.000	10.750	36.91	0.6303
		140	1.125	10.500	41.08	0.6013
		160	1.312	10.126	47.14	0.5592
14	14.0	10	0.250	13.500	10.80	0.9940
		20	0.312	13.376	13.42	0.9750
		30	0.375	13.250	16.05	0.9575
		40	0.437	13.126	18.61	0.9397
		60	0.593	12.814	24.98	0.8956
		80	0.750	12.500	31.22	0.8522
		100	0.937	12.126	38.45	0.8020
		120	1.062	11.876	43.17	0.7693
		140	1.250	11.500	50.07	0.7213
		160	1.406	11.188	55.63	0.6827

* Based on A.S.A. Standards B36.10.
† Designates former "standard" sizes.
‡ Former "extra strong."

TABLE A-7
Properties of the Atmosphere *

Altitude, ft	Altitude, miles	Absolute Temperature, R	Absolute Pressure, lb$_f$/sq ft	Pressure Ratio	Density, lb$_m$/cu ft	Density Ratio	Speed of Sound, ft/sec
0	0	518	2,116	1.00	7.65×10^{-2}	1.00	1,120
5,000	0.947	500	1,758	8.32×10^{-1}	6.60×10^{-2}	8.61×10^{-1}	1,100
10,000	1.894	483	1,456	6.87×10^{-1}	5.66×10^{-2}	7.38×10^{-1}	1,080
20,000	3.788	447	972	4.59×10^{-1}	4.08×10^{-2}	5.33×10^{-1}	1,040
30,000	5.682	411	628	2.97×10^{-1}	2.88×10^{-2}	3.76×10^{-1}	997
40,000	7.576	392	392	1.85×10^{-1}	1.88×10^{-2}	2.45×10^{-1}	973
50,000	9.470	392	243	1.15×10^{-1}	1.16×10^{-2}	1.52×10^{-1}	973
60,000	11.364	392	151	7.13×10^{-2}	7.32×10^{-3}	9.45×10^{-2}	973
70,000	13.258	392	94.5	4.47×10^{-2}	4.51×10^{-3}	5.90×10^{-2}	974
80,000	15.152	392	58.8	2.78×10^{-2}	2.80×10^{-3}	3.67×10^{-2}	974
90,000	17.045	392	36.6	1.73×10^{-2}	1.67×10^{-3}	2.28×10^{-2}	974
100,000	18.939	392	22.8	1.08×10^{-3}	1.1×10^{-3}	1.4×10^{-2}	975
150,000	28.409	575	3.2	1.5×10^{-3}	9.7×10^{-4}	1.3×10^{-3}	1,190
200,000	37.879	623	0.73	3.6×10^{-4}	2.2×10^{-5}	2.9×10^{-4}	1,240
300,000	56.818	487	0.017	9.0×10^{-6}	6.9×10^{-7}	9.0×10^{-6}	1,110
400,000	75.758	695	0.0011	5.2×10^{-7}	2.7×10^{-8}	3.5×10^{-7}	1,430
500,000	94.697	910	1.2×10^{-4}	8.5×10^{-8}	3.1×10^{-9}	4.1×10^{-8}	....
600,000	113.64	1,130	4.1×10^{-5}	1.9×10^{-8}	5.7×10^{-10}	7.5×10^{-9}	....
700,000	132.58	1,350	1.3×10^{-5}	6.2×10^{-9}	1.5×10^{-10}	1.9×10^{-9}	....
800,000	151.52	1,570	4.6×10^{-6}	2.2×10^{-9}	4.6×10^{-11}	6.0×10^{-10}	....
900,000	170.45	1,800	1.9×10^{-6}	9.0×10^{-10}	1.7×10^{-11}	2.2×10^{-10}	....

* Sources of Atmospheric Property Data:
   1. C. N. Warfield, "Tentative Tables for the Properties of the Upper Atmosphere," *NACA TN* 1200, 1947.
   2. H. A. Johnson, M. W. Rubesin, F. M. Sauer, E. G. Slack, and L. Fossner, "The Thermal Characteristics of High Speed Aircraft," AAF, AMC, Wright Field, TR 5632, 1947.
   3. J. P. Sutton, *Rocket Propulsion Elements*, 2d ed., New York: McGraw-Hill Book Company Inc., 1957.

Index